Foundations of elementary school arithmetic

Foundations
of
elementary school
arithmetic

HENRY VAN ENGEN
University of Wisconsin

MAURICE L. HARTUNG *leslie* , *1902 –*
University of Chicago

JAMES E. STOCHL
University of Minnesota

Scott, Foresman and Company

Chicago, Atlanta, Dallas, Palo Alto, Fair Lawn, N.J.

Preface

For several years the manuscript for this book was used experimentally at the University of Wisconsin and elsewhere in mathematics classes for elementary-school teachers. On the basis of this experimental use, we have revised the manuscript so that the approach to certain mathematical ideas is somewhat less formal and somewhat more intuitive than in the original manuscript. It is our hope that we have now achieved the proper balance between a precise formulation of mathematical concepts and an informal presentation of the content. By an "informal presentation," we mean the use of many examples, both mathematical and non-mathematical, and considerable reliance upon the "common sense" of the reader rather than upon rigorous mathematical proof.

This book is intended both for college students who expect to become elementary-school teachers and for teachers who have already had some experience in the classroom. We have planned the book so that it may be used either for independent study or in a course with the aid of an instructor. The book is suitable for either a one-semester or a two-semester course. In a one-semester course, the instructor will find it necessary to omit some material or to have his students read certain chapters or sections without benefit of classroom discussion. In a two-semester course, the books listed in the Bibliography may be assigned to supplement and enrich the text.

Because the chapters and topics have been developed in a logical sequence, the instructor who finds it necessary to omit some of the material must exercise caution. Many of the ideas discussed in the chapter on numeration systems, for example, are needed in the subsequent chapter on the theory of computing; some topics in the chapter on number theory are needed for the development of rational numbers; the chapter on geometry is preceded by the chapter on measurement so that we can make a distinction between metric and nonmetric geometry. These are but a few examples of the structure and organization of the material that make it necessary to use care in omitting or rearranging any of the topics that are included. For a few topics, such as the product of two natural numbers, we have given alternative treatments. Whenever this was done, we have so indicated in a footnote; an instructor or individual teacher may consider both treatments or he may omit one of them if time limitations make it impossible to cover both treatments.

This book is not a "methods" book, although we occasionally touch upon the relationship between a mathematical concept and the way it should be presented to children. For instance, when we discuss addition and multiplication of natural numbers, we point out that the underlying mathematical ideas concerning set operations may be used as a guide to proper teaching methods. Because the book includes a discussion of the major topics of elementary-school arithmetic, it should be extremely useful as a source book for a methods class.

Just as this book is not a methods book, so also it is not a book for teaching elementary arithmetic to teachers; rather, it is a book for teaching teachers the foundations of arithmetic. We have assumed that the user of this book already has some command of the skills of elementary arithmetic, and we believe that it is much more important to discuss mathematical ideas than to provide drill exercises. Thus, the reader of this book will not find practice exercises for developing or reviewing computational skills.

Since this is a book on the theoretical foundations of elementary arithmetic, the main topics are the natural numbers, the rational numbers of arithmetic (sometimes referred to as the non-negative rational numbers), numeration systems, number systems, and sets of number pairs called proportional relations. For each of the number systems considered, we have presented a complete development of the operations and the properties of the operations. Because we feel that the elementary-school teacher ought to have some acquaintance with other sets of numbers, we have also presented a brief treatment of the system of rational numbers, which includes both the non-negative and the negative rational numbers, and the system of real numbers, which includes the rational and the irrational numbers. Our treatment of the rational and real numbers is less than complete because the main concern of the elementary-school teacher is with the natural numbers and the rational numbers of arithmetic. For this reason, we have naturally allotted more time and space to these two sets of numbers and their properties.

Technically, the topics of measurement and geometry do not belong in a study of the mathematical foundations of arithmetic. However, the present interest in the teaching of these topics in the elementary school and their obvious practical value made us feel that their inclusion is justifiable.

In writing a book of this kind, we were faced with many choices concerning the content and ways of presenting it. In certain instances, we decided not to use the mathematical terminology and symbolism that would have enabled us to express an idea more concisely because we did not wish to overwhelm the reader with too much technical language. We introduced new symbolism and terminology only when we felt that it resulted in a genuine gain in communication. Again, in our development of the natural numbers, we chose to use the approach through sets, rather than the Peano postulates, because the natural numbers are developed from sets of objects in elementary arithmetic. Hence, the approach through sets to the natural numbers is more fruitful in suggesting good instructional techniques for the classroom. We also decided to develop the rational numbers of arithmetic independently from the set of all rational numbers because the rationals of arithmetic have always been taught in the elementary school. We do not claim that our choices have always been the best ones or that anyone else would make the same choices as we have; but we have kept in mind the content that is appropriate and teachable for the teacher of young children.

Obviously, this book is not the work of the authors alone. The ideas and suggestions of a number of people have been incorporated at various stages in the development of the book. The authors wish to acknowledge the assistance that they have received at every stage from these persons. In particular, the following graduate students at the University of Wisconsin, who taught from the original manuscript, provided useful criticisms and suggestions: Mary Konrad, Donovan Lichtenberg, Robert Prelipp, G. Edith Robinson, Marilyn Zweng, and Dora Helen Skypek.

HENRY VAN ENGEN
MAURICE L. HARTUNG
JAMES E. STOCHL

Contents

Illustrations

Portion of Babylonian tablet showing
Babylonian numerals, page 122

A simple computing device, "Napier's Rods,"
and a modern computer, page 151

Three division algorisms from 1729 arithmetic text
by Isaac Greenwood, page 162

Page from the 1608 English edition of *The Art of Tenths:
Decimall Arithmetick* by Simon Stevin, page 280

*The other illustrations in this book were done
by Janet LaSalle*

Chapter one

The mathematical and educational setting

The reform in arithmetic content
The reform in arithmetic teaching
Abstraction and symbolization
Number and numeral

Recently there have been significant changes in both the content of the elementary arithmetic program and the methods of teaching arithmetic. New content has been introduced into the arithmetic program for two major reasons: the changes that have occurred in mathematics, and the need for trained mathematicians as a result of the technological advances of the last two decades.* The new methods are a result of changes in the psychology of learning and in the goals of arithmetic instruction. In this chapter we will first consider the changes that are taking place in arithmetic as a result of the mathematical and technological revolutions. Because our main concern in this book is with content rather than with methods of teaching, we will not consider the effect that new theories of learning have had upon the teaching of arithmetic; but we will observe how changes in the goals and content of arithmetic have been instrumental in altering the methods of instruction.

---

* A more complete discussion of these two topics can be found in the following article: "Progress in Mathematics and Its Implications for Schools" by G. Baley Price, *The Revolution in School Mathematics*, pp. 1-14. Complete information concerning this article and all other articles and books referred to in the text is given in the Bibliography on pages 395-398. This article is item 1 of the Bibliography.

The reform in arithmetic content

The idea that arithmetic and mathematics have changed might be puzzling to some of you. Mathematics seems to deal in "eternal truths," such as *2 + 2 = 4* and *the square of the hypotenuse of a right triangle is equal to the sum of the squares of the other two sides.* It is perhaps difficult for non-mathematicians to see how mathematics can change, but it has. Such topics as finite geometries, topology, and decision theory are relative new-comers in the field of mathematics. Mathematics has been reëxamined within the framework of set theory, and many mathematical concepts have been redefined in terms of set ideas. These are but a few of the changes that have occurred in mathematics.

The new developments in mathematics are one stimulus for the reform in arithmetic. The arithmetic taught in the elementary schools should relate more closely to the ideas that mathematicians of today find most useful and powerful.* Specifically, this means that instruction in arithmetic should concern itself with more than computation, standard units of measure, and social and business applications, which have received so much attention in the past. Along with these topics, instruction in arithmetic should provide for the development of a meaningful concept of number, an understanding of numeration systems, the meaning of operations on numbers, the properties of number systems, and a systematic approach to problem solving. Unfortunately, mathematical ideas of contemporary interest have been introduced only recently into the arithmetic program. Schools are just now beginning to bring the arithmetic program up to date so that it more nearly reflects the mathematician's view of mathematics. Changes in the arithmetic program based upon changes in mathematics will probably be made more rapidly in the immediate future.†

The second stimulus for change in arithmetic instruction is the technological advance that has occurred in the past twenty years.‡ The invention of the electronic computer, developments in the fields of nuclear physics and rocketry, the exploration of space, along with many other discoveries in science and technology, have created an unprecedented demand for trained mathematicians and technicians—a demand that has not yet been satisfied and that has revealed a serious shortage of such personnel.

---

* For additional comment on this point, see "Twentieth Century Mathematics in the Elementary School" by H. Van Engen. Item 2 of Bibliography
† R. L. Swain discusses the possible changes in the elementary-school mathematics curriculum in "Modern Mathematics and School Arithmetic," *Twenty-Fifth Yearbook of NCTM*, pp. 270-295. Item 3 of Bibliography
‡ For a brief but exciting view of some of these advances, see *Mathematics* (Life Science Library). Item 4 of Bibliography

The shortage of qualified mathematicians and technicians forced the educational world to investigate the arithmetic taught in elementary schools. Both educators and mathematicians agreed that the schools were not teaching arithmetic as it should be taught. Soon the demand for reform became widespread among those responsible for school curriculums. The agitation for reform, while in many cases erratic, inconsistent, and misdirected, produced a favorable climate for the work of both educators and laymen interested in a sound program in mathematics for the elementary schools. The reform movement was of great benefit to the schools because it attracted the interest and support of the public and encouraged the schools to adopt modern arithmetic programs. The schools began to realize that learning to compute is not the only—or, indeed, the most important—purpose of studying elementary-school arithmetic. Of course children must know how to compute, but computation is important only as a means to an end. The ability to compute assists children in arriving at generalizations about numbers; but, in the end, it is the generalizations and abstractions that are of primary importance.

The reform in arithmetic teaching

Along with the reform in the content of the arithmetic program have come improved methods of teaching arithmetic. When the primary objective of teaching arithmetic was the development of speed and skill in computation, methods of teaching arithmetic consisted chiefly in giving the children rules for computation and much practice. The recent emphasis on thinking, creativity, and "discovery" is at least partially the result of revised notions about the purpose of instruction in arithmetic. After all, if the main objective is the development of ideas and understanding rather than merely computational skill and the recall of seemingly unrelated facts, then the methods of teaching must necessarily be altered. We do not intend to discuss teaching methods in any detail, since this book is devoted mainly to exposition of the mathematical understandings upon which sound methods must be built. From time to time, however, we will point out some implications the discussion has for the choice of methods.

Consider, for example, the notion that a child should be taught that "three plus five equals eight" simply by telling him this fact and having him commit it to memory. Perhaps you reject the "telling" approach to teaching an arithmetic basic fact such as this because you believe that the child should understand *why* three plus five equals eight. In other words, you reject the "telling" method of teaching because you think that the goal of education in arithmetic is understanding.

Once you have decided that understanding deserves more emphasis than does the memorization of facts, you must give careful attention to the choice of concepts that are to be developed. Then you must plan classroom activities so that the children can understand the concepts you have selected. Thus, it is apparent that the new objectives in the teaching of elementary arithmetic have played an important rôle in the reform in teaching methods. The remainder of this chapter will be devoted to a brief discussion of some ideas that will be important for you to keep in mind throughout the book.

Abstraction and symbolization*

Helping children make worth-while abstractions and generalizations is a major task of the schools. Much of one's adult life is spent dealing with abstractions. Ideas of beauty, honesty, humanity, and courage, for example, are abstractions. Such abstractions are arrived at over a period of years and after many experiences with particular instances. Arithmetic, a branch of mathematics, is a subject that is concerned mainly with abstractions that are also arrived at after many experiences with specific examples in the physical world.

Mathematical abstractions are gained from the study of many situations that have a common element. The child learns to give this common element a name; that is, he gives a name to an abstraction. For example, the child learns to give the name "circle" to such plane figures as those represented below. He learns that all circles have a common property;

namely, that, in each circle, the distance from the center of the circle to all points in the circle is the same. Further, he comes to realize that the size of the figure does not make it a circle; the color of the lead used to draw the figure does not make it a circle; the position of the figure (on the wall, floor, or paper) does not make it a circle; the color of the interior of the figure does not make it a circle. These and all other physical aspects are ignored in determining whether or not a given figure is a circle. In other words, the child learns to abstract a property that is common to many figures. Those geometric figures that possess this property he learns to

---

* A thorough discussion of this topic can be found in "The Formation of Concepts" by H. Van Engen, *Twenty-First Yearbook of NCTM*, pp. 69-98. Item 5 of Bibliography

call circles. When he is able to generalize in this way, we say that he has made an abstraction because he has achieved insight into the element common to many, many geometric figures.

The schools must teach children to make abstractions—in particular, those abstractions that are important in mathematics. Ordinarily, children do not make the abstractions needed for the study of mathematics unless instruction in arithmetic is explicitly oriented towards abstraction as a goal.

As a further illustration of what we mean by a mathematical abstraction, let us consider again the example that was introduced earlier, "three plus five equals eight." The child must understand what is meant by the terms *plus, three, five, eight, three plus five,* and *equals.* And, since the meaning of a sentence is more than the simple union of the individual meanings of the words, he must also understand the meaning of the sentence made up of these words. The words refer to concepts, which are abstractions. For the child, three plus five equals eight, or $3 + 5 = 8$, is an idea that must be abstracted from many, many illustrations from the physical world. For example, he sees many illustrations of a set of five objects (blocks, pennies, apples, etc.) joining a set of three objects and learns that the symbol $3 + 5$ is associated with situations of this kind. In a sense, he learns a very general name for the experience "five things join three things" and that "$3 + 5$" is another name for the number whose common name is "8." Thus, the initial ideas of mathematics are drawn from the physical world by a process of abstraction and generalization.

Man has invented symbols to represent events so that he can communicate ideas without the occurrence of the events themselves.* The meaning of these symbols becomes very generalized. To return to our example, "$3 + 5$" is a symbol conveying the idea that a set of 5 objects has joined a set of 3 objects. We say that "$3 + 5$" is a name of the number associated with these combined sets of objects, and that "8" is a standard name of the same number. To indicate that "8" and "$3 + 5$" are names for the same number, we write the sentence

$$3 + 5 = 8.$$

You should note the use of the symbol for equality ($=$). It is inserted between two symbols to indicate that we have two names for the same number. Thus, we can write "$4 = IV$" or "$2 + 2 = 4$" or "$3 + 1 = 4$" because in each instance the symbols appearing on either side of the symbol for equality are names for the same number.

---

* For an excellent discussion of symbolism in mathematics, see "Language and Symbolism in Mathematics" by R. S. Fouch and E. D. Nichols. *Twenty-Fourth Yearbook of NCTM,* pp. 327-369. Item 6 of Bibliography

You may not be familiar with the use of "4 + 1" as a symbol for a number. Previously, you have probably thought of 4 + 1 as an addition "example." Certainly, the connotation of "4 + 1" is that of a set of one object having joined a set of four objects, but "4 + 1" is a name of the number associated with the combined set of objects. We can also use "5" to name the number associated with the set, but this name does not have the connotation that "4 + 1" has. The symbol 4 + 1 reveals the way we arrived at the number five in this particular instance.

Because a great deal of specialized symbolism occurs in mathematics, there is often a tendency to introduce symbols too early and too rapidly.* Insofar as possible, the children should be given many experiences with a concept before they are required to form a generalization about it or to use a symbol for it. Without extensive use of examples, there is considerable danger that the children will not understand the meaning of many of the symbols they are required to use, but will accept them simply as symbols, and not as symbols or names of abstractions drawn from experiences.

Number and numeral

Even more fundamental than the connotation of "3 + 5" or "4 + 1" is the concept of number itself. Perhaps because it is so fundamental, the concept of number is one of the most difficult to understand. Certainly, most educated adults know how to use numbers, but if you ask them what a number *is*, you are likely to be greeted with silence. Suppose, for example, you have several sets of objects, such as 4 apples, 4 dogs, 4 chairs, etc. The objects themselves do not consitute the number 4. The concept 4 does not involve the dogs as dogs, the apples as apples, or the chairs as chairs. However, the *numerousness* of each of these sets is one particular instance or use of the number 4. In a later chapter, we will give a better answer to such questions as "What is the number 4?" For the time being, we assume that you have a working knowledge of numbers sufficient for the discussion in this chapter.

In teaching arithmetic, you will be confronted with the distinction between symbols and the ideas for which the symbols stand, that is, their *referents*. Difficulties occur in talking about numbers and the symbols that represent them. One of the difficulties we have in mind can be illustrated by discussing the word *dog* and the animal named by the word. When you

---

* For additional comment on this problem, see "Formalism in Arithmetic Programs" by M. L. Hartung. Item 7 of Bibliography

say, "Rover is a dog," you mean that Rover belongs to that class of animals which people designate as dogs. Again, if you say, "Dogs can run," then you are evidently referring to the members of a class of animals. However, when you say, " 'Dog' has three letters," you are evidently talking about the word and not about the animal as such. In this book, when we are talking about symbols, we will use quotation marks around them if there is a possibility that the meaning of the sentence might be misinterpreted. With this agreement in mind, consider the two sentences below:

Sue has three letters.
"Sue" has three letters.

They have quite different meanings. The first one conveys the idea that someone named Sue has three letters or messages. The second sentence conveys the idea that the word *Sue* contains three letters. The sentence, "The word *Sue* has three letters," is another way of writing the second of the above sentences.

In mathematics, also, we distinguish between a name and the idea possessing the name. For example, "Write 'four' on the chalkboard" and "Write four on the chalkboard" are two sentences that look very much alike, but that have different meanings. The first sentence conveys the command that a symbol for the number four should be written on the board. This, of course, can be done. The second sentence demands that the number four should be written on the board. This, of course, cannot be done, because the number four is an *idea*, not a symbol. We can write "four" four times on the chalkboard; in other words, we can write the symbol four four times on the chalkboard. To see the point of this example, think about the following three sentences. You can easily see that the first of these sentences does not make any sense, but that the last two do.

Write cow on the chalkboard.
Write "cow" on the chalkboard.
Write the word *cow* on the chalkboard.

In any language, sentences contain words that are symbols or names for things. We have a special name for these words or symbols; we call them "nouns." In mathematics, we have a special name for those nouns that are symbols for numbers. We call them "numerals." Numerals are symbols. The configuration you see below is a numeral, *not* a number. The numeral 5 enables you to think of the mathematical idea of five just as the word *cow* enables you to think of the animal named by this word.

5

CONCLUSION

The fundamental problem of the classroom teacher of arithmetic is to select the activities and manage the communication problem so that the child can easily abstract from these activities the mathematical ideas the teacher has in mind. Our discussion in this chapter has several purposes. We have tried to show you that the teacher of arithmetic must be aware of the changes that are occurring in the arithmetic program. He must himself understand the mathematical concepts he is trying to teach. Only when the teacher has the concepts clearly in mind can he select the methods of instruction to be used. In planning the instruction, the teacher is faced with the double problem of teaching abstractions and teaching the appropriate symbols to convey ideas. He must, therefore, discuss symbols as well as the ideas they stand for. He must make a distinction between a word and the idea it represents, and in particular, a distinction between a numeral and a number.

The remaining chapters of this book will be devoted largely to mathematical concepts and to the theory of arithmetic. As noted above, we will discuss teaching implications whenever appropriate. In the main, however, it is our intention to discuss the *content* of a modern arithmetic program for the elementary school rather than the methods for teaching such a program.

CHAPTER QUIZ

A "chapter quiz" is presented at the end of each chapter. The responses for these quizzes are given in the back of the book, beginning on page 426.

1 Certain topics that might appear in an arithmetic textbook are listed below. Some of the topics are concerned with social and business applications; some, with computational procedures; and some, with mathematical concepts. For each topic, decide whether you would expect to find it included in a "traditional" or in a "modern" arithmetic text, or in both. In each case, give reasons for your decision.

A Computing compound interest
B Numeration systems
C Area of a triangle
D Properties of addition and multiplication
E Short division
F Computing with decimals
G The family budget
H One-to-one correspondence between sets

   I Automobile insurance

   J Basic facts for addition

   K Checking addition by casting out nines

2 List some of the ways mathematics is used in a science book for the upper elementary grades. Make a similar list for a social studies book.

3 React to each of the following hypothetical classroom situations in light of the discussion in this chapter; that is, evaluate the teacher's choice of method for presenting the material. Give reasons for your evaluation.

   A Teacher A teaches second graders how to subtract by telling them, "To subtract 4 from 6, we think how much to add to 4 to get 6."

   B. Teacher B shows fifth graders how to find the area of a rectangle and then gives them a rule, "To find the area of a rectangle, multiply the length by the width."

   C Miss C teaches her first graders how to count by first having them learn the numerals in sequence from 1 through 10. Then she asks them to count various groups of objects.

4 Imagine that you are a teacher and that you will be required to teach a sequence of lessons on one of the topics listed below. For one of the three topics, tell what important ideas and skills are to be taught in connection with it. While all these ideas will be discussed in full in some chapter of this book, this exercise will help you to see what some of the basic problems are.

   A Subtraction involving borrowing

   B Long division

   C Area of a parallelogram

5 Suppose that a child thinks that 4 "added to" 2 is 24. Do you think he understands the meaning of addition? Do you think he understands the distinction between numbers and numerals?

6 The numbers 1, 3, 5, 7, 9, etc., are the odd numbers, and the numbers 2, 4, 6, 8, 10, etc., are the even numbers. Find the sums of several pairs of even numbers. What conclusion can you draw about the sum of two even numbers? Find the sums of several pairs of odd numbers. What generalization can you make about the sum of two odd numbers?

7 Draw four triangles of different sizes. For each triangle, measure the length of each of the three sides. Then find the sum of the lengths of the two shorter sides and compare this sum with the length of the longest side. What can you decide about triangles and the lengths of their sides?

SUPPLEMENTARY READINGS

For additional information and other points of view on the topics discussed in this chapter, the following references are helpful.

Banks, J. Houston, *Learning and Teaching Arithmetic*, chapter 1. This chapter contains a discussion of the present status of mathematics education in relationship to past events. It also includes a discussion of present-day issues in the teaching of arithmetic. Item 8 of Bibliography

Marks, John L., Purdy, D. Richard, and Kinney, Lucien B., *Teaching Arithmetic for Understanding*, chapter 1. A good discussion of the major goals of arithmetic teaching. Item 9 of Bibliography

Van Engen, Henry, "Which Way Arithmetic?" This article contains a discussion of how changes in learning theory are changing the arithmetic program. It also contains examples of teaching mathematical ideas by using new principles of learning. Item 10 of Bibliography

Wheat, Harry G., "The Fallacy of Social Arithmetic." This article presents a strong argument against a social approach to arithmetic. Item 11 of Bibliography

Chapter two

Natural numbers

Sets and subsets
Mapping
Equivalent sets
The union of two sets
The intersection of two sets
The Cartesian product of two sets
Standard sets
Finite and infinite sets
Order
Ordinal and other uses of numerals

Imagine that this is the first day of a new school year. The school bell has just called the children to order. You glance around and find that each of your pupils is seated at a desk. You also notice that each desk is occupied. At once, you know that there are exactly as many desks as there are children in the room. Suppose someone were to ask you how you know this without counting pupils or desks.

Perhaps your first reaction to this question is that it is too simple. However, you may find the question hard to answer, even though there is a perfectly definite answer. To find the answer, it is necessary to analyze the basic ideas involved in the situation. You intuitively used several very fundamental mathematical concepts in arriving at your conclusion about the number of desks and the number of children in the classroom.

In this book, we intend to answer the question under discussion, along with those we raised in Chapter 1 concerning some other important concepts of mathematics, such as the idea of number and the meaning of the operation of addition. In this chapter, we will begin to answer certain questions about some basic ideas of mathematics.

Sets and subsets

Throughout the book you will find that the notion of a set is extremely useful. Many ideas of mathematics can be simplified and unified when they are viewed in terms of sets of objects. In this chapter, for example, you will see how the idea of number, the order of numbers, and the process of counting can be explained within the framework of sets.

We will begin with a discussion of some of the terminology mathematicians use when they talk about sets. A set is any definite collection of objects. Many commonly used words, such as *group, bundle, family*, and *class*, convey a somewhat similar idea. In mathematics, the word *set* is used in connection with mathematical objects such as numbers or points that share some property or satisfy some relation. Thus, the pupils in a class, the desks in the classroom, the rooms in the school building, the teachers in the school, and the numbers from 1 through 10 are all examples of sets of objects. When we wish to talk about the specific objects that belong to a set, we refer to them as *members* of the set. There are two principal methods of specifying the members of a set.

First, it may be possible to list, or *tabulate*, the names of the members of a set. Suppose, for example, the set of children in the Smith family consists of Sam, Sue, Jimmy, Clara, and John. You can symbolize this set in the following manner:

$$\{Sam, Sue, Jimmy, Clara, John\}$$

Notice the braces that are used to enclose the names of the members of the set. Braces will be used whenever we are tabulating a set. The symbol is read "the set whose members are Sam, Sue, Jimmy, Clara, and John." The order in which the names of the members are listed is not important. The set tabulated below is the same as the set listed above, even though the order of the names has been changed.

$$\{Jimmy, Clara, Sam, Sue, John\}$$

Similarly, if a, b, and c represent the members of a set, $\{b, c, a\}$ is the same set as $\{a, b, c\}$. We can use the symbol for equality to show that we have two names for the same set. Thus,

$$\{Sam, Sue, Jimmy, Clara, John\} = \{Jimmy, Clara, Sam, Sue, John\},$$

and

$$\{a, b, c\} = \{b, c, a\}.$$

It is convenient to use letters to name sets that have many members; we will therefore agree to use the capital letters of the alphabet. We can write the sentences

$$A = \{Sam, Sue, Jimmy, Clara, John\},$$

and

$$B = \{Sue, Jimmy, John, Clara, Sam\}.$$

Since A is the same set as B, we can also write

$$A = B.$$

Second, you can specify the members of a set by giving a rule that enables you to determine whether or not a given object is a member. Consider, for example, "the set consisting of the first six Presidents of the United States." The phrase "the first six Presidents of the United States" enables you to determine whether or not a given individual belongs to this set. We will say that this phrase gives us a *description* of the set. A tabulation of the set just described, which we can call set C, is given below.

$$C = \{George\ Washington,\ John\ Adams,\ Thomas\ Jefferson,$$
$$James\ Madison,\ James\ Monroe,\ John\ Quincy\ Adams\}.$$

From the description of set C, you know that such men as Andrew Jackson, Abraham Lincoln, Daniel Webster, and Henry Clay are not members of the set.

Again, consider the set of all Presidents of the United States whose last names begin with the letter W. This set is given below.

$$\{George\ Washington,\ Woodrow\ Wilson\}$$

Sometimes there are no objects that satisfy a given description. For example, suppose we ask you for the set of all Presidents of the United States whose last names begin with the letter X. Since there has been no President whose last name begins with X, we say that this set is the *empty set*. The set of baseball players who are simultaneously members of the Chicago White Sox and the New York Yankees is another example of the empty set. A symbol for the empty set is shown below. This symbol is read "the empty set," or "the null set." The symbol $\emptyset$ is also used for the empty set.

$$\{ \ \}$$

Whether a set is specified by listing the names of its members or by giving a description, it must always be possible to decide whether or not a specific object is a member of the set. This is what we mean when we say a set is a *definite* collection of objects.

One of the interesting and useful ideas related to sets is the idea of a *subset*. Each of the sets mentioned above can be considered a subset of some other set. The set of children in the Smith family is a subset of all the members of the Smith family; the set of the first six Presidents of the United States is a subset of all the Presidents of the United States; and so on.

If D = {1, 2, 3, 4, 5, 6, 7, 8} and E = {1, 4, 8}, then E is a subset of D because every member of E is a member of D. If F = {1, 7, 8, 9}, then F is not a subset of D because one member of F—namely, 9—is not a member of D. For any two sets X and Y, X is a subset of Y if each member of X is a member of Y.

We will have occasion to use two special subsets of a given set. Consider the set X = {1, 2, 3, 4, 5, 6}. We will say that X is a subset of itself since every member of X is a member of X. By the same line of reasoning, every set is a subset of itself. We will also say that the empty set is a subset of X because the empty set obviously has no members that are not members of X. In fact, the empty set is a subset of every set, including the empty set itself. Set A is called a *proper subset* of B if A is a subset of B and if A is not equal to B. Hence, a set is not a proper subset of itself; set B is called an *improper subset* of itself. The empty set is a proper subset of every set except itself.

Notice that a subset is itself a set. Thus, {3, 6} is a set whose members are 3 and 6. Only if {3, 6} is considered in relation to some other set, such as {0, 3, 6, 9, 12, 15}, do we call it a subset. Further, it is important to keep in mind that being a member of a set and being a subset of a set are quite different concepts. For example, the *number* 2 is a *member* of {1, 2, 3}; but the *set* whose only member is 2—that is {2}—is a *subset* of {1, 2, 3}.

You will find several blocks of exercises like the following one in each chapter. These exercises are labeled consecutively throughout the book. The responses for these exercises are given in the back of the book, beginning on page 399.

1 Describe the following sets in words:

  a {1, 2, 3, 4, 5, 6, 7}
  b {2, 4, 8, 16, 32}
  c {Saturday, Sunday}
  d {a, e, i, o, u, y}
  e {14, 35, 21, 28, 7}

2 Tabulate the following sets:

a The states of the United States whose names begin with the letter *I*

b The even numbers less than 16 and greater than 2

c The squares of all the counting numbers less than 9

d The female Presidents of the United States

e The months of the year that have exactly 30 days

3 Is it possible to determine whether or not a specific object is a member of each of the sets described below?

a All persons who weigh more than 150 pounds

b All persons with light hair

c All even numbers greater than 101

d All numbers greater than 42 and also less than 6

4 Suppose that A = {2, 4, 6}. Use A to form subsets B, C, D, and E that meet the requirements expressed below.

a A = B.

b C is a proper subset of B.

c D is a subset of C, and C is a subset of D.

d E is an improper subset of B.

5 Name all the subsets of each of the following sets.

a A = {Sam, Wayne}.

b B = {Nancy, Carl, Ed, Marie}.

6 Suppose that A = {5, 6, 7}. List the proper and improper subsets of A. How many subsets does A have?

7 Determine a rule for deciding how many subsets—both proper and improper—a set has if the number of members in the set is known. You should be able to arrive at the rule if you consider several specific examples. First determine the number of subsets a set with one member has; then, the number of subsets a set with two members has; next, the number of subsets a set with three members has; and so on.

Mapping

We have talked about one relation that may exist between two sets; that is, the sets may be related in the sense that one of the sets is a subset of the other. We can determine another useful relation between two sets by the process of *mapping* the members of the sets onto each other.

By matching each member of a set A with a member of a set B, we map A *into* B. The diagram at the top of page 16 illustrates a mapping

of A into B. The direction of the arrows indicates that A is mapped into
B rather than B into A. We say that each member of A is mapped *onto*
a member of B.

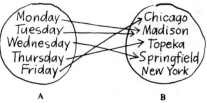

A   B

Notice that Monday is mapped onto Madison; hence, Madison is the
image of Monday. Similarly, Madison is the image of Tuesday, Springfield
is the image of Wednesday, and so on. However, Madison is not mapped
onto Monday, so Monday is *not* the image of Madison; nor is any of the
other days the image of the city onto which it is mapped. Notice also that
Monday and Tuesday are mapped onto Madison; that is, Madison is the
image of both Monday and Tuesday. Because one member of B is the
image of more than one member of A, this mapping is an example of a
many-to-one mapping.

Mappings such as the one illustrated above are not very interesting nor,
for our purposes, very important. A much more interesting and important
kind of mapping is illustrated below. Note the double-headed arrows,
which indicate that we have two mappings. We have mapped each member
of S onto a member of T, and we have mapped each member of T onto a
member of S. Notice that 10 is the image of Harry, and Harry is the image
of 10; 12 is the image of Pete, and Pete is the image of 12; and so on.
You will remember that the mapping illustrated above was called a mapping of A *into* B. That mapping is an "into" mapping because B has a
member—New York—that is not an image of a member of A. By contrast, the mappings illustrated in the diagram below are a mapping of
S *onto* T because each member of T is an image of a member of S and
also a mapping of T *onto* S because each member of S is an image of a
member of T.

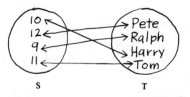

S   T

The mappings of S onto T and T onto S are related in a special manner;
we say that the mapping of T onto S is the *inverse* of the mapping of S

onto T because the mapping of T onto S may be determined from the mapping of S onto T by interchanging images. That is, a given member of S is mapped onto a member of T if and only if the same member of T is mapped onto the given member of S. Likewise, the mapping of S onto T is the inverse of the mapping of T onto S.

You can see that each member of T is the image of only one member of S and that each member of S is the image of only one member of T; therefore, both mappings are *one-to-one* mappings. Also, in this case, each member of S has one and only one image in T, and each member of T has one and only one image in S. We say that these two mappings constitute a *one-to-one correspondence* between sets S and T because both mappings are one-to-one and both are onto.

The diagrams below provide further examples of various kinds of mappings. For each diagram, we have described the kind of mapping or mappings illustrated. Each of the first three diagrams illustrates a single

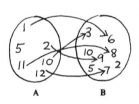
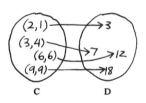

One-to-one mapping
A is mapped into B.

One-to-one mapping
C is mapped onto D.

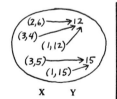
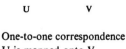

Many-to-one mapping
X is mapped onto Y.

One-to-one correspondence
U is mapped onto V.
V is mapped onto U.

mapping from the first set into the second. The fourth diagram, however, illustrates two mappings—a mapping from the first set onto the second and the inverse mapping from the second set onto the first.

Equivalent sets

Whenever the members of two sets, such as S and T discussed in the preceding section, can be put in one-to-one correspondence, we will say that the sets are *equivalent*. Note that we can decide whether two sets are equivalent without knowing how many objects are in the sets simply by determining whether or not their members can be put in one-to-one correspondence. Also note that, unlike *equal* sets, equivalent sets need not contain the same members.

Now we can return to the classroom situation described at the beginning of this chapter. Because each child is seated at a desk and each desk is occupied by one child, you know that the set of children is mapped onto the set of desks and the set of desks is mapped onto the set of children. Or, stated in other words, each desk is the image of one and only one child, and each child is the image of one and only one desk. Thus, the set of desks and the set of children are equivalent, and it is possible to decide that the number of children and the number of desks is the same without actually determining this number.

8 Form a set of numbers X, a set of people Y, and a mapping from X into Y so that the mapping of X into Y is one-to-one.
9 Form a set of numbers X, a set of people Y, and a mapping of Y into X so that the mapping is many-to-one.
10 Form a set of numbers X and a set of people Y so that X is equivalent to Y.
11 Decide whether each of the sentences below expresses a true or a false statement about the mapping exhibited by the following diagram.

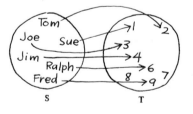

a Tom is an image of 2.
b 2 is an image of Tom.
c S is equivalent to T.
d S is mapped onto a subset of T.
e S is a subset of T.
f S is equivalent to a subset of T.
12 Suppose that R = {Bob, 5, pencil, Sara, the sun}. Use this set to form the sets described in exercises a and b on page 19.

a Set K so that K is equivalent to a subset of R.

b Set D so that R is equivalent to a subset of D.

13 Several mappings are illustrated below. Check each one to determine whether the mapping is many-to-one or one-to-one, and tell whether or not the mapping is onto.

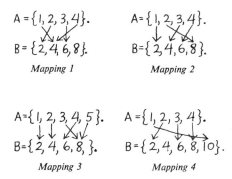

Mapping 1 Mapping 2

Mapping 3 Mapping 4

14 Several pairs of mappings are illustrated below. Check each pair to determine if the mappings are inverses of each other and if they constitute a one-to-one correspondence.

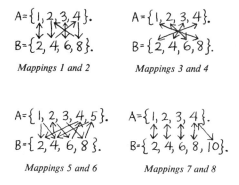

Mappings 1 and 2 Mappings 3 and 4

Mappings 5 and 6 Mappings 7 and 8

The union of two sets

Now that we have examined some of the ways in which sets can be related, we can consider some of the operations that can be performed on sets. One of the most important operations on sets is that of forming the *union* of two sets. In nonmathematical terms, you are forming the union of two sets when you put the coins you have in your hand with the coins you have in your pocket or when you put the books on the table with the books in the bookcase.

In discussing the union of sets, we will find it convenient to refer to the four sets tabulated below. The letters a, b, c, d, and so on, represent objects.

$$F = \{a, b, c, d, e\}. \qquad\qquad H = \{d, e, f, i\}.$$
$$G = \{f, g, h\}. \qquad\qquad\quad I = \{k, h\}.$$

Notice that sets F and G have no members in common. Such sets are *disjoint sets*. In general, any two sets are disjoint if no member of either set is a member of the other set. Sets F and H are obviously not disjoint because d and e are members of both sets. Sets that have one or more members in common are said to *meet*. For sets F, G, H, and I, you should be able to tell by simple inspection which of the other pairs of sets are disjoint and which pairs meet.

When you form the union of two sets, you generate a third set composed of all the members of each set. Thus, the set tabulated below is the union of F and G because it contains all the members of F and all the members of G.

$$F \cup G = \{a, b, c, d, e, f, g, h\}.$$

Notice the symbol $F \cup G$, used to indicate the union of sets F and G. This symbol is read "F union G," or, since $\cup$ resembles a cup, it is sometimes read "F cup G." You should have no difficulty in remembering the symbol used for the union of two sets since it resembles the letter U.

Now consider $F \cup H$. You might be tempted to write the following:

$$F \cup H = \{a, b, c, d, e, d, e, f, i\}.$$

Notice, however, that because sets F and H meet, d and e, which represent the same objects in H as they do in F, occur twice. Remember that we defined the union of two sets as the set composed of all the members of each set. If two sets, like F and H, have members in common, these common members need be named only once in tabulating the set that is the union of the two sets. Hence, the set indicated below is the union of F and H.

$$F \cup H = \{a, b, c, d, e, f, i\}.$$

From these two examples, you should be able to form the union of the following pairs of sets: F and I, G and H, G and I, H and I.

You will remember that we said earlier that the order in which the names of the members of a set are listed does not make any difference. From this, you should see that $G \cup F$ is the same set as $F \cup G$. More specifically,

$$\{a, b, c, d, e, f, g, h\} = \{f, g, h, a, b, c, d, e\}.$$

In fact, this is true for any two sets in general. Thus, for any two sets C and D,

$$C \cup D = D \cup C.$$

Since the union of two given sets contains all the members of each set, it should be apparent that each of the given sets is a subset of the set formed by the union. Hence, both F and G are subsets of $F \cup G$.

You should also be able to see that the union of a non-empty set with the empty set is equal to the non-empty set. For example,

$$\{5, 10, 15, 20\} \cup \{\ \} = \{5, 10, 15, 20\}.$$

Also, the union of the empty set with itself is the empty set:

$$\{\ \} \cup \{\ \} = \{\ \}.$$

From the examples given in this section, you can probably infer that the union of two disjoint sets bears some relationship to the sum of two numbers. In Chapter 4 we will examine sums and products. At that time we will develop the relationship between the sum of two numbers and the union of two disjoint sets.

The intersection of two sets

Another important operation on sets is that of forming their *intersection*. When you form the intersection of two sets, the result is a third set that consists of those members, and only those members, that belong to both the given sets.

Consider, for example, the following two sets whose members are on two committees at a given school:

Student Council = S = {Don, Ruth, Joe, Carl, Nancy, Jim}.
College Life Committee = C = {Don, Sally, Joe, Wayne}.

Notice that Don and Joe are on both committees and, hence, are members of both sets. Don and Joe are members of a third set, which is the intersection of S and C. This set is indicated below:

$$S \cap C = \{Don, Joe\}.$$

Notice the symbol, $S \cap C$, used to represent the intersection of sets S and C. This symbol is read "S intersection C," or, because the symbol $\cap$ resembles a peak or a cap, it is sometimes read "S cap C."

Let us consider some other examples. Suppose that

$$A = \{1, 2, 3, 4, 6, 12\},$$

and that
$$B = \{1, 2, 3, 5, 6, 10, 15, 30\}.$$

The intersection of A and B is the following set:
$$A \cap B = \{1, 2, 3, 6\}.$$

Now consider the following two sets:
$$X = \{2, 4, 6, 8, 10\},$$

and
$$Y = \{1, 3, 5, 7, 9\}.$$

Notice that X and Y are disjoint sets. Since the intersection of two sets contains those objects, and only those objects, that belong to both sets, it should be apparent that the intersection of X and Y is the empty set. Hence, we can write
$$X \cap Y = \{ \ \}.$$

You should be able to satisfy yourself that it is the case that the intersection of two disjoint sets is always the empty set. By the same line of reasoning, the intersection of any given set with the empty set will be the empty set. This is so because two such sets are obviously disjoint. *

The Cartesian product of two sets

A third important operation that can be performed on sets is that of generating the *Cartesian set* or *Cartesian product* of two given sets.† We will first explain this concept by using a nonmathematical example.

Suppose that four couples meet for an evening of bridge. They plan to change partners during the course of the evening so that each man has each woman as his partner at some time. The problem is to determine the number of pairs of bridge partners that will be formed.

First, we will indicate the two sets, one composed of the four men and the other composed of the four women.

$$M = \{\text{Roger, John, Ralph, Jim}\}.$$
$$W = \{\text{Ann, Janet, Harriet, Alice}\}.$$

---

* For a geometric interpretation of union and intersection of sets by means of Venn diagrams, see *Modern Mathematics: Introductory Concepts and Their Implications* by A. B. Evenson, pp. 9-22. Item 12 of Bibliography

† The word *Cartesian* is derived from the name of René Descartes, the seventeenth century French philosopher-mathematician, who developed the methods of analytic geometry.

It is quite apparent that Roger must be partners with Ann, Janet, Harriet, and Alice in turn. This will also be true for John, Ralph, and Jim. The set of all possible pairs of bridge partners is exhibited below. Parentheses are used to enclose the names of the members of each pair of bridge partners.

{(Roger, Ann), (Roger, Janet), (Roger, Harriet), (Roger, Alice),
(John, Ann), (John, Janet), (John, Harriet), (John, Alice),
(Ralph, Ann), (Ralph, Janet), (Ralph, Harriet), (Ralph, Alice),
(Jim, Ann), (Jim, Janet), (Jim, Harriet), (Jim, Alice)}

You will note that there are sixteen pairs of partners. These pairs are called *ordered pairs* because the names of the members of each pair are listed in a definite order—man first and woman second. This set of ordered pairs is the Cartesian set, or *cross product*, of the two sets M and W. The cross product of M and W is symbolized as shown below. The symbol

$$M \times W$$

M × W is read "M cross W."* You should also note that the members of the set M × W are pairs of objects, rather than single objects, where the first object is a member of set M and the second object is a member of set W.

We have said that the cross product of two sets, like M and W, results in a set of ordered pairs. Since order is important and (Roger, Ann) is different from (Ann, Roger), for example, you can probably infer that W × M is a different set of ordered pairs from M × W. You should form the set W × M for yourself and compare it with M × W, exhibited above.

We will illustrate the cross product of two sets with another example. Consider the following sets C and D:

$$C = \{a, b, c\}.$$
$$D = \{1, 2\}.$$

First, we will form the cross product of C and D.

$$C \times D = \{(a, 1), (a, 2), (b, 1), (b, 2), (c, 1), (c, 2)\}.$$

Note that the first member of each ordered pair is a member of C, while the second member is a member of D.

---

* Note that the symbol for the cross product of two sets is the same as the symbol for the product of two numbers. There should be no confusion if you keep in mind that this symbol represents a cross product when used in connection with sets and that it represents a product when used in connection with numbers.

Next, consider the cross product of D and C:

$$D \times C = \{(1, a), (1, b), (1, c), (2, a), (2, b), (2, c)\}.$$

Note that, in this case, the first member of each ordered pair is a member of D, while the second member is a member of C. $(a, 1)$ is a different ordered pair from $(1, a)$ because the members occur in a different order. Hence, C $\times$ D and D $\times$ C are different sets because they contain different ordered pairs, but they are equivalent sets, as shown below.

$$C \times D = \{(a, 1), (a, 2), (b, 1), (b, 2), (c, 1), (c, 2)\}.$$
$$D \times C = \{(1, a), (1, b), (1, c), (2, a), (2, b), (2, c)\}.$$

We can also form the Cartesian product of a set with itself. For example, suppose that

$$A = \{0, 2, 4\}.$$

Then the Cartesian set of A—that is, A $\times$ A—is formed by matching each member of A with each member of A in turn. Thus,

$$
\begin{aligned}
A \times A = \{&(0, 0), (0, 2), (0, 4),\\
&(2, 0), (2, 2), (2, 4),\\
&(4, 0), (4, 2), (4, 4)\}.
\end{aligned}
$$

We can generalize the notion of the Cartesian product of two sets to say that, for any two non-empty sets A and B, the Cartesian product A $\times$ B is a set of ordered pairs that is obtained by associating each member of A with each member of B in turn.

Just as the union of disjoint sets is related to the sum of two numbers, the cross product of two sets is related to the product of two numbers. Remember that M and W, discussed earlier, each have 4 members, and M $\times$ W has 4 $\times$ 4, or 16, members. Similarly, C has 3 members, D has 2 members, and C $\times$ D has 6 members. Also, A has 3 members and A $\times$ A has 9 members. This relationship between the cross product of two sets and the product of two numbers will be examined again in Chapter 4, where sums and products are discussed.

15 Tabulate as indicated the union and the cross product of the sets tabulated below.

$H = \{a, b, c\}.$ $R = \{1, 2\}.$ $K = \{\ \}.$ $M = \{\text{Sue, Doris, Tad, Tom}\}.$
a H $\times$ K   **b** H $\cup$ K   **c** M $\times$ R   **d** R $\times$ M   **e** R $\cup$ R

16 Tabulate as indicated the intersection and the union of the sets tabulated at the top of page 25.

X = {1, 2, 3, 4, 5, 6}.   Y = {1, 3, 5, 7, 9}.   Z = {2, 4, 6, 8, 10}.

a $X \cap Y$ **c** $Z \cap Y$ **e** $Y \cup Z$

b $X \cup Y$ **d** $Z \cap X$ **f** $Y \cap X$

17 Use the sets you formed for exercise 16 to answer the following questions:

a Is $X \cap Y = Y \cap X$?

b Which of the sets you formed is the same as $Y \cap Z$?

c Which of the sets you formed is the same as $X \cap Z$?

18 If C and D are any two sets, is it always true that $C \cup D = D \cup C$? Use specific sets of numbers to illustrate your answer.

19 If C and D are any two sets, is it always true that $C \cap D = D \cap C$? Use specific sets to illustrate your answer.

20 Is it ever true that, for any sets C and D, $C \times D = D \times C$? Give an illustration to explain your answer.

21 Give an example of sets C and D so that $C \cap D = C \cup D$.

Standard sets

Earlier in this chapter you learned how to determine whether two sets are equivalent without counting the members of each set. For example, if you know that every seat in a certain auditorium is occupied by just one person and that no one is standing, then you conclude at once that the set of persons in the audience is equivalent to the set of seats in the auditorium. In a sense, the set of seats in the auditorium is used as a standard for comparison. If we know the *number* of members in the set of seats, then we can conclude that the same number should be used to represent the number of members in the set of people in the audience.

We will now examine more closely the idea of a set used as a standard. Let us agree to use the sets tabulated below. In these tabulations, each symbol represents a different object. Let us further agree that, when you

Kay = {☆}.   Ming = {☆ △}.   Roo = {☆ △ ○}.
Hi = {☆ △ ○ □}.   El = {☆ △ ○ □ ◊}.

are asked to determine the number of objects in a set, such as the number of fingers on your left hand, you are to find a set tabulated in the above display that is equivalent to the set of fingers. In this example, your response would obviously be "El." If you knew that "El" was always associated with the set tabulated above, then it would not be necessary to have the "El" set always on display. You would know from repeated experience how many objects are needed to form a set equivalent to the "El" set.

We will now use the idea of certain sets as standards and the properties and operations of sets previously discussed to develop the natural numbers. All of you, of course, have a working knowledge of the natural numbers; you became acquainted with them in childhood and have used them for many years. You already know that numerousness is not related to the nature of physical objects. Thus, you would not hesitate to use the natural number 5 to represent the numerousness of each set of objects pictured below.

You may have an intuitive notion of a number as being associated with many different sets that are alike with respect to numerousness. This is a good beginning for an understanding of the way in which natural numbers can be identified with sets. Keep in mind that our goal is to lay the foundation of a system and also that the identification of natural numbers with sets leads to many interesting mathematical relationships.*

We have said that number is somehow related to the numerousness of sets. In fact, we identify natural numbers with special kinds of sets— namely, *standard sets*. The meaning of "standard sets" will become clear a bit later, but first we need to examine the make-up of a set more closely.

It is important that you distinguish between a set and its members. For example, the Brady family has as its members, Mr. Brady, Mrs. Brady, Howard, and Sue. The family as a set is one entity—

{Mr. Brady, Mrs. Brady, Howard, Sue}

—but the members of the family, or set, are four separate entities of a different kind.

In fact, sets themselves are frequently members of other sets. Consider, for example, the set of couples present at a party:

{the Allens, the Millers, the Kings, the Robinsons}

Each member of the set exhibited above is itself a set. The following set is the same set as the one above:

---

* The discussion that follows represents *one* approach to the development of the natural numbers. Other approaches are, of course, possible. A more sophisticated and rigorous discussion of this development can be found in Chapter 2 of *Set Theory: The Structure of Arithmetic*, by Norman Hamilton and Joseph Landin. Item 13 of Bibliography

$\{$ (Bill Allen, Jane Allen), (Walter Miller, Donna Miller),
(Jim King, Carol King), (Ralph Robinson, Mary Robinson)$\}$

It is sometimes convenient to think of a set that contains both individual objects and also the set containing those objects as a member. Suppose, for example, that David, John, and Joe perform as a musical trio. We will call this set A.

$$A = \{David, John, Joe\}.$$

Suppose, further, that their income is distributed in the following manner: one share to each member of the trio and one share to the trio itself for operating expenses. We will give the name B to the set of those sharing in the income.

$$B = \{David, John, Joe, \{David, John, Joe\}\}.$$

Notice that one member of B is A; thus, B could have been symbolized in the following way:

$$B = \{David, John, Joe, A\}.$$

The idea of forming a set composed of the individual members of a given set and the given set itself will be useful in our development of standard sets. You should be able to think of other examples like set B above, such as the set consisting of all the members of a swimming team and the team itself as the set of recipients of trophies, or the members of a business partnership and the partnership itself as a set for legal purposes.

One further tool that we need before we develop the standard sets of natural numbers is a systematic way of constructing a set that in some sense succeeds or "follows" a given set. We will call such a set the *successor set* of the given set and will define it to be the set that includes the members of the given set and the set itself. Thus, set B, described above and exhibited again below,

$$B = \{David, John, Joe, A\},$$

is the successor set of A. It includes the individual members of A and A itself as a member. From now on, we will symbolize the successor set of a given set in the following way: The successor set of a given set A will be named A' (this symbol is read "A prime"); the successor set of a given set B will be named B'; and so on. (Using this notation, we would call the successor set exhibited above A' rather than B.)

The following examples may further clarify the idea of a successor set. Suppose that

$$K = \{a, b, c, d\}.$$

Then the successor set of K is K′:

$$K' = \{a, b, c, d, \{a, b, c, d\}\} = \{a, b, c, d, K\}.$$

Suppose that

$$L = \{\text{five, three}\}.$$

Then the successor set of L is L′:

$$L' = \{\text{five, three, L}\}.$$

Notice that we obtain the successor set of a given set by forming the union of two sets. We do this by forming the union of a set having certain members with the set itself. Thus, $K' = K \cup \{K\}$, and $L' = L \cup \{L\}$. We now generalize this notion and define the successor set of a given set P as follows:

If P is any set, then the successor set $P' = P \cup \{P\}$.

By means of the successor set, we can form a sequence of standard sets with which natural numbers can be identified. First, we must decide which set we will use to start the sequence. It seems quite natural to start with the empty set—the set that has no members. We will identify the natural number zero with the empty set. Then we can write the following:

$$\{\ \} = 0.$$

Next, we will construct 0′, the successor set of 0. We will identify the natural number 1 with this set, and we can write the following:

$$0' = 0 \cup \{0\} = \{\ \} \cup \{0\} = \{0\} = 1.$$

Note that {0} is not the empty set, but is a set that has one member, the number zero. Also keep in mind that we are developing natural numbers in terms of *standard sets* for the natural numbers. Any set equivalent to a standard set will have the same natural number as the standard set. Thus, any set equivalent to {0} will also have the natural number 1 associated with it. That is, it will have exactly one member.

Next, we construct the successor set of 1—namely, 1′—which is identified with the natural number 2. We write the following:

$$1' = 1 \cup \{1\} = \{0\} \cup \{1\} = \{0, 1\} = 2.$$

Again, remember that any set equivalent to {0, 1}, such as {a, b} or {(Alice, Tom), (Susan, Fred)} or {cat, dog}, will have the natural number 2 associated with it.

In a similar manner, we can proceed as follows:

$$2' = 2 \cup \{2\} = \{0, 1\} \cup \{2\} = \{0, 1, 2\} = 3.$$
$$3' = 3 \cup \{3\} = \{0, 1, 2\} \cup \{3\} = \{0, 1, 2, 3\} = 4.$$
$$4' = 4 \cup \{4\} = \{0, 1, 2, 3\} \cup \{4\} = \{0, 1, 2, 3, 4\} = 5.$$
$$5' = 5 \cup \{5\} = \{0, 1, 2, 3, 4\} \cup \{5\} = \{0, 1, 2, 3, 4, 5\} = 6.$$

We can generalize the above procedure by noting that the successor set of any standard set can be constructed by forming the union of the standard set and the set containing the standard set as its sole member. Using mathematical notation, we can develop the natural number x as shown below. The three dots in the symbol $\{0, 1, 2 \ldots, x - 2\}$ represent the members of the set, if any, that are not named in the tabulation.

$$(x - 1)' = (x - 1) \cup \{x - 1\}$$
$$= \{0, 1, 2, \ldots, x - 2\} \cup \{x - 1\}$$
$$= \{0, 1, 2, 3, \ldots, x - 1\} = x.$$

Here, x represents any natural number greater than 1. You will understand this notation better if you use several natural numbers as replacements for x. For example, suppose you replace x in $(x - 1)'$ by 15. You would then obtain the following:

$$14' = 14 \cup \{14\}$$
$$= \{0, 1, 2, 3, 4, 5, 6, 7, 8, 9, 10, 11, 12, 13\} \cup \{14\}$$
$$= \{0, 1, 2, 3, 4, 5, 6, 7, 8, 9, 10, 11, 12, 13, 14\}$$

Hence, we know that 15, the successor of 14, is identified with the standard set $\{0, 1, 2, 3, \ldots, 14\}$.

The set of standard sets whose members are developed in this way is the set of natural numbers. We can symbolize the set of natural numbers in the following way. The three dots within the braces are used to indicate that the sequence of numbers goes on and on without end.

$$N = \{0, 1, 2, 3, 4, 5, 6, 7, \ldots\}.$$

You should realize that each of the numbers in the set tabulated above is identified with a standard set, and you should be able to construct the standard set that is equal to any particular natural number.

Next, we will see how natural numbers are used to determine the number of objects in a given set. Let us suppose, for example, that we want to determine the number of objects in the set exhibited below.

$$Q = \{a, b, c, d, e, f, g, h, i\}.$$

We first find a standard set that is equivalent to Q. After some experimentation, we find that the following one-to-one correspondence can be set up.

$$\{a, b, c, d, e, f, g, h, i\}$$
$$\updownarrow \updownarrow \updownarrow \updownarrow \updownarrow \updownarrow \updownarrow \updownarrow \updownarrow$$
$$\{0, 1, 2, 3, 4, 5, 6, 7, 8\}$$

The second set, we know, is the standard set that is identified with the natural number 9. Because Q is equivalent to the standard set 9, we say that Q has 9 members.

22 Explain how each of the following can be interpreted as a set of sets.
a The National Baseball League
b The Butler family reunion
c The population of Canada
d The faculty of a university

23 Tabulate the successor set of each of the following sets.
a { }
b {1, 2}
c {{a}, {a, b}}

24 Exhibit the standard set that can be put in one-to-one correspondence with each of the following sets.
a {Alice, Margaret, {Alice, Margaret}}
b {1, 2, 3, 4}
c {(6, 0), (6, 1), (6, 2), (5, 0), (5, 1), (5, 2)}

25 a Tabulate the successor of the successor of 1.
b Tabulate the successor of the successor of the successor of 21.

26 Tabulate the standard set identified with each of the natural numbers named below.
a 12   **b** 7   **c** 1   **d** 8   **e** 10

Finite and infinite sets

Now that we have identified natural numbers with standard sets, we can make an important distinction between kinds of sets. Any set that is the empty set or that is equivalent to a standard set is a *finite set*. Another way of saying this is to say that a natural number is associated with every finite set. We will say that an *infinite set* is a set that is not finite. Hence, an infinite set is not associated with a natural number.

Let us first consider finite sets and the way in which we determine the natural number that is associated with a finite set. From our discussion, you can see that, because any finite set of objects can be put in one-to-one correspondence with a standard set that is a natural number, any finite set has a natural number associated with it. The natural number that is associated with the given set is identified with the standard set to which the given set is equivalent. Let us say this in another way. If A is a set of objects, we will say that the number of A is the same as the standard set that is equivalent to A. We will use a to represent the number of set A. Symbolically, we write "n[A] = a." This sentence is read, "The number of A equals a." More specifically, if

$$A = \{Henry, Harold, Sue, Clara, Russell\},$$

then the number of A is 5 because A can be put in one-to-one correspondence with the standard set 5, which is $\{0, 1, 2, 3, 4\}$. You can express the fact that the number of A is 5 by writing n[A] = 5. This sentence is read, "The number of A is equal to 5." Similarly, if the number of set B is b, then we can write n[B] = b.

In general, if any two finite sets S and T are equivalent, we can write n[S] = n[T]. Suppose, for example,

$$S = \{cat, dog, rat, mouse\}$$

and

$$T = \{fish, bird, horse, cow\}.$$

Since n[S] = 4 and n[T] = 4, you can readily see that n[S] = n[T].

Of course, after a certain amount of experience in childhood, we learn short cuts for ascertaining the number of members in a given set. One of the short cuts is counting, which we will discuss a little later in this chapter.

27 Given two finite sets A and B such that A is equivalent to an improper subset of B and B is equivalent to an improper subset of A, what do you know about A and B? About n[A] and n[B]?

28 Suppose that you are given two finite sets R and S and that R is equivalent to a subset of S, but S is not equivalent to a subset of R. What do you know about R and S? About n[R] and n[S]?

29 Suppose that you are given two finite sets X and Y and that X is equivalent to Y. What do you know about n[X] and n[Y]?

30 Let A = $\{a, b, c, d, e, f\}$ and let B = $\{1, 2, 3, 4, 5, 6, 7, 8\}$. Use A and B to name each of the natural numbers indicated below.

a n[A]   e n[A $\times$ B]

b n[B]   f n[A $\cap$ B]

c n[A $\cup$ B]   g n[B $\times$ A]

d n[B $\cup$ A]

Now let us consider infinite sets. In the following discussion, we will use what you have learned about equivalent sets to show that the set of natural numbers, the set of even numbers, and the set of odd numbers are examples of infinite sets. You cannot, of course, list all the names of the members of an infinite set; if you could do so, the set would not be infinite. But we use the three dots as "shorthand" notation to show that the members of the set go on and on.

$$N = \{0, 1, 2, 3, 4, 5, 6, \ldots\}.$$

It is important to list the names of enough members of a set so that there will be no question of how to find subsequent members. The set of even numbers, which we call set S, is tabulated below.

$$S = \{0, 2, 4, 6, 8, \ldots\}.$$

From these two examples, you should be able to show how the set of odd numbers can be tabulated.

You know that any two finite sets are equivalent if the members of the two sets can be put in one-to-one correspondence. It should also be evident that a proper subset of a given finite set cannot be equivalent to the given set because the members of the proper subset and the members of the given set cannot be put in one-to-one correspondence. For example, consider $A = \{0, 1, 2, 3, 4, 5\}$ and $B = \{0, 1, 5\}$. B is a proper subset of A, and it is obviously impossible to put the members of A and B into one-to-one correspondence.

As a further example, consider the set of blocks shown in the picture below. The black blocks can be thought of as a proper subset of the set containing all the black and white blocks. It is quite apparent that the set of black blocks cannot be put in one-to-one correspondence with the entire set of blocks.

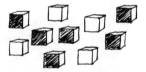

Thus, we can say that, for any given finite set, a proper subset cannot be equivalent to the given set. However, this is not the case with infinite sets. Consider, for example, set N, the set of natural numbers, and set S, the set of even numbers, which we described previously. Set S is certainly a proper subset of set N because every member of S is a member of N, but every member of N is not a member of S. Now let us examine the diagram below, which shows that N and S can be put in one-to-one correspondence by matching each member of N with its "double" in S. This

$$N = \{0, 1, 2, 3, 4, 5, 6, 7, 8, 9, 10, 11, 12 \ldots\}.$$
$$S = \{0, 2, 4, 6, 8, 10, 12, 14, 16, 18, 20, 22, 24 \ldots\}.$$

means that S, which is a proper subset of N, is equivalent to N. But this conclusion conflicts with our findings for finite sets. Therefore, we say that only infinite sets have the property that a proper subset of an infinite set can be equivalent to the given set. In fact, mathematicians use this property to define an infinite set. Any set that can be put in one-to-one correspondence with a proper subset of itself is defined as an infinite set, and any set for which this is not the case is a finite set.

From the preceding discussion, you know that N is an infinite set because it can be put in one-to-one correspondence with a proper subset of itself, namely, set S. We can use this same technique to show that set S is also infinite. Consider set F, for example. This is the set of natural numbers each of which is divisible by 4.

$$F = \{0, 4, 8, 12, 16, \ldots\}.$$

It is evident that F is a proper subset of S because every member of F is a member of S, but not every member of S is a member of F. The diagram below shows how S and F can be put in one-to-one correspondence.

$$S = \{0, 2, 4, 6, 8, 10, 12, 14, 16, 18, 20, \ldots\}.$$
$$F = \{0, 4, 8, 12, 16, 20, 24, 28, 32, 36, 40, \ldots\}.$$

Thus, since set S is equivalent to set F, which is a proper subset of S, we know that S is an infinite set. You should be able to use the device demonstrated in this diagram and in the diagram at the top of the page to show that the set of odd numbers is infinite. For example, you can show that $\{1, 3, 5, 7, 9, 11, \ldots\}$ is equivalent to $\{3, 9, 15, 21, 27, 33, \ldots\}$, which is a proper subset of the set of odd numbers.

31 Decide whether each of the following sets is finite or infinite.
  a The fractions between 0 and 1
  b The population of the world
  c The counting numbers divisible by 7
  d The stars in the universe

32 Set up a one-to-one correspondence between the following pairs of infinite sets.

a The multiples of 5 and the multiples of 15

b The counting numbers and the counting numbers greater than 1003

33 Suppose that $U = \{1, \frac{1}{2}, \frac{1}{3}, \frac{1}{4}, \frac{1}{5}, \ldots\}$. Find a proper subset of U that is equivalent to U.

Order

Now that we have developed the natural numbers in terms of standard sets, we will investigate a very important property of numbers—the property of order. We can first define order in an informal way. We assume that this represents a plausible explanation of the way children learn how numbers are ordered.

Even before children are able to tell you the number of objects in a given set, they are able to say which of two sets has more objects. For example, if a four- or five-year-old child were offered his choice of the two sets of gumdrops pictured below, he would not hesitate to choose the set with the greater number of gumdrops.

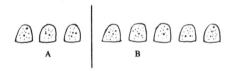

We can use our knowledge of one-to-one correspondence, proper subsets, and natural numbers to explain how a child probably arrives at such a decision.

The two sets of gumdrops are again pictured below. Note that the members of A have been put in one-to-one correspondence with a proper subset of B. Thus, the child who does not know the number of members in either set A or set B can decide that there are more gumdrops in B because some are "left over" after he has matched the members of the two sets.

We can give an informal definition of "less than" for natural numbers on the basis of the example of the gumdrops. Because the members of A can be put in one-to-one correspondence with a proper subset of B, we will say that the number of A is less than the number of B. This idea can be symbolized as $n[A] < n[B]$. The symbol $<$ is read "is less than." Specifically, since $n[A] = 3$ and $n[B] = 5$, we can say "3 is less than 5," or "$3 < 5$."

So far, we have given you an informal notion of the order of natural numbers. Now we can define order more precisely in terms of the idea of "greater than" and the idea of successor sets.

Really, the concept of order is implicit in the way in which we have developed the natural numbers through successor sets. We know that 1 is the successor of 0; hence, we say that 1 is greater than 0. This is symbolized as $1 > 0$. We know that 5 is the successor of 4, so we say that $5 > 4$. The successor of any given natural number is greater than the number which it succeeds. Further, if a first number is greater than a second number and the second number is greater than a third number, then the first number is also greater than the third number. Symbolically, we can write, if $a > b$ and $b > c$, then $a > c$, where a, b, and c represent natural numbers. For example, $9 > 8$ and $8 > 7$; hence, $9 > 7$. This procedure can be generalized, and we can say that a number which is the successor of the successor of the successor . . . is greater than each of the other numbers in the "chain" of successors.

The term "less than" is now easily defined in terms of "greater than." If $5 > 4$, for example, then we know that $4 < 5$. Similarly, if $12 > 8$, then $8 < 12$. In general, if $a > b$, then $b < a$ for any two natural numbers a and b.

Now that we have established the idea of the order of the natural numbers, we can formulate the following sequence:

$$0 < 1 \text{ and } 1 < 2 \text{ and } 2 < 3 \text{ and } 3 < 4 \text{ and } 4 < 5 \ldots$$

or, more concisely,

$$0 < 1 < 2 < 3 < 4 < 5 < 6 < 7 < 8 < 9 \ldots$$

This sequence is read "zero is less than one, is less than two, is less than three . . . ."*

Earlier, we remarked that counting is one of the short cuts for ascertaining the number of members in a given set. We explained that the numerousness of a given set could be determined by finding the equivalent

---

* For a more complete treatment of ordered sets, see *Introduction to the Theory of Sets* by Joseph Breuer, pp. 55-68. Item 14 of Bibliography

standard set. However, when children learn to count, they memorize the names of the natural numbers in order. They can then form a one-to-one correspondence between the members of the set that is being counted and the names of the natural numbers. The following diagram illustrates the technique of counting. Note that quotation marks are used because numerals are used in counting. Note, also, that "0" is not used in counting.

$$\{a, b, c, d, e, f, g\}$$
$$\updownarrow \ \updownarrow \ \updownarrow \ \updownarrow \ \updownarrow \ \updownarrow \ \updownarrow$$
$$\text{"1" "2" "3" "4" "5" "6" "7"}$$

As a matter of fact, the set of natural numbers, with 0 omitted, is frequently called the set of counting numbers.

Ordinal and other uses of numerals

You know that natural numbers are used to answer such questions as "How many members are in this set?" However, we make other uses of the names of natural numbers.

Recall that the names of the natural numbers can be ordered. This means that we can arrange the names in a specified sequence, which is a useful instrument for arranging the members of other sets in a definite order. Thus, if the children in a class are entering a room in single file, we can give each child a numeral as he comes in, giving "1" to the first child, "2" to the second child, "3" to the third child, and so on. The picture below shows how the names and the children are matched. In this case, we are primarily interested in using the name of a standard set to indicate order.

We are interested in the fact that Johnny holds "1" and thus was first to walk into the room. Mary holds "2," so Mary was the second child to come into the room. Louise holds "3," so Louise was the third child, and so on. This procedure establishes an order in which each child has come into the room. The result, therefore, is an *ordinal* use of the set of names for natural numbers. The ordinal use of numerals for natural numbers is, of course, related to their meaning as natural numbers. We would not say that Mary is the second child to enter the room unless there were two children in the room after her arrival, nor that Louise is the third child unless there were three children in the room after her arrival.

The expression *ordinal numbers* is commonly associated with this use of number names. We frequently use the numerals *first, second, third, fourth*, and so on, when we are indicating order. However, we can also use the names of the naturals themselves to express order; that is, "1," "2," "3," "4," may be used in an ordinal sense. In a given situation it should be evident whether the primary emphasis is upon numerousness or order.

The names of the natural numbers are also used for purposes of identification in cases where neither numerousness nor order is important. In such instances, the numerals are simply labels.

The members of a basketball team, for example, usually have numerals on their jerseys. If Jack Wagner has the numeral 14 on his jersey, this does not mean that he is the fourteenth member of the squad or that the squad consists of 14 or more members. For obvious practical reasons, such as brevity and use of a uniform by different players in different years, numerals are a more useful means of identification than are the names of the players. The program for a basketball game will establish a one-to-one correspondence between two equivalent sets—a set of numerals and the set of players' names. For instance, the program might show this correspondence:

Player Numeral	Player Name
2	Jim Johanssen
5	Sam Riccardo
6	Walter Hanson
11	Steve Kowalski
12	Herman Miles
14	Jack Wagner

If "Player 12" commits a foul, the spectators can look at their programs to find his name. They use the correspondence between the numerals and the names of the players to find out who committed the foul.

The above example is an instance of the "identification" use of names for natural numbers. House "numbers," telephone "numbers," and room "numbers" are other uses of numerals that may have some ordinal significance, but that are mainly "identification" numerals.

CONCLUSION

We have attempted in this chapter to give you an understanding of one way in which the natural numbers may be developed. There are alternative approaches to the numerical concepts we have analyzed here. But it is our belief that the development of number ideas through sets is meaningful and fruitful. You will find that we return often to sets for understanding of concepts in subsequent chapters, and you will learn that set notation is one of the most powerful tools of the mathematician.

You must keep in mind that the purpose of this material is to provide you with insight into the meaning of arithmetical concepts. Obviously, it is not expected that you will give your pupils the sort of development presented here. We do hope and expect that you will gain mastery of this material so that you will be capable of planning your teaching in such a way that the children will understand and enjoy arithmetic.

CHAPTER QUIZ

1 In how many ways can you put a set of three objects in one-to-one correspondence with the set $\{1, 2, 3\}$? Exhibit all of these ways.

2 Use a diagram to illustrate the following:

A A many-to-one mapping.

B A two-to-one mapping.

C A one-to-one correspondence.

3 Form two finite sets S and T so that S is a proper subset of T.

4 Form two finite sets V and W such that V is a subset of W and such that W is a subset of V. What other relationship exists between V and W?

$K = \{3, 5, 6, 8, 10\}$. $L = \{\ \}$. $M = \{1, 5, 8\}$. Use sets K, L, and M to form each of the following sets.

5 $K \cup M$ 9 $K \times M$

6 $K \cap M$ 10 $L \cap M$

7 $L \times M$ 11 $M \cap M$

8 $L \cup K$ 12 $L \times L$

13 If $A = \{0, 1, 2\}$ and $B = \{0, 1, 2, 3, 4\}$, what is $n[A \times B]$?

14 Suppose that $F = \{\frac{1}{2}, \frac{1}{3}, \frac{1}{4}, \frac{1}{5}, \ldots, \frac{1}{n}, \ldots\}$.

A Exhibit a one-to-one correspondence between the members of F and the set of natural numbers.

B Exhibit a one-to-one correspondence between a subset of F and the set of natural numbers.

C Show that F is an infinite set.

Name the natural number that is the successor of the number associated with each set named below.

15 $\{a, b, c, \{a, b, c\}\}$ 18 $\{1, 2, 3, 4, 5, 6\}$

16 $\{(0, 0), (0, 1)\}$ 19 $\{Jim, Ken\} \cap \{Bob, Sandra\}$

17 $\{\ \} \cup \{0\}$ 20 $10 \cup \{10\}$

21 Use set notation to show how to construct the standard set of n', the successor of n.

22 Are the following examples of natural numbers, ordinal "numbers," or identification numerals? (Remember, some identification numerals have ordinal or natural implications.)

A Eleven men on a football team

B Room 3012 in the Prescott Building

C Police car 66

D The numeral on the wing of an airplane

E A telephone number

F 5671

G The population of the state of Alaska

SUPPLEMENTARY READINGS

There are many sources where you might find additional material pertaining to this chapter. A few worth-while references are listed below.

Johnson, D. A., and Glenn, W. H., *Sets, Sentences, and Operations*, pp. 1-34. This booklet not only contains very interesting exercises, but also is very simply written. It might be a good source of material for teaching some of these ideas in the elementary school. Item 15 of Bibliography

Mathematics for the Elementary School, Grade 4; School Mathematics Study Group, Chapter 1, "Concept of Sets." This material is based on ideas similar to those presented in this chapter and has been written for elementary school use. Item 16 of Bibliography

"Operating with Sets," *Insights into Modern Mathematics* (Twenty-Third Yearbook of NCTM), pp. 36-64. This is a sophisticated approach to sets and their relation to number. Item 17 of Bibliography

Chapter three

Numerical expressions and conditions

Number sequences
Numerical expressions
Open sentences and conditions
General statements

In mathematics we are often interested in making generalizations that are true for every member of the set of objects with which we are working. Such generalizations are often called theorems or properties, and specialized notation has been developed for expressing them. In this chapter you will consider some of these generalizations and learn some of the notation that constitutes the technical language of mathematics. The symbolism of mathematics is extremely important because very complex ideas and generalizations can be expressed succinctly and clearly when one is familiar with mathematical symbolism.

As a teacher of arithmetic, you will often need to make a statement that is true for each member of a set of numbers. For example, you may wish to say that the product of any natural number and 1 is equal to the given number. This true statement about numbers is fairly easy to express in words. But, as you will see later, this statement can be expressed even more easily in mathematical symbolism. An example of an idea that is more difficult to express is the generalization that the square of the sum of two numbers minus the sum of the squares of the two numbers is equal to twice the product of the two numbers.

As a further example, suppose that you want to make a general statement, that is true for all natural numbers, of the idea illustrated by each of the following statements:

$$5 + 5 = 2 \times 5.$$
$$6 + 6 = 2 \times 6.$$
$$8 + 8 = 2 \times 8.$$
$$0 + 0 = 2 \times 0.$$
$$15 + 15 = 2 \times 15.$$

As your general statement, you might suggest one of the sentences below:

Any number added to itself equals two times the number.

The sum of a number and that same number
equals two times that number.

These two sentences are somewhat cumbersome and lacking in clarity. Furthermore, it is difficult to perform mathematical activities, like computing or developing proofs, with sentences of this kind. Again, one of the purposes of this chapter is to show you how the language of mathematics facilitates the expression of ideas like this one. First, we will consider some examples of the kinds of mathematical ideas that we often want to generalize.

Number sequences

All of you have probably had some experience with number sequences. On general aptitude tests or intelligence tests, you may have been asked to determine the next term in such sequences as A and B, displayed below. Remember that the three dots to the right of the last numeral indicate that the numbers in the sequence continue in the same pattern.

A: 3, 5, 9, 17, 33, ...
B: 1, 4, 9, 16, ...

For the first of these sequences, one way to find the term that follows 33 is to multiply 33 by 2 and subtract 1 from the product. For the second sequence, you can find the term that follows 16 by observing that 1 is the square of 1, 4 is the square of 2, 9 is the square of 3, and 16 is the square of 4. Hence, the term that follows 16 can be obtained by finding the square of 5.

In finding succeeding terms in the sequences named above, you must determine the *pattern* for the sequence. Because mathematicians are often interested in the patterns exhibited by sequences of numbers, they have developed symbolism that enables them to express these patterns once they are determined. The number sequence expressed below is one of the more interesting and has been studied extensively.

$$1, 1, 2, 3, 5, 8, 13, 21, 34, \ldots$$

This sequence of numbers is known as the Fibonacci sequence because it was studied by Fibonacci,* an Italian mathematician of the Middle Ages. He used the sequence in the solution of a problem concerning the number of descendants produced, under certain specified conditions, by a single pair of rabbits in one year.

The Fibonacci sequence is of interest because of certain properties that it possesses. Notice that each number in the sequence, beginning with the third number, is equal to the sum of the two preceding numbers. Once you have observed this pattern, you can determine as many numbers in the sequence as you wish. Later in this chapter you will learn how to express this pattern in mathematical symbolism. There are certain other relationships among the numbers in the Fibonacci sequence that are rather amazing. For example, suppose that you choose any three consecutive members of the sequence, find the product of the first and third numbers, and then find the difference of this product and the square of the second number.

First, we will choose the first three numbers of the sequence and determine the difference:

$$(1 \times 2) - 1^2 = 1.$$

Next, we choose the second, third, and fourth numbers:†

$$(1 \times 3) - 2^2 = -1.$$

Next, the third, fourth, and fifth numbers:

$$(2 \times 5) - 3^2 = 1.$$

Next, the fourth, fifth, and sixth numbers:

$$(3 \times 8) - 5^2 = -1.$$

Next, the fifth, sixth, and seventh numbers:

$$(5 \times 13) - 8^2 = 1.$$

---

* Leonardo da Pisa, better known as Leonardo Fibonacci (c. 1170-1248).
† Negative numbers will be discussed in a later chapter. For the purposes of this discussion, we assume that you have some knowledge of negative numbers. We assume, for example, that you know that $3 - 4$ is equal to -1 in the set of integers.

Next, the sixth, seventh, and eighth numbers:

$$(8 \times 21) - (13)^2 = -1.$$

If we continued this process, we would see that the pattern exhibited above would continue. We can state this property of the Fibonacci sequence in the following way.

For any three consecutive numbers in the Fibonacci sequence,
the difference of the number
that is the product of the first and third numbers
and the number that is the square of the second number
is equal either to 1 or to -1.

The above statement of this property of the Fibonacci sequence is awkward and rather difficult to follow. The property can be stated much more simply in mathematical symbols, as you will learn later in this chapter. In making general statements about number sequences, you can use a certain kind of mathematical expression that is discussed in the following section.

Numerical expressions

We will begin this discussion of mathematical symbolism with a simple example. We will first consider the following sequence of numbers:

$$6, 11, 16, 21, 26, 31, 36, 41, \ldots$$

Notice that each succeeding number in the sequence is obtained by adding 5 to the preceding number. Suppose that you wish to know the thousandth number in this sequence. You could, of course, determine the thousandth number by writing the names of the first 999 numbers and then adding 5 to the 999th number. Obviously, this would be an extremely tedious process; it would be even more tedious to determine the millionth or billionth number in this fashion.

Let us now see if we can develop mathematical symbolism that will enable us to find any number in the sequence quickly and easily. We shall call each number in the sequence a *term* and indicate the number of each term in the sequence as shown below.

Number of the term:	1	2	3	4	5	6	7	8	9	10	11 ...
Term of the sequence:	6,	11,	16,	21,	26,	31,	36,	41,	46,	51,	56, ...

Let us compare each term in the sequence with the number indicating which term of the sequence it is. If we multiply the number of the term by 5 and add 1, then we obtain the corresponding term in the sequence. Thus, the seventh term in the sequence is equal to $5 \times 7 + 1$, or 36. Now we are ready to write a pattern, or form, which we will call a *numerical expression*, that can be used for expressing any term in the sequence. The numerical expression for naming a particular term in the sequence is shown below.

$$5 \times n + 1$$

In the expression $5 \times n + 1$, the letter n is called a *placeholder*; it holds a place for any numeral for a member of the set of counting numbers. Remember that the set of counting numbers, set C, is an infinite set of numbers that contains every natural number except 0. We say that set C is the *universe* that contains all those numbers whose names may be used as replacements for n. Throughout this book, we will use the letter U to name the universe. For this example, we can write

Counting numbers, page 36

$$U = \{1, 2, 3, \ldots\}.$$

Or, because $\{1, 2, 3, \ldots\} = C$, we can write

$$U = C.$$

If we replace n in $5 \times n + 1$ by the numeral 2, we obtain $5 \times 2 + 1$, or 11, which is the second term of the sequence. Again, if we replace n by the numeral 10, we obtain $5 \times 10 + 1$, or 51, which is the tenth term of the sequence.

Now we can easily find the thousandth term of the sequence. If we replace the n in $5 \times n + 1$ by 1000, we obtain $5 \times 1000 + 1$, or 5001, which is the thousandth term of the sequence. You should use this procedure to determine the millionth and the 1,567,444th terms of the sequence.

In numerical expressions, the letter n is not the only symbol used as a placeholder. Almost any symbol, such as those shown in the following expressions, will do, but the letters of the alphabet are customarily used in mathematics. Also, we usually eliminate the symbol for multiplication in an expression like $5 \times n + 1$ and write $5n + 1$.

$$5 \times \underline{\quad} + 1$$
$$5 \times P + 1$$
$$5 \times \square + 1$$
$$5 \times ☆ + 1$$

Now we can use our numerical expression to indicate the pattern of the sequence we have been considering:

Number of the term: 1   2   3   4   5   ...   n   ...
Term of the sequence: 6,   11,   16,   21,   26,   ..., $5n + 1$,   ...

If you compare the following two sentences, it should be obvious to you how much simpler and more useful the expression $5n + 1$ is for describing the nth, or *general*, term of the sequence:

To find any term of the sequence,
multiply the number of the term by 5 and add 1.

The general term of the sequence is $5n + 1$.

You can also use numerical expressions to determine the general term of each of the sequences presented on page 41 of this chapter. For the first sequence, the general term is $2^n + 1$. For the second sequence, the general term is n^2. In each case, the universe for n is the set of counting numbers.

34 For each of the following sequences, use the given expression to find the 10th term, the 134th term, and the 5987th term.
Number of the term: 1   2   3   4,   ..., n,   ...
Sequence A: 2,   3,   4,   5,   ..., $n + 1$,   ...
Sequence B: 12,   14,   16,   18,   ..., $2n + 10$,   ...
Sequence C: 1,   4,   9,   16,   ..., $n \times n$,   ...

35 Find a numerical expression for the general term in each of the following sequences:
Sequence D: 1,   4,   7,   10,   13,   16,   19, ...
Sequence E: 2,   4,   6,   8,   10,   12,   14, ...
Sequence F: 3,   5,   7,   9,   11,   13,   15, ...

36 From the set of counting numbers, generate sequences whose general terms are named by the following expressions. Write the names of the first ten terms of each sequence. Remember that $C = \{1, 2, 3, \ldots\}$.
Expression A: $2n + 6$
Expression B: $n \times n - 1$
Expression C: $n(n - 1)$
Expression D: $0 \times n$

Open sentences and conditions

The idea of a numerical expression is helpful for developing further the symbolism of mathematics. You can think of a numerical expression as playing the same rôle in mathematical language as a phrase plays in the English language. We are now ready to consider the kind of sentences that mathematicians find useful.

We often use a sentence that contains one or more placeholders to express a generalization in mathematics. Such a sentence is called an *open sentence*. The following sentences are examples of open sentences:

> ~~~ wrote *War and Peace.*
>
> $x - 15 < 45.$
>
> ~~~ was the 15th President of the United States.
>
> $7 \times 12 = n.$

Notice that none of these open sentences expresses a statement that can be classified as true or false; it is only after the placeholder has been replaced by a name or a numeral that we can decide whether the resulting *statement* is true or false.

Once the placeholder in an open sentence has been replaced by the name of a member of the universe, then we obtain a *closed sentence* that does express a statement that is either true or false. Just as we use numerical expressions to generate numerals for numbers, we will use open sentences to generate sentences that express statements.

With open sentences, as with numerical expressions, we need to specify the universe from which replacements can be obtained. We will first consider a nonmathematical example.

> The universe: The 50 states of the United States
> The open sentence: ~~~ is a state whose name begins
> with the letter *M.*

Below are some of the closed sentences that can be obtained by using the names of the members of the universe as replacements for the placeholder in the open sentence. Again, the truth or falsity of the statements expressed by these closed sentences can now be ascertained.

> Ohio is a state whose name begins with the letter *M.*
> New York is a state whose name begins with the letter *M.*
> California is a state whose name begins with the letter *M.*
> Maine is a state whose name begins with the letter *M.*
> Michigan is a state whose name begins with the letter *M.*

Next, we will consider a mathematical example.

> The universe: {0, 1, 2, 3, 4, 5, 6}
> The open sentence: $5a + 1 = 11.$

The following closed sentences are obtained when the placeholder a in the open sentence is replaced by a numeral for a member of the universe:

$$5 \times 0 + 1 = 11.$$
$$5 \times 1 + 1 = 11.$$
$$5 \times 2 + 1 = 11.$$
$$5 \times 3 + 1 = 11.$$
$$5 \times 4 + 1 = 11.$$
$$5 \times 5 + 1 = 11.$$
$$5 \times 6 + 1 = 11.$$

Notice that only one of the above sentences expresses a true statement.

So far in this section, we have been talking about symbols—that is, numerals, placeholders, and open sentences. However, ideas are more important in mathematics than are the symbols used to express them. Hence, from now on, we will discuss ideas such as *variables* and *conditions* rather than symbols such as placeholders and open sentences. Let us now consider an example of a condition.

In this example, we will use an infinite universe, the set of natural numbers, or N.

$$U = \{0, 1, 2, 3, \ldots\}.$$
The condition: $2x < 8$.

Some of the statements that can be obtained from this condition are expressed below. Of course, we cannot express all of the statements, because the set of permissible replacements for x is infinite.

$$2 \cdot 0 < 8.$$
$$2 \cdot 1 < 8.$$
$$2 \cdot 2 < 8.$$
$$2 \cdot 3 < 8.$$
$$2 \cdot 4 < 8.$$
$$2 \cdot 5 < 8.$$
$$2 \cdot 6 < 8.$$

Notice that the first four sentences express true statements, while the last three express false statements. It should be apparent that, if x is replaced by any natural number greater than 3, then a true statement is not obtained from the given condition. *

---

* Those who wish to study the ideas presented in this section more thoroughly should refer to *Modern Mathematics, Introductory Concepts and Their Implications*, A. B. Evenson, pp. 55-74. Item 12 of Bibliography

37 Which members of the following universe yield true statements from each of the conditions expressed below?

$$U = \{0, 1, 2, 3, 4, 5, 6, 7, 8\}.$$

a $6x = 24.$ **c** $2x > 9.$ **e** $8x + 3 < 51.$
b $6x - 3 = 2 + 5x.$ **d** $4x = 14.$ **f** $2x - 11 > 9.$

38 Use mathematical notation to express each of the following conditions.
  a The product of three and a natural number is greater than 25.
  b When seven is subtracted from a natural number, the difference is less than fifteen.
  c When twelve is added to the product of a natural number and five, the sum is forty-seven.
  d The sum of a natural number and eleven is equal to six.

General statements

We will now consider certain kinds of conditions that often arise in mathematics. First we will work with some examples.

$$U = \{0, 1, 2, 3\}.$$
The condition: $M + 2 = 2 + M.$

In the condition expressed above, the variable M occurs twice. We will agree to replace M by the same number both times. When you replace M by members of the universe, you obtain the following sentences:

$$0 + 2 = 2 + 0.$$
$$1 + 2 = 2 + 1.$$
$$2 + 2 = 2 + 2.$$
$$3 + 2 = 2 + 3.$$

Notice that all the sentences express true statements; hence, we can make the following generalization:

For each replacement of M, $M + 2 = 2 + M.$

You must keep in mind that the only replacements you may make are those numbers that are members of the universe. For this example, you can see that, if the universe were the entire set of natural numbers, you would obtain a true statement for each replacement of M. Let us now examine another condition for which this is not the case.

$$U = \{0, 1, 2, 3, 4, 5\}.$$
The condition: $x + 3 < 9.$

You obtain the statements expressed below when you use the members of the universe as replacements for x.

$$0 + 3 < 9.$$
$$1 + 3 < 9.$$
$$2 + 3 < 9.$$
$$3 + 3 < 9.$$
$$4 + 3 < 9.$$
$$5 + 3 < 9.$$

Again, because each of these sentences expresses a true statement, you can make the following generalization *for the given universe*:

For each replacement of x, $x + 3 < 9$.

However, this example differs from the preceding one in that if you extend the universe to the entire set of natural numbers, you do not obtain a true statement for each replacement of x. In fact, if you replace x by any natural number greater than 5, you obtain a false statement. Thus, it is always important to keep the universe in mind when you are making general statements about numbers.

In the following discussion, it will be convenient to use several different universes. We will distinguish among them by giving them names, such as U_1, U_2, U_3, and so on. When we wish to refer to one of the universes tabulated below, we will simply use its name rather than give a tabulation of it.

$$U_1 = \{0, 1, 2, 3, 4, 5, 6, 7, 8, 9, 10\}.$$
$$U_2 = \{0, 1, 2, 3, \ldots, 200\}.$$
$$U_3 = \{0, 1, 2, 3, \ldots, 1000\}.$$
$$U_4 = \{0, 1, 2, 3, \ldots, 1,000,000\}.$$
$$U_5 = \{0, 1, 2, 3, \ldots\}.$$

Notice that U_5, the set of natural numbers, is the only infinite set among the universes that are tabulated.

Now we will consider the condition

$$a + b = b + a.$$

Remember that a condition yields a true or a false statement only after every variable has been replaced by a member of the universe. Also remember that, if a variable is used more than once in a condition, then it must be replaced by the same member of the universe each time it occurs in the condition.

Below are some of the statements that can be obtained when U_1 is the universe for each variable.

$$0 + 1 = 1 + 0.$$
$$5 + 10 = 10 + 5.$$
$$9 + 6 = 6 + 9.$$
$$7 + 3 = 3 + 7.$$

Each of these sentences expresses a true statement. With U_1 as the universe for each variable, it is possible to obtain a total of 11×11, or 121, true statements from the condition $a + b = b + a$.

If U_2 is the universe, you can obtain 40,401 true statements from $a + b = b + a$. Similarly, you could determine all the statements that can be obtained from $a + b = b + a$ when U_3 or U_4 is the universe, although this would be an exceedingly tedious task. If you wrote all these sentences, you would find that each one expresses a true statement.

Now, however, consider the sentences that can be obtained from $a + b = b + a$ when U_5 is the universe for each variable. Because U_5, the set of natural numbers, is an infinite set, it is not possible to write all of the closed sentences that can be obtained from $a + b = b + a$. In Chapter 4 we will use the idea of the union of disjoint sets to see that the following statement is true when the universe is U_5, or N.

For each a and b, $a + b = b + a$.

When you study the properties of addition of natural numbers, you will learn that the sentence just given is a statement of the commutative property of addition. Notice how simply this generalization is expressed by the sentence "For each a and b, $a + b = b + a$." Compare it with the following way of expressing the same generalization: "For any two natural numbers, the sum of the first number and the second number is equal to the sum of the second number and the first number." As you learn more about properties of number systems, you will appreciate more fully the mathematical notation that enables you to state such generalizations so easily and briefly.

39 From the statements expressed below, make a generalization and express it in mathematical notation.
a $8 \times 0 = 0.$ **c** $5 \times 0 = 0.$
b $3 \times 0 = 0.$ **d** $2 \times 0 = 0.$

40 Use the following sentences to form a generalization.
a $2 + 2 + 2 + 2 = 4 \times 2.$ **c** $12 + 12 + 12 + 12 = 4 \times 12.$
b $6 + 6 + 6 + 6 = 4 \times 6.$ **d** $7 + 7 + 7 + 7 = 4 \times 7.$

41 Use the following sentences to form a generalization.

a $1 \cdot 2 > 1^2$. **c** $6 \cdot 7 > 6^2$.

b $3 \cdot 4 > 3^2$. **d** $10 \cdot 11 > 10^2$.

42 Use the following sentences to form a generalization.

a $3^2 + 4^2 < (3 + 4)^2$. **c** $9^2 + 10^2 < (9 + 10)^2$.

b $8^2 + 9^2 < (8 + 9)^2$. **d** $4^2 + 5^2 < (4 + 5)^2$.

43 Suppose that A is any finite subset of a given universe U and that { } is the empty set. Tell whether each of the following sets is equal to A, U, or { }.

a $A \cup U$ **c** $A \cup A$ **e** $A \cup \{ \}$

b $A \cap U$ **d** $A \cap A$ **f** $A \cap \{ \}$

Union and intersection of sets, pages 20 and 21

Disjoint sets, page 20

Proper subset, page 14

44 If A and B are disjoint sets, then what is $A \cap B$?

45 If A is a proper subset of B, then what is $A \cap B$? What is $A \cup B$?

Now we will return to the Fibonacci sequence mentioned in the opening pages of this chapter. Your newly acquired knowledge of conditions and variables will help you make some generalizations about this sequence. The sequence is exhibited again below. Notice that this time we have also given each term a name, such as S_1, S_2, S_3, and so on.

Number of the term:	1	2	3	4	5	6	7	8	9	10 ...
Term of the sequence:	1	1	2	3	5	8	13	21	34	55 ...
Name of the term:	S_1	S_2	S_3	S_4	S_5	S_6	S_7	S_8	S_9	S_{10} ...

Using the names of the terms, we can write the following sentences.

$$S_1 + S_2 = S_3.$$
$$S_2 + S_3 = S_4.$$
$$S_3 + S_4 = S_5.$$
$$S_4 + S_5 = S_6.$$
$$S_5 + S_6 = S_7.$$
$$S_6 + S_7 = S_8.$$

Note that, in each of these sentences, the subscripts are numerals for three consecutive natural numbers.

Now we can construct a definition of the Fibonacci sequence of numbers. Let S_n, S_{n+1}, and S_{n+2} represent any three consecutive terms of the sequence. The universe for n is $\{1, 2, 3, 4, \ldots \}$.

For each n, $S_n + S_{n+1} = S_{n+2}$, and $S_1 = 1$ and $S_2 = 1$.

This definition gives you all the information you need for finding any term of the Fibonacci sequence. From the definition, you know that the first term is 1 and the second term is 1. You also know that $S_1 + S_2 = S_3$; and, since S_1 is 1 and S_2 is 1, S_3 is $1 + 1$, or 2. Similarly, $S_2 + S_3 = S_4$;

and, since S_2 is 1 and S_3 is 2, S_4 is $1 + 2$, or 3. You can continue to obtain succeeding terms of the sequence in this fashion.

Compare the definition given above with the following description of the Fibonacci sequence: "The first term of the sequence is 1, the second term is 1, and the third term, and each succeeding term of the sequence, is equal to the sum of the two preceding terms." Obviously, the definition expressed in mathematical notation is much more concise and, when properly understood, more useful than the description in words.

In our earlier discussion of the Fibonacci sequence, you will recall that we stated this property of the sequence: "For any three consecutive numbers in the Fibonacci sequence, the difference of the number that is the product of the first and third numbers and the number that is the square of the second number is equal either to $+1$ or to -1." You can now use mathematical notation to state this property more concisely.

Before stating the property, consider the following examples:

$$S_1 \times S_3 - (S_2)^2 = +1.$$
$$S_2 \times S_4 - (S_3)^2 = -1.$$
$$S_3 \times S_5 - (S_4)^2 = +1.$$
$$S_4 \times S_6 - (S_5)^2 = -1.$$
$$S_5 \times S_7 - (S_6)^2 = +1.$$
$$S_6 \times S_8 - (S_7)^2 = -1.$$

An examination of these sentences should enable you to see the pattern exhibited by any three consecutive terms when you find the product of the first and third terms and then subtract the square of the second term from it. This property can now be expressed in mathematical notation. Again, we will use S_n, S_{n+1}, and S_{n+2} to represent any three consecutive terms of the sequence. The universe for n is $\{1, 2, 3, 4, \ldots \}$.

If n is replaced by an odd number,
then $S_n \times S_{n+2} - (S_{n+1})^2 = +1$.
If n is replaced by an even number,
then $S_n \times S_{n+2} - (S_{n+1})^2 = -1$.

CONCLUSION

From the examples that we have considered in this chapter, it should be evident that mathematical symbolism is extremely useful in stating generalizations about numbers. Once you have mastered this symbolism, you will find not only that you can state mathematical concepts more clearly and concisely, but also that you can remember them more easily.

CHAPTER QUIZ

Use the four universes tabulated below in connection with exercises 1 through 9. For each universe, tell whether the sentence in each exercise expresses a true statement.

$$U_1 = \{0, 1, 2, 3, 4, 5, 6, 7, 8\}.$$
$$U_2 = \{2, 4, 6, 8, 10, 12, 14\}.$$
$$U_3 = \{5, 10, 15, 20, \ldots, 100\}.$$
$$U_4 = \{1, 3, 5, 7, 11, 13, 17, 19\}.$$

1 For each replacement of s, s is less than 20.
2 For each replacement of k, k is a prime number. [Remember that a prime number is divisible only by itself and one.]
3 For each replacement of M, M is a multiple of 5.
4 For each replacement of x and of y, $x + y < 40$.
5 For each replacement of a and of b, $2ab$ is an even number.
6 For each replacement of x, $x \cdot 1 = x$.
7 For each replacement of x, $x^2 - x$ is divisible by 2.
8 For each replacement of x and of y, $xy = yx$.
9 For each replacement of n, $n + 0 = n$.

The universe for the following exercises is the set of counting numbers. Use the expression given in each exercise to list the first ten terms of a sequence. Also formulate a true statement about the relation between any two consecutive terms of the sequence. For exercise 10, for example, you could write, $S_n + 2 = S_{n+1}$.

10 $2n$ 13 $n \div (n + 1)$
11 n^2 14 $3n + 1$
12 $\dfrac{2n}{n + 1}$ 15 $1 + \dfrac{1}{n}$

In each of the following exercises, you are given the first five terms of a sequence. First, find the numerical expression that fits these five terms. Then use this expression to list the next five terms of the sequence.

16 1, 2, 3, 4, 5   20 $0, \frac{1}{2}, 1, \frac{3}{2}, 2$
17 0, 1, 2, 3, 4   21 5, 6. 7, 8, 9
18 0, 2, 4, 6, 8   22 2, 2, 2, 2, 2
19 1, 3, 5, 7, 9   23 1, 2, 5, 10, 17

The following sentences express statements that might be made in an arithmetic class. Express these statements in mathematical terminology. Use N as the universe.

24 The quotient of any non-zero number and itself is one.

25 The sum of any number and zero is that number.

26 The quotient of zero and any non-zero number is zero.

27 The product of zero and any number is zero.

28 The product of one and any number is that number.

SUPPLEMENTARY READINGS

Additional information concerning the material in this chapter can be obtained in the following references.

Report of the Commission of Mathematics, Appendices, pp. 2-7. This report shows how the ideas discussed in this chapter can be used to clarify the teaching of algebra. Item 18 of Bibliography

Tarski, Alfred, *Introduction to Logic*. This book includes a more rigorous approach to the ideas of this chapter, which may be of interest to some students. Item 19 of Bibliography

University of Chicago College Mathematics Staff, *Concepts and Structure of Mathematics*. Although this book may be difficult to obtain, it is an excellent source for the ideas in this chapter. Item 20 of Bibliography

Van Engen, Henry, *et al*, *Seeing Through Mathematics, Book 1*, pp. 5-120. Even though this is a junior high school text, there is a wealth of material for the person who may be unfamiliar with modern mathematics. Item 21 of Bibliography

Workbook in Modern Mathematics, by Howard Marston, pp. 1-21. This workbook contains many good exercises. Item 22 of Bibliography

Chapter four

Sums and products

In Chapter 2 you saw how natural numbers can be identified with standard _{Standard} sets. For example, you learned that the natural number 3 is the standard ^{sets, page 28} set {0, 1, 2} and that 3 is also associated with any set that can be put in one-to-one correspondence with this standard set. This means that if A = {a, b, c}, then the number of A, that is n[A], is 3.

You also studied certain operations with sets in Chapter 2. In this chapter, we will make use of two set operations—the union of two disjoint sets and the Cartesian product of two sets—to define the sums and the products of natural numbers.

Sum of two natural numbers

A teacher might introduce the concept of the sum of two natural numbers, such as 3 and 2, by showing the children a set of 3 objects, a different set of 2 objects, and then the set of 5 objects that can be formed by "joining" the two sets. Using physical examples of this kind is a good classroom technique. As a teacher, you will want to understand the abstract, mathematical ideas that underlie such physical examples.

We will first consider the two sets that are tabulated below.

$$A = \{Bruce, Jim, Fred\}.$$
$$B = \{Tom, Herman\}.$$

You will recall that disjoint sets have no common members; hence, A and B are disjoint sets. Disjoint sets, page 20

If you form the union of A and B, you obtain Union of sets, page 20

$$A \cup B = \{Bruce, Jim, Fred, Tom, Herman\}.$$

We define the sum of the number of A and the number of B to be the number of $A \cup B$. This means that the sum of n[A] and n[B], or n[A] + n[B], is equal to n[A $\cup$ B]. In mathematical notation, we write

$$n[A] + n[B] = n[A \cup B].$$

In this example, because n[A] = 3 and n[B] = 2, we can write,

$$3 + 2 = n[A \cup B].$$

Next, consider these two sets:

$$C = \{pencil, eraser, chalk, ruler\}.$$
$$D = \{book, notebook\}.$$

Again, we form the union of these two sets.

$$C \cup D = \{pencil, eraser, chalk, ruler, book, notebook\}.$$

Because C and D are disjoint sets, we know that

$$n[C] + n[D] = n[C \cup D].$$

Also, because n[C] = 4 and n[D] = 2, we can write,

$$4 + 2 = n[C \cup D].$$

We can express this idea by using single letters to represent natural numbers; for example, we can use r to represent n[R], s to represent n[S], a to represent n[A], and so on. We can now state the following definition of the *sum of any two natural numbers*.

For any two disjoint sets R and S,
$$n[R] + n[S] = n[R \cup S].$$
Also, if n[R] = r and n[S] = s,
then $r + s = n[R \cup S]$.

The following example will make clear why it is necessary that sets R and S be disjoint. Consider the following sets that are *not* disjoint.

$$R = \{3, 4, 5\}.$$
$$S = \{0, 1, 2, 3, 4\}.$$

You learned in Chapter 2 that, when you tabulate the union of two sets with common members, you list the names of the common members only once. Therefore,

$$R \cup S = \{0, 1, 2, 3, 4, 5\}.$$

Notice that, in this case, because R and S are not disjoint sets, $n[R] + n[S]$ is *not* equal to $n[R \cup S]$.

Order in Sums

Now that we have defined the sum of two natural numbers, we find that certain properties of sums of natural numbers are based on the definition. First we will consider a property concerning the order in which the sum of two numbers is obtained.

We will use the following two sets to illustrate this property.

$$G = \{a, b, c, d, e, f\}.$$
$$H = \{0, 1\}.$$

Now we form the union of G and H.

$$G \cup H = \{a, b, c, d, e, f, 0, 1\}.$$

Next we form the union of H and G.

$$H \cup G = \{0, 1, a, b, c, d, e, f\}.$$

As illustrated by the diagram below, the members of the set $G \cup H$ can be put in one-to-one correspondence with the members of $H \cup G$.

$$G \cup H = \{a, \ b, \ c, \ d, \ e, \ f, \ 0, \ 1\ \}.$$
$$H \cup G = \{0, \ 1, \ a, \ b, \ c, \ d, \ e, \ f\ \}.$$

Thus, $G \cup H$ and $H \cup G$ are equivalent sets, and the same number is associated with each set. (In fact, $G \cup H$ and $H \cup G$ are equal sets because they contain exactly the same members, but we need be concerned only with their equivalence.) Hence,

Equivalent sets, page 18

$$n[G \cup H] = n[H \cup G].$$

Further, because n[G] = 6 and n[H] = 2, you can use the definition of the sum of two natural numbers to obtain

$$6 + 2 = n[G \cup H]$$

and

$$2 + 6 = n[H \cup G].$$

But, because G $\cup$ H and H $\cup$ G are equivalent, n[G $\cup$ H] = n[H $\cup$ G]. So you can obtain

$$6 + 2 = 2 + 6.$$

You have seen that, for the specific sets G and H, n[G $\cup$ H] and n[H $\cup$ G] are the same. You can generalize this concept to show that, for any two disjoint sets R and S, n[R $\cup$ S] = n[S $\cup$ R]. This is true because R $\cup$ S contains exactly the same members as S $\cup$ R. A set can be put into one-to-one correspondence with itself; so two sets that are equal can be put in one-to-one correspondence. Thus, the two sets are equivalent and must have the same natural number associated with them. This property of sums of natural numbers is expressed below.

For any two natural numbers a and b, $a + b = b + a$.

This property concerning the order in sums involves an infinite set of true statements about the sums of pairs of natural numbers. Each of these true statements, such as those exhibited below, concerns the sum of two natural numbers.

$$1 + 2 = 2 + 1.$$
$$3 + 5 = 5 + 3.$$
$$0 + 6 = 6 + 0.$$
$$15 + 15 = 15 + 15.$$
$$142 + 455 = 455 + 142.$$

Thus, because R $\cup$ S and S $\cup$ R are equivalent for any two disjoint sets R and S, we see that n[R] + n[S] = n[S] + n[R].

Sum of three natural numbers

When we are finding the sum of three or more numbers, we must group them in some way so that we find the sum of only two numbers at a time. For example, suppose that we want to find the sum of 3, 8, and 7. We might first find the sum of 3 and 8 and then add 7 to this sum, or we might first find the sum of 8 and 7 and then add this sum to 3.

Every school child quickly learns that, if he is finding the sum of more than two numbers, he arrives at the same total no matter how he groups the numbers when he adds. We can use the idea of the union of disjoint sets to show that the sum of three or more natural numbers is the same, no matter how the numbers are grouped in finding the sum.

Let us consider a specific example. We will use the three disjoint sets tabulated below.

$$A = \{3, 5, 7\}.$$
$$B = \{2, 4, 6, 8\}.$$
$$C = \{0\}.$$

We want to form the union of A, B, and C. But we can form the union of only two sets at a time because the operation of forming the union of sets is defined in terms of two sets. We first form $A \cup B$.

$$A \cup B = \{3, 5, 7, 2, 4, 6, 8\}.$$

Next, we form the union of $A \cup B$ and C. We will use $(A \cup B) \cup C$ to symbolize the union of $A \cup B$ and C.

$$(A \cup B) \cup C = \{3, 5, 7, 2, 4, 6, 8, 0\}.$$

Note that the parentheses in the symbol $(A \cup B) \cup C$ indicate the way in which we grouped the sets to form the union of these three sets.

Now we will form the union of these three sets in a different way. This time we will first form the union of B and C.

$$B \cup C = \{2, 4, 6, 8, 0\}.$$

Now we will form the union of A and $B \cup C$.

$$A \cup (B \cup C) = \{3, 5, 7, 2, 4, 6, 8, 0\}.$$

An inspection of the tabulations of $(A \cup B) \cup C$ and $A \cup (B \cup C)$ should convince you that these two sets are equivalent. Hence,

$$n[(A \cup B) \cup C] = n[A \cup (B \cup C)].$$

We can also state this in terms of the sums of the numbers associated with sets A, B, and C. Thus $n[A] = 3$, $n[B] = 4$, and $n[C] = 1$. We can therefore write the sentences below and at the top of page 60, each of which can be justified by the way in which the union of sets and the sum of two natural numbers are defined.

$$n[A \cup B] = 3 + 4.$$
$$n[(A \cup B) \cup C] = (3 + 4) + 1.$$

$$n[B \cup C] = 4 + 1.$$
$$n[A \cup (B \cup C)] = 3 + (4 + 1).$$

But we already know that $n[(A \cup B) \cup C] = n[A \cup (B \cup C)]$; therefore, we know that

$$(3 + 4) + 1 = 3 + (4 + 1).$$

We have now shown that, for the three specific natural numbers 3, 4, and 1, the sum of the first and second numbers and the third number, namely, $(3 + 4) + 1$, is the same as the sum of the first number and the second and third numbers, namely, $3 + (4 + 1)$.

We could use the same procedure to show that this is true for any three natural numbers. This property of sums is expressed below.

For any three natural numbers r, s, and t,
$$(r + s) + t = r + (s + t).$$

This property of sums involves an infinite set of true statements about natural numbers. Each of these statements, like those expressed below, concerns the sum of three natural numbers.

$$(3 + 4) + 2 = 3 + (4 + 2).$$
$$(5 + 16) + 7 = 5 + (16 + 7).$$
$$(128 + 352) + 45 = 128 + (352 + 45).$$

46 Use the properties of sums for natural numbers to find in an easy manner the number named by each of the following expressions.

a $8 + (2 + 34)$
b $(19 + 42) + 81$
c $(22 + 49) + (51 + 33)$
d $68 + (33 + 51) + 32$

47 Which of the conditions expressed below result in true statements for each replacement of a, b, and c by natural numbers? For those conditions that result in true statements for all a, b, and c, what property or properties enable you to obtain the expression at the right of the "equals sign" from the expression at the left?

a $a + b = b + c.$
b $(a + b) + c = c + (a + b).$
c $(a + b) + c = (a + c) + b.$
d $a + (b + c) = (a + b) + (a + c).$
e $a + (b + c) = a + (c + b).$
f $c + b + a = a + b + c.$

Product of two natural numbers

We will now relate the product of two natural numbers to the Cartesian Cartesian product, page 22 product of two sets. In Chapter 2 you learned that the Cartesian product of two sets is formed by matching each member of the first set with each member, in turn, of the second set. The following example will help you recall this process.

$$P = \{a, b, c, d\}.$$
$$Q = \{x, y, z\}.$$

When you form the Cartesian product of P and Q, you obtain P × Q. (Remember that the symbol P × Q is read "P cross Q.") This set of ordered pairs is tabulated below:

$$P \times Q = \{(a, x), (a, y), (a, z),$$
$$(b, x), (b, y), (b, z),$$
$$(c, x), (c, y), (c, z),$$
$$(d, x), (d, y), (d, z)\}.$$

Now, we will relate this process to the numbers associated with each of the three sets, P, Q, and P × Q. The product of n[P] and n[Q], that is, n[P] × n[Q], is defined as n[P × Q]. In other words, the number that is the product of the number of P and the number of Q is equal to the number of the Cartesian set P × Q, and we write,

$$n[P] \times n[Q] = n[P \times Q].$$

It is easy to verify this for the given example. You know that n[P] = 4 and that n[Q] = 3; you can count the number of members in P × Q to see that n[P × Q] = 12.

We can now use mathematical notation to define the *product of any two natural numbers.*

For any two sets R and S, n[R] × n[S] = n[R × S].
Also, if n[R] = r and n[S] = s,
then r × s = n[R × S].

Notice that, in defining a product, it is not necessary to restrict the definition to disjoint sets, as is the case in defining a sum. This is true because, even if two sets have exactly the same members, the set of ordered pairs that you obtain is different from either of the given sets. For example, if J = {2, 4} and K = {2, 4}, then

$$J \times K = \{(2, 2), (2, 4), (4, 2), (4, 4)\}.$$

Thus, even though J and K are not disjoint, it is still true that

$$n[J] \times n[K] = n[J \times K].$$

48 Use sets A and B, tabulated below, to develop the product of 4 and 5.

$$A = \{0, 1, 2, 3\}.$$
$$B = \{0, 1, 2, 3, 4\}.$$

49 Use the standard set 2 and the empty set to develop the product of 2 and 0.

Order in products*

Now that we have defined the product of two natural numbers, we can use this definition to develop certain properties of products. As you might expect, there is an "order in products" property that is analogous to the "order in sums" property. We will use the two sets tabulated below to illustrate this property.

$$S = \{0, 1, 2, 3\}.$$
$$T = \{3, 5\}.$$

First, we form the Cartesian set $S \times T$.

$$S \times T = \{(0, 3), (0, 5), (1, 3), (1, 5),$$
$$(2, 3), (2, 5), (3, 3), (3, 5)\}.$$

From the definition of a product, you know that

$$n[S] \times n[T] = n[S \times T].$$

Next, we form the Cartesian set $T \times S$.

$$T \times S = \{(3, 0), (3, 1), (3, 2), (3, 3),$$
$$(5, 0), (5, 1), (5, 2), (5, 3)\}.$$

Again, according to the definition of a product, you know that

$$n[T] \times n[S] = n[T \times S].$$

If we can show that $n[S \times T] = n[T \times S]$, we will be able to show that $n[S] \times n[T] = n[T] \times n[S]$. Notice that $S \times T$ and $T \times S$ are *not* the same sets because the ordered pairs that are contained in $S \times T$ are different

---

* An alternative definition of a product in terms of a sum of equal addends is given in the section beginning on page 68. There, we develop, in terms of the alternative definition, the properties that are developed in this section and in the two following sections. If you wish, you may omit this section and the two following ones and turn immediately to the treatment on page 68. Or, you may wish to consider both treatments.

from the ordered pairs that are contained in T × S. However, S × T and T × S *are* equivalent sets, as shown by the diagram below.

$$S \times T = \{(0, 3), (0,5), (1,3), (1,5), (2,3), (2,5), (3,3), (3,5)\}.$$
$$T \times S = \{(3,0), (5,0), (3,1), (5,1), (3,2), (5,2), (3,3), (5,3)\}.$$

You will recall that, if two sets are equivalent, then they have the same number associated with them. Therefore, the number associated with S × T is the same as the number associated with T × S; that is,

$$n[S \times T] = n[T \times S].$$

Finally, because $n[S] \times n[T] = n[S \times T]$, $n[T] \times n[S] = n[S \times T]$, and $n[S \times T] = n[T \times S]$, we are able to say that

$$n[S] \times n[T] = n[T] \times n[S].$$

This last sentence tells us that the product of the number of S and the number of T is equal to the product of the number of T and the number of S. Because $n[S] = 4$ and $n[T] = 2$, we know that

$$4 \times 2 = 2 \times 4.$$

We could generalize this procedure to obtain the property of products of natural numbers that is expressed below.

For any two natural numbers a and b, $ab = ba$.

This property of products involves an infinite set of sentences concerning the products of pairs of natural numbers. Each of these sentences, like those shown below, expresses a true statement.

$$6 \times 3 = 3 \times 6.$$
$$5 \times 12 = 12 \times 5.$$
$$9 \times 1 = 1 \times 9.$$
$$15 \times 65 = 65 \times 15.$$

Thus, we have shown that, because S × T and T × S are equivalent for any two sets S and T, $n[S] \times n[T] = n[T] \times n[S]$.

Product of three natural numbers

Now we can use the idea of Cartesian products to develop another property of products. This property is analogous to the property that we developed for the sum of three natural numbers.

We will first use the sets tabulated below to develop a specific example of this property.

$$A = \{0, 1\}.$$
$$B = \{1, 3, 5\}.$$
$$C = \{0, 2, 4\}.$$

First, we form the cross product of A and B. We must form the Cartesian set of only two sets at a time because this operation is defined for just two sets.

$$A \times B = \{(0, 1), (0, 3), (0, 5), (1, 1), (1, 3), (1, 5)\}.$$

Next, we form the Cartesian product of A $\times$ B and C. When we do this, we obtain the set tabulated below. Notice that (A $\times$ B) $\times$ C is a set of ordered pairs, but that the first component of each pair is itself an ordered pair while the second component is a single number.

$$
\begin{aligned}
(A \times B) \times C = \{ & \big((0, 1), 0\big), \big((0, 1), 2\big), \big((0, 1), 4\big), \\
& \big((0, 3), 0\big), \big((0, 3), 2\big), \big((0, 3), 4\big), \\
& \big((0, 5), 0\big), \big((0, 5), 2\big), \big((0, 5), 4\big), \\
& \big((1, 1), 0\big), \big((1, 1), 2\big), \big((1, 1), 4\big), \\
& \big((1, 3), 0\big), \big((1, 3), 2\big), \big((1, 3), 4\big), \\
& \big((1, 5), 0\big), \big((1, 5), 2\big), \big((1, 5), 4\big) \}.
\end{aligned}
$$

From the definition of a product, you know that

$$n[A \times B] \times n[C] = n[(A \times B) \times C].$$

Now we form the Cartesian product of B and C.

$$
\begin{aligned}
B \times C = \{ & (1, 0), (1, 2), (1, 4), \\
& (3, 0), (3, 2), (3, 4), \\
& (5, 0), (5, 2), (5, 4) \}.
\end{aligned}
$$

If you form the Cartesian product of A and B $\times$ C, you will obtain a set of ordered pairs in which the first component of each pair is a single number while the second component is itself an ordered pair. Thus, while A $\times$ (B $\times$ C) and (A $\times$ B) $\times$ C are not the *same* set, it is true that A $\times$ (B $\times$ C) is *equivalent* to (A $\times$ B) $\times$ C. Because these two sets are equivalent, you know that they have the same number of members. Therefore,

$$n[(A \times B) \times C] = n[A \times (B \times C)].$$

But because

$$n[A \times B] \times n[C] = n[(A \times B) \times C],$$

and because

$$n[A] \times n[B \times C] = n[A \times (B \times C)],$$

you know that

$$n[A \times B] \times n[C] = n[A] \times n[B \times C].$$

For the particular sets A, B, and C with which we have been working, we know that n[A] = 2, n[B] = 3, and n[C] = 3. Therefore, we know that

$$(2 \times 3) \times 3 = 2 \times (3 \times 3).$$

We can generalize this concept to obtain the property of products that is expressed below.

For any three natural numbers a, b, and c, $(ab)c = a(bc)$.

This property of products, like the similar property of sums, enables you to find the product of three or more natural numbers in more than one way. The sentences below express some of the statements that you can obtain from this property.

$$(3 \times 2) \times 4 = 3 \times (2 \times 4).$$
$$(28 \times 12) \times 6 = 28 \times (12 \times 6).$$
$$(4 \times 5) \times 100 = 4 \times (5 \times 100).$$
$$(68 \times 25) \times 4 = 68 \times (25 \times 4).$$

50 Use the properties of products for natural numbers to find in an easy manner the number named in each of the following expressions.

a $4 \times (5 \times 7)$
b $(25 \times 19) \times 4$
c $(11 \times 50) \times (20 \times 63)$
d $50 \times (26 \times 6) \times 40$

51 Which of the conditions expressed below result in true statements for each replacement of a, b, and c by natural numbers? For those conditions that result in true statements for all a, b, and c, what property or properties enable you to obtain the expression at the right of the "equals sign" from the expression at the left?

a $(ab)c = c(ab)$.   **d** $ab = cb$.
b $a(bc) = (ab)(ac)$.   **e** $a(bc) = a(cb)$.
c $cba = abc$.   **f** $(ab)c = (ac)b$.

Combining sums and products

Thus far, you have studied two properties of sums and two similar properties of products. Another important property concerns sums and products jointly and enables us to interpret expressions like $2 \times (5 + 7)$ that involve both a sum and a product. In an expression like $2 \times (5 + 7)$, you can either find the sum of 5 and 7 first and then find the product of 2 and this sum; or you can first find the product of 2 and 5 and the product of 2 and 7 and then find the sum of these two products. The results are the same in either case. We will now use the ideas of the union of two sets and the Cartesian product of two sets to investigate this relation between sums and products.

We will use the three sets tabulated below to illustrate this property of sums and products.

$$P = \{a, b, c\}.$$
$$Q = \{0, 1\}.$$
$$R = \{3, 5, 7, 9\}.$$

First we will show that $P \times (Q \cup R) = (P \times Q) \cup (P \times R)$. The necessary steps are given below.

$Q \cup R = \{0, 1, 3, 5, 7, 9\}.$
$P \times (Q \cup R) = \{(a, 0), (a, 1), (a, 3), (a, 5), (a, 7), (a, 9),$
$(b, 0), (b, 1), (b, 3), (b, 5), (b, 7), (b, 9),$
$(c, 0), (c, 1), (c, 3), (c, 5), (c, 7), (c, 9)\}.$

$P \times Q = \{(a, 0), (a, 1), (b, 0), (b, 1), (c, 0), (c, 1)\}.$
$P \times R = \{(a, 3), (a, 5), (a, 7), (a, 9),$
$(b, 3), (b, 5), (b, 7), (b, 9),$
$(c, 3), (c, 5), (c, 7), (c, 9)\}.$
$(P \times Q) \cup (P \times R) = \{(a, 0), (a, 1), (b, 0), (b, 1), (c, 0), (c, 1),$
$(a, 3), (a, 5), (a, 7), (a, 9), (b, 3), (b, 5),$
$(b, 7), (b, 9), (c, 3), (c, 5), (c, 7), (c, 9)\}.$

If you compare sets $P \times (Q \cup R)$ and $(P \times Q) \cup (P \times R)$, you will see that the two sets have the same members; hence,

$$n[P \times (Q \cup R)] = n[(P \times Q) \cup (P \times R)].$$

Next, we will work with the expressions $n[P \times (Q \cup R)]$ and $n[(P \times Q) \cup (P \times R)]$. We have labeled the steps for convenience in referring to them.

So far, you know that
1) $n[P \times (Q \cup R)] = n[(P \times Q) \cup (P \times R)].$

By the definition of a product you know that

2) $n[P \times (Q \cup R)] = n[P] \times n[Q \cup R]$.

By the definition of a sum, you know that $n[Q \cup R] = n[Q] + n[R]$. Therefore, you can obtain

3) $n[P \times (Q \cup R)] = n[P] \times (n[Q] + n[R])$.

By the definition of a sum, you know that

4) $n[(P \times Q) \cup (P \times R)] = n[P \times Q] + n[P \times R]$.

By the definition of a product, you know that $n[P \times Q] = n[P] \times n[Q]$ and that $n[P \times R] = n[P] \times n[R]$. Therefore,

5) $n[(P \times Q) + (P \times R)] = (n[P] \times n[Q]) + (n[P] \times n[R])$.

From steps 1, 3, and 5, you can obtain

6) $n[P] \times (n[Q] + n[R]) = (n[P] \times n[Q]) + (n[P] \times n[R])$.

This last step is what we started out to establish. For the three sets with which we have been working, we know that $n[P] = 3$, $n[Q] = 2$, and $n[R] = 4$. Hence, we obtain

7) $3 \times (2 + 4) = (3 \times 2) + (3 \times 4)$.

Thus, we have shown that, for the three natural numbers associated with sets P, Q, and R, the product of 3 and $2 + 4$ is equal to the sum of 3×2 and 3×4. We can generalize this idea and state this property for all natural numbers.

For any three natural numbers a, b, and c,
$$a(b + c) = ab + ac.$$

52 Use the property discussed in this section to find in an easy manner the number named by each of the following expressions.

a $37 \times 82 + 37 \times 18$

b $239 \times 124 + 239 \times 876$

c $25 \times (8 + 5)$

d $5137 \times 56 + 5137 \times 44$

53 In which of the following open sentences is the property discussed in this section illustrated for all natural numbers a, b, and c?

a $a(bc) = (ab) \times (ac)$.

b $a(b + c) = (a + b) \times (a + c)$.

c $a + (b \times c) = (a + b) \times (a + c)$.

d $a + (b + c) = (a + b) + (a + c)$.

e $a \times (b + c) = (a \times b) + (a \times c)$.

54 Knowing that, if a, b, and c are natural numbers, then $ab = ba$ and $a(b + c) = ab + ac$, prove that $(a + b)c = ac + bc$.

55 Show, by giving a specific example, that $a + (b \times c) = (a + b) \times (a + c)$ does not express a true statement for all natural numbers a, b, and c.

Another treatment of products

In an earlier section, the product of two natural numbers was defined in terms of the Cartesian product of two sets. This definition of products has certain advantages from a mathematical point of view, but it is a rather sophisticated notion for elementary-school children to grasp. From a pedagogical point of view, a definition of products in terms of sums has many advantages. For example, children can more easily understand the notion of 3×5 as meaning $5 + 5 + 5$, than they can understand 3×5 as meaning the number of elements in a Cartesian set. Thus, as teacher, it is important that you understand how the product of two natural numbers can be related to a sum of equal addends.

It seems quite natural to say that the sum of 5 and 5 ought to be the same as 2×5. Similarly, it makes sense to think that the sum of 5, 5, 5, and 5 ought to be the same as 4×5. Hence, we want the following sentences to express true statements.

$$5 + 5 = 2 \times 5.$$
$$5 + 5 + 5 + 5 = 4 \times 5.$$

In fact, for any number of addends of 5, we want the following to be true:

$$\underbrace{5 + 5 + \ldots + 5}_{n \text{ addends of } 5} = n \times 5.$$

We can generalize this idea even further and develop the following definition of the product of any two natural numbers in terms of a sum of equal addends.

For any two natural numbers a and b,
$$\underbrace{b + b + \ldots + b}_{a \text{ addends of } b} = a \times b, \text{ or } ab.$$

Notice that this definition of a product as a sum of equal addends has meaning only when the universe is the set of natural numbers. The definition would be meaningless if a were replaced by a rational number like $\frac{5}{2}$ since it does not make sense to talk about $\frac{5}{2}$ equal addends. Of course, the definition in terms of a Cartesian product has the same limitation. Now let us see whether we can use this definition of the product of two natural numbers to develop certain generalizations relating to products.

First of all, suppose that we replace the b in the definition of the product of two natural numbers by 0. Let us see what generalization we can state about the product of any natural number a and 0. If we replace b by 0, we obtain

$$\underbrace{0 + 0 + \ldots + 0}_{a \text{ addends of } 0} = a \times 0.$$

Later in this chapter, we will use the union of disjoint sets to develop the idea that the sum of any natural number and 0 is equal to the given number. This means that $0 + 0 = 0$, that $0 + 0 + 0 = 0$, and so on. Therefore, we see that

$$\underbrace{0 + 0 + \ldots + 0}_{a \text{ addends of } 0} = 0.$$

Hence, we know that, for any natural number a,

$$a \times 0 = 0.$$

Now suppose that we replace the b in the definition of product by 1. When we do this, we obtain

$$\underbrace{1 + 1 + \ldots + 1}_{a \text{ addends of } 1} = a \times 1.$$

We must now interpret the expression at the left of the "equals" sign in the above sentence. We know that the sum of 2 ones is 2, the sum of 3 ones is 3, the sum of 50 ones is 50, and so on. Thus, we can conclude that the sum of a ones is a. Remember that a is a variable for a natural number. Thus,

$$a = 1 \times a.$$

In other words, the product of 1 and any natural number is equal to the given number.

Next we can use the definition of product and certain properties of sums to interpret an expression like $3 \times (5 + 4)$ that involves both a sum and a product. From the definition of products, $3 \times (5 + 4)$ is equal to the sum of 3 addends of $(5 + 4)$. That is,

$$3 \times (5 + 4) = (5 + 4) + (5 + 4) + (5 + 4).$$

We can now use the properties that we established earlier concerning the order in sums and the way in which 3 or more addends are grouped to show that

Order in sums and sum of three natural numbers, pages 57 and 60

$$(5 + 4) + (5 + 4) + (5 + 4) = (5 + 5 + 5) + (4 + 4 + 4).$$

But, from the definition of product, we know that $(5 + 5 + 5) = (3 \times 5)$ and that $(4 + 4 + 4) = (3 \times 4)$. Therefore, we can conclude that

$$3 \times (5 + 4) = (3 \times 5) + (3 \times 4).$$

From this last statement, we know that the product of 3 and $(5 + 4)$ is the same as the sum of (3×5) and (3×4).

Let us now see if we can illustrate that, for any three natural numbers a, b, and c, the following is true:

$$a \times (b + c) = ab + ac.$$

First of all, from the definition of product, we know that $a \times (b + c)$ means a addends of $(b + c)$. That is,

$$a \times (b + c) = \underbrace{(b + c) + (b + c) + \ldots + (b + c)}_{a \text{ addends of } (b + c)}.$$

But we can now use the properties concerning sums to regroup the addends in the following way.

$$\underbrace{(b + c) + (b + c) + \ldots + (b + c)}_{a \text{ addends of } (b + c)} = \underbrace{(b + \ldots + b)}_{a \text{ addends of } b} + \underbrace{(c + \ldots + c)}_{a \text{ addends of } c}.$$

From the definition of product, we know that

$$\underbrace{(b + b + \ldots + b)}_{a \text{ addends of } b} = ab.$$

and that

$$\underbrace{(c + c + \ldots + c)}_{a \text{ addends of } c} = ac.$$

Therefore, we know that

$$\underbrace{(b + b + \ldots + b)}_{a \text{ addends of } b} + \underbrace{(c + c + \ldots + c)}_{a \text{ addends of } c} = (ab) + (ac).$$

Finally,

$$a \times (b + c) = ab + ac.$$

This is the generalization that we wished to illustrate, and we now can say that, for any three natural numbers a, b, and c, the product of a and $b + c$ is equal to the sum of ab and ac.

This property concerning the way in which sums and products are combined can be generalized even further to sums of more than two addends. Thus, if a, b, c, and d are natural numbers, we could easily show that $a(b + c + d) = ab + ac + ad$.

Next we shall see if our definition of product enables us to state an order of products property that is similar to the order of sums property we stated earlier. Certainly, when we consider specific examples, we agree that $2 \times 4 = 4 \times 2$, that $6 \times 8 = 8 \times 6$, that $100 \times 22 = 22 \times 100$, and so on. But now we want to see whether we can say that, for *any* two natural numbers a and b, the product ab is equal to the product ba.

From the definition of the product of two natural numbers, we know that

$$ab = \underbrace{b + b + \ldots + b.}_{a \text{ addends of } b}$$

Earlier, we saw that the product of any natural number and 1 is equal to the given number. Therefore, we know that $b \times 1 = b$. So, we know that

$$\underbrace{b + b + \ldots + b}_{a \text{ addends of } b} = \underbrace{b \times 1 + b \times 1 + \ldots + b \times 1.}_{a \text{ addends of } b \times 1}$$

Now we can use the general form of the property we just developed concerning sums and products to show that

$$\underbrace{b \times 1 + b \times 1 + \ldots + b \times 1}_{a \text{ addends of } b \times 1} = b \times \underbrace{(1 + 1 + \ldots + 1).}_{a \text{ addends of } 1}$$

Further, we know that

$$\underbrace{(1 + 1 + \ldots + 1)}_{a \text{ addends of } 1} = a.$$

Therefore,

$$b \times \underbrace{(1 + 1 + \ldots + 1)}_{a \text{ addends of } 1} = ba.$$

Finally, we can now say that, for any two natural numbers a and b,

$$ab = ba.$$

Thus, there is an order in products property that is similar to the order in sums property we developed earlier.

We also showed earlier that, when we are working with three or more addends, we get the same sum no matter how we group the addends. In other words, we know that, for any three natural numbers, a, b, and c, $(a + b) + c = a + (b + c)$. Although it would be a tedious process, we could use the definition of product and certain properties to illustrate that, when three factors are involved, the way in which we group the factors does not affect the product. That is,

For any three natural numbers a, b, and c, $(ab)c = a(bc)$.

The generalization just expressed enables you to decide, without computing, that sentences like the following do express true statements.

$$(3 \times 2) \times 5 = 3 \times (2 \times 5).$$
$$15 \times (10 \times 14) = (15 \times 10) \times 14.$$
$$(72 \times 8) \times 25 = 72 \times (8 \times 25).$$

In this section, we have given an alternative to the definition of the product of two natural numbers in terms of Cartesian sets. This definition related products to sums in a way that is appropriate to the study of elementary arithmetic. With this definition, we have been able to develop the same properties as we can develop with the Cartesian product definition.

56 a Express 5×8 as the sum of five equal addends.
   b Express 8×5 as a sum of eight equal addends.
   c Use the method presented in this section to show that $5 \times 8 = 8 \times 5$.
57 a Express $4 \times (1 + 2)$ as a sum of four equal addends.
   b Show that the sum you found for part a can be expressed as the sum of two products.
58 Sums and products have properties that are analogous. Explain what this statement means to you.
59 Use the methods of this section to show that the product of an odd number and an even number is even. [Use $2x$ to represent an even natural number and $2x + 1$ to represent an odd natural number.]
60 Use the definitions and properties that you have learned so far in this chapter concerning sums and products to show that the following statements are true.
   a $(5 + 2) + 6 = 2 + (5 + 6)$.
   b $6 \times (1 + 4) = (4 \times 6) + 6$.
   c $6 \times (a + 1) = 6 + 6a$.
   d $(4 \times 3) + (4 \times 5) = 4(5 + 3)$.
   e $(a \times 2) + 5a = (5 + 2)a$.
   f $ac + cb = c(b + a)$.

61 Show how to generalize $a(b + c) = ab + ac$ to three addends. That is, show that, for any four natural numbers a, b, c, and d,

$$a(b + c + d) = ab + ac + ad.$$

Some special properties of sums and products

If you were working with a condition like $a + 3 = 15 + 3$, you would probably "cancel out the threes" to obtain $a = 15$. Similarly, if you were working with a condition like $5r = 40$, you would "divide both sides by 5" to obtain $r = 8$. In this section, we will discuss the properties that enable you to perform these manipulations.

The cancellation property of sums states that if, for any three given numbers, the sum of the first number and the third number is equal to the sum of the second and third numbers, then the first number is equal to the second number. We can easily show that this is the case by using any three finite sets A, B, and C, such that A and C are disjoint and B and C are disjoint.

First, we start with the idea that $n[A] + n[C] = n[B] + n[C]$. We want to show that, if this is the case, then $n[A] = n[B]$. By the definition of a sum, you know that $n[A] + n[C] = n[A \cup C]$ and also that $n[B] + n[C] = n[B \cup C]$. Therefore,

$$n[A \cup C] = n[B \cup C].$$

This means that $A \cup C$ and $B \cup C$ are equivalent sets. Since C is obviously equivalent to itself, A and B must be equivalent to each other. Hence,

$$n[A] = n[B].$$

The last sentence is what we wanted to show. We now state the cancellation property of sums as follows:

> For any three natural numbers a, b, and c,
> if $a + c = b + c$, then $a = b$.

This property enables you to determine the solution of a condition like $n + 5 = 32$. You know that $32 = 27 + 5$, so you can obtain $n + 5 = 27 + 5$ from $n + 5 = 32$. Then, by the property of sums just expressed, you can obtain $n = 27$ from $n + 5 = 27 + 5$. Thus, 27 is the solution of $n + 5 = 32$.

There is a property of products that is similar to the property of sums that we just established. This property enables you to conclude that, for any three natural numbers, if the third number is not 0 and if the product of the first and third numbers is equal to the product of the second and third numbers; then the first number is equal to the second number.

To illustrate this property in terms of Cartesian products, we will use any three finite sets A, B, and C. Suppose that $a = $ n[A], $b = $ n[B], and $c = $ n[C].

By the definition of a product in terms of a Cartesian set, you know that, if $ac = bc$, then

$$n[A \times C] = n[B \times C].$$

This means that $A \times C$ and $B \times C$ are equivalent sets. $A \times C$ is formed by matching each member of A with each member of C, and $B \times C$ is formed by matching each member of B with each member of C. Since A and B are matched with the same set, set C, and since $A \times C$ and $B \times C$ have the same number of members, it follows that A and B must have the same number of members. Therefore,

$$n[A] = n[B], \text{ and } a = b.$$

You will remember that we said that c cannot be 0; this means that C cannot be the empty set. If C were the empty set, then both $A \times C$ and $B \times C$ would be the empty set, no matter what n[A] or n[B] might be. This is true because the empty set has no members to match with the members of the other set, and, hence, there are no ordered pairs in the Cartesian set. Thus, if $C = \{\ \}$, we could not validly argue that $n[A] = n[B]$ or that $a = b$.

Thus, we have used the definition of products in terms of Cartesian sets to illustrate the cancellation property of products that is expressed below.

For any three natural numbers a, b, and c,
if $c \neq 0$ and if $ac = bc$, then $a = b$.

It is left as an exercise for you to develop the property just expressed in terms of the alternative definition of products given on page 68.

This property of products enables you to determine solutions of conditions of the form $3n = 45$. You know that $45 = 15 \times 3$; hence, you can obtain $3n = 15 \times 3$. By the order of products property, you know that $3n = n \times 3$; hence, you can obtain $n \times 3 = 15 \times 3$. Then, by the property of products just expressed, you can obtain $n = 15$. Thus, 15 is the solution of $3n = 45$.

62 Use the cancellation properties for natural numbers to draw a conclusion in the form of an open sentence that can be derived from each of the following open sentences. Your conclusion for exercise a, for example, would be the sentence $x = 5$.

a $x + 8 = 5 + 8$.
b $5x = 5 \cdot 7$.
c $6 + x = z + x$.
d $xy = 9x, x \neq 0$.
e $(z + 4) + 3 = 11 + 3$.

f $(x + y) + 8 = (x + y) + z$.
g $4 + y + 5 = x + 4$.
h $6y = 6z$.
i $(4y) \cdot 3 = 8 \cdot 3$.
j $xyz = y \cdot y, y \neq 0$.

63 Show how the cancellation properties of natural numbers may be used to determine solutions for the open sentences listed below. The universe is N.

a $5x = 55$.
b $2x + 3 = 15$.
c $7 + 4x = 35$.

d $3x + 5 = 23$.
e $3a + 11 = 14$.
f $43b + 14 = 100$.

64 Use the definition of products given on page 68 to prove that for any three natural numbers a, b, and c, if $c \neq 0$, and if $ac = bc$, then $a = b$.

Special sums and products

We can use the idea of the union of disjoint sets to develop a property that concerns the sum of any natural number and 0. You know that 0 is the number of the empty set; that is, $n[\{ \ \}] = 0$. You also know that $\{ \ \}$ Number of and any set are disjoint because they have no common members. Now empty set, page 28 suppose that we form the union of $\{ \ \}$ and any other set, which we will call set A.

$$A \cup \{ \ \} = A.$$

Therefore,

$$n[A \cup \{ \ \}] = n[A],$$
$$n[A] + n[\{ \ \}] = n[A],$$

and

$$n[A] + 0 = n[A].$$

We can state this again, using a to represent $n[A]$.

$$a + 0 = a.$$

Thus, we have the property of sums that is expressed below.

For any natural number a, $a + 0 = a$.

We have already developed a similar property concerning the product Product of any natural of any natural number and 1 by using the definition of a product in terms number and 1, of a sum of equal addends. Now we can use the idea of a Cartesian product page 69 to develop this property in another way. We will consider any set A and set B, which has exactly one member. Because B has only one member to be matched with each member of A, the Cartesian set A × B consists of a set of ordered pairs that contains the same number of members as A. Thus, because A × B is equivalent to A,

$$n[A \times B] = n[A].$$

From the definition of a product, you know that $n[A \times B] = n[A] \times n[B]$. Therefore,

$$n[A] \times n[B] = n[A].$$

You know that $n[B] = 1$, and you can use a to represent $n[A]$ to obtain

$$a \times 1 = a.$$

Thus, we have the following property of products.

For any natural number a, $a \times 1 = a$.

Earlier, we also developed a property concerning the product of any given natural number and 0. Now we can use Cartesian sets to develop this property in another way. Suppose that A is any set, that $n[A] = a$, and that B = { }.

You know that

$$n[A] \times n[B] = n[A \times B].$$

But, because B = { }, $n[B] = 0$, A × B = { } and $n[A \times B] = 0$. Therefore,

$$a \times 0 = 0.$$

Thus, we have the following property of products.

For any natural number a, $a \times 0 = 0$.

Standard names of sums

You know that expressions like $2 + 4$, $3 + 1$, and $5 + 3$ are names of sums. You know, however, that such sums also have standard names that are numerals for natural numbers. Certainly, you already know that 6 is the standard name of $2 + 4$, that 4 is the standard name of $3 + 1$, and so on; but we must now give a mathematical analysis of how we arrive at standard names.

One way to find the standard name of a sum like $2 + 4$ is to use the ideas of standard sets and equivalent sets. Suppose that C = {a, b} and that $D = \{c, d, e, f\}$. From the definition of a sum, you know that

$$n[C] + n[D] = n[C \cup D].$$

But, because C is equivalent to the standard set $\{0, 1\}$, $n[C] = 2$. Also, because D is equivalent to the standard set $\{0, 1, 2, 3\}$, $n[D] = 4$. Therefore, you can obtain

$$2 + 4 = n[C \cup D].$$

Now the problem is to find the standard set that is equivalent to $C \cup D$. From the definition of the union of two sets, we obtain

$$C \cup D = \{a, b, c, d, e, f\}.$$

$\{a, b, c, d, e, f\}$ is equivalent to the standard set $\{0, 1, 2, 3, 4, 5\}$; hence, $n[C \cup D] = 6$. Therefore, you can write

$$2 + 4 = 6.$$

Another way to arrive at the standard name of a sum is to use the idea of the successor of a natural number and what you already know about the standard names of certain sums. From the property about the sum of any given natural number and 0, you already know how to find the standard name of the sum of the given number and 0. For example, you know that $3 + 0 = 3$. Also, because of the order in sums property, you know that $0 + 4 = 4 + 0$, that $0 + 8 = 8 + 0$, and so on. Therefore, the standard name of the sum of a given natural number and 0 or of 0 and a given natural number is also the name of the given number.

Next, we will use the successor idea to determine standard names of sums like $2 + 1$, $6 + 1$, $1 + 5$, and $1 + 4$. In Chapter 2 you learned that, for any set A, the successor of A is $A \cup \{A\}$. From the definition of a sum, you know that $n[A \cup \{A\}] = n[A] + n[\{A\}]$. But, because $\{A\}$ has exactly 1 member, you know that $n[\{A\}] = 1$. Therefore, $n[A \cup \{A\}] = n[A] + 1$, and the successor of $n[A]$ is $n[A] + 1$. In Chapter 2 we also established the order of the natural numbers in terms of the successor idea. Recall that, for the natural numbers,

Successor set, page 27

$$0 < 1 < 2 < 3 < 4 < 5 < 6 < 7 < 8 < 9 < 10 < 11 < 12 \ldots.$$

Thus, we know that the sum of any given natural number and 1 is equal to the successor of the given number. This means that we know that $5 + 1 = 6$ because 6 is the successor of 5; we know that $8 + 1 = 9$ because 9 is the successor of 8; and so on.

We can also find the standard names of sums like $1 + 7$ and $1 + 3$ by using the order in sums property. $1 + 7 = 7 + 1$; therefore, the standard name of $1 + 7$ is 8 because 8 is the standard name of $7 + 1$. Similarly, because $1 + 3 = 3 + 1$, the standard name of $1 + 3$ is 4 because 4 is the standard name of $3 + 1$.

Thus, you know that the standard name of the sum of a given natural number and 1 or of 1 and a given natural number is the name of the successor of the given number.

So far, we know how to find standard names of sums that include either 0 or 1 as one or both addends. Now, we must build upon this so that we have a method for finding a standard name of a sum like $2 + 2$.

First, we establish that, because $1 + 1 = 2$,

$$2 + 2 = 2 + (1 + 1).$$

Next, by the property that concerns the sum of three numbers, we know that $2 + (1 + 1) = (2 + 1) + 1$. Therefore, Sum of three numbers, page 60

$$2 + 2 = (2 + 1) + 1.$$

But we already know that $2 + 1$ is the successor of 2, or 3; thus,

$$2 + 2 = 3 + 1.$$

Finally, we know that $3 + 1 = 4$, and hence,

$$2 + 2 = 4.$$

You should be able to justify each of the following steps in finding the standard name of $6 + 2$.

$$6 + 2 = 6 + (1 + 1).$$
$$6 + 2 = (6 + 1) + 1.$$
$$6 + 2 = 7 + 1.$$
$$6 + 2 = 8.$$

Now we can generalize the procedure for finding the standard name of the sum of any natural number a and 2.

$$a + 2 = a + (1 + 1).$$
$$a + 2 = (a + 1) + 1.$$

If we symbolize the successor of a by a', then we can write

$$a + 2 = a' + 1.$$

But $a' + 1$ is the successor of a', which is the successor of a. Therefore, if we use $(a')'$ to symbolize the successor of the successor of a, then we have

$$a + 2 = (a')'.$$

We can say, therefore, that the standard name of the sum of any given natural number and 2 is the name of the successor of the successor of the given number. The order in sums property also enables us to say that the standard name of the sum of 2 and any given natural number is the name of the successor of the successor of the given number.

Now we can use what we already know to determine the standard name of the sum of any given natural number and 3. Consider the sum $5 + 3$. Because $3 = 2 + 1$, you know that

$$5 + 3 = 5 + (2 + 1).$$

By the property that concerns the sum of three numbers, you know that $5 + (2 + 1) = (5 + 2) + 1$. Therefore,

$$5 + 3 = (5 + 2) + 1.$$

But you already know that $5 + 2$ is equal to the successor of the successor of 5, or 7. Therefore,

$$5 + 3 = 7 + 1.$$

Finally, you know that $7 + 1$ is equal to the successor of 7, or 8. Therefore,

$$5 + 3 = 8.$$

Again, we can generalize to say that the sum of any given natural number and 3 is equal to the successor of the successor of the successor of the given number.

Theoretically it would be possible to find the standard name of the sum of any two natural numbers by repeated use of the successor notion. Practically, of course, it would be exceedingly cumbersome to use this method to find the standard name of $2,345,198 + 459,982$, for example. Actually, we determine the standard names for sums by means of a computational short cut. We shall discuss methods of computation involving natural numbers in Chapter 7.

65 Use the successor idea to show how to find the standard name of each sum named below.

a $5 + 7$ **b** $6 + 6$ **c** $3 + 4$ **d** $4 + 5$

66 Show that $5 + 10$ and $10 + 5$ have the same successor.

Standard names of products

If a product is thought of in terms of a Cartesian set, you can use the ideas of a standard set and equivalent sets to find the standard name of a product. Suppose, for example, that A = {a, b, c} and B = {d, e}. From the definition of a product, you know that

$$n[A] \times n[B] = n[A \times B].$$

Because A is equivalent to the standard set {0, 1, 2}, you know that n[A] = 3. Because B is equivalent to the standard set {0, 1}, you know that n[B] = 2. Therefore,

$$3 \times 2 = n[A \times B].$$

Next, we tabulate A × B so that we can find a standard set that is equivalent to it.

$$A \times B = \{(a, d), (a, e), (b, d), (b, e), (c, d), (c, e)\}.$$

The following diagram shows that A × B is equivalent to the standard set that is identified with the natural number 6.

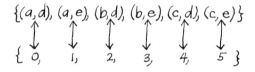

Thus, n[A × B] = 6, and

$$3 \times 2 = 6.$$

In the elementary school, a product like 3 × 5 is often given a physical interpretation in terms of the combining of 3 sets, each containing 5 objects. Thus, to find the standard name of the product 3 × 5, we can find the standard name of the sum 5 + 5 + 5. Similarly, to find the standard name of 6 × 8 (6 sets of 8 each), we can find the standard name of the sum 8 + 8 + 8 + 8 + 8 + 8. In the following discussion, we will use the information we already have concerning the product of any natural number and 1 to give a mathematical explanation of this "adding" method of finding the standard name of a product.

First, however, we should point out that, by the property concerning the product of any number and 0, you already know that the standard name of a product of the form a × 0 is 0. By the order in products property, you also know that the standard name of a product of the form 0 × a is 0.

Further, by the property concerning the product of any number and 1, you know that the standard name of any product of the form a × 1 is a. And, by the order in products property, you know that the standard name of any product of the form 1 × a is also a.

Next, consider a product like 2×2. You know that $2 = 1 + 1$; therefore, you can write,

$$2 \times 2 = 2 \times (1 + 1).$$

By the property that concerns combining sums and products, you know that $2 \times (1 + 1) = (2 \times 1) + (2 \times 1)$. Therefore, Combining sums and products, page 66

$$2 \times 2 = (2 \times 1) + (2 \times 1).$$

But you know that $2 \times 1 = 2$. Hence, $(2 \times 1) + (2 \times 1) = 2 + 2$, and

$$2 \times 2 = 2 + 2.$$

From our previous work with addition, you know that $2 + 2 = 4$; thus,

$$2 \times 2 = 4.$$

You should be able to justify each step in the following example:

$$5 \times 2 = 5 \times (1 + 1).$$
$$5 \times 2 = (5 \times 1) + (5 \times 1).$$
$$5 \times 2 = 5 + 5.$$

The methods discussed in the previous section on standard names of sums can now be used to show that $5 + 5 = 10$. Hence,

$$5 \times 2 = 10.$$

In general, we can find the product of any given natural number a and 2 in the following way.

$$a \times 2 = a \times (1 + 1).$$
$$a \times 2 = (a \times 1) + (a \times 1).$$
$$a \times 2 = a + a.$$

By continuing this procedure, we could develop a method for determining the standard name of the product of any two natural numbers. As we pointed out in connection with sums, the usual method involves the use of computational procedures that will be discussed in a later chapter. Our purpose in showing you how to develop standard names of sums and products is to demonstrate how a mathematician can construct complex and powerful results from a few basic ideas.

67 In the manner used in this section, show how to find the standard name of each product named below.

a 8×2 **c** 5×5
b 4×3 **d** 6×4

82

CONCLUSION

The relationships between set operations and the properties of sums and products that have been discussed in this chapter should give you an understanding of why the definition of a natural number as a standard set is such a useful one. With this definition and the definitions of operations on sets, we have been able to establish many important properties of sums and products. Of course, you will not use many of these ideas—at least in the form presented—with elementary-school children. But the background of ideas given here should help you understand better the ideas that you will be presenting in the classroom.

CHAPTER QUIZ

1 For each of sets A, B, C, and D, tabulated below, tell what the number of the set is.

A = { }.   B = {0}.   C = {a, b, c, d}.   D = {Carl, Wayne}.

Let A, B, C, and D refer to the sets tabulated in exercise 1. Give another name for each natural number expressed in exercises 2 through 10.

2 n[A ∪ B]   5 n[A × A]   8 n[C ∪ D]
3 n[A × B]   6 n[B × B]   9 n[D × C]
4 n[B ∪ C]   7 n[A ∪ A]   10 n[B ∪ B]

11 Suppose that S = {a, b}, R = {Sue, Jane, Carol}, and L = {Don, Nancy}. Show how the members of S × R can be matched with the members of L × R so as to set up a one-to-one correspondence. What is the name of the relation that exists between S × R and L × R? What can you say about n[S × R] and n[L × R]?

State why you think the following sentences might express true statements for each replacement of the variables by natural numbers.

12 $a + (b + c) = a + (c + b)$.
13 $s(ry) = (sr)y$.
14 $s(ry) = (ys)r$.
15 $(a + b) + c = c + (a + b)$.
16 $(a + b) + c = c + (b + a)$.
17 $a(b + c) = (b + c)a$.
18 $a(b + c) = ba + ac$.
19 $a(b + c) = ac + ab$.
20 $a(b + c) = ca + ba$.
21 $2c + 2d = 2(c + d)$.
22 $(kl + kn) + (ry + sy) = k(l + m) + (r + s)y$.

Suppose that R,S,A,and B are mutually disjoint sets and that n[R] = r, n[S] = s, n[A] = a, and n[B] = b. In terms of r, s, a, and b, write another symbol for each natural number named in exercises 23 through 28.

23 n[R $\times$ S] 26 n[R $\cup$ A]

24 n[(R $\times$ S) $\times$ A] 27 n[(S $\times$ A) $\cup$ B]

25 n[(A $\times$ B) $\cup$ (R $\times$ S)] 28 n[(A $\cup$ B) $\times$ (R $\cup$ S)]

29 If A = {cat} and B = {dog, rat, mouse}, show that the members of A $\times$ B can be put in one-to-one correspondence with B.

Justify each of the following by using the properties that have been developed in this chapter.

30 $2 \times 3 = 3 \times 2$. 32 $5 \times 6 = 20 + 10$.

31 $5(4 + 3) = 20 + 15$. 33 $6 \times 5 \times 2 = 30 \times 2$.

SUPPLEMENTARY READINGS

Gibb, E. G., *et al.*, *The Growth of Mathematical Ideas: Grades K-12* (Twenty-Fourth Yearbook of NCTM), pp. 20-28. Discusses the relationship of sums and products of natural numbers to operations on sets. Item 6 of Bibliography

Levi, Howard, *Elements of Algebra*, Ch. II. Although the terminology is slightly different, the approach is essentially the same as that used in this chapter. Item 23 of Bibliography

Russell, Bertrand, *Introduction to Mathematical Philosophy*, Ch. 1 and 2. Uses the successor idea to develop sums and products. Item 24 of Bibliography

For an axiomatic approach to addition and multiplication of natural numbers, see either of the following references.

Hamilton, Norman and Landin, Joseph, *Set Theory: The Structure of Arithmetic*, pp. 106-112. Item 13 of Bibliography

Kerschner, R. B. and Wilcox, L. R., *The Anatomy of Mathematics*, pp. 101-123. Item 25 of Bibliography

Chapter five

Fundamental operations

The operation of addition
The teaching of addition
The operation of multiplication
The teaching of multiplication
Some comments about addition and multiplication
The natural-number system
Properties of equality
Subtraction and division
Clock arithmetic
Another finite number system

In Chapter 4 the sum of two natural numbers was defined in terms of the union of disjoint sets, and the product of two natural numbers was defined in terms of the Cartesian product of two sets. In this chapter we will first explain what we mean by an arithmetical *operation* and then show how the operations of addition and multiplication are related to sums and products.

The operation of addition

You will recall that, at the end of the last chapter, we developed a method for finding the standard name of a sum. In your elementary-school days, you may have worked with an "addition table" like the one shown below. It provides a convenient summary of the standard names of the sums of all pairs of numbers that can be formed from the natural numbers 0 through 12. To find the standard name of the sum of 4 and 6, for example, you locate the numeral that is to the right of the numeral 4 in column A

Standard names of sums, page 76

and also below the numeral 6 in row A. This numeral is, of course, 10, which is the standard name of the sum 4 + 6.

Using methods such as those described in Chapter 4, you could extend this table indefinitely. We will imagine that the table has been extended to include the standard name of the sum of any two natural numbers we care to think about. Thus, if N is the set of all natural numbers, then N × N is the set of all possible ordered pairs of natural numbers; and we will assume that the sum of the components of each pair of members of N × N is named in our imaginary table.

Column A	Row A 0	1	2	3	4	5	6	7	8	9	10	11	12	...
0	0	1	2	3	4	5	6	7	8	9	10	11	12	...
1	1	2	3	4	5	6	7	8	9	10	11	12	13	...
2	2	3	4	5	6	7	8	9	10	11	12	13	14	...
3	3	4	5	6	7	8	9	10	11	12	13	14	15	...
4	4	5	6	7	8	9	10	11	12	13	14	15	16	...
5	5	6	7	8	9	10	11	12	13	14	15	16	17	...
6	6	7	8	9	10	11	12	13	14	15	16	17	18	...
7	7	8	9	10	11	12	13	14	15	16	17	18	19	...
8	8	9	10	11	12	13	14	15	16	17	18	19	20	...
9	9	10	11	12	13	14	15	16	17	18	19	20	21	...
10	10	11	12	13	14	15	16	17	18	19	20	21	22	...
11	11	12	13	14	15	16	17	18	19	20	21	22	23	...
12	12	13	14	15	16	17	18	19	20	21	22	23	24	...
:	:	:	:	:	:	:	:	:	:	:	:	:	:	:

The addition table shows clearly that such numbers as 3 and 2 have been paired, and that this pair is matched with its sum, the number 5. There are many ways in which pairs of natural numbers can be matched with a single natural number; addition is just one of the ways. We will use a diagram like the following one to indicate an addition matching, or mapping.

$$(3, 2) \xrightarrow{+} 5$$

This diagram is read, "The ordered pair of natural numbers 3, 2 is mapped onto 5 by addition." In the diagram, the symbol + above the arrow indicates that (3, 2) is mapped onto 5 *by addition*.

Mapping, page 15

Several other diagrams that can be obtained from the addition table are shown below.

$$(1, 1) \xrightarrow{\ +\ } 2$$
$$(5, 5) \xrightarrow{\ +\ } 10$$
$$(6, 3) \xrightarrow{\ +\ } 9$$
$$(11, 10) \xrightarrow{\ +\ } 21$$
$$(6, 4) \xrightarrow{\ +\ } 10$$
$$(2, 7) \xrightarrow{\ +\ } 9$$
$$(12, 9) \xrightarrow{\ +\ } 21$$
$$(11, 11) \xrightarrow{\ +\ } 22$$

There are 13×13, or 169, such diagrams to be obtained from the table on page 85. Of course, if you considered all possible pairs of natural numbers, there would be an infinite set of such diagrams. The diagrams below illustrate several of the mappings that are not exhibited in the addition table.

$$(116, 1) \xrightarrow{\ +\ } 117$$
$$(5000, 215) \xrightarrow{\ +\ } 5215$$
$$(0, 87) \xrightarrow{\ +\ } 87$$
$$(105, 12) \xrightarrow{\ +\ } 117$$

Notice that the mapping of ordered pairs of natural numbers onto sums maps more than one pair onto the same sum. For example, both (6, 3) and (2, 7) are mapped onto 9; both (116, 1) and (105, 12) are mapped onto 117. You can find many other examples of several different ordered pairs that are mapped onto the same sum. Hence, the mapping of or- Many-to-one dered pairs of natural numbers onto sums is an example of a many-to-one _{mapping,} page 16 mapping.

Now we can state generally what we mean by the *operation of addition*.

> The operation of addition is a many-to-one mapping
> whereby every ordered pair of natural numbers
> is mapped onto a natural number that is their sum.

Another way of expressing the same idea is to say that, by the operation of addition, the members of $N \times N$ are mapped onto the members of N. Obviously, this statement is not so complete or specific as the definition given above because addition is only one of many possible ways of mapping the members of $N \times N$ onto N.

Now that we have defined the operation of addition, we will turn our attention to certain properties of addition. Included in the definition of the addition operation is the idea that the sum of any two natural numbers is itself a natural number. We say, therefore, that the set of natural numbers is closed under the operation of addition, or, to put it another way, that addition of natural numbers has the *closure property*. We express closure of addition in the following way.

For any two natural numbers a and b, $a + b \in N$.

In the above sentence, a and b represent any two natural numbers; N represents the set of natural numbers; and the symbol ϵ expresses the idea "is a member of." The entire sentence is read, "For any two natural numbers a and b, the sum of a and b is a member of the set of natural numbers."

In Chapter 4 you learned that, for any two natural numbers a and b, $a + b = b + a$. Hence, we say that addition of natural numbers is *commutative*, or that addition has the commutative property. You can find many illustrations of the commutative property in the addition table on page 85. For example, the numeral 17 appears to the right of the numeral 8 and below the numeral 9; the numeral 17 also appears to the right of the numeral 9 and below the numeral 8. This verifies that

Order in sums, page 57

$$8 + 9 = 17 = 9 + 8.$$

Another property you studied in Chapter 4 is: For any three natural numbers a, b, and c, $(a + b) + c = a + (b + c)$. This property is known as the *associative property of addition* of natural numbers, or we may simply say that addition is associative.

Sum of three natural numbers, page 58

The teaching of addition

It is quite obvious that the methods used here for developing mathematical definitions of a sum and of the operation of addition are not appropriate for elementary-school children. It is possible, however, to use these ideas as a *guide* in planning an instructional program for children.

You have seen how numbers and operations with numbers are closely associated with sets and operations with sets. You will recall, for example, that the sum of two natural numbers is defined in terms of the union of disjoint sets. Further, we were able to use this idea to develop the commutative property of addition of natural numbers because the way in which you form the union of two sets does not affect the number of the set you obtain. In other words, because, for any two sets A and B, $A \cup B$ is equivalent to $B \cup A$, $n[A \cup B] = n[B \cup A]$.

Sum of two natural numbers, page 56

Now we will give an illustration of the kind of classroom activity that might be used to help children understand the concepts we have been discussing.

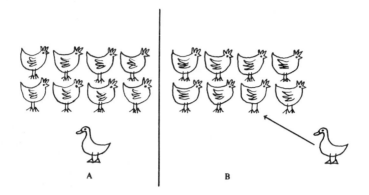

A   B

Children should have repeated experiences with objects or with pictures like those above. They should see many different examples in which a set of 8 objects and a set of 1 object are combined to form a set of 8 + 1, or 9, objects. In this way, the children will soon be able to abstract the idea that, whenever 8 objects are combined with 1 object, the result is a set of 9 objects. In connection with such experiences, they should associate the operation of addition with the "combining" or "joining" action in which two groups are involved. Later, they should associate the meaning of the symbol + and the word *sum* with the result of the action.

Now compare the two pictures above with those below. Picture C is the same as picture A, but picture D differs from picture B in that it shows the set of 8 joining the set of 1, rather than the other way around. With pictures like C and D, children will learn to associate the sum 1 + 8. After many experiences, they will be able to see that, although the actual situations are different, the same number results when a set of 8 joins a set of 1 as when a set of 1 joins a set of 8. They will naturally conclude that 8 + 1 = 1 + 8 and begin to understand the commutative property of addition.

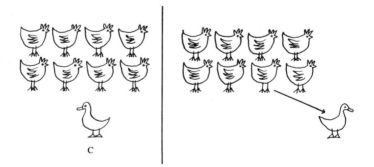

C

Notice that the expressions $8 + 1$ and $1 + 8$ preserve the sense of what has happened in each instance. Thus, $8 + 1$ indicates that 1 has been combined with 8; while $1 + 8$ indicates that 8 has been combined with 1. In each case, we know that the numeral 9 is the standard name of the sum, although the numeral 9 does not convey the same sense as either of the expressions $8 + 1$ or $1 + 8$.

The ideas that the children are to gain from illustrations such as those above are the same ideas that you learned in a more abstract way when we discussed the union of disjoint sets. We will use the following sets to help you recall how this was done.

Union of disjoint sets, page 20

$$F = \{a, b, c\}.$$
$$G = \{x, y\}.$$
$$F \cup G = \{a, b, c, x, y\}.$$

By the definition of a sum, you know that

$$n[F] + n[G] = n[F \cup G].$$

Therefore, because $n[F] = 3$ and $n[G] = 2$,

$$n[F \cup G] = 3 + 2.$$

Next, we form the union of G and F.

$$G \cup F = \{x, y, a, b, c\}.$$

Again, by the definition of a sum,

$$n[G] + n[F] = n[G \cup F].$$

Since $n[G] = 2$ and $n[F] = 3$,

$$n[G \cup F] = 2 + 3.$$

But, if you compare $F \cup G$ with $G \cup F$, you find that $F \cup G$ and $G \cup F$ are equivalent sets; hence,

$$n[F \cup G] = n[G \cup F].$$

Finally,

$$3 + 2 = 2 + 3.$$

Thus, through the use of many examples of a physical or concrete nature, children can intuitively develop certain important mathematical concepts, such as the meaning of addition, the meaning of a sum, and the commutativity of addition of natural numbers.

In exercises 68 through 72, we will use N to designate the set of natural numbers. Remember that the operation of addition of natural numbers is a mapping of N × N onto N.

68 In this mapping, (0, 0) is mapped onto 0. Do any other members of N × N map onto 0 by addition?

69 How many pairs of natural numbers map onto the number 1 under this mapping? What are these pairs?

70 What pairs map onto 2 under the addition mapping?

71 How many pairs map onto 3? What are these pairs?

72 What generalization can you make about the number of pairs that map onto a number n under the addition mapping?

73 The following diagrams illustrate addition mappings from N × N onto N. Find proper replacements for x and y.

a $(3, 21) \xrightarrow{+} x$ **e** $(x, y) \xrightarrow{+} 7$

b $(x, 6) \xrightarrow{+} 10$ **f** $(0, x) \xrightarrow{+} 6$

c $(5, y) \xrightarrow{+} 8$ **g** $(y, 0) \xrightarrow{+} 1$

d $(x, y) \xrightarrow{+} 0$ **h** $(x, y) \xrightarrow{+} 120$

The operation of multiplication

In Chapter 4 we also developed a method for finding the standard name of a product. The "multiplication table" shown on page 91 summarizes the standard names of the products of all ordered pairs of numbers that can be formed from the natural numbers 0 through 12.

Standard names of products, page 79

Just as the addition table shows the mapping of an ordered pair of natural numbers onto their sum, so the multiplication table exhibits the mapping of an ordered pair of natural numbers onto their product. For example, you can see from the table that the ordered pair 6, 3 is mapped onto the product 18. We will use the following diagram to represent this mapping.

$$(6, 3) \xrightarrow{\times} 18$$

This diagram is read, "The ordered pair of natural numbers 6, 3 is mapped onto 18 by multiplication." Note that this time we use the symbol × above the arrow. In this way we can distinguish a multiplication mapping from an addition mapping.

Several other diagrams that can be obtained from the multiplication table are shown at the top of page 91.

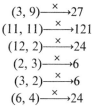

$$(3, 9) \xrightarrow{\times} 27$$
$$(11, 11) \xrightarrow{\times} 121$$
$$(12, 2) \xrightarrow{\times} 24$$
$$(2, 3) \xrightarrow{\times} 6$$
$$(3, 2) \xrightarrow{\times} 6$$
$$(6, 4) \xrightarrow{\times} 24$$

A total of 169 such diagrams can be obtained from the given multiplication table. Of course, an infinite set of such diagrams could be made if you consider all the members of N × N.

You can find in the multiplication table many examples of different ordered pairs that are mapped onto the same product. For example, both (2, 3) and (3, 2) are mapped onto 6; similarly, both (12, 2) and (6, 4) are mapped onto 24. Hence, the mapping of ordered pairs of natural numbers onto products is also an example of a many-to-one mapping, although it is a different mapping from the addition mapping.

Column A	Row A 0	1	2	3	4	5	6	7	8	9	10	11	12	
0	0	0	0	0	0	0	0	0	0	0	0	0	0	...
1	0	1	2	3	4	5	6	7	8	9	10	11	12	...
2	0	2	4	6	8	10	12	14	16	18	20	22	24	...
3	0	3	6	9	12	15	18	21	24	27	30	33	36	...
4	0	4	8	12	16	20	24	28	32	36	40	44	48	...
5	0	5	10	15	20	25	30	35	40	45	50	55	60	...
6	0	6	12	18	24	30	36	42	48	54	60	66	72	...
7	0	7	14	21	28	35	42	49	56	63	70	77	84	...
8	0	8	16	24	32	40	48	56	64	72	80	88	96	...
9	0	9	18	27	36	45	54	63	72	81	90	99	108	...
10	0	10	20	30	40	50	60	70	80	90	100	110	120	...
11	0	11	22	33	44	55	66	77	88	99	110	121	132	...
12	0	12	24	36	48	60	72	84	96	108	120	132	144	...
⋮	⋮	⋮	⋮	⋮	⋮	⋮	⋮	⋮	⋮	⋮	⋮	⋮	⋮	⋮

We can now state generally what we mean by the *operation of multiplication* for natural numbers.

The operation of multiplication is a many-to-one mapping
whereby every ordered pair of natural numbers
is mapped onto a natural number that is their product.

Another way of expressing this idea is to say that, under the operation of multiplication, the members of N × N are mapped onto the members of N.*

The idea that the product of any two natural numbers is a natural number is included in the definition of the multiplication operation. Hence, the set of natural numbers is closed under multiplication. We can use *a* and *b* to represent any two natural numbers and express the *closure property of multiplication* of natural numbers in the following way.

For any two natural numbers *a* and *b*, *ab* ε N.

The above sentence is read "For any two natural numbers *a* and *b*, the product of *a* and *b* is a member of the set of natural numbers."

In Chapter 4 you learned that, for any two natural numbers *a* and *b*, *ab* = *ba*. As you might guess, this property is the *commutative property of multiplication*. The fact that multiplication of natural numbers is commutative is also illustrated in the multiplication table on page 91. For example, you can see that both (10, 3) and (3, 10) are mapped onto 30. This verifies that

$$10 \times 3 = 3 \times 10.$$

You also learned in Chapter 4 that, for any three natural numbers *a*, *b*, and *c*, *(ab)c* = *a(bc)*. This property is the *associative property of multiplication* of natural numbers; or we may simply say that multiplication is associative.

Order in products, page 62

Product of three natural numbers, page 63

The teaching of multiplication

As we said in connection with addition, it is unwise to teach abstract definitions of such ideas as product or the operation of multiplication to very young children. But it is possible to base the teaching of these ideas upon sound mathematical foundations.

In the elementary school, multiplication can be taught as a "simultaneous joining" of sets that have the same number of objects. Examples like those shown in pictures A and B below can be used in teaching young children the meaning of multiplication.

---

* *Theory of Arithmetic* by Peterson and Hashisaki, pp. 81-100, contains a development of the operations on natural numbers as mappings that is similar to the one given here. Item 26 of Bibliography

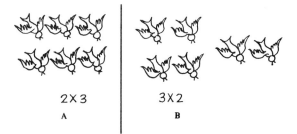

2 X 3   3 X 2

A   B

As the children work with objects and with pictures like those above, they learn to associate the operation of multiplication with the joining of equivalent sets and to associate the symbol $\times$ and the word *product* with the results of such action. For example, with pictures like picture A, the children learn to associate 2×3 with the joining of 2 sets of 3 objects each. With pictures like picture B, they associate 3×2 with the joining of 3 sets of 2 objects each. After many experiences of this kind, they see that, although the actual situations are different, the same number results when 2 sets of 3 are joined as when 3 sets of 2 are joined. Eventually, the children realize that $2 \times 3 = 3 \times 2$ and begin to understand that multiplication of natural numbers is commutative.

The relationship between multiplication and Cartesian products can be demonstrated by means of physical situations, although you would not want to do this with children who are just beginning their study of multiplication. You will recall that the product of two natural numbers is associated with the Cartesian product of two sets. In Chapter 4 we used the idea of a Cartesian product to establish the commutative property of multiplication. We will now give an illustration of how these concepts can be translated into a physical situation that relates to the idea of a pairing of objects.

Cartesian product, page 22

A   B   1   2   3

The idea of a Cartesian product can be used to determine the ways in which the skirts and blouses pictured above can be matched or paired with each other. These pairings are exhibited below:

Skirt A—Blouse 1   Skirt B—Blouse 1
Skirt A—Blouse 2   Skirt B—Blouse 2
Skirt A—Blouse 3   Skirt B—Blouse 3

You can see that, because there are 2 skirts and 3 blouses, there are 2 × 3, or 6, ways of pairing skirts with blouses. Obviously, if you paired blouses with skirts, you would find that there are 3 × 2, or 6, ways of pairing blouses with skirts. When you pair blouses with skirts, you obtain different ordered pairs from those obtained by pairing skirts with blouses. In each case, however, the number of pairs is the same.

Of course, this latter kind of example is not so useful with young children as the more intuitive approach presented earlier in this section. One important advantage to the idea of "simultaneous joining" of equivalent sets is that the total number of objects in the separate sets is the same as the number of objects in the combined sets. Thus, if 6 × 3 is thought of as 6 sets of 3 each, then there are 18 objects in all, and 6 × 3 = 18. By contrast, in our example with skirts and blouses, which illustrates the Cartesian product idea, there are only 5 objects in all, although we can determine 6 ways in which the objects can be paired.

In connection with exercises 74 through 79 keep in mind that the operation of multiplication is a mapping of N × N onto N.

74 There is one member of N that is the image of infinitely many pairs under the multiplication mapping. What number is this?

75 There is one member of N that is the image of just one member of N × N. What number is this? Of what pair is it the image?

76 How many pairs map onto 2 under the multiplication mapping? What are these pairs?

77 What members of N × N map onto 3? Onto 4? Onto 5? Onto 6? Onto 7? Onto 8?

78 How many pairs map onto 11? Onto 13? Onto 17? Onto 37?

79 How many pairs map onto 9? Onto 16? Onto 20?

80 If A = {a, b, d}, show a mapping of A × A onto A.

81 The following diagrams illustrate multiplication mappings from N × N onto N. Find proper replacements for x and y.

a $(4, 7) \xrightarrow{\times} x$ f $(1, y) \xrightarrow{\times} 8$

b $(x, 8) \xrightarrow{\times} 24$ g $(y, 1) \xrightarrow{\times} 12$

c $(2, x) \xrightarrow{\times} 12$ h $(x, y) \xrightarrow{\times} 90$

d $(x, y) \xrightarrow{\times} 36$ i $(x, 0) \xrightarrow{\times} 9$

e $(x, y) \xrightarrow{\times} 1$ j $(x, 0) \xrightarrow{\times} y$

Some comments about addition and multiplication

Both addition and multiplication are defined in terms of the mapping of ordered *pairs* of numbers onto numbers. In other words, the operation of addition involves only two numbers, and the operation of multiplication involves only two numbers. For this reason, each of these operations is called a *binary* operation.

Even though addition and multiplication are binary operations, you can determine sums or products when more than two addends or factors are involved. You do this by grouping the numbers so that you find the sum or the product of only two numbers at a time. Thus, you must group the addends or factors when you determine the sums or products represented by expressions like those shown below. The associative properties that we expressed earlier assure that you will obtain the same sum or the same product no matter how you group the numbers.

$$6 + 4 + 8$$
$$9 \times 3 \times 7$$
$$7 + 5 + 3 + 6$$
$$2 \times 4 \times 5 \times 8$$

Another property developed in Chapter 4 is the property that enables you to work with expressions that involve both sums and products. You learned that, for any three natural numbers a, b, and c, $a(b + c) = ab + ac$. This important property is called the *distributive property of multiplication over addition* of natural numbers. Or, more simply, we express this property by saying that multiplication distributes over addition of natural numbers. *(Combining sums and products, page 66)*

At this point it is convenient to give the names of some of the other properties that you studied in Chapter 4. One special property provides that, for any natural number a, $a + 0 = a$. The number 0 is called the *identity element for addition of natural numbers* because the sum of any natural number and 0 is the same as, or identical with, the given number. *(Identity elements, pages 75 and 76)* You also learned that, for any natural number a, $a \times 1 = a$. Similarly, the number 1 is called the *identity element for multiplication of natural numbers* because the product of any natural number and 1 is the same as the given number.

For any three natural numbers a, b, and c, if $a + c = b + c$, then $a = b$. This property is called the *cancellation property of addition*. For any three natural numbers a, b, and c, if c is non-zero and $ac = bc$, then $a = b$. As you can probably guess, this property is called the *cancellation property of multiplication*. *(Special properties of sums and products, page 73)*

Now we have the operations and properties we need for illustrating what is meant by a number system.

The natural-number system

In general terms, a number system consists of a set of numbers; two operations under which the set is closed; commutative and associative properties for the two operations; and a property that relates the two operations. The chart below summarizes the requirements for a number system. Notice that we have used the letter S to represent the set of numbers in the system. It should be apparent that the set of natural numbers, together with addition and multiplication and their properties, does form a number system. This is so because both addition and multiplication of natural numbers are closed, commutative, and associative operations and because multiplication does distribute over addition.

Properties of a number system

	Addition	Multiplication
Closure $\longrightarrow$	$a + b \in S.$	$ab \in S.$
Commutativity $\longrightarrow$	$a + b = b + a.$	$ab = ba.$
Associativity $\longrightarrow$	$(a + b) + c =$ $a + (b + c).$	$(ab)c = a(bc).$
Distributivity $\longrightarrow$		$a(b + c) = ab + ac.$

The identity-element properties and cancellation properties of addition and multiplication are given in the chart below. These properties, while useful and important, are not essential for a number system.

Special properties of addition and multiplication
of natural numbers

	Addition	Multiplication
Identity-element $\longrightarrow$	$a + 0 = a.$	$a \times 1 = a.$
Cancellation $\longrightarrow$	If $a + c = b + c,$ then $a = b.$	If $c \neq 0$ and $ac = bc,$ then $a = b.$

We will return to the idea of a number system when we work with sets of numbers like the rational numbers and the real numbers. In each case, we will see that the operations on rational and real numbers do fulfill the requirements for a number system. Hence, we will be justified in calling the elements of these sets numbers.

In Chapter 7 on the theory of computing, we will use certain properties—namely, the commutative, associative, and distributive properties—to explain methods of computing with numerals for natural numbers. We will present one example at this time to give you an idea of how these properties are involved.

Suppose that you want to find the product of 3 and 21. Of course, you long ago learned to record the computation in the following manner:

$$\begin{array}{r} 21 \\ \underline{3} \\ 63 \end{array}$$

But let us analyze the process that you use when you obtain 63 as the product of 3 and 21.

21 can be expressed as $(2 \times 10) + 1$, so you can write

$$3 \times 21 = 3 \times [(2 \times 10) + 1].$$

Using the distributive property, you obtain

$$3 \times 21 = 3 \times (2 \times 10) + 3 \times 1.$$

You know that $3 \times 1 = 3$; therefore, you can write

$$3 \times 21 = 3 \times (2 \times 10) + 3.$$

Then, because multiplication is associative, you know that $3 \times (2 \times 10) = (3 \times 2) \times 10$. Hence, you can obtain

$$3 \times 21 = (3 \times 2) \times 10 + 3.$$

Next, because $(3 \times 2) = 6$, you can obtain

$$3 \times 21 = 6 \times 10 + 3.$$

You know that $6 \times 10 = 60$; therefore, you can write

$$3 \times 21 = 60 + 3.$$

Finally, because $60 + 3 = 63$, you obtain

$$3 \times 21 = 63.$$

Properties of equality

In essence, the basic properties of addition and multiplication provide rules for the use of these operations. For example, we might find it more convenient to work with the expression $3 \times (4 + 5)$ than with the expression $3 \times 4 + 3 \times 5$. The distributive property tells us that these two expressions name the same number; hence, we can replace either expression by the other.

Just as the operations of addition and multiplication possess certain properties, so the relation of equality also has certain properties. In fact, when we developed the properties of addition and multiplication, we used certain of the properties of equality without telling you what they were. The five basic properties of equality are listed below. The universe for a, b, and c is N.

Properties of equality

Reflexive property $\longrightarrow$ For each a, $a = a$.

Symmetric property $\longrightarrow$ For each a and b, if $a = b$, then $b = a$.

Transitive property $\longrightarrow$ For each a, b, and c, if $a = b$ and $b = c$, then $a = c$.

Addition property $\longrightarrow$ For each a, b, and c, if $a = b$, then $a + c = b + c$.

Multiplication property $\longrightarrow$ For each a, b, and c, if $a = b$, then $ac = bc$.

The first of these properties—the reflexive property of equality—may seem obvious and trivial, but it is a property not possessed by all relations between numbers. The relation of "less than," for example, does not have this property; it is not true that, for each a, $a < a$.

The second property, the symmetric property of equality, may also seem trivial. But, when you are working with mathematical ideas, it is very important to be clear about the properties of the operations and relations that are involved. Just as the relation of "less than" does not have a reflexive property, neither does it have a symmetric property. Thus, it is not true that, for each a and b, if $a < b$, then $b < a$.

The transitive property of equality enables you to conclude, for example, that, because $8 + 6 = 14$ and because $14 = 2 \times 7$, $8 + 6 = 2 \times 7$.

The addition property of equality tells you something about the operation of addition as well as something about the relation of equality. The following rule, which you undoubtedly learned in high school, is actually the addition property: "If equals are added to equals, then their sums are equal." When you study the rational-number system in a later chapter, you will find that this property is a very useful one.

The multiplication property serves the same purpose with respect to multiplication as the property just discussed serves with respect to addition. You may have learned this property as the rule, "If equals are multiplied by equals, then their products are equal." As with the addition property of equality, you will find that the multiplication property has many applications in the set of rational numbers and the set of real numbers. You should compare these properties with the cancellation properties of addition and multiplication of natural numbers that are shown in the chart on page 96.

From now on, any time we are working with the equality relation, we will be able to use any one of these five properties. Later you will study other relations between numbers that possess some or all of these properties. But, for now, we will simply say that these five properties provide the rules whereby we can use the equality relation, just as the properties of the operations provide the rules for using addition and multiplication of natural numbers.

The addition and multiplication properties of equality* are sometimes rather difficult to interpret in complicated situations. For this reason, we will introduce a *substitution property* that will be useful in developing the properties of natural numbers.

> In any true statement about numbers,
> if a meaningful symbol for a number
> is replaced by another symbol for the same number,
> the resulting statement is also true.

As an example of the substitution property, suppose that we are working with a statement that contains the expression $5 \times (4 + 6)$ and that we wish to simplify the expression. Because $4 + 6 = 10$, we can use the substitution property to rewrite this expression as 5×10. Note that we can obtain 5×10 from $5 \times (4 + 6)$ by using the multiplication property of equality. Thus, if we begin with the equation

$$4 + 6 = 10,$$

then we can multiply both sides of the equation by 5 to obtain

$$5 \times (4 + 6) = 5 \times 10.$$

Hence, by the multiplication property of equality, the expressions $5 \times (4 + 6)$ and 5×10 name the same number.

At this point, it might be well to summarize the important concepts that we have dealt with so far in this chapter. We have established the following characteristics of the natural-number system:

1) The system includes a set of objects, called numbers, that are elements of $\{0, 1, 2, 3, \ldots\}$.

---

* The addition property of equality is frequently called the "well-defined property of addition," and the multiplication property of equality is often called the "well-defined property of multiplication."

2) There are two operations, addition and multiplication, that provide for two different ways in which each pair of natural numbers is mapped onto a single natural number.

3) There are certain properties—including two commutative and two associative properties and a distributive property—that govern the use of the two operations.

4) There are five properties—the reflexive, symmetric, transitive, addition, and multiplication properties—concerning the use of the equality relation between natural numbers.

82 Which of the following subsets of N are closed with respect to addition?
  a The even numbers
  b The multiples of 7
  c The numbers that are perfect squares
  d The odd numbers

83 Find two more subsets of N that are not closed with respect to addition.

84 Which of the subsets of N listed in exercise 82 are closed with respect to multiplication?

85 Find two subsets of N that are not closed with respect to multiplication.

86 Which of the following everyday situations are commutative?
  a Putting on a shirt and putting on a tie
  b Putting on stockings and putting on shoes
  c Turning on the light and opening the window

87 Describe two more pairs of events like those given in exercise 86 that are not commutative.

88 The following ingredients of a lunch are certainly not associative:
  "(Hot dog and mustard) and lemonade" and
  "Hot dog and (mustard and lemonade)."
Describe another situation that is not associative.

89 Consider the set of all even numbers,

$$E = \{0, 2, 4, 6, 8, \ldots\}.$$

Is addition closed, commutative, and associative in set E? Is multiplication closed, commutative, and associative in E? Does multiplication distribute over addition in E? Does E, together with addition and multiplication, form a number system?

90 Repeat exercise 89 for the set of all odd numbers,

$$P = \{1, 3, 5, 7, 9, \ldots\}.$$

91 Repeat exercise 89 for the set of all natural numbers that are multiples of 3,

$$T = \{0, 3, 6, 9, 12, \ldots\}.$$

92 Repeat exercise 89 for the set of all natural numbers that are not multiples of 3,

$$V = \{1, 2, 4, 5, 7, 8, \ldots\}.$$

93 We will invent two binary operations on the elements of the set of natural numbers. Let the operation $\oplus$ ("circle plus") be defined so that the "circle sum" of any two natural numbers is 0. Let the operation $\otimes$ ("circle times") be defined so that the "circle product" of any two natural numbers is the first number raised to the second number as a power. Thus, for the natural numbers a and b,

$$a \oplus b = 0,$$

and

$$a \otimes b = a^b.$$

Does the set of natural numbers, together with these two operations, form a number system?

94 Show how the distributive property enables you to find easily the standard name of each of the products expressed below.
a 5×102 **b** 20×91 **c** 25×14

95 Multiplication is distributive with respect to addition; that is, $a \times (b + c) = ab + ac$. Is addition distributive with respect to multiplication; that is, is $a + (b \times c) = (a + b) \times (a + c)$?

96 Is multiplication distributive with respect to multiplication; that is, does $a \times (b \times c) = (a \times b) \times (a \times c)$?

97 Is the operation of forming the union of sets distributive over itself; that is, does $A \cup (B \cup C) = (A \cup B) \cup (A \cup C)$?

98 Is the operation of forming the Cartesian product of sets distributive over the operation of forming the union? That is, does $A \times (B \cup C) = (A \times B) \cup (A \times C)$?

99 Make up four problems in which the distributive property can be used to explain why the problem can be solved in two ways.

100 Given the properties of equality and of the natural-number system and the special properties in the charts on pages 96 and 98, prove that $0 + a = a$ for all natural numbers.

101 Prove that $1 \times a = a$ for all natural numbers.

Subtraction and division

It may seem curious to you that the operations of subtraction and division are not considered to be essential ingredients of the natural-number system. In fact, neither subtraction nor division is an operation within the system because under neither of these operations is the set of natural numbers closed.

You will recall that we defined both addition and multiplication as special kinds of mappings whereby every member of N × N is mapped onto a member of N. However, for the natural numbers, subtraction and division cannot be defined in such a way that N is closed under either of these operations. For example, there is no member of N onto which (2, 4) can be mapped by subtraction; that is, the expression $2 - 4$ does not name a natural number. Similarly, for division there are many pairs of natural numbers that do not have quotients in the set of natural numbers. For example, there is no member of N onto which (6, 5) can be mapped by division; this means that the expression $6 \div 5$ does not name a natural number. Technically, then, neither subtraction nor division is an operation on the set of natural numbers, although they are often called operations in the elementary school.

First, we will show how subtraction can be related mathematically to addition of natural numbers. You know that you can use the following sentence to express the fact that 8 is equal to the sum of 3 and 5.

$$3 + 5 = 8.$$

Suppose, however, that you want to determine the proper replacement for c so that the following condition will yield a true statement.

$$c + 2 = 11.$$

Remember that in this condition c must be replaced by a natural number. Obviously, c must be replaced by 9 because the sum of 9 and 2 is equal to 11.

But, instead of the condition expressed above, we could have used the following one.

$$c = 11 - 2.$$

We agree that the number that satisfies $c = 11 - 2$ is the same as the number that satisfies $c + 2 = 11$. Thus, we define subtraction in terms of addition and say that, because the *sum* of 9 and 2 is 11, the *difference* of 11 and 2 is 9.

Let us consider another example. Either the condition

$$x + 5 = 7$$

or the condition

$$x = 7 - 5$$

involves the idea that some number, together with 5, has a sum of 7. We say that, because the sum of 2 and 5 is equal to 7, the difference of 7 and 5 is equal to 2.

Subtraction and addition are often said to be *opposite* operations. As we remarked earlier, subtraction is not closed in the set of natural numbers. To find the proper replacements for the variables in conditions like those expressed below, it is necessary to have negative numbers in the universe.

$$x + 7 = 2.$$
$$n = 8 - 12.$$
$$y = 0 - 7.$$
$$5 + c = 1.$$

In fact, negative numbers were introduced some 1300 years ago in response to such questions as, "What number added to 6 gives a sum of 2?"

Mathematically, it is preferable to define subtraction in terms of addition. But this is a rather subtle concept, and it is not a good idea to use this approach with young children. In elementary school, subtraction is usually associated with some sort of "take away" activity. You can, however, give children an intuitive idea of the way in which addition and subtraction are related by explaining that subtraction is, in one sense, the "undoing" of addition. That is, once you have taught the children that $3 + 2 = 5$, you can relate this addition fact to the subtraction fact $5 - 2 = 3$.

Our discussion of subtraction should give you a clue as to how division is related to multiplication. We will begin with the following example.

$$n \times 3 = 12.$$

Suppose that you want to know by what number 3 can be multiplied to obtain 12 as the product. Obviously, n must be replaced by 4, because the product of 4 and 3 is 12.

By definition, the condition expressed below has the same solution as $n \times 3 = 12$.

$$n = 12 \div 3.$$

Thus, division is defined in terms of multiplication. We say that, because the *product* of 4 and 3 is 12, the *quotient* of 12 and 3 is 4. Since division can be defined in terms of multiplication, it may be called the opposite operation of multiplication.

Either of the conditions expressed below involves the idea that the product of some number and 5 is 35.

$$x \times 5 = 35.$$
$$x = 35 \div 5.$$

In each of these conditions, x should be replaced by the same number. Again, we can conclude that, because the product of 7 and 5 is 35, the quotient of 35 and 5 is 7.

We remarked earlier that negative numbers are needed before we can find the proper replacement for the variable in a condition like $n + 5 = 1$. Now consider the following:

$$a \times 3 = 4.$$
$$p = 6 \div 5.$$
$$y \times 2 = 13.$$
$$d = 22 \div 7.$$

Obviously, when the universe is N, there are no replacements that enable you to obtain true statements from these conditions. However, once rational numbers like $1\frac{1}{3}$, $\frac{6}{5}$, and so on, have been introduced, it is possible to determine the quotient of such pairs of numbers as 4 and 3 or 6 and 5.

Division is usually presented to young children as a process of "separating into equivalent sets." However, the children can be given some notion of division as the opposite of multiplication very early. For example, pairs of facts, like $3 \times 2 = 6$ and $6 \div 2 = 3$ or $8 \times 5 = 40$ and $40 \div 5 = 8$, can be compared to give an understanding of the way in which the two operations are related.

So far in this section, we have seen that neither subtraction nor division of natural numbers has the closure property. We will next determine whether either of these operations has the commutative or the associative property. Because a property is a generalization about *all* members of the given universe, it is very easy to show that an operation does *not* have a certain property. You do this simply by finding just one example that contradicts the generalization. For example, if subtraction did have the commutative property, then it would be true for any two natural numbers a and b that $a - b = b - a$. Suppose that we select the two numbers 8 and 5. You know that $8 - 5 = 3$, but that $5 - 8$ does not equal 3 because this would mean that $3 + 8$ is equal to 5. Therefore, you know that the difference of 8 and 5 is not equal to the difference of 5 and 8. Because $8 - 5 \neq 5 - 8$, you can decide immediately that subtraction is not commutative.

Similarly, you need only one contradictory example to show that division is not commutative. For example, $6 \div 3 = 2$, but $3 \div 6$ is not a natural number; hence, you know that the quotient of 6 and 3 is not equal to the quotient of 3 and 6. Thus, division is not commutative.

It is likewise easy to decide whether or not subtraction has the associative property. If subtraction is associative, then, for any three natural numbers

a, b, and c, $(a - b) - c$ would be equal to $a - (b - c)$. Suppose that you choose the three numbers 14, 8, and 2. You know that $(14 - 8) - 2 = 4$ and that $14 - (8 - 2) = 8$. Therefore, $(14 - 8) - 2 \neq 14 - (8 - 2)$, and subtraction does not have the associative property.

If division of natural numbers had the associative property, then, for any three natural numbers a, b, and c, it would be true that $(a \div b) \div c$ would be equal to $a \div (b \div c)$. It is left as an exercise for you to give an example to show that division is not associative.

Because subtraction and division are not defined for all pairs of natural numbers, these operations have limited use when N is the universe. When a condition involves either subtraction or division, you must be careful about the replacements you make for the variable. If you are working with conditions like $13 - c < 5$ or $24 \div n > 6$, you find that certain replacements lead to difficulties. In the first example, if c is replaced by 14, then you obtain the expression $13 - 14$, which is meaningless in the set of natural numbers. In the second example, you also obtain expressions that are meaningless in N if you replace the variable by a number other than 1, 2, 3, 4, 6, 8, 12, or 24.

Thus, we see that subtraction and division of natural numbers differ from addition and multiplication in several important ways. First of all, if the universe is N, we know that $a + b$ and $a \times b$ represent natural numbers no matter what replacements we make for a and b. By contrast, we know that $a - b$ and $a \div b$ do not represent natural numbers for every replacement of a and b. We also know that both addition and multiplication have commutative and associative properties, while neither subtraction nor division has either of these properties.

102 What are the opposites of the following activities?
  a Sit down
  b Drive two miles north
  c Go up three floors
  d Withdraw $10 from a savings account
  e Sell ten shares of stock
103 What are some other illustrations of everyday situations and their opposites? Give at least 5 examples.
104 For each statement expressed below, write two sentences that express the opposite of the given statement. For statement a, you can write $10 - 7 = 3$ and, because $3 + 7 = 7 + 3$, you can also write $10 - 3 = 7$.
  a $3 + 7 = 10$.　　**d** $x + 3 = 14$.
  b $0 + 5 = 5$.　　**e** $6 + y = 13$.
  c $8 + 1 = 9$.　　**f** $x + y = z$.

105 Repeat exercise 104 for the statements expressed below. (Since division by
zero is not permissible, you can write only one sentence for part c.)

a $5 \times 6 = 30$.   **d** $1 \times 4 = 4$.
b $2 \times 7 = 14$.   **e** $9 \times 5 = 45$.
c $0 \times 8 = 0$.   **f** $12 \times 3 = 36$.

106 Give an example to show that the operation of division is not associative
in the set of natural numbers.

Clock arithmetic

So far in this chapter, we have developed a number system whose set of
elements—the set of natural numbers—is infinite. There are finite sets of
numbers that also satisfy all the properties of a number system. In this section we will consider one such example so that you will better understand
numbers and number systems.

We will use the twelve natural numbers that are named on the face of a
clock as the set of numbers in this system. This means that the universe for
the system is the set of natural numbers from 1 through 12. That is,

$$U = \{1, 2, 3, 4, 5, 6, 7, 8, 9, 10, 11, 12\}.$$

We now need to agree on definitions for operations on this set of
numbers. In terms of mappings, we first need to agree on a mapping for
the operation of addition so that a pair of numbers like (3, 4) is mapped
onto another element of the universe. Stated in terms with which you are
familiar, we must determine a mapping of $U \times U$ onto U and call this
mapping the operation of addition.

To illustrate the mapping, we will use the face of a clock like the one
pictured below. Furthermore, we will think of this clock as having only an
hour hand. The numeral for 12 on the clock will be the origin, or starting

position, for the first of every pair of consecutive moves of the hand, and all
moves for addition will be in a clockwise direction. Now consider a pair of
consecutive moves of the hand. If the hand is moved from 12 to 4 and then
is moved 3 more hours, it will come to rest at 7. It seems quite natural to
think of this as a kind of "addition" and to write

$$(4, 3) \xrightarrow{+} 7,$$

or, in more familiar notation,

$$4 + 3 = 7.$$

In a similar manner, a move of the hand from 12 to 5 followed by a move of 4 more hours can be associated with the following:

$$(5, 4) \xrightarrow{\;+\;} 9,$$

and

$$5 + 4 = 9.$$

So far there seems to be nothing new or startlingly different about this new kind of addition. But now suppose that we move the hand from 12 to 9 and then continue the move for 6 more hours. The hand comes to rest on 3. In terms of the previous examples, it is reasonable to say that the "sum" of 9 and 6 is 3. Thus, we write

$$(9, 6) \xrightarrow{\;+\;} 3,$$

and

$$9 + 6 = 3.$$

In this example, we obtain a result that is different from the result we obtain when we are working with natural numbers, where $(9, 6)$ is mapped onto 15, not 3. Thus, we see that "clock arithmetic" is different from our familiar arithmetic. Let us consider another example and find the sum of 11 and 8 in clock arithmetic. Visualize moving the hand of the clock from 12 to 11 and, from there, moving it 8 more hours. Obviously, the hand will come to rest on 7, and, in accordance with our previous examples, we can write

$$(11, 8) \xrightarrow{\;+\;} 7,$$

and

$$11 + 8 = 7.$$

We can now define the operation of addition in clock arithmetic as a mapping of the elements of U × U onto the elements of U as shown in the table on page 108. The table summarizes all of the possible pairs of consecutive moves of the hand and, hence, includes all of the addition mappings in clock arithmetic.

There are several observations that you can make from the addition table about the operation of addition in clock arithmetic. First, the operation of addition is closed. This means that the following is true.

For each a and b of U, $a + b \in U$.

You can check this by looking at the table because we are working with a finite universe that contains exactly 12 numbers. All 144 mappings from U $\times$ U onto U are shown, and in no case is any pair mapped onto a number that is not a member of U.

Addition table for clock arithmetic

+	1	2	3	4	5	6	7	8	9	10	11	12
1	2	3	4	5	6	7	8	9	10	11	12	1
2	3	4	5	6	7	8	9	10	11	12	1	2
3	4	5	6	7	8	9	10	11	12	1	2	3
4	5	6	7	8	9	10	11	12	1	2	3	4
5	6	7	8	9	10	11	12	1	2	3	4	5
6	7	8	9	10	11	12	1	2	3	4	5	6
7	8	9	10	11	12	1	2	3	4	5	6	7
8	9	10	11	12	1	2	3	4	5	6	7	8
9	10	11	12	1	2	3	4	5	6	7	8	9
10	11	12	1	2	3	4	5	6	7	8	9	10
11	12	1	2	3	4	5	6	7	8	9	10	11
12	1	2	3	4	5	6	7	8	9	10	11	12

Second, the operation of addition is commutative. Again, if we check the table, we see that $9 + 6 = 6 + 9$, that $11 + 12 = 12 + 11$, that $8 + 1 = 1 + 8$, and so on. In terms of any two members of U represented by a and b, we can state the following generalization.

For each a and b of U, $a + b = b + a$.

Third, the operation of addition is associative. Let us use the table to check some examples.

Example A: $(4 + 9) + 5 = 4 + (9 + 5)$.
$1 + 5 = 4 + 2$.
$6 = 6$.

Example B: $(11 + 8) + 7 = 11 + (8 + 7)$.
$7 + 7 = 11 + 3$.
$2 = 2$.

We could check all possible combinations of three numbers to see that addition is associative in every case. However, this will not be necessary. You should be familiar with the way we state this property for all possible members of U.

For each a, b, and c of U, $(a + b) + c = a + (b + c)$.

Keep in mind that we are attempting to fulfill all of the requirements of a number system. Thus far, we have been able to define the operation of addition in such a way that, for addition in U, we have closure, commutativity, and associativity. Next we need to decide what we mean by the operation of multiplication in clock arithmetic and to develop a multiplication table.

Let us again think of the 12 numbers in U as being represented on the face of a clock. Suppose that we also think of the product of two numbers in clock arithmetic in terms of a sum of equal addends as we did in the natural number system. This means that $2 \times 4 = 4 + 4$, that $5 \times 7 = 7 + 7 + 7 + 7 + 7$, and so on. Now let us start at 12 and make 2 moves of 4 hours each. The hand stops at 8; therefore, it seems proper to write the following: Another treatment of products, page 68

$$2 \times 4 = 8.$$

In terms of a multiplication mapping, we symbolize this in the following way:

$$(2, 4) \xrightarrow{\times} 8.$$

As a further example, let us see where the hand would stop if we made 3 moves of 5 hours each. If you visualize the face of the clock again, it should be apparent to you that the hand stops at 3. Thus, we can write the following:

$$(3, 5) \xrightarrow{\times} 3,$$

and

$$3 \times 5 = 3.$$

The results of considering all possible pairs of members of U are summarized in the multiplication table shown on page 110.

We can now define the operation of multiplication for clock arithmetic as the mapping whereby every element of $U \times U$ is mapped onto an element of U as exhibited in the multiplication table. In the natural-number system, you learned that multiplication in N is closed, associative, and commutative. Let us check to see if these properties also hold in the system we are developing for clock arithmetic.

The table for multiplication shows that every pair (a, b) of U $\times$ U is mapped onto an element of U. For example, $(11, 11) \xrightarrow{\times} 1$, or $11 \times 11 = 1$; $10 \times 12 = 12$; $3 \times 6 = 6$; etc. Hence, we can state the following generalization.

For each a and b of U, $a \times b \in$ U.

Thus, the operation of multiplication in U is closed.

Multiplication table for clock arithmetic

×	1	2	3	4	5	6	7	8	9	10	11	12
1	1	2	3	4	5	6	7	8	9	10	11	12
2	2	4	6	8	10	12	2	4	6	8	10	12
3	3	6	9	12	3	6	9	12	3	6	9	12
4	4	8	12	4	8	12	4	8	12	4	8	12
5	5	10	3	8	1	6	11	4	9	2	7	12
6	6	12	6	12	6	12	6	12	6	12	6	12
7	7	2	9	4	11	6	1	8	3	10	5	12
8	8	4	12	8	4	12	8	4	12	8	4	12
9	9	6	3	12	9	6	3	12	9	6	3	12
10	10	8	6	4	2	12	10	8	6	4	2	12
11	11	10	9	8	7	6	5	4	3	2	1	12
12	12	12	12	12	12	12	12	12	12	12	12	12

Checking a few examples in the multiplication table should convince you that multiplication in U is commutative. For example, $8 \times 2 = 2 \times 8$ and $5 \times 6 = 6 \times 5$. Because we are working with a finite set of numbers, we could check all possible pairs in U $\times$ U to show that multiplication is in fact commutative. Thus, we can state the following property.

For each a and b of U, $a \times b = b \times a$.

Next we need to decide if the operation of multiplication in clock arithmetic is associative. An example will help convince you that multiplication in U is associative.

$$5 \times (3 \times 4) = (5 \times 3) \times 4.$$
$$5 \times 12 = 3 \times 4.$$
$$12 = 12.$$

Although it would be time consuming and not very interesting, we could verify that multiplication in clock arithmetic is associative by checking all possible examples. Thus, we can state the following property of multiplication.

For each a, b, and c of U, $(a \times b) \times c = a \times (b \times c)$.

As for addition, we have been successful in defining multiplication in clock arithmetic so that it is closed, commutative, and associative. The final property that we need to complete our number system for clock arithmetic is a property that relates the two operations. In other words, we need to know whether one of our two operations distributes over the other. Let us see whether multiplication distributes over addition as it does in the system of natural numbers.

If multiplication does distribute over addition in U, then the following statement will be true.

$$2 \times (5 + 6) = (2 \times 5) + (2 \times 6).$$

By using the addition and multiplication tables, you can verify that the statement above leads to the following true statements.

$$2 \times 11 = 10 + 12.$$
$$10 = 10.$$

Again, by using the tables, you should verify that the following statements are true.

$$3 \times (8 + 4) = (3 \times 8) + (3 \times 4).$$
$$12 \times (12 + 12) = (12 \times 12) + (12 \times 12).$$
$$7 \times (5 + 9) = (7 \times 5) + (7 \times 9).$$

It would be possible to check the distributive property for all possible combinations of three numbers in U. However, this would be a tedious task, and we merely state that, in general, multiplication in clock arithmetic distributes over addition.

For each a, b, and c of U, $a \times (b + c) = (a \times b) + (a \times c)$.

Thus, our *number system for clock arithmetic* is complete. We have two operations in U, multiplication and addition, with each operation closed, commutative, and associative, and with multiplication distributing over addition. Therefore, these properties and the clock arithmetic numbers form a number system. It is called a *finite number system* because we have only a finite number of elements—12—in the universe.

Even though we have seen that there are similarities between the clock-arithmetic number system and the natural-number system, there are some very interesting differences which we will now discuss.

You will recall that in the arithmetic of natural numbers, there are Identity elements for addition and multiplication pages 75 and two identity elements; namely, 0, the identity element for addition, and 1, the identity element for multiplication. Let us now see whether clock arithmetic also has identity elements. If clock arithmetic has an identity element for addition, there must be some element k of U such that, for each a of U,

$$a + k = a.$$

An examination of the addition table on page 108 will reveal that the number 12 is the proper replacement for k in the above condition. For example, $5 + 12 = 5$ and $12 + 10 = 10$. Hence, the number 12 is an identity element for addition in clock arithmetic, and we can state the following generalization.

For each a in U, $a + 12 = a$.

It is left as an exercise for you to examine the multiplication table on page 110 to determine the identity element for multiplication in clock arithmetic.

For the arithmetic of natural numbers, we define subtraction in terms Subtraction related to addition, page 102 of addition. For example, if there is a natural number n such that

$$n + 5 = 15,$$

then, the same replacement for n also satisfies

$$n = 15 - 5.$$

Notice that, because there is only one replacement for n that satisfies $n + 5 = 15$, it is also true that there is only one replacement for n that satisfies $n = 15 - 5$. Now let us see whether we can define subtraction in terms of addition in clock arithmetic. First, we examine the addition table to see what number satisfies

$$n + 7 = 3.$$

Notice that the number 8 is the only replacement for n that satisfies this condition. If we define subtraction in clock arithmetic in terms of addition, then we will say that, because

$$8 + 7 = 3,$$
$$8 = 3 - 7.$$

If you think of subtraction as the opposite of addition, you can think of subtraction as moving the hand on the face of the clock in a counterclockwise direction. Thus, the result $8 = 3 - 7$ seems natural. We should note, however, that, unlike subtraction in N, subtraction in U is closed. In other words, for each a and b in U, $a - b \in$ U. You should use the addition table and the relationship between addition and multiplication to verify this for yourself.

If we continue our analogy between clock arithmetic and the arithmetic of natural numbers, it is logical to consider next whether the operation of division can be defined in terms of multiplication. However, before investigating this, we should note something about the operation of multiplication in clock arithmetic.

When we consider a condition like $n \times 5 = 20$ in the arithmetic of natural numbers, we know that only one number, namely, 4, satisfies this condition. From the relationship between multiplication and division in the arithmetic of natural numbers, it follows that 4 is the only number that satisfies $n = 20 \div 5$. But, if we examine the multiplication table for clock arithmetic, we find that each of the following statements is true.

$$2 \times 3 = 6.$$
$$6 \times 3 = 6.$$
$$10 \times 3 = 6.$$

Suppose that we relate division to multiplication and say that, because $n \times 3 = 6$, $n = 6 \div 3$. From the sentences above, we know that there are three numbers that satisfy $n \times 3 = 6$; hence, we must conclude that there are also three numbers that satisfy $n = 6 \div 3$. This means that, if we try to say that division for clock arithmetic is the opposite operation of multiplication, we will not be able to find a unique answer as we can in the arithmetic of natural numbers. This is why we cannot define division in terms of multiplication in clock arithmetic.

There are other differences between clock arithmetic and the arithmetic of natural numbers. Some of these differences we will return to in Chapter 9 when we discuss elementary number theory. Other differences are left for you to investigate as exercises. We hope that the material presented in this section not only increases your understanding of what a number system is, but also provides you with material that you may find useful in the teaching of children.

107 Find all the natural numbers that satisfy each of the following conditions. Find the members of U in clock arithmetic that satisfy each of these conditions.

a $2n + 2 = 8$.   **b** $6n + 1 = 7$.   **c** $3n + 3 = 12$.

108 How many numbers named in the multiplication table for clock arithmetic have just two factors? (For purposes of this exercise, do not consider 1 as a factor.)

109 Do the following properties hold for clock arithmetic?
a For each a, b, and c in U, if $a = b$, then $a + c = b + c$.
b For each a, b, and c in U, if $a = b$, then $ac = bc$.
c For each a, b, and c in U, if $ac = bc$ and if $c \neq 12$, then $a = b$.
d For each a, b, and c in U, if $a + c = b + c$, then $a = b$.
110 Make a clock with the numerals 1, 2, 3, 4, 5, 6, and 7 on its face; that is, make a seven-hour clock. Construct addition and multiplication tables and investigate the properties of these operations as they were investigated for the twelve-hour clock in this section. What differences, if any, do you find?

Another finite number system*

We have considered two number systems so far in this chapter. In one system the set of numbers was the infinite set N. In the second system, the set of numbers was a finite subset of N, the natural numbers from 1 through 12. In this section we will construct another finite system with two "numbers" and two new "operations." We will arbitrarily choose two symbols to represent these numbers and two other symbols to represent the operations in the system. We will also develop tables similar to the addition and multiplication tables to show how the operations are to be performed on the numbers. Then we will see whether these two operations have the same properties as addition and multiplication have in the natural-number system.

1) We will represent the numbers in the new system by α (read as "alpha") and β (read as "beta").
2) We will use $\triangledown$ (read as "arrowhead") and $\star$ (read as "star") to symbolize the two operations in the system.
3) The tables below show the results you obtain from the operations arrowhead and star in the system.

$\triangledown$	α	β
α	α	β
β	β	α

$\star$	α	β
α	α	α
β	α	β

You interpret these tables in the same way that you interpreted the addition and multiplication tables presented earlier in this chapter. Thus, according to the arrowhead table given above, you know that

$$\alpha \triangledown \alpha = \alpha,$$
$$\alpha \triangledown \beta = \beta,$$
$$\beta \triangledown \alpha = \beta,$$

and

$$\beta \triangledown \beta = \alpha.$$

Notice that, whenever the operation arrowhead is performed, the ordered pairs of numbers in our system are mapped onto single numbers that are also in our system. Thus, operation arrowhead has the closure property. Now let us see if this is also true of operation star. From the star table given above, you know that

$$\alpha \star \alpha = \alpha,$$
$$\alpha \star \beta = \alpha,$$
$$\beta \star \alpha = \alpha,$$

and

$$\beta \star \beta = \beta.$$

Again, you can see that the ordered pairs of numbers in our system are mapped onto single numbers in our system by operation star; hence, operation star has the closure property.

Next we will check to see if the operation arrowhead is commutative and associative. Because our system has only two numbers, we can easily check for commutativity. We need consider only the following examples.

$$\alpha \triangledown \alpha = \alpha \triangledown \alpha.$$
$$\alpha \triangledown \beta = \beta \triangledown \alpha.$$
$$\beta \triangledown \beta = \beta \triangledown \beta.$$

Each of these sentences expresses a true statement; therefore, arrowhead is a commutative operation.

We can also determine whether operation arrowhead has the associative property. We will do this by first showing that

$$(\alpha \triangledown \beta) \triangledown \alpha = \alpha \triangledown (\beta \triangledown \alpha).$$

You know that $\alpha \triangledown \beta = \beta$; therefore,

$$(\alpha \triangledown \beta) \triangledown \alpha = \beta \triangledown \alpha.$$

You also know that $\beta \triangledown \alpha = \beta$; thus,

$$(\alpha \triangledown \beta) \triangledown \alpha = \beta.$$

Now we must see if $\alpha \triangledown (\beta \triangledown \alpha)$ is also equal to β. From the arrowhead table, you know that $\beta \triangledown \alpha = \beta$, so

$$\alpha \triangledown (\beta \triangledown \alpha) = \alpha \triangledown \beta.$$

Because $\alpha \triangledown \beta = \beta$,

$$\alpha \triangledown (\beta \triangledown \alpha) = \beta.$$

Therefore, because both $(\alpha \triangledown \beta) \triangledown \alpha$ and $\alpha \triangledown (\beta \triangledown \alpha)$ are equal to β,

$$(\alpha \triangledown \beta) \triangledown \alpha = \alpha \triangledown (\beta \triangledown \alpha).$$

To establish that arrowhead has the associative property for all possible combinations, it is also necessary to show that each of the following sentences expresses a true statement. Check to see whether this is so.

$$(\alpha \triangledown \alpha) \triangledown \alpha = \alpha \triangledown (\alpha \triangledown \alpha).$$
$$(\alpha \triangledown \alpha) \triangledown \beta = \alpha \triangledown (\alpha \triangledown \beta).$$
$$(\alpha \triangledown \beta) \triangledown \beta = \alpha \triangledown (\beta \triangledown \beta).$$
$$(\beta \triangledown \alpha) \triangledown \alpha = \beta \triangledown (\alpha \triangledown \alpha).$$
$$(\beta \triangledown \alpha) \triangledown \beta = \beta \triangledown (\alpha \triangledown \beta).$$
$$(\beta \triangledown \beta) \triangledown \alpha = \beta \triangledown (\beta \triangledown \alpha).$$
$$(\beta \triangledown \beta) \triangledown \beta = \beta \triangledown (\beta \triangledown \beta).$$

Now we will check to see if operation star has the commutative and associative properties. We need to verify only the following examples to show that star is commutative.

$$\alpha \star \alpha = \alpha \star \alpha.$$
$$\alpha \star \beta = \beta \star \alpha.$$
$$\beta \star \beta = \beta \star \beta.$$

From the star table, you can see that each of the above sentences does express a true statement. Thus, operation star is commutative.

It is left as an exercise for the reader to verify that each of the following sentences expresses a true statement. Once you have checked these sentences, you will have established the associative property of operation star.

$$(\alpha \star \alpha) \star \alpha = \alpha \star (\alpha \star \alpha).$$
$$(\alpha \star \alpha) \star \beta = \alpha \star (\alpha \star \beta).$$
$$(\alpha \star \beta) \star \alpha = \alpha \star (\beta \star \alpha).$$
$$(\alpha \star \beta) \star \beta = \alpha \star (\beta \star \beta).$$
$$(\beta \star \alpha) \star \alpha = \beta \star (\alpha \star \alpha).$$
$$(\beta \star \alpha) \star \beta = \beta \star (\alpha \star \beta).$$
$$(\beta \star \beta) \star \alpha = \beta \star (\beta \star \alpha).$$
$$(\beta \star \beta) \star \beta = \beta \star (\beta \star \beta).$$

To complete our number system, we still need to show that one of the operations distributes over the other. In fact, operation star distributes over operation arrowhead. We will show that this is the case for one example. We want to establish that

$$\alpha \star (\beta \triangledown \alpha) = (\alpha \star \beta) \triangledown (\alpha \star \alpha).$$

First, we will work with $\alpha \star (\beta \triangledown \alpha)$. You know that $\beta \triangledown \alpha = \beta$, so

$$\alpha \star (\beta \triangledown \alpha) = \alpha \star \beta.$$

$\alpha \star \beta = \alpha$; therefore,

$$\alpha \star (\beta \triangledown \alpha) = \alpha.$$

Next, if we can show that $(\alpha \star \beta) \triangledown (\alpha \star \alpha)$ is also equal to α, we will have shown that the two expressions are equal. Because $\alpha \star \beta = \alpha$ and $\alpha \star \alpha = \alpha$,

$$(\alpha \star \beta) \triangledown (\alpha \star \alpha) = \alpha \triangledown \alpha.$$

But $\alpha \triangledown \alpha = \alpha$; therefore,

$$(\alpha \star \beta) \triangledown (\alpha \star \alpha) = \alpha.$$

Hence,

$$\alpha \star (\beta \triangledown \alpha) = (\alpha \star \beta) \triangledown (\alpha \star \alpha).$$

You should use the above method to show that each of the following sentences expresses a true statement.

$$\beta \star (\alpha \triangledown \beta) = (\beta \star \alpha) \triangledown (\beta \star \beta).$$
$$\alpha \star (\beta \triangledown \beta) = (\alpha \star \beta) \triangledown (\alpha \star \beta).$$

Although it would be tedious, we could show that in every instance operation star does distribute over operation arrowhead. Hence, we have another example of a finite number system.

Note that we have called α and β numbers in our number system. Of course, we have not established that $\alpha < \beta$ or that $\alpha > \beta$, nor have we associated α and β with sets as we did the natural numbers. This number system is a useful one only insofar as it gives you insight into number systems in general. You will find that in later chapters we will use the same set of criteria to establish other, more useful number systems.*

---

* *Finite Mathematical Systems* by M. Scott Norton contains an elementary presentation of several finite arithmetics, with some interesting exercises and applications. Item 27 of Bibliography. *Prelude to Mathematics* by W. W. Sawyer is also a good source for additional information on finite arithmetics. Item 28 of Bibliography

111 Use the tables for operations arrowhead and star that are given in this section to find the following:

    a $\alpha \triangledown \beta$ **b** $\alpha \star \beta$ **c** $\beta \triangledown \beta$ **d** $\alpha \star \alpha$

112 Show that operation arrowhead is not distributive with respect to operation star in the finite number system.

CONCLUSION

In one sense, the material in this chapter completes our study of the natural numbers. Our study of the natural-number system, which began with a development of natural numbers in terms of standard sets, included definitions of sums and products and the corresponding operations and a discussion of the properties of these operations. In Chapters 6 and 7, we will continue to work with the natural numbers; in those chapters, we will consider systematic ways of naming numbers and methods of computing standard names for such numbers as $252 + 85$ or 76×38 or $1540 \div 77$.

CHAPTER QUIZ

For each pair of natural numbers named below, first make a diagram to represent the addition mapping of the pair onto its sum. Then make a diagram to represent the multiplication mapping of the pair onto its product.

  1 (6, 12)   3 (10, 10)   5 (55, 3)

  2 (0, 14)   4 (18, 1)   6 (78, 39)

  7 For each pair of natural numbers named in exercises 1 through 6, is the difference of the first and second numbers a natural number? For each pair, is the quotient of the first and second numbers a natural number?

  8 One child remembers that $6 \times 8 = 48$ by recalling that $3 \times 8 = 24$ and then doubling 24. Which properties of the natural-number system is he using?

  9 Another child remembers that $6 \times 8 = 48$ by recalling that $3 \times 8 = 24$ and then adding 24 to 24. Which properties is this child using?

  10 Assume that you have forgotten that $9 \times 8 = 72$. By using the basic properties of the natural-number system, give at least four different ways to find the answer.

Perform the operations that are indicated in exercises 11, 12, and 13.

  11 $4 + 3 \times 2$ 12 $5 \times 6 + 8$ 13 $3 \times 4 + 6 \times 2$

14 Is more than one answer possible for exercises 11, 12, and 13? Now consider the following ways of rewriting each of these exercises.

11 $4 + (3 \times 2)$ and $(4 + 3) \times 2$
12 $(5 \times 6) + 8$ and $5 \times (6 + 8)$
13 $(3 \times 4) + (6 \times 2)$ and $3 \times (4 + 6) \times 2$

Do the parentheses specify the order of operations? What convention must we adopt to make sure that everyone gets the same answers to exercises like these?

15 Is the operation of forming the Cartesian product of two sets commutative? That is, is $A \times B = B \times A$ for all sets A and B?

16 Use the sets $A = \{1, 2\}$, $B = \{a, b, c\}$, and $C = \{k\}$ to investigate whether or not the following is true for sets A, B, and C.

$$(A \times B) \times C = A \times (B \times C).$$

Do you think that the operation of forming a Cartesian product is associative for all sets X, Y, and Z?

SUPPLEMENTARY READINGS

Freund, John, *A Modern Introduction to Mathematics*, pp. 16-44 and 62-79. A sound treatment of the natural numbers, accompanied by some good exercises. Item 29 of Bibliography

Schaaf, W. L., *Basic Concepts of Elementary Mathematics*, Chapter 4, pp. 97-129. An easy-to-read axiomatic treatment of the natural-number system. Item 30 of Bibliography

Van Engen, Henry, *et al.*, *Seeing Through Mathematics*, Book 1, Unit 6, pp. 245-306. A systematic development of the natural-number system, written at an elementary level. Item 21 of Bibliography

Chapter six

Systems of numeration

The Babylonian system of numeration
The Egyptian numeration system
The Roman numeration system
The Hindu-Arabic numeration system
More about decimal numerals
Bases other than ten

In the preceding chapters we devoted our attention to the meaning of natural numbers and to an analysis of operations with these numbers. Eventually, we brought all these ideas together in the development of the natural-number system. Here we will be concerned not with number systems, but with numeration systems. By a numeration system, we mean a collection of symbols and a systematic way in which these symbols are employed to express numbers. To help you understand our own decimal (base-ten) system of numeration, we will first consider some of the characteristics of the Babylonian, Egyptian, and Roman systems. The following discussion of these numeration systems will be brief, and you might be interested in learning more about one or all of them by reading some of the books listed in the footnotes and supplementary reading list for this chapter.

Natural-number system, page 96

The Babylonian system of numeration

As early as 1600 B.C., the Babylonians had developed an efficient system of numeration. Because the Babylonians wrote with a stylus on a clay tablet, all of their symbols, including their numerals, were wedge-shaped in appearance. Thus, their writing is called cuneiform (wedge-shaped) writing and their numerals are called cuneiform numerals. The discovery of clay tablets containing cuneiform symbols has enabled archaeologists to make some plausible speculations about the meanings of these symbols.

The numerals shown below are taken from a Babylonian tablet some 3500 years old.* Note that, for the first 9 groups of wedges, the number of wedges in each succeeding group increases by one. Thus, it is assumed

that these groups of symbols are names for the numbers 1, 2, 3, 4, 5, 6, 7, 8, and 9. The next symbol, which is a horizontal rather than a vertical wedge, must be the numeral for 10. The next three symbols are evidently numerals for 11, 12, and 13.

So far in our description of the Babylonian numeration system, we have seen how many different numbers can be expressed by the use of just two symbols—the vertical and the horizontal wedge. We can deduce from what we have seen so far how the numerals for numbers from 14 through 19 can be formed by using combinations of these two symbols. For example, the Babylonian numeral for 19 would be written as follows:

The same clay tablet from which were taken the cuneiform numerals shown above also contains the numerals shown below. You will remember that we read the single horizontal wedge as the numeral for 10. Apparently, then, these symbols, from left to right, should be read as the names for 10,

20, 30, 40, and 50. We can also assume that the Babylonians would write the symbol shown below to name 36.

* The discussion presented here of the translation of Babylonian numerals follows closely the account presented in *The Exact Sciences in Antiquity* by Otto Neugebauer. Item 31 of Bibliography

Portion of Babylonian tablet showing groups
of three numbers, called Pythagorean triples,
that satisfy the relation $a^2 + b^2 = c^2$.

Plimpton Collection, 322, Columbia University Libraries

From our analysis up to this point, we can arrive at certain conclusions about the Babylonian system of numeration. First of all, the Babylonians employed an *additive system* of numeration. This means that the number expressed by a group of symbols is determined by adding together the numbers expressed by each symbol in the group. For example, the numeral for 23 was written as,

𒌋𒌋𒐗

which is interpreted as $10 + 10 + 1 + 1 + 1$.

We might now assume that the Babylonian numeral for 60 would be composed of 6 horizontal wedges. Instead, we find that the numerals for

multiples of ten from 10 through 50 are followed by these symbols.

The asterisks indicate that some of the symbols on the tablet have been destroyed. If we assume that these numerals continue on from the preceding ones, we must interpret these numerals as names for 60, 70, 80, 120, and 130. This means that the vertical wedge, which previously was the numeral for 1, now becomes the numeral for 60. Thus, the Babylonian numeral for 70 is written as $60 + 10$, the numeral for 80 is written as $60 + 10 + 10$, the numeral for 120 as $60 + 60$, and the numeral for 130 as $60 + 60 + 10$.

We can also deduce that the symbols that were effaced from the tablet would be symbols for 90, 100, and 110, which would be written as follows.

This interpretation of the numerals for the numbers beyond 59 reveals certain other characteristics of the Babylonian numeration system. One of these properties is that the number named by a symbol is dependent upon the position of the symbol with respect to other symbols included in the numeral. For example, if the vertical wedge is placed to the right of the horizontal wedge, as shown below, then the number named is $10 + 1$, or 11.

If, however, the symbols are reversed, as shown below, then the number

named is 60 + 10, or 70. When the value of a symbol in a numeration system is dependent upon the position of the symbol, then the numeration system is said to be a *place-value* system. The Babylonians were forerunners in the development of a place-value numeration system. The importance of place value lies in the fact that you can name many different numbers with the use of only a few symbols which express different numbers when they are rearranged.

By the way in which the numerals beyond 59 were written, we can also see that the Babylonian numeration system had two bases—both a base of 10 and a base of 60. The system had a base of 10—that is, a decimal base—because the single horizontal wedge was used in place of a group of 10 vertical wedges. The base of 60, or sexagesimal base, is evidenced by the fact that 60 ones can be expressed as 1 sixty, 120 ones can be expressed as 2 sixties, etc.; thus, the vertical wedge, depending upon its position, was used to express 1, 60, 60 × 60, and so on.

The most serious weakness of the Babylonian numeration system was that the system had no zero symbol. Because there was no zero symbol, it might be difficult to know what number was named by certain numerals. For example, the Babylonian numeral shown below could be a name for 2 × 60 + 20, for 3600 + 60 + 20, or 3680; or for 2 × 3600 + 20, or 7220.

In a numeral like this one, if the scribe meant each vertical wedge to represent 3600 rather than 60, he would usually leave a space between the two vertical wedges and the horizontal wedges. Sometimes, however, no such space was left, and the reader had to be able to interpret the meaning of the numeral from its context.

Some vestiges of the sexagesimal system of the Babylonians are still found in certain of our standard units of measure. For example, we still have 60 minutes in 1 hour, 60 minutes in 1 degree, 60 seconds in 1 minute, and so on.

113 Write Babylonian numerals for the numbers represented by the following decimal numerals.

a 14   c 67   e 89   g 752
b 53   d 144   f 231   h 5137

114 Use the Babylonian numerals to find the following sums.

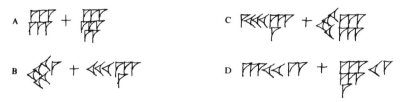

The Egyptian numeration system

The best source of information about the Egyptian numeration system is the Rhind papyrus written about 1800 B.C. The chart below shows the hieroglyphic symbols that were commonly used by the Egyptians to name certain numbers.

$\lvert -1$	$\int -10,000$
$\cap -10$	$\text{🐦} -100,000$
$\text{②} -100$	
$\text{🪷} -1000$	$\text{🧍} -1,000,000$

The numeral for 1 is thought to represent a vertical staff; the numeral for 10, a heelbone; the numeral for 100, a papyrus scroll or a coil of rope; the numeral for 1000, a lotus flower; the numeral for 10,000, a bent reed or a finger pointing to the sky; the numeral for 100,000, a bird (an alternate symbol for 100,000 was 🐟, called a burbot or tadpole); and the numeral for 1,000,000, a man with arms upraised in astonishment.

The following chart displays the Egyptian names for certain numbers.

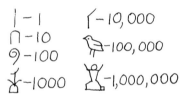

From the list of numerals given above, it is apparent that the Egyptian system of numeration was a decimal system. For example, 10 ones could be expressed by a single numeral for 1 ten. The Egyptian system also had an additive principle. For example, the numeral for 30 was composed of 3 heelbones; that is, $10 + 10 + 10$.

However, the Egyptian system did not make use of place value. Thus, the order in which the symbols in a numeral were written did not affect the value of the symbols. For example, 32 could be written in any one of the four ways shown below.

ΠΙΛΛΙ   ΙΛΛΙΛ   ΛΛΛΙΙ   ΙΙΛΛΛ

Because the Egyptian system was not a place-value system, it was not so efficient as the Babylonian system. In the Egyptian system many symbols were required in writing numerals for large numbers. For example, the numeral for 3612 required 12 symbols in Egyptian notation (3 lotus flowers, 6 scrolls, 1 heelbone, and 2 vertical staffs). By comparison, the same number could be expressed in Babylonian notation with only 4 symbols.

Γ ⊀ ΓΓ

Therefore, for reasons of economy of notation, the property of place value is manifestly a useful one for a numeration system to have.

115 Write Egyptian numerals for the following decimals.

    a 14   **b** 89   **c** 144   **d** 231   **e** 752   **f** 5137

116 Use Egyptian numerals to find the following sums.

    a |||||||| + |||||||

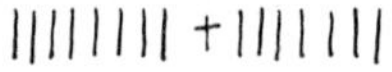

    b ΛΛΛΛΛΛ | + ΛΛΛΛΛΛΛ |||||||

    c 9999ΛΛΛ||||| + 999ΛΛΛΛ||||

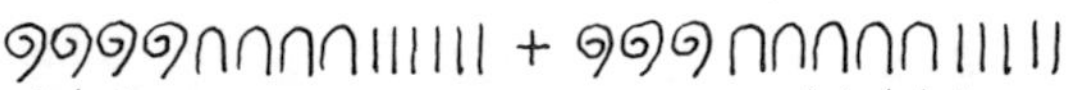

    d ⚇⚇⚇999999ΛΛΛΛ||||| + ⚇⚇⚇⚇⚇99999Λ|||||

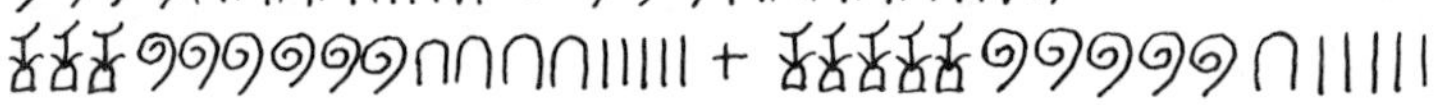

The Roman numeration system

Because you are probably quite familiar with the Roman system of numeration, we will mention it only briefly. The most commonly used Roman numerals are shown below.

$$I - 1$$
$$V - 5$$
$$X - 10$$
$$L - 50$$
$$C - 100$$
$$D - 500$$
$$M - 1000$$

The Roman system, like the other systems we have considered so far, used the additive principle. For example, the Roman numeral for 22 is XXII, or $10 + 10 + 1 + 1$.

The Roman system was not a place-value system except in special cases where the relationship between two adjacent symbols was significant. You are probably aware of this special kind of notation frequently used in writing Roman numerals. This is the method whereby, if a symbol of lesser value is written at the *left* of a symbol of greater value, then the number represented by the symbol at the left is to be subtracted from the number represented by the symbol at the right. For example, if the symbol I is written to the left of the symbol V, then the numeral IV expresses $5 - 1$, or 4. Similarly, if the symbol X is written to the left of the symbol C, then the numeral XC expresses $100 - 10$, or 90.

There is evidence that this kind of notation was not used consistently by the Romans and that it was a late development in the system. In many instances, the numeral IIII, rather than IV, was used to express 4, and the numeral XVIIII, rather than XIX, was used to express 19. The use of this kind of notation was also restricted. For example, the symbol I was used at the left of only the symbols V and X; the symbol X could precede only the symbols L and C; the symbol C could precede only the symbols D and M. Furthermore, symbols that represent multiples of 5—such as V or L or D—were not used in this way.

The Roman numeration system was a system with a mixed base because groups of numbers were expressed in different bases. The numerals for the numbers from 1 through 4 were essentially tally numerals; the numbers from 5 through 9 were expressed by base-five numerals; those from 10 to 50 were expressed by a combination of base-five and base-ten numerals; and so on.

117 Write Roman numerals for each of the following decimals.

a 14	**c** 144	**e** 752	**g** 1965	**i** 1492
b 89	**d** 231	**f** 5137	**h** 493	**j** 2899

The Hindu-Arabic numeration system

Our system of numeration, the Hindu-Arabic system, was brought to the Western world by the Arabs at the time of their conquests in North Africa and Spain. It is called the Hindu-Arabic system because the Arabs apparently obtained the numerals and the place-value concepts from the Hindus in India. The Hindu-Arabic system is a *decimal system* because it is a base-ten system.

In our study of the Babylonian, Egyptian, and Roman numeration systems, we considered some of the important characteristics of the Hindu-Arabic system. We will now discuss these properties one by one.

The Hindu-Arabic system is an additive system. For example, the numeral 323 names the number $300 + 20 + 3$, and the numeral 8258 names the number $8000 + 200 + 50 + 8$.

The Hindu-Arabic system is also a place-value system. For example, in the numeral 33, each digit represents a different number. The first digit from the left represents 3 tens and the second digit represents 3 ones. Because of the principle of place value, digits may be used repeatedly since they express different numbers depending upon their location with respect to the other digits in the numeral.

As we remarked earlier, the Hindu-Arabic numeration system has 10 as its base; thus, 10 ones are equal to 1 ten, 10 tens are equal to 1 one-hundred, etc. Furthermore, only ten different digits are employed in the Hindu-Arabic system. By means of these ten digits, the additive principle, and the principle of place value, it is possible to express any natural number.

There is one important characteristic of the Hindu-Arabic system that is not shared by any of the numeration systems we studied earlier. This is the fact that our numeration system has a zero symbol. You will recall that we said earlier that sometimes it might be difficult to determine what number is expressed by certain numerals in the Babylonian system. We also said that this ambiguity resulted from the lack of a zero symbol in the system. (At a period later than the one we have been considering, a zero symbol was introduced into the Babylonian numeration system, along with certain other modifications.) In the Hindu-Arabic system, no such ambiguity can occur, because there is a zero symbol. Hence, in the numeral 508, the digit 5 represents 5 hundreds, not 5 tens, and the digit 0 represents 0 tens. In the numeral 58, however, the digit 5 represents 5 tens, not 5 hundreds. If we did not have the zero symbol, it would be difficult to decide whether the numeral 1, for example, expressed 1 one, 1 ten, 1 one-hundred, or some other power of ten.

We now see that there are certain necessary characteristics for an efficient numeration system. A numeration system that contained a single, distinct symbol for each number would be quite cumbersome; therefore, it is desirable that a numeration system contain only a few symbols which can be used repeatedly and that the numbers represented by the digits in the numeral can be added. Thus, it is important for a numeration system to have relatively few different symbols and to be additive. It is also desirable for a numeration system to be a place-value system. With this property, numerals for large numbers can be written with a minimum of symbols. Finally, if a numeration system does use place value, then it is important for the system to have a zero symbol so that you can interpret numerals without ambiguity.

118 Name each of these numbers first in Babylonian symbols, then in Egyptian symbols, and finally in Roman symbols.

   a 48   **b** 72   **c** 3642   **d** 102   **e** 100   **f** 1964

119 Write the numerals for the first 15 numbers in each of the Babylonian, Egyptian, and Roman numeration systems.

120 Express 4 hours 10 minutes 55 seconds in seconds. What bases did you use in this problem?

121 Add 58 and 39. Now write these numerals in Babylonian, Egyptian, and Roman symbols and again find the sum. What conclusions can you draw about the efficiency of the various numeration systems from this exercise?

More about decimal numerals

We have established that our numeration system is a decimal system. Sometimes, however, we make use of other bases, such as base two for electronic computers or base twelve for certain kinds of measures. Before we examine several of these different bases, we will develop a new way of expressing decimal numerals that will be helpful in the study of other bases.

First, we will develop some useful symbolism. You are probably already familiar with such numerals as 6^2, 10^3, 2^5, etc. And you probably already know that $6^2 = 6 \times 6$, that $10^3 = 10 \times 10 \times 10$, and that $2^5 = 2 \times 2 \times 2 \times 2 \times 2$. In 2^5, the numeral 2 names the *base* of the number, the numeral 5 expresses the *exponent*, and the number 2^5 is the fifth *power* of 2. We can use variables to represent natural numbers to obtain the following general form.

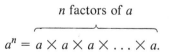

$$a^n = a \times a \times a \times \ldots \times a.$$

If you replace a by 7 and n by 6, you obtain

$$7^6 = 7 \times 7 \times 7 \times 7 \times 7 \times 7.$$

The symbolism a^n is called *exponential notation*. Thus, the numeral 2^3 is exponential notation for $2 \times 2 \times 2$, or 8; and the numeral 10^2 is exponential notation for 10×10, or 100.

Next, we will develop a convenient way to determine products and quotients when numbers are expressed in exponential notation. For example, suppose that you want to consider the following product as a power of 4.

$$4^3 \times 4^2$$

You know that $4^3 = 4 \times 4 \times 4$ and that $4^2 = 4 \times 4$. Therefore,

$$4^3 \times 4^2 = (4 \times 4 \times 4) \times (4 \times 4).$$

But $(4 \times 4 \times 4) \times (4 \times 4) = 4^5$. Hence,

$$4^3 \times 4^2 = 4^5.$$

Thus, the exponent of the product of 4^3 and 4^2 is equal to the sum of the exponents of 4^3 and 4^2. That is,

$$4^3 \times 4^2 = 4^{3+2}, \text{ or } 4^5.$$

You should use the method described above to verify that each of the following sentences expresses a true statement.

$$10^7 \times 10^3 = 10^{7+3}.$$

$$5^4 \times 5^5 = 5^9.$$

$$1^3 \times 1^8 = 1^{3+8}.$$

$$3^2 \times 3^4 = 3^6.$$

For any 3 natural numbers represented by a, n, and m, if $a \neq 0$, we can make the following generalization.

$$a^m \times a^n = a^{m+n}.$$

Next, let us see what happens when we work with quotients that are expressed in exponential notation. Suppose that we want to consider the quotient $6^5 \div 6^3$ as a power of 6. For convenience, we will indicate this quotient as shown below.

$$\frac{6^5}{6^3}$$

This symbol represents a quotient and is read as "6^5 over 6^3," or "6^5 divided by 6^3," or "the quotient of 6^5 and 6^3."

You know that $6^5 = 6 \times 6 \times 6 \times 6 \times 6$ and that $6^3 = 6 \times 6 \times 6$. Hence,

$$\frac{6^5}{6^3} = \frac{6 \times 6 \times 6 \times 6 \times 6}{6 \times 6 \times 6}.$$

But, $\dfrac{6 \times 6 \times 6 \times 6 \times 6}{6 \times 6 \times 6} = 6 \times 6$, or 6^2. Therefore,

$$\frac{6^5}{6^3} = 6^2.$$

Thus, the exponent of the quotient of 6^5 and 6^3 is equal to the difference of the exponents of 6^5 and 6^3. That is,

$$\frac{6^5}{6^3} = 6^{5-3}, \text{ or } 6^2.$$

You should use the method described above to verify that each of the following sentences expresses a true statement.

$$2^5 \div 2^4 = 2^1.$$
$$\frac{10^8}{10^2} = 10^{8-2}.$$
$$4^6 \div 4^1 = 4^{6-1}.$$

For any three natural numbers represented by a, m, and n, if $a \neq 0$ and if m is greater than or equal to n, then we can make the following generalization.

$$a^m \div a^n = a^{m-n}.$$

We must specify that m be greater than or equal to n only so long as we are dealing with natural numbers. This is necessary because $m - n$ is not defined for natural numbers if n is greater than m. If negative numbers were contained in the universe, we would not need this restriction.

Note that we have said that m can be equal to n. Let us see what happens when this is the case. Suppose that we replace a by 3 and m and n by 4. We obtain

$$3^4 \div 3^4 = 3^{4-4}.$$

Because $4 - 4 = 0$, we can obtain

$$3^4 \div 3^4 = 3^0.$$

We must now decide what number is named by the symbol 3^0. Certainly, it does not make sense to talk about 0 factors of 3. It does make sense, however, for the quotient of 3^4 and 3^4 to equal 1. Therefore, if a is not equal to 0, we define the zero power of a natural number to be equal to 1; that is,

$$\text{if } a \neq 0, \text{ then } a^0 = 1.$$

Obviously, this is a satisfactory definition when we are finding the quotient of two natural numbers expressed in exponential notation. For example, $10^2 \div 10^2 = 1$; therefore, 10^{2-2}, or 10^0, should be equal to 1. Let us see if this definition of a^0 also works when we are finding the product of two numbers expressed in exponential notation.

From our earlier generalization about products, you know that

$$2^4 \times 2^0 = 2^{4+0}, \text{ or } 2^4.$$

Hence, it does make sense to define 2^0 as 1 because the product of 2^4 and 1 is certainly equal to 2^4.

Now we will use the exponential notation that we have just developed to help us learn more about the numerals in our numeration system. We have already seen that the Hindu-Arabic system is an additive system that makes use of the place-value principle and that it is a base-ten, or decimal, system.

Consider the numeral 53,839. This numeral expresses a sum in the following way.

$$53,839 = 50,000 + 3000 + 800 + 30 + 9.$$

Also, $50,000 = 5 \cdot 10,000$; $3000 = 3 \cdot 1000$; $800 = 8 \cdot 100$; $30 = 3 \cdot 10$; and $9 = 9 \cdot 1$. Hence, you can write

$$53,839 = 5 \cdot 10,000 + 3 \cdot 1000 + 8 \cdot 100 + 3 \cdot 10 + 9 \cdot 1.$$

Further, you know that $10,000 = 10^4$, that $1000 = 10^3$, that $100 = 10^2$, that $10 = 10^1$, and that $1 = 10^0$. Therefore, by the substitution property, you can write

Substitution property, page 99

$$53,839 = 5 \cdot 10^4 + 3 \cdot 10^3 + 8 \cdot 10^2 + 3 \cdot 10^1 + 9 \cdot 10^0.$$

In this sentence, the expression at the right of the symbol for equality is called the *expanded form* of the decimal numeral 53,839. Note in particular the pattern of the numerals for the exponents in the expanded form. You can see that each place in the numeral has a "value" that is ten times as great as the value of the place immediately to its right; thus, the exponent of the power of 10 is greater by 1.

Several more examples of decimal numerals written in expanded form are given below. Study these examples carefully so that you can understand the basic pattern.

$$3906 = 3 \cdot 10^3 + 9 \cdot 10^2 + 0 \cdot 10^1 + 6 \cdot 10^0.$$
$$754,325 = 7 \cdot 10^5 + 5 \cdot 10^4 + 4 \cdot 10^3 + 3 \cdot 10^2 + 2 \cdot 10^1 + 5 \cdot 10^0.$$
$$60,030 = 6 \cdot 10^4 + 0 \cdot 10^3 + 0 \cdot 10^2 + 3 \cdot 10^1 + 0 \cdot 10^0.$$

From these examples, you see that each digit in a base-ten numeral may be associated with a power of 10. Later, when negative numbers have been introduced, you will see how this pattern can be extended to include negative exponents so that numerals like 175.362 can be written in expanded form.*

122 Rewrite each of the products expressed below in exponential notation.

a $3 \times 3 \times 3 \times 3$ e $10 \times 10 \times 10$

b 5×5 f $5 \times 10 \times 10$

c 6×8 g $9 \times 4 \times 4 \times 4 \times 4$

d $2 \times 2 \times 2 \times 5 \times 5$ h $7 \times 7 \times 8 \times 6 \times 6$

123 For each of the products and quotients expressed below, use exponential notation to express the product or quotient.

a $8^1 \times 8^9$ d $35^8 \div 35^7$

b $10^6 \times 10^8$ e $5^2 \times 5^1$

c $15^5 \div 15^2$ f $4^3 \times 4^3$

124 Write the standard name of each of the numbers named below.

a 5^3 d $16^5 \div 16^3$

b $4^2 \times 4^3$ e $5^0 \times 6^2$

c $6^2 \times 56^1$ f $45^5 \div 45^4$

125 The table below shows what replacements to make in the form $a \cdot 10^3 + b \cdot 10^2 + c \cdot 10^1 + d \cdot 10^0$. Make the appropriate replacements and then write the numerals as decimals.

	a	b	c	d
a	1	5	6	0
b	0	9	0	9
c	0	0	0	1
d	6	1	1	1

Bases other than ten

In this section we will consider several numeration systems that have all of the properties of our decimal system, but which have bases other than ten. The primary purpose of studying systems in bases other than ten is to increase your understanding of the decimal system, not to develop skill in computing in other bases.

When we use a decimal to name the number of objects in a set, we group the objects in terms of powers of 10. (Grouping by tens and powers of ten probably has its basis in the fact that man has 10 fingers. Thus,

---

* *Seeing Through Mathematics*, *Book 1*, is a good source of information on powers, exponents, and expanded form of numerals. Pages 226 *et seq*. Item 21 of Bibliography

once primitive man had "used up" all ten fingers when counting, he would naturally begin all over again and form a new group of 10.) As an example of what we mean, consider the objects shown in pictures A and B below. When we use the numeral 23 to describe the number of objects in this set, we have—at least mentally—grouped the objects as shown in picture B.

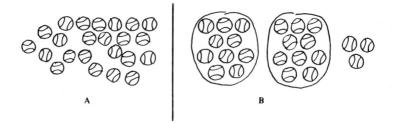

A   B

Similarly, when we use the decimal 650 to describe the number of objects in a set, we have mentally grouped the objects into 6 groups of ten tens, or 6 groups of one hundred, and 5 groups of ten.

Now suppose that, instead of grouping by tens, we group the objects by fives. In the picture below, we have again grouped the set of objects shown above; this time we have formed groups of 5 objects. If we now

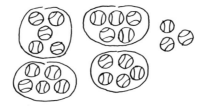

use the numeral 43 to describe the number of objects in the set, we are using a *base-five* numeral in which the digit 4 represents 4 groups of five and the digit 3, as before, represents 3 ones. The base-five numeral 43 is read "four, three," not "forty-three," since "forty" means "four tens."

Next suppose that we group the objects in this set by twos and powers of two, as shown below. The *base-two* numeral that we use to describe the

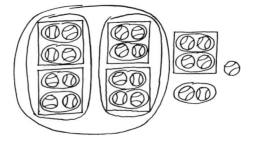

number of objects in the set is 1011. This numeral is read "one, zero, one, one." In this numeral, the digits from left to right represent 1 group of 2^4, 0 groups of 2^3, 1 group of 2^2, 1 group of 2^1, and 1 one.

As a final example, suppose that we group the objects in the set by eights, as shown below. As you might guess, the *base-eight* numeral that

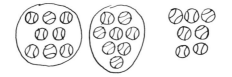

we use to describe the number of objects in this set is 27. In the numeral 27, the digit 2 represents 2 groups of eight, and the 7 represents 7 ones.

Now we will consider several numeration systems with bases other than ten in some detail. We will begin with a base-five system.

In the chart below we have tabulated a series of sets in which each set contains one more member than the set that precedes it. Then, in the column labeled "Base ten," we have written the decimal name of the natural number associated with each of these sets. Finally, in the column labeled "Base five," we have indicated how the number associated with each set is named in a base-five numeration system.

Natural numbers associated with sets, page 28

	Base ten	Base five
{ }	0	0
{a}	1	1
{a, b}	2	2
{a, b, c}	3	3
{a, b, c, d}	4	4
{a, b, c, d, e}	5	10
{a, b, c, d, e, f}	6	11
{a, b, c, d, e, f, g}	7	12
{a, b, c, d, e, f, g, h}	8	13
{a, b, c, d, e, f, g, h, i}	9	14
{a, b, c, d, e, f, g, h, i, j}	10	20
{a, b, c, d, e, f, g, h, i, j, k}	11	21

To distinguish a base-five numeral from a base-ten numeral, we will use the numeral 5 as a subscript. Thus, we will use the symbols 0_5, 1_5, 2_5, and so on, for the base-five numerals. Of course, if there is no possible confusion, as in the chart, then we will omit the subscripts. Note that in the base-five system, we have used the familiar symbols 0, 1, 2, 3, and 4 to name the numbers associated with the first five sets. However, the next numeral in our base-five system is not 5, but the numeral 10. This numeral should be read "one, zero, base five"; it should not be read as "ten," which is the name for this numeral in base ten. Just as the numeral 10 represents one group of ten in the base-ten system, the numeral 10_5 represents one group of five in the base-five system. Therefore, 10_5 names the same number as the numeral 5 in the base-ten system, and we can write $10_5 = 5$. Similarly, the numeral 11_5 (read "one, one, base-five") represents 1 group of 5 and 1 one; the numeral 12_5 represents 1 group of 5 and 2 ones; the numeral 21_5 represents 2 groups of 5 and 1 one.

Using the additive principle and the idea of place value, you can construct a base-five numeration system that enables you to name numbers in much the same way as they are named by base-ten numerals.

We can also establish methods for finding sums and products of the numbers named by base-five numerals. The "addition table" for the base-five system is shown below.

Addition and multiplication tables for base ten, pages 85 and 91

Addition table for base five

+	0	1	2	3	4
0	0	1	2	3	4
1	1	2	3	4	10
2	2	3	4	10	11
3	3	4	10	11	12
4	4	10	11	12	13

Some of the addition facts that you can obtain from the addition table are expressed below. In all, there are 25 addition basic facts for the base-five system as compared to the 100 basic facts for base ten.

$$3_5 + 4_5 = 12_5.$$
$$1_5 + 4_5 = 10_5.$$
$$4_5 + 3_5 = 12_5.$$

The "multiplication table" for our base-five system is shown below.

Multiplication table for base five

×	0	1	2	3	4
0	0	0	0	0	0
1	0	1	2	3	4
2	0	2	4	11	13
3	0	3	11	14	22
4	0	4	13	22	31

Some of the multiplication facts that you can obtain from the table are expressed below.

$$0_5 \times 4_5 = 0_5.$$
$$2_5 \times 3_5 = 11_5.$$
$$4_5 \times 1_5 = 4_5.$$
$$4_5 \times 4_5 = 31_5.$$

As for addition, there are 25 multiplication basic facts for the base-five system.

We can also write base-five numerals in expanded form in much the same way we did base-ten numerals. The expanded forms for several base-five numerals are given below.

$$23_5 = 2 \cdot 10^1 + 3 \cdot 10^0.$$
$$140_5 = 1 \cdot 10^2 + 4 \cdot 10^1 + 0 \cdot 10^0.$$
$$3201_5 = 3 \cdot 10^3 + 2 \cdot 10^2 + 0 \cdot 10^1 + 1 \cdot 10^0.$$
$$10442_5 = 1 \cdot 10^4 + 0 \cdot 10^3 + 4 \cdot 10^2 + 4 \cdot 10^1 + 2 \cdot 10^0.$$
$$330124_5 = 3 \cdot 10^{10} + 3 \cdot 10^4 + 0 \cdot 10^3 + 1 \cdot 10^2 + 2 \cdot 10^1 + 4 \cdot 10^0.$$

Note that the pattern for the expanded form of a base-five numeral is like the pattern for base-ten numerals. You must keep in mind, however, that the powers of 10 in each of these forms are powers of 10_5 (which is equal to 5, base ten), and not powers of ten. Note also that the first digit in the numeral 330124_5 is associated with 10^{10}, *not* with 10^5. This is so because the exponent of the "fifth" power of a number is expressed in base five by the numeral 10, not by the numeral 5, which is not a base-five symbol but a base-ten symbol.

Next, we will develop methods for rewriting base-five numerals as base-ten numerals and base-ten numerals as base-five numerals. This process is usually called "converting" from one base to another. To convert from base five to base ten, we can alter the expanded forms of the base-five numerals so that they are expressed in terms of base-ten numerals.

Instead of using powers of 10_5 in the expanded forms of the numerals, we will use powers of the base-ten numeral 5, thereby converting the numerals to base-ten numerals. Below, we have used the same numerals whose expanded forms were given above. This time, we have given the expanded forms in terms of powers of 5.

$$23_5 = 2 \cdot 5^1 + 3 \cdot 5^0.$$
$$140_5 = 1 \cdot 5^2 + 4 \cdot 5^1 + 0 \cdot 5^0.$$
$$3201_5 = 3 \cdot 5^3 + 2 \cdot 5^2 + 0 \cdot 5^1 + 1 \cdot 5^0.$$
$$10442_5 = 1 \cdot 5^4 + 0 \cdot 5^3 + 4 \cdot 5^2 + 5 \cdot 5^1 + 2 \cdot 5^0.$$
$$330124_5 = 3 \cdot 5^5 + 3 \cdot 5^4 + 0 \cdot 5^3 + 1 \cdot 5^2 + 2 \cdot 5^1 + 4 \cdot 5^0.$$

When you examine these expanded forms, you see that the numerals can easily be rewritten in the usual base-ten form by performing a few simple computations. For example, you can find the base-ten numeral that is equal to 23_5 by finding the product of 2 and 5^1, the product of 3 and 5^0, and finally the sum of these two products. Therefore, $23_5 = 10 + 3$, or 13. Similarly, you can use the expanded forms given at the bottom of page 137 to verify that each of the following statements is true.

$$140_5 = 45.$$
$$3201_5 = 426.$$
$$10442_5 = 747.$$
$$330124_5 = 11289.$$

The following example shows how a base-ten numeral can be converted to a base-five numeral. Suppose that you want to find the base-five numeral that names the same number as 742. Because the decimal numeral 742 has three digits, we know that the base-five numeral will have more than three digits. We will begin by guessing that the base-five numeral has five or six digits. If the base-five numeral has six digits, then the sixth digit from the right would be associated with 5^5, or 3125. However, 3125 is greater than 742, so we know that the base-five numeral does not have six digits. If the base-five numeral has five digits, then the fifth digit from the right is associated with 5^4, or 625. Since 625 is less than 742, the base-five numeral does have five digits. Therefore, we can write the following pattern for the numeral.

$$a \cdot 5^4 + b \cdot 5^3 + c \cdot 5^2 + d \cdot 5^1 + e \cdot 5^0.$$

Now we must find the proper replacements for a, b, c, d, and e, which may be replaced by 0, 1, 2, 3, or 4.

We can see immediately that the replacement for a is the numeral 1 because 625 is "contained in" 742 only once. When we subtract 625 from 742, we obtain 117. Next, we must decide what digit is associated with 5^3, or 125. Because 117 is less than 125, we know that b must be replaced by the numeral 0 because no 125 is "contained in" 117. We can now see that c must be replaced by the numeral 4 because there are four 25's in 117. When we subtract 100 from 117, we obtain 17. Thus, it is evident that d must be replaced by the numeral 3 and that e must be replaced by the numeral 2. We have now obtained the following base-ten expanded form of the base-five numeral.

$$1 \cdot 5^4 + 0 \cdot 5^3 + 4 \cdot 5^2 + 3 \cdot 5^1 + 2 \cdot 5^0.$$

Therefore, we can conclude that $742 = 10432_5$. You can verify this by determining whether or not the expanded form of the base-five numeral does name the same number as the base-ten numeral 742.

In general, you can convert a decimal numeral to a base-five numeral by first deciding upon the number of digits there are in the base-five numeral and then by using division and subtraction to determine the digits associated with each power of 5 expressed in the numeral.

126 Convert the base-five numerals below to base-ten numerals.

   a 34   **c** 3042   **e** 4321

   b 231   **d** 443   **f** 10413

127 Convert the base-ten numerals below to base-five numerals.

   a 14   **c** 144   **e** 752   **g** 1231

   b 89   **d** 231   **f** 5137   **h** 62

We remarked earlier that many electronic computers use base-two numerals in their operations. Base-two numerals are used because the two digits 0 and 1 of the binary system can be made to correspond to the two conditions of electric circuits (off and on). Therefore, we shall give some attention to a base-two system of numeration that has the same properties as our decimal system. In the chart given below, a series of sets is tabulated. The base-ten numerals and the base-two numerals that name the number of members in each set are also listed in the chart. Analogous to the method we used for base five, we will use the subscript 2 for base-two numerals whenever there might be confusion. Thus, the base-two numerals will be represented by 0_2, 1_2, 10_2, etc.

	Base ten	Base two
{ }	0	0
{a}	1	1
{a, b}	2	10
{a, b, c}	3	11
{a, b, c, d}	4	100
{a, b, c, d, e}	5	101
{a, b, c, d, e, f}	6	110
{a, b, c, d, e, f, g}	7	111
{a, b, c, d, e, f, g, h}	8	1000

Note that we use only the digits 0 and 1 in our base-two numerals. The third numeral, 10 (read "one, zero, base two), is associated with the set that has two members and indicates that we think of this number as 1 group of two. Just as the base-ten numeral 10 represents one group of ten, the base-two numeral 10_2 represents one group of two. Therefore,

10_2 and the decimal 2 name the same number, so we can write $10_2 = 2$. From the numerals in the chart, you should be able to determine the pattern for writing base-two numerals and to continue the list to include the base-two numerals that name the numbers through 20.

We can also establish the rules for addition and multiplication for a base-two system. The addition and multiplication tables for base two are shown below.

Addition table for base two   *Multiplication table for base two*

+	0	1
0	0	1
1	1	10

×	0	1
0	0	0
1	0	1

From these tables, you can see that there are only four addition facts and four multiplication facts in the table for the base-two system.

We can also write base-two numerals in expanded form just as we did base-ten and base-five numerals. For example,

$$11010_2 = 1 \cdot 10^{100} + 1 \cdot 10^{11} + 0 \cdot 10^{10} + 1 \cdot 10^1 + 0 \cdot 10^0.$$

In this expanded form, keep in mind that the numeral 10 represents the base-two numeral for the same number as the base-ten numeral 2. Note also that the exponents of the powers of 10 are expressed as base-two numerals.

To convert base-two numerals to base ten, we will alter the expanded form and replace the base-two numerals by base-ten numerals. Thus,

$$11010_2 = 1 \cdot 2^4 + 1 \cdot 2^3 + 0 \cdot 2^2 + 1 \cdot 2^1 + 0 \cdot 2^0.$$

Therefore, $11010_2 = 26$. Several other examples are shown below.

$$1111_2 = 1 \cdot 2^3 + 1 \cdot 2^2 + 1 \cdot 2^1 + 1 \cdot 2^0.$$
$$10111_2 = 1 \cdot 2^4 + 0 \cdot 2^3 + 1 \cdot 2^2 + 1 \cdot 2^1 + 1 \cdot 2^0.$$
$$101_2 = 1 \cdot 2^2 + 0 \cdot 2^1 + 1 \cdot 2^0.$$
$$1010_2 = 1 \cdot 2^3 + 0 \cdot 2^2 + 1 \cdot 2^1 + 1 \cdot 2^0.$$

Using the expanded forms of the numerals given above, we can easily find the base-ten numerals that are equal to the given base-two numerals. You should verify that each of the following statements is true.

$$1111_2 = 15.$$
$$10111_2 = 23.$$
$$101_2 = 5.$$
$$1010_2 = 10.$$

Next, we will give an example of how a base-ten numeral can be converted to a base-two numeral. Suppose that you want to convert the decimal 114 to a base-two numeral. First you use your knowledge of the powers of 2 to estimate the number of digits in the base-two numeral. You might first assume that there will be either 7 or 8 digits in the base-two numeral. $2^6 = 64$ and $2^7 = 128$; therefore, 2^6 is the greatest power of 2 that is associated with a digit in the base-two numeral. This means that there are seven digits in the base-two numeral. We can now write the following pattern for the base-two numeral.

$$a \cdot 2^6 + b \cdot 2^5 + c \cdot 2^4 + d \cdot 2^3 + e \cdot 2^2 + f \cdot 2^1 + g \cdot 2^0$$

Remember that a, b, c, etc., in the expanded form of the base-two numeral can be replaced only by the numerals 0 and 1. You already know that a should be replaced by 1. When you subtract 64 from 114, you obtain 50; hence, b should also be replaced by 1 because there is one 32 in 50. $50 - 32 = 18$; therefore, c should be replaced by 1 because there is one 16 in 18. Since $18 - 16 = 2$, both d and e should be replaced by 0. Finally, f should be replaced by 1 because there is one 2 in 2; and g should be replaced by 0. Thus, you obtain the following base-ten expanded form of the base-two numeral.

$$1 \cdot 2^6 + 1 \cdot 2^5 + 1 \cdot 2^4 + 0 \cdot 2^3 + 0 \cdot 2^2 + 1 \cdot 2^1 + 0 \cdot 2^0$$

We can use this expanded form to obtain the true statement expressed by the following sentence.

$$114 = 1110010_2.$$

By the method just described, any base-ten numeral can be expressed as a base-two numeral.

128 Convert the following base-two numerals to base-ten numerals.
    a 11001   **b** 11101   **c** 1101   **d** 1111101   **e** 1000101
129 Convert the following base-ten numerals to base-two numerals.
    a 31   **b** 50   **c** 7   **d** 99   **e** 12   **f** 64

We will consider very briefly one other numeration system—the base-twelve system—that has the same properties as our decimal system. Because we want to use the numeral 10_{12} to represent 1 twelve in this system and the numeral 11_{12} to represent 1 twelve and 1 one, we need two more digits in our system. We need a digit to name the number associated with a group of ten objects and a digit to name the number associated with a group of eleven objects. Two such digits that are commonly used are $\mathcal{X}$ (dek) for ten and $\mathcal{E}$ (el) for eleven. The first 16 numerals in the base-twelve system are named below, together with the decimal numerals for the same numbers.

Base ten	Base twelve
0	0
1	1
2	2
3	3
4	4
5	5
6	6
7	7
8	8
9	9
10	χ
11	ε
12	10
13	11
14	12
15	13

You should extend this list to include the names of the first 25 numbers in base-twelve symbols.

It is left as an exercise for the reader to develop the addition and multiplication tables for the base-twelve system basic facts.

The expanded forms of base-twelve numerals follow the same pattern as those for numerals in other bases. Thus,

$69\,\varepsilon\,3_{12} = 6 \cdot 10^3 + 9 \cdot 10^2 + \varepsilon \cdot 10^1 + 3 \cdot 10^0$, where $10_{12} = 12$.

In the following examples, we have used base-ten numerals in the expanded forms so that you can convert the base-twelve numerals to decimals by performing the indicated computations.

$$69\,\varepsilon\,3_{12} = 6 \cdot 12^3 + 9 \cdot 12^2 + \varepsilon \cdot 12^1 + 3 \cdot 12^0.$$
$$34\,\chi_{12} = 3 \cdot 12^2 + 4 \cdot 12^1 + \chi \cdot 12^0.$$
$$7682_{12} = 7 \cdot 12^3 + 6 \cdot 12^2 + 8 \cdot 12^1 + 2 \cdot 12^0.$$
$$\varepsilon\,0_{12} = \varepsilon \cdot 12^1 + 0 \cdot 12^0.$$

You should also be able to use the methods developed for base five and base two to develop a method for converting a decimal numeral to a base-twelve numeral.

CONCLUSION

In this chapter we have discussed briefly the various systems that man has devised for naming natural numbers. The Hindu-Arabic system, which had its origins many centuries ago, has survived and is now used throughout the Western world. It has endured because it is an efficient system that employs only a few symbols, has a symbol for 0, and incorporates the desirable characteristics of a numeration system. Although we commonly use base-ten numerals, numerals in certain other bases—such as two, eight, and twelve—are sometimes useful.*

CHAPTER QUIZ

1 Write the names of the first 20 natural numbers in a base-six numeration system. In a base-three system.

2 Use sets of objects to show that $13_8 = 11$.

3 What numeral may be used to name the number of elements in the set tabulated below in each of the following bases?
$$\{a, b, c, d, e, f, g, h, i, j, k, l, m, n, o, p, q, r\}$$
A base six   C base two   E base eighteen
B base three   D base nine

4 Tabulate a set whose number is named by the numeral 33_4. Do the same for 33_6.

5 Construct the addition and multiplication tables for base three.

6 Find the decimal that is equal to each of the numbers named below.
A 11111_2 C 303_5 E 11_{11}
B 33_4 D 1010_2 F $13\mathcal{E}_{12}$

7 Convert 45 to a numeral in each of the following bases.
A base nine   B base five   C base three   D base two

8 What can you say about a numeration system with a base of one?

9 What advantages might there be to using a base-twelve numeration system?

10 Write the names of the first 16 natural numbers in a base-eight system and then in a base-two system. Compare the numerals in the two systems to see if you can see why base-eight numerals are easily converted to base-two numerals and vice versa. For this reason, base-eight numerals are often used as an intermediate step in coding numbers for a base-two computer.

---

* *Understanding Numeration Systems* by Donovan A. Johnson and William H. Glenn contains a development of numeration systems with bases two, five, and twelve and some excellent exercise material. Item 32 of Bibliography

SUPPLEMENTARY READINGS

They Wrote on Clay by Edward Chiera presents an account of life in the ancient Near East as revealed by clay tablets. Item 35 of Bibliography

Numbers and Numerals by David E. Smith and J. Ginsburg tells how numbers came into use and what the first crude numerals meant. Pages 1-38. Item 33 of Bibliography

Science Awakening: Egyptian, Babylonian and Greek Mathematics by B. L. Van Der Waerden presents a history of mathematics from the Egyptians through the decline of the Greeks. Chapters I and II. Item 34 of Bibliography

Chapter seven

Theory of computing

Addition
Subtraction
Multiplication
Division
A comment on subtraction and division

Much of elementary school arithmetic is concerned with finding standard names of sums, differences, products, and quotients. The expression $25 + 12$ does represent the sum of 25 and 12; however, when you write the sentence $25 + 12 = 37$, you are indicating that computation has been performed to obtain the numeral 37 as the *standard name* of $25 + 12$. In this chapter we will discuss methods for finding standard names of sums, differences, products, and quotients of natural numbers.

Addition

In Chapter 5 we presented an addition table that included the standard names of the sums of certain ordered pairs of natural numbers, with the understanding that the table could theoretically be extended to include the standard name of the sum of every pair of natural numbers. The mappings from $N \times N$ onto N by addition that involve the numbers from 0 through 9 are called the *basic facts* for addition. These are the addition "facts" that you committed to memory in elementary school. When we want to find standard names of sums that involve addends greater than 9, we use these

Mapping from N X N onto N by addition, page 86

basic facts, together with the properties of the natural-number system and the properties of the decimal numeration system. Frequently, we use computational short cuts without being aware of the mathematical justifications for these short cuts. It is our purpose in this chapter to analyze computational procedures and to explain why we can compute in the way that we do.

In explaining how we find the standard name of the sum of two numbers such as 34 and 52, we will first use the properties of the decimal numeration system to express each number in expanded form. Then we will use certain properties of the natural-number system to arrive at the standard name of the sum. You already know that the numeral 86 is the standard name of $34 + 52$, but the following analysis will show how we arrive at the standard name.

We know that, in expanded form,

Expanded forms of decimals, page 132

$$34 = 3 \cdot 10^1 + 4 \cdot 10^0,$$

and also that

$$52 = 5 \cdot 10^1 + 2 \cdot 10^0.$$

By the substitution property we obtain

Substitution property, page 99

$$A \quad 34 + 52 = (3 \cdot 10^1 + 4 \cdot 10^0) + (5 \cdot 10^1 + 2 \cdot 10^0).$$

You know that, when you find the sum of 34 and 52, you usually add the numbers in ones' place to obtain 6 ones and you add the numbers in tens' place to obtain 8 tens. In the work that follows, we will use several properties of the natural-number system to justify this procedure.

Note that, in sentence A above, the sum of four products is expressed at the right of the symbol for equality. Because addition is associative, we know that the sum remains the same no matter how we group the addends. We next obtain

Associative property of addition, page 87

$$B \quad 34 + 52 = \left(3 \cdot 10^1 + (4 \cdot 10^0 + 5 \cdot 10^1)\right) + 2 \cdot 10^0.$$

Next, because we want to find the sum of the numbers associated with 10^1 and the sum of the numbers associated with 10^0, we need to change the order of the addends in the sum $4 \cdot 10^0 + 5 \cdot 10^1$. Because addition is commutative, we know that $4 \cdot 10^0 + 5 \cdot 10^1 = 5 \cdot 10^1 + 4 \cdot 10^0$. Therefore,

Commutative property of addition, page 87

$$C \quad 34 + 52 = \left(3 \cdot 10^1 + (5 \cdot 10^1 + 4 \cdot 10^0)\right) + 2 \cdot 10^0.$$

Again using the associative property of addition, we obtain

$$D \quad 34 + 52 = (3 \cdot 10^1 + 5 \cdot 10^1) + (4 \cdot 10^0 + 2 \cdot 10^0).$$

Now we need to show that the sum expressed at the right in sentence D is equal to $8 \cdot 10^1 + 6 \cdot 10^0$. Because multiplication distributes over addition, we know that

Distributive property, page 95

$$3 \cdot 10^1 + 5 \cdot 10^1 = (3 + 5)10^1$$

and that

$$4 \cdot 10^0 + 2 \cdot 10^0 = (4 + 2)10^0.$$

Therefore, by the substitution property, we obtain

E $34 + 52 = (3 + 5)10^1 + (4 + 2)10^0.$

From our knowledge of the basic facts for addition we know that $3 + 5 = 8$ and that $4 + 2 = 6$. Thus, by the substitution property,

F $34 + 52 = 8 \cdot 10^1 + 6 \cdot 10^0.$

Finally, from the properties of the decimal numeration system, we know that $8 \cdot 10^1 + 6 \cdot 10^0 = 86$. Therefore, we can use the transitive property of equality to obtain

Transitive property of equality, page 98

G $34 + 52 = 86.$

This example should make it quite obvious that we do indeed use a great many short cuts when we compute! In the next example, we will combine some of the steps, but we will also introduce a new complication to show what happens when we "carry" in addition. Suppose that we want to find the standard name of the sum $476 + 84$. First we write the numerals in expanded form and use the substitution property to obtain

$$476 + 84 = (4 \cdot 10^2 + 7 \cdot 10^1 + 6 \cdot 10^0) + (8 \cdot 10^1 + 4 \cdot 10^0).$$

Then, by the commutative and associative properties of addition and the distributive property, we rearrange and group the addends to obtain

$$476 + 84 = \left(4 \cdot 10^2 + (7 + 8)10^1\right) + (6 + 4)10^0.$$

From our knowledge of the basic facts we know that $7 + 8 = 15$ and that $6 + 4 = 10$. Hence, we use the substitution property to obtain

$$476 + 84 = 4 \cdot 10^2 + 15 \cdot 10^1 + 10 \cdot 10^0.$$

However, in the expanded form of a numeral, the digit associated with each power of ten must be one of the digits from 0 through 9. Thus, before we can write the standard name that is represented by the expanded form given above, we must do some further work. What we do next in this example shows what is involved when we "carry" in addition. We know that $10 \cdot 10^0 = 1 \cdot 10^1 + 0 \cdot 10^0$. Similarly, $15 \cdot 10^1 = 1 \cdot 10^2 + 5 \cdot 10^1$.

Therefore, by the substitution property, we can obtain

$$476 + 84 = 4 \cdot 10^2 + 1 \cdot 10^2 + 5 \cdot 10^1 + 1 \cdot 10^1 + 0 \cdot 10^0.$$

Then, by the associative property of addition and the distributive property,

$$476 + 84 = (4 + 1)10^2 + (5 + 1)10^1 + 0 \cdot 10^0.$$

Next, because $4 + 1 = 5$, and $5 + 1 = 6$,

$$476 + 84 = 5 \cdot 10^2 + 6 \cdot 10^1 + 0 \cdot 10^0.$$

Finally, because of the properties of the decimal numeration system, $5 \cdot 10^2 + 6 \cdot 10^1 + 0 \cdot 10^0 = 560$. Hence, we use the transitive property of equality to obtain

$$476 + 84 = 560.$$

Usually, when we find a sum, we use an algorism, or pattern for computation, like the one shown below. (The "carried" figures need not be written as they are in this example.)

$$
\begin{array}{r}
{}^{1\,1}476 \\
84 \\
\hline
560
\end{array}
$$

Note that the way in which we write the figures when we compute indicates that we have already used the commutative and associative properties. Thus, the numerals that are associated with 10^0 are grouped together in a column; the numerals that are associated with 10^1 are grouped in a column; and so on. When we begin to compute, the arrangement of the work and the order of the steps take care of all of the necessary rearranging of the numerals. Also notice that, because of the way in which the numerals are arranged, we simplify the regrouping procedure that must be done when we carry. In the above example, we immediately wrote the numeral for 1 ten above the column in which all the numerals that are associated with 10^1 are written. We did the same with the numeral for 1 hundred.

When we use the traditional addition algorism, it is customary to begin by finding the sum of the ones, next the sum of the tens, next the sum of the hundreds, and so on. The following "long" form for addition, shown on page 149, permits us to find the sum of the numbers associated with each power of ten in the original addends in any order we please. In this algorism, instead of writing the "carried" figures above the proper columns, we write the numeral for each of the partial sums beneath the

769	769	769	769
935	935	935	935
14	1600	1600	90
90	90	14	1600
1600	14	90	14
1704	1704	1704	1704

original numerals. This algorism shows clearly that, when we find the sum of the numerals associated with 10^1, we are really finding the sum of 60 and 30, not the sum of 6 and 3. Similarly, the algorism shows that we are finding the sum of 700 and 900, not the sum of 7 and 9. Once we have expressed all of the partial sums, then it is necessary to use the associative and distributive properties when finding the final sum.

Finding the sum represented by a column of numerals like those shown below is traditionally called "column addition."

$$\begin{array}{r} 9 \\ 6 \\ 7 \\ 8 \\ \underline{5} \\ 35 \end{array}$$

Children are usually taught that they can start either at the top or at the bottom of the column and find the sum by adding the numbers two at a time. Actually, we make use of several properties of addition when we perform column addition. Let us see how these properties are used in the example given above. First we will show what happens when we begin at the top of the column.

Because addition is a binary operation, we can add only two numbers at a time. Therefore, we use the associative property to obtain

Binary operation, pages 94-95

$$9 + 6 + 7 + 8 + 5 = \big([(9 + 6) + 7] + 8\big) + 5.$$

Next, because $9 + 6 = 15$, we replace $9 + 6$ by 15 to obtain

$$9 + 6 + 7 + 8 + 5 = \big((15 + 7) + 8\big) + 5.$$

$15 + 7 = 1 \cdot 10^1 + 12 \cdot 10^0$, and $1 \cdot 10^1 + 12 \cdot 10^0 = 2 \cdot 10^1 + 2 \cdot 10^0$, or 22, so

$$9 + 6 + 7 + 8 + 5 = (22 + 8) + 5.$$

We can similarly show that $22 + 8 = 30$; therefore,

$$9 + 6 + 7 + 8 + 5 = 30 + 5.$$

Finally, because $30 + 5 = 35$, we use the transitive property of equality to obtain

$$9 + 6 + 7 + 8 + 5 = 35.$$

We next want to show why it is also possible to begin at the bottom of the column of numerals and obtain the same sum. If we can show that the following sentence expresses a true statement, then we will have shown that the sum obtained when we start at the bottom of the column is the same as that obtained when we start at the top of the column.

$$\big([(5 + 8) + 7] + 6\big) + 9 = \big([(9 + 6) + 7] + 8\big) + 5.$$

The steps given below show how we can obtain the true statement expressed above. We have indicated the properties that we used (one or more times) following each step.

1 $\big([(5 + 8) + 7] + 6\big) + 9 = 9 + \big([(5 + 8) + 7] + 6\big).$
   Commutative property of addition
2 $9 + \big([(5 + 8) + 7] + 6\big) = 9 + \big(6 + [7 + (8 + 5)]\big).$
   Commutative property and substitution property
3 $9 + \big(6 + [7 + (8 + 5)]\big) = \big([(9 + 6) + 7] + 8\big) + 5.$
   Associative property of addition

Because equality is transitive, we know that the expression at the left of the symbol for equality in step 1 is equal to the expression at the right in step 3. Hence, we obtain

4 $\big([(5 + 8) + 7] + 6\big) + 9 = \big([(9 + 6) + 7] + 8\big) + 5.$

Since the sentence in step 4 expresses a true statement, it is evident that the sum will be the same, no matter whether we begin at the top or at the bottom of the column of numerals. The method that we used for this example could be generalized to show that this is always the case when we are finding the sum of 3 or more numbers.

130 Show the use of the properties of the natural number system and the decimal numeration system in the computations indicated below. Then show the usual addition algorism.
   a $15 + 43$ c $293 + 172$
   b $27 + 65$ d $4 + 8 + 9 + 3$

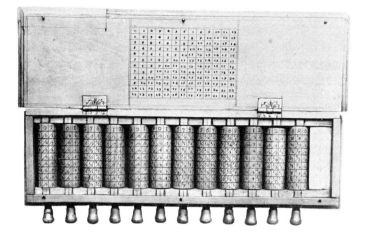

From the abacus of ancient times to the modern-day computer,
various devices have been developed to assist man in making
computations and to eliminate the need for human computing.
At the top is a simple device for multiplying, known as
"Napier's Rods," invented by the Scottish mathematician
John Napier in the seventeenth century. *The Bettmann
Archive, Inc.* Below is a modern computer designed to
handle business, engineering, and scientific problems.
Courtesy of International Business Machines Corporation

Subtraction

You will recall that, in Chapter 5, we defined subtraction in terms of its relation to addition. We said that, because the sum of 9 and 5 is 14, for example, the difference of 14 and 5 is 9. If we use the way in which these two operations are related, we can devise a set of subtraction "basic facts" that correspond to the basic facts that are included in our addition table. These subtraction facts are expressed in the subtraction table shown below. Theoretically, of course, we do not need the subtraction basic facts

Subtraction related to addition, page 102

−	0	1	2	3	4	5	6	7	8	9	10	11	12	13	14	15	16	17	18
0	0	1	2	3	4	5	6	7	8	9									
1		0	1	2	3	4	5	6	7	8	9								
2			0	1	2	3	4	5	6	7	8	9							
3				0	1	2	3	4	5	6	7	8	9						
4					0	1	2	3	4	5	6	7	8	9					
5						0	1	2	3	4	5	6	7	8	9				
6							0	1	2	3	4	5	6	7	8	9			
7								0	1	2	3	4	5	6	7	8	9		
8									0	1	2	3	4	5	6	7	8	9	
9										0	1	2	3	4	5	6	7	8	9

because we can always use our knowledge of the addition facts instead. However, to facilitate computation, we commit the subtraction facts to memory and use them just as we use the addition basic facts. When we compute to find standard names of differences like $63 - 47$, we use these facts and the properties of the number and numeration systems.

However, before we consider an example of how standard names of differences are computed, we need to say more about the relationship between addition and subtraction. When we consider negative numbers in Chapter 12, you will find that subtraction can be defined in terms of addition involving additive inverses. For example, the difference of 8 and 6 is defined as the sum of 8 and -6; that is, $8 - 6 = 8 + (-6)$. Similarly, $7 - 12 = 7 + (-12)$, and so on. The commutative, associative, and distributive properties hold for addition and multiplication involving negative numbers, as well as for these operations on natural numbers. Therefore, we can use these properties in connection with examples involving subtraction, so long as we understand what we are doing.

We gave examples in Chapter 5 to show that subtraction is neither commutative nor associative. Thus, $10 - 3 \neq 3 - 10$, and $(7 - 4) - 3 \neq$

$7 - (4 - 3)$. But $10 - 3 = 10 + (-3)$, and it is true that $10 + (-3) = -3 + 10$. Furthermore, $(7 - 4) - 3 = (7 + (-4)) + (-3)$, and it is true that $(7 + (-4)) + (-3) = 7 + (-4 + (-3))$. So, when we use various properties of addition in the examples that follow, it is with the understanding that the examples could have been rewritten as addition examples involving negative addends.

Let us now see how we can use the basic facts for subtraction and various properties to show that $63 - 47 = 16$. Note that it is necessary to "borrow" in this example. Some of the following steps will show what happens when we "borrow" in subtraction. The justification of each step follows the step.

1   $63 - 47 = (6 \cdot 10^1 + 3 \cdot 10^0) - (4 \cdot 10^1 + 7 \cdot 10^0)$.

Expanded form of numerals and substitution property

2   $63 - 47 = ((5 + 1) 10^1 + 3 \cdot 10^0) - (4 \cdot 10^1 + 7 \cdot 10^0)$.

Basic facts for addition and substitution property
This step is necessary because we need to "borrow" from tens' place in 63. By the basic facts for addition, we know that $6 = 5 + 1$; therefore, we can replace 6 in the product $6 \cdot 10^1$ by $5 + 1$.

3   $63 - 47 = (5 \cdot 10^1 + 1 \cdot 10^1 + 3 \cdot 10^0) - (4 \cdot 10^1 + 7 \cdot 10^0)$.

Distributive property and substitution property

4   $63 - 47 = (5 \cdot 10^1 + 13 \cdot 10^0) - (4 \cdot 10^1 + 7 \cdot 10^0)$.

Meaning of expanded form of a numeral and substitution property
We have replaced $1 \cdot 10^1 + 3 \cdot 10^0$ by $13 \cdot 10^0$.

5   $63 - 47 = (5 \cdot 10^1 - 4 \cdot 10^1) + (13 \cdot 10^0 - 7 \cdot 10^0)$.

Commutative and associative properties of addition*

6   $63 - 47 = (5 - 4)10^1 + (13 - 7)10^0$.

Distributive property and substitution property

7   $63 - 47 = 1(10^1) + 6(10^0)$.

Basic facts for subtraction and substitution property

8   $63 - 47 = 16$.

Meaning of expanded form and transitive property of equality

The subtraction algorism with which we are all familiar is shown in the next example, $256 - 68$. Note that, just as for the addition

---

* That is, the expression at the right of the "equals" sign in step 4 is equal to $(5 \cdot 10^1 + 13 \cdot 10^0) + ((-4)10^1 + (-7)10^0)$. By the associative property of addition, $(5 \cdot 10^1 + 13 \cdot 10^0) + ((-4)10^1 + (-7)10^0) = (5 \cdot 10^1 + [13 \cdot 10^0 + (-4)10^1]) + (-7)10^0$. By the commutative property, $(5 \cdot 10^1 + [13 \cdot 10^0 + (-4)10^1]) + (-7)10^0 = (5 \cdot 10^1 + [(-4)10^1 + 13 \cdot 10^0]) + (-7)10^0$. Again, by the associative property, $(5 \cdot 10^1 + [(-4)10^1 + 13 \cdot 10^0]) + (-7)10^0 = (5 \cdot 10^1 + (-4)10^1) + (13 \cdot 10^0 + (-7)10^0)$. But this last expression is equal to $(5 \cdot 10^1 - 4 \cdot 10^1) + (13 \cdot 10^0 - 7 \cdot 10^0)$, which is shown at the right of the "equals" sign in step 5.

algorism, we write the numerals in such a way that the digits associated with 10^0 are aligned, those associated with 10^1 are aligned, and so on. Note also the way in which we indicate that we have "borrowed" from the tens' column and from the hundreds' column. This algorism is called the "subtractive decomposition" method.

$$\begin{array}{r} {\scriptstyle 1 \ \ 14 \ \ 1} \\ \cancel{2}\cancel{5}6 \\ 68 \\ \hline 188 \end{array}$$

We will now use the expanded form of the numerals to show more clearly what has been done. The example becomes

$$\begin{array}{r} 2 \cdot 10^2 + 5 \cdot 10^1 + 6 \cdot 10^0 \\ 6 \cdot 10^1 + 8 \cdot 10^0 \\ \hline \end{array}$$

Because $6 \cdot 10^0 - 8 \cdot 10^0$ is not a natural number, we rewrite the expanded form of 256 as shown below. Then we find the difference of the numbers in ones' place.

$$\begin{array}{r} 2 \cdot 10^2 + 4 \cdot 10^1 + 16 \cdot 10^0 \\ 6 \cdot 10^1 + \ \ 8 \cdot 10^0 \\ \hline 8 \cdot 10^0 \end{array}$$

Again, $4 \cdot 10^1 - 6 \cdot 10^1$ is not a natural number, so we rewrite the expanded form of 256 as shown in the next step. Then we can complete the computation.

$$\begin{array}{r} 1 \cdot 10^2 + 14 \cdot 10^1 + 16 \cdot 10^0 \\ 6 \cdot 10^1 + \ \ 8 \cdot 10^0 \\ \hline 1 \cdot 10^2 + 8 \cdot 10^1 + \ \ 8 \cdot 10^0 \end{array}$$

Certain other subtraction methods have been used in the past and are of some historical interest. We will discuss one of them briefly. The method that we wish to describe, which can be used when it is necessary to borrow, is known as the "subtractive equal additions" method of subtraction. This technique involves the principle that we may add the same number to both the minuend (the number from which we subtract) and the subtrahend (the number we subtract) without affecting the difference. For example, $16 - 5 = 11$, and $(16 + 10) - (5 + 10) = 11$. In general, $a - b = (a + c) - (b + c)$.

When you use this technique in an example in which you must borrow before you can find the difference in ones' place, you add 10 ones to the minuend and 1 ten to the subtrahend.

Thus, by the subtractive decomposition method, 56 − 39 becomes

$$
\begin{array}{cc}
& 4\,{}_{1} \\
56 & \cancel{5}6 \\
\underline{39} & \underline{39} \\
& 17
\end{array}
$$

But, by the subtractive equal additions method, you would add 10 ones to 56 and 1 ten to 39. Thus,

$$
\begin{array}{c}
\overset{1}{5}6 \\
4 \\
\cancel{3}9 \\
\hline
17
\end{array}
$$

If you study the subtraction examples given below, you should be able to see how this method can be used for any problem involving subtraction. By the subtractive equal additions method, 725 − 393 becomes

$$
\begin{array}{cc}
725 & \overset{1}{7}25 \\
\underline{393} & 4 \\
& \cancel{3}93 \\
\cline{2-2}
& 332
\end{array}
$$

The following two steps show how to find the difference 871 − 484 by the subtractive equal additions method.

$$
\begin{array}{ccc}
871 & 8\overset{1}{7}1 & 8\overset{1}{7}\overset{1}{1} \\
\underline{484} & 9 & 5 \\
& \cancel{4}\cancel{8}4 & \cancel{4}\cancel{8}4 \\
\cline{2-3}
& 7 & 387
\end{array}
$$

If you are interested in learning about other methods of subtraction that have been used in the past, you will find that some of these methods are described in certain of the books listed in the bibliography for this chapter.

131 Show the use of expanded forms for the computations indicated below. Then show the usual subtraction algorism.

    a 847 − 514   **b** 31 − 19   **c** 625 − 268

132 Use the "subtractive equal additions" method for the examples given in exercise 131.

Multiplication

Along with the addition table that was given in Chapter 5, we presented a multiplication table. This table contained the standard names of the products of ordered pairs of natural numbers that can be formed from the numbers 0 through 12, with the understanding that such a table could theoretically be extended to include the products of all ordered pairs of natural numbers. The products formed by ordered pairs composed of the numbers from 0 through 9 are called the *basic facts* for multiplication. These are the multiplication basic facts that you memorized in elementary school. When we want to find the standard name of a product that is not included among the basic facts, we resort to some computational procedure.

In explaining how we find the standard name of a product like 6×78, we will first express the numbers in expanded form. To simplify our notation a bit, we will now dispense with the zero power of 10 in the expanded form and simply write the ones' digit of a numeral by itself. For this example, we will use just 6 instead of $6 \cdot 10^0$ as the expanded form of 6. Also, instead of using $7 \cdot 10^1 + 8 \cdot 10^0$ as the expanded form of 78, we will use

$$78 = 7 \cdot 10^1 + 8.$$

Hence,

$$6 \times 78 = 6 \times (7 \cdot 10^1 + 8).$$

Then we use the distributive property to obtain

$$6 \times 78 = (6 \times 7 \cdot 10^1) + (6 \times 8).$$

By the associative property of multiplication, we obtain

$$6 \times 78 = (6 \times 7) \cdot 10^1 + (6 \times 8).$$

Next, because $6 \times 7 = 42$ and $6 \times 8 = 48$, we can use the substitution property to obtain

$$6 \times 78 = (42 \cdot 10^1) + 48.$$

But $42 \cdot 10^1 = 4 \cdot 10^2 + 2 \cdot 10^1$ and $48 = 4 \cdot 10^1 + 8$. Thus,

$$6 \times 78 = (4 \cdot 10^2 + 2 \cdot 10^1) + ((4 \cdot 10^1) + 8).$$

Next, by the associative property of addition and the distributive property, we obtain

$$6 \times 78 = 4 \cdot 10^2 + (2 + 4)10^1 + 8.$$

We know that $2 + 4 = 6$, so

$$6 \times 78 = 4 \cdot 10^2 + 6 \cdot 10^1 + 8.$$

Finally, we know that $4 \cdot 10^2 + 6 \cdot 10^1 + 8 = 468$; therefore, by the transitive property of equality,

$$6 \times 78 = 468.$$

We have used the properties of the natural-number system and of the decimal numeration system to show how to find the standard name of a product. A long and involved procedure would be necessary to analyze an example like 742×635 in this fashion. However, you should be able to see that, although more steps would be required, the same properties that were used for the product 6×78 would be used for a more complicated example.

Next we will consider some multiplication algorisms. The two algorisms that are most commonly used are given below. When children are taught to use the algorism at the left, they are usually given the rule that each

```
   346          346
    32           32
  -----        -----
   692          692
  1038        10380
 ------       ------
 11072        11072
```

successive partial product is "moved one place to the left." Frequently, the reason for this procedure is not clearly explained. The algorism at the right has the advantage of making it clear that the second partial product is formed by multiplying 346 by 30, not by 3. Thus, the product of 346 and 30 is 10380, not 1038.

In the two algorisms given above, we multiplied first by the number associated with 10^0, next by the number associated with 10^1, and so on. Also, we were required to multiply the number represented by each digit in the numeral for the multiplicand in proper order. If we use the longer algorism given at the top of page 158, we can find the partial products in any order we please.

722		722		722	
456		456		456	
12	6 × 2	280000	400 × 700	800	400 × 2
120	6 × 20	8000	400 × 20	8000	400 × 20
4200	6 × 700	800	400 × 2	280000	400 × 700
100	50 × 2	35000	50 × 700	100	50 × 2
1000	50 × 20	1000	50 × 20	1000	50 × 20
35000	50 × 700	100	50 × 2	35000	50 × 700
800	400 × 2	4200	6 × 700	12	6 × 2
8000	400 × 20	120	6 × 20	120	6 × 20
280000	400 × 700	12	6 × 2	4200	6 × 700
329232		329232		329232	

If you compare these examples with those given earlier, you see that the commonly used algorisms are much more economical in terms of time and effort. The traditional algorisms require less time because they incorporate more short cuts and require a minimum of writing. However, it should also be obvious that the most efficient algorism is not by any means the clearest in terms of what is actually being done. When you are first teaching computational procedures to young children, you should always keep in mind that the introduction of too many short cuts at an early stage may obscure the meaning of the process and make it puzzling to children.

133 Show the use of the properties in the computations indicated below.
    a 8 × 63   **b** 10 × 759
134 Use each of the three algorisms for multiplication described in this section for the examples given in exercise 133.
135 Use the algorism shown at the top of this page for each of the computations indicated below.
    a 89 × 36   **c** 709 × 235
    b 325 × 84   **d** 1234 × 562

Division

In Chapter 5 we defined division in terms of its relation to multiplication. For example, we said that, because 6 × 8 = 48, it is also true that 48 ÷ 8 = 6. We can list a set of division "basic facts" that correspond to the basic facts included in our multiplication table. (There are no division basic facts that correspond to the multiplication basic facts of the form $a \times 0 = 0$; this is the case because division by 0 is not defined. You will learn why this is so later in this chapter.) The division basic facts are displayed in the chart on page 159.

Division related to multiplication page 103

÷	1	2	3	4	5	6	7	8	9
0	0	0	0	0	0	0	0	0	0
1	1								
2	2	1							
3	3		1						
4	4	2		1					
5	5				1				
6	6	3	2			1			
7	7						1		
8	8	4		2				1	
9	9		3						1
10		5			2				
12		6	4	3		2			
14		7					2		
15			5		3				
16		8		4				2	
18		9	6			3			2
20				5	4				
21			7				3		
24			8	6		4		3	
25					5				
27			9						3
28				7			4		
30					6	5			
32				8				4	
35					7		5		
36				9		6			4
40					8			5	
42						7	6		
45					9				5
48						8		6	
49							7		
54						9			6
56							8	7	
63							9		7
64								8	
72								9	8
81									9

As we remarked in connection with subtraction, we do not really need the division basic facts because we can use the multiplication facts instead. But, for speed and efficiency, we memorize and use the division basic facts when we compute.

We will not take the time to give an explanation of the computational procedures that we use when we divide as we did for the other operations. Such an explanation would require us to introduce rational numbers of the form $\frac{a}{b}$.

In elementary arithmetic, children are often taught that division is a process of repeated subtraction whereby a given number (the divisor) is subtracted from the total (the dividend) a certain number of times (the quotient). The example below shows how you can find the quotient of 18 and 3 by repeatedly subtracting 3 from 18 and recording the total number of times that this can be done. The work shows that the quotient of 18 and 3 is 6.

$$
\begin{array}{rl}
18 & \\
\underline{3} & 1 \\
15 & \\
\underline{3} & 1 \\
12 & \\
\underline{3} & 1 \\
9 & \\
\underline{3} & 1 \\
6 & \\
\underline{3} & 1 \\
3 & \\
\underline{3} & \underline{1} \\
0 & 6 \\
\end{array}
$$

Textbooks of today usually present one of two algorisms for division. We will use the same example (26112 ÷ 64) to display each of these algorisms. The first one, given below, is the algorism commonly used in the past.

$$
\begin{array}{r}
408 \\
64\overline{)26112} \\
\underline{256} \\
512 \\
\underline{512} \\
\end{array}
$$

The second algorism is shown below. We have provided several versions to show that it is possible to compute in more than one way when this algorism is used.

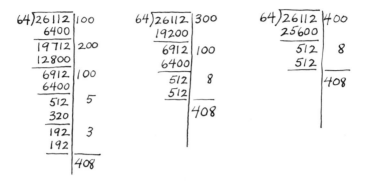

The first algorism is an adaptation of a method that appeared in an arithmetic text written by an Italian named Calandri and published in 1491. Although it has the advantage of being slightly more condensed than the second one, it is frequently difficult for children to learn because it incorporates many short cuts. The second algorism is one presented in the Isaac Greenwood *Arithmeticks* published in 1729. This algorism, which is not so economical as that of Calandri, does have an advantage for children who are learning the division process because it makes clearer what really happens when they divide.

Let us now investigate to see why we said earlier that division by 0 is not defined. We have said that division is related to multiplication in the following way: For any three natural numbers, a, b, and c, $a \div b = c$ means $a = c \times b$. Now suppose that we replace a by 5 and b by 0 and that we want to find the proper replacement for c. In other words, we want to find the replacement for c that satisfies $5 \div 0 = c$. Let us make the same replacements in $a = c \times b$ and see what happens: $5 = c \times 0$. Certainly we know that, whatever replacement we make for c, $c \times 0 = 0$ because the product of any number and 0 is 0. Thus, we reach the unacceptable conclusion that $5 = 0$. Next, suppose that we replace both a and b by 0. Then any replacement for c results in a true statement. This is also unacceptable because it means that $0 \div 0$ is any number we wish. No matter what replacements we choose for a and c, if we replace b by 0, the result is unsatisfactory. For this reason, mathematicians agree to leave division by 0 undefined.

136 Use the method of repeated subtraction, illustrated in the example on page 160, to show that the quotient of 20 and 4 is 5.

reaſon of the *Periods* ſo plac'd in this *Example.* And having thus particularly conſider'd the *Manner,* I proceed to the Reaſon of theſe Operations; which will be very obvious to any One that ſhall conſider a little, the following *Form of Expreſſing* the ſame *Example.*

Diviſor	Dividend	Quotient

8) 6 8 5 5 2 (8000 The Firſt *Quotient.*

Subſtract | | 4 | 0 | 0 | 0 { The *Product* of the *Diviſor* into the *Quotient*, viz. 8 into 8000 ; for the *Quotient* Figure is always of the Value of the Figure, under which the *Units* Place of its *Product* ſtands.

Diviſor 8) | 4 | 5 | 5 | 2 (500 Second *Quotient* Figure;
Subſtract | 4 | 0 | 0 | 0 (Being the *Product* of 8 into 500.

Diviſor 8) | 5 | 5 | 2 (60 Fourth *Quotient* Figure;
Subſtract | 4 | 8 | 0 (The *Product* of 8 into 60.

Diviſor 8) | 7 | 2 (9 Laſt *Quotient* Figure;
Subſtract | 7 | 2 (The *Product* of 8 into 9.

Remains   0 0 Now the *Sum* of all theſe ſeveral
Qotients Viz.   8000 + 500 + 60 + 9 = 8569.

EXAMPLE II.

To divide 590624922 by 7563. This is performed as follows.

Diviſor	Dividend	Quotient
7563)	590624922	(78094
	52941····	
	61214	
	60504	
	71092	
	68067	
	30252	
	30252	
	00000	

T2

THE *Learner* may obſerve from theſe Two *Examples*, (1) *That the chief Difficulty in Diviſion lies in making Choice of a true* Quotient Figure. The *Rule* relating hereunto, I have made as extenſive as was poſſible; however, in *common Practice* it will be ſufficient, to have regard only to the Two Firſt *Figures* of the *Diviſor*, for by them all the reſt are generally regulated; Except the Second *Figure* chance to be 2, 3, or 4. and at the ſame time the Third *Figure*, 7. 8, or 9. (2) *That for every* Figure, or Cypher wh ch is brought down from the Dividend *in Order to a now Operation, there muſt always be either a* Figure, *or Cypher ſet down in the* Quotient.

THE foregoing *Examples* are ſuch that the *Dividend* is exactly meaſured, or *divided off* by the *Diviſor* : In ſuch Caſes where this cannot be done, there will be a *Remainder* which is generally ſet over the *Diviſor*, with a ſeparating Line betwixt them; and Adjoined to the *Quotient.* The *Examples* following are of this Kind : and the Method of managing them will be taught when we come to the *Doctrine of Fractions.*

The SHORT ITALIAN Method.

EXAMPLE III.

To divide 462358234 by .12485. This is perform'd as follows.

Diviſor	Dividend	Quotient
12485)	462358234	(37033.
	87808	
	41323	
	28684	
Remainder	1229	

12·9
12485

D 2   *EXAMPLE*

Three division algorisms from arithmetic text
by Isaac Greenwood
Published by T. Hancock in Boston, New England, 1729.
University of Chicago Library

137 Use both the Calandri and the Greenwood algorisms to determine each of the following quotients.

a $400 \div 16$ **b** $2052 \div 19$ **c** $3450 \div 115$

A comment on subtraction and division

So far in this book, we have dealt almost exclusively with natural numbers. In earlier chapters, we considered the properties of natural numbers, of operations on natural numbers, of the system of natural numbers, and of the decimal numeration system. In this chapter, we have studied the methods whereby we find standard names for the sums, products, differences, and quotients of natural numbers. We will use the word *process* to refer to the procedure of finding a standard name of a sum, product, difference, or quotient. Thus, the process of addition is the method we use to find the standard name of a sum and is quite distinct from the operation of addition. The *operation* of addition is the mapping of an ordered pair of numbers onto a number called its sum. For example, (18, 17) is mapped onto the sum $18 + 17$. The *process* of addition, however, is the method we use to determine 35 as the standard name of the sum $18 + 17$. Whenever we are concerned with finding the standard name of a number that results from an operation, such as $8 + 13$, 12×9, $16 - 5$, or $175 \div 5$, we are concerned with a process.

Operation of addition, page 86

You will recall that both addition and multiplication are closed in the set of natural numbers. That is, the sum of any two natural numbers is again a natural number, and the product of any two natural numbers is likewise a natural number. This means that, when we process sums and products involving natural numbers, we can always find a standard name that expresses a natural number. You should also recall, however, that neither subtraction nor division is closed in the set of natural numbers. This implies that, for some pairs of natural numbers, differences and quotients do not exist.

Closure for addition and multiplication, pages 86-87 and 92

Let us first consider some subtraction examples. Because the difference $45 - 15$, for example, is a natural number, we can use the process of subtraction to determine 30 as the standard name of this difference. The symbol $7 - 12$, however, does not name a natural number; therefore, there is no standard name that corresponds to it. Hence, we say that an expression like $7 - 12$ or $0 - 5$ or $213 - 482$ is not meaningful when the universe is N, the set of natural numbers.

Similar situations arise when we consider division. The expression $36 \div 3$, for example, is meaningful when the universe is N, because the quotient $36 \div 3$ is a natural number, and the numeral 12 is the standard name of this quotient. By contrast, the expression $17 \div 5$ is not meaningful when the universe is N, because the symbol $17 \div 5$ does not name a natural number. Such expressions as $17 \div 5$ or $3 \div 8$ or $780 \div 11$ are meaningful only when the universe is the set of rational numbers.

Children are introduced to differences like $7 - 12$ or $0 - 5$ only when they begin to study positive and negative numbers. With division, however, children are often taught special methods for expressing quotients like $3 \div 8$ or $17 \div 5$ before they have studied rational numbers. This is done because there are many practical situations that are a part of children's experiences in which such examples arise. For example, sharing 10 pennies among 3 children or determining the number of 2-cent candies that can be bought with 15 cents are everyday situations in which the division process does not "come out even" when we are limited to natural numbers.

Children are often taught to use the following algorism in solving problems of this type.

$$\begin{array}{r} 5)\overline{17}\,|3 \\ \underline{15}\quad| \\ 2\,|3 \end{array}$$

The quotient is then expressed as "3, with 2 remainder." Although the quotient $17 \div 5$ is not a natural number, the result—3, with 2 remainder—can be interpreted meaningfully with respect to most practical situations. In fact, this result would be more appropriate than the quotient $3\frac{2}{5}$ for certain practical situations in which a rational-number answer might not make sense.

The idea that $17 \div 5$ is equal to 3, with 2 remainder, can also be expressed as follows:

$$17 = 3 \times 5 + 2.$$

In fact, there is an important theorem of arithmetic that establishes that any natural number can be expressed in the following way:

$$a = q \times b + r, \text{ where } 0 \leqq r < b.$$

In this sentence, a represents the dividend, b the divisor, q the quotient, and r the remainder. We will discuss this theorem in some detail in the chapter on elementary number theory, Chapter 9.

138 Express each of the following in the form $a = q \times b + r$.

a $462 \div 16$ c $20 \div 21$

b $4289 \div 364$ d $372 \div 12$

CONCLUSION

A major portion of the study of arithmetic in the elementary school is devoted to the acquisition of skill in computation. From the material presented in this chapter, you should see that computational procedures, which often appear mysterious to a child, can be explained in terms of certain mathematical properties. It has also been our intention in this chapter to show that the computational algorisms with which we are familiar are certainly not the only possible algorisms and that sometimes they are not the best for teaching children to compute. The more efficient and concise an algorism is, the more short cuts it incorporates; and, hence, the more puzzling it may be to the child.

CHAPTER QUIZ

1 A = {Sam, Jane, Sue, John, Jim}. B = {cat, dog, mouse, rat}.
 C = {book, pencil}. D = {slate, pencil, eraser, pen, 4, 10}.
 A What is n[A]? What is n[B]? What is n[C]? What is n[D]?
 B Give the standard name of each number named below.
  n[A ∪ B] n[B] + n[D] n[A ∪ C]
  n[A ∪ D] n[C] + n[B] n[D] + n[A]
 C Why is it not correct to write n[C] + n[D] = n[C ∪ D]?
2 Write each of the following numerals in expanded form.
 A 345 B 15,690 C 5000 D 409 E 1
3 Use expanded forms to find the sum of 56 and 11. Be able to tell what properties you use.
4 Use parentheses to show the different ways in which you can express the sum of 6, 9, and 3. What properties are you using?
5 Repeat exercise 4 for the product of 6, 9, and 3.
6 Use the expanded forms of 45 and 14 to find their product.
7 Which of the following generalizations about numbers are correct? If the generalization is not correct, give an example that contradicts it.
 A For each replacement of n by a natural number, $n + 1 = 1 + n$.
 B For all numbers except zero, any number divided by itself is 1.
 C If the product of two numbers is 4, then one of the numbers must be 2.
 D For all n, 0 divided by n equals 0.
 E Any number divided by itself is 1.
 F The sum of two odd numbers is always an even number.
 G The product of an even number and 0 is always 0.

8 Use both Calandri's method and Greenwood's method to find the following quotients. If the quotient is not a natural number, express the answer in the form $a = q \times b + r$.

A $965 \div 16$ D $20400 \div 66$

B $1004 \div 34$ E $44000 \div 12$

C $45600 \div 199$ F $51210 \div 16$

9 Find the squares of ten different odd numbers. Subtract 1 from each of these squares. Is each difference an even number? An odd number? Always divisible by 4? By 3? Find the greatest common divisor of the differences. Do you think this result holds generally?

10 Formulate a generalization about the sum, product, difference, and quotient of any two odd numbers. Formulate a similar generalization for any two even numbers.

11 The following forms are ambiguous. Rewrite each one in two ways so that each way names a different number.

A $5 \times 6 + 5$ D $15 - 3 \times 4$ G $36 \times 6 \div 6$

B $12 \div 3 + 1$ E $15 \times 6 \div 2$ H $52 - 5 \times 3$

C $5 + 6 \times 7$ F $16 - 5 \times 2$ I $12 \div 4 - 1$

12 Some of the following expressions may be meaningless. Select these expressions and explain why they are meaningless.

A $45 \times 0 + 55$ D $16 + 0/0$ G $0 \times 0 + 5$

B $15 \div 0$ E 5^0 H $\dfrac{9}{0} + \dfrac{0}{9}$

C $0 \div 5 + 9$ F $\dfrac{5 - 1}{0}$ I $(4 \times 6) + 1 \times (8 - 9) \div 0$

SUPPLEMENTARY READINGS

Glenn, William H. and Johnson, Donovan A., *Short Cuts in Computing*. This pamphlet contains many "trick" ways of computing in special cases and explanations of why the methods work in terms of the properties of the number system. It also contains various ways to check answers, including that of casting out nines. Item 36 of Bibliography

Johnson, Donovan A. and Glenn, William H., *Computing Devices*. This booklet contains a discussion of various devices from the abacus to the electronic computer that have been used to perform computations. Item 37 of Bibliography

Larsen, Harold D. and Ludlow, H. Glenn, *Arithmetic for Colleges.* This is a good source of information on various algorisms for addition, subtraction, and multiplication, including the historical background for each algorism. Chapters 3, 4, and 5. Item 38 of Bibliography

Peterson, John A. and Hashisaki, Joseph, *Theory of Arithmetic.* This book contains a good explanation of how the algorisms of addition and multiplication are related to the properties of the natural number system and of the decimal numeration system. Pages 100-107. Item 26 of Bibliography

Swain, Robert L., *Understanding Arithmetic.* Chapters 4 and 5 of this book contain explanations of why algorisms work and also compares present-day algorisms to those used in the past. Item 39 of Bibliography

Chapter eight

Relations

Sets of number pairs
Proportional relations
Applications of proportional relations
Other kinds of relations
Properties of relations

In the earlier chapters of this book, we were concerned mainly with the natural-number system—with the set of natural numbers, with the operations and the properties of the operations on natural numbers, with systems of naming natural numbers, and with methods of computation involving natural numbers. These topics constitute the major portion of the arithmetic that a child learns in the first four years of elementary school. However, once a child has mastered the fundamental operations of arithmetic and the basic computational procedures, he is ready to move on to other important aspects of arithmetic. One such aspect is concerned with sets of number pairs that arise in connection with various kinds of physical and social situations. The study of these sets leads to certain important mathematical ideas as well as to practical solutions of problems, since pairs of numbers that belong to the same set may be compared to observe trends, clustering, scatter, and so on. We will begin with an illustration of what we mean by the study of sets of number pairs.

Sets of number pairs

In a certain city, the normal range of temperatures for the month of May is from 50° to 85°. Suppose that, at a weather station in this city, the temperature to the nearer degree is recorded every hour of the day. The following table shows the results for one day in May. Note that pairs of numbers are named in the chart under the heading (t, d). The first number of each pair is the hour in terms of a 24-hour clock, and the second number is the temperature to the nearer degree. Thus, from the number pair (9, 59), we know that the temperature at 9 A.M. was 59°. We will use the symbol (t, d) to represent any pair in the chart. The letter t in the symbol (t, d) can be replaced by any of the numerals from 1 through 24 that expresses an hour of the day. The letter d may be replaced by any of the numerals from 50 through 85 that express the temperature measured in degrees.

Time-Temperature Chart

A. M.			P. M.		
Time	Temperature	(t, d)	Time	Temperature	(t, d)
1	54	(1, 54)	13	83	(13, 83)
2	50	(2, 50)	14	83	(14, 83)
3	50	(3, 50)	15	84	(15, 84)
4	51	(4, 51)	16	84	(16, 84)
5	50	(5, 50)	17	80	(17, 80)
6	55	(6, 55)	18	79	(18, 79)
7	56	(7, 56)	19	74	(19, 74)
8	58	(8, 58)	20	70	(20, 70)
9	59	(9, 59)	21	65	(21, 65)
10	65	(10, 65)	22	61	(22, 61)
11	67	(11, 67)	23	58	(23, 58)
12	74	(12, 74)	24	57	(24, 57)

We can think of the pairs of numbers given in the chart as a set of ordered pairs. If we use the letter T for the set of numbers that designate the hours, we know that

$$T = \{1, 2, 3, \ldots, 24\}.$$

Similarly, if we use the letter D for the set of numbers that designate the temperatures in the normal range, we know that

$$D = \{50, 51, 52, \ldots, 85\}.$$

If we form the set of all possible pairs of numbers whose first components refer to hours and whose second components refer to temperatures, we obtain the Cartesian set $T \times D$. You will recall that the number of mem- bers in a Cartesian set like $T \times D$ is equal to the product of the number of members in T and the number of members in D. Thus, because T has

Cartesian set, page 61

24 members (the number of hours) and D has 36 members (the number of possible temperatures in the normal range), T × D has 24 × 36, or 864, members. Because it would be tedious to tabulate T × D, we will not do so; we will assume that your previous study of Cartesian sets will enable you to think about the members of this set without our tabulating the set.

Each of the 24 ordered pairs of numbers named in the chart above is a member of T × D; hence, the set of ordered pairs named in the chart is a subset of T × D. The subset of T × D whose members are named in the chart is called a *relation*. It is a relation of temperature to time. In mathematics, a relation involves some sort of rule or condition whereby a set of ordered pairs is "selected out" of a given Cartesian set, or universe. Later in this chapter, we will give a more formal definition of a relation. Now, however, we will consider another way of representing the relation that we have been discussing.

Subset of a set, page 14

The data presented in the time-temperature chart can also be given in a graph. The graph of this data is shown on page 171. Certainly you are familiar with various kinds of graphs, such as bar graphs, line graphs, and so on. Several important mathematical ideas are employed in the construction of a graph. We will examine this graph in detail to make clear what these ideas are.

Along the horizontal line, called the "horizontal axis," we have located 24 points at equal intervals with which we have associated the natural numbers 1 through 24. These points indicate the 24 hours for which the temperatures were recorded. Along the vertical line, called the "vertical axis," we have located 36 points at equal intervals to represent the normal range of temperature readings from 50 through 85. Using the points in the two axes, we have constructed a *grid* that consists of 864 points that are associated with the 864 ordered pairs in the Cartesian set T × D. Thus, the point associated with (5, 50) is located directly above 5 on the horizontal axis and directly to the right of 50 on the vertical axis; the point associated with (15, 84) is located directly above 15 on the horizontal axis and directly to the right of 84 on the vertical axis. Because there is a one-to-one correspondence between the points in the grid and the members of T × D, we can use the number pairs to identify the points; for example, we will call the point that is associated with (7, 56) "point (7, 56)." Similarly, point (24, 57) is the point associated with (24, 57).

Notice that some of the points in the grid have been encircled; these points are those associated with the ordered pairs named in the time-temperature chart. The encircled points are the *graph* of the relation of temperature to time. Just as the relation of temperature to time is a subset

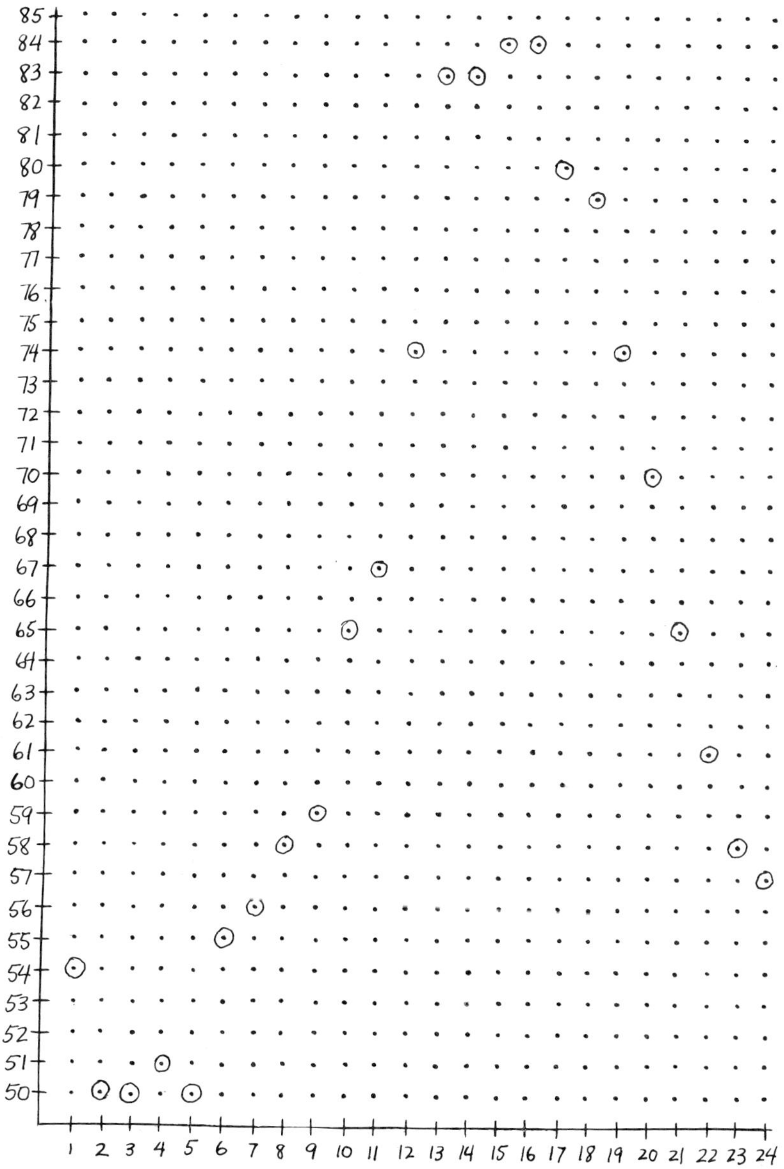

85
84
83
82
81
80
79
78
77
76
75
74
73
72
71
70
69
68
67
66
65
64
63
62
61
60
59
58
57
56
55
54
53
52
51
50

1 2 3 4 5 6 7 8 9 10 11 12 13 14 15 16 17 18 19 20 21 22 23 24

of T $\times$ D, the set of points in the graph is a subset of the set of points in the grid. The grid can be thought of as a graph of T $\times$ D.

From both the time-temperature chart and the graph that we have been discussing, it should be clear that this relation is a selection of certain ordered pairs of numbers from among many possible ordered pairs of numbers. For example, hour 4 could have been paired with any one of the 36 temperature readings, but, in fact, it is paired with 51 in the relation;

again, hour 18 could have been paired with any one of the 36 numbers that refer to temperatures, but it is paired with 79 in the relation. It is in this sense that a relation like that of temperature to time is a subset of a set of ordered pairs.

Next we will present a non-mathematical example of a relation of the type we sometimes consider in everyday life. Suppose that the following sets of men and women are planning to play bridge. Suppose also that the bridge partners are to be members of the opposite sex. We will consider the relation determined by "is the bridge partner of."

$$M = \{Jim, Joe, Sam, Fred\}.$$
$$W = \{Sally, Alice, Sue, Marie\}.$$

We do not yet know whether Sally is the partner of Jim, of Sam, or of one of the other two members of set M. We do know, however, that each member of W is the partner of one and only one of the members of M. By forming the Cartesian set M $\times$ W, we will have the universe, which is the set of all possible ordered pairs of bridge partners. M $\times$ W is tabulated below.

M $\times$ W = {(Jim, Sally), (Jim, Alice), (Jim, Sue), (Jim, Marie),
(Joe, Sally), (Joe, Alice), (Joe, Sue), (Joe, Marie),
(Sam, Sally), (Sam, Alice), (Sam, Sue), (Sam, Marie),
(Fred, Sally), (Fred, Alice), (Fred, Sue), (Fred, Marie)}.

Now we want to determine the subset of M $\times$ W that is the relation "is the bridge partner of." Suppose that the statements expressed below are true.

Marie is the partner of Jim.
Sally is the partner of Joe.
Alice is the partner of Sam.
Sue is the partner of Fred.

We can now tabulate the relation determined by "is the bridge partner of," which is a subset of M $\times$ W.

{(Jim, Marie), (Joe, Sally), (Sam, Alice), (Fred, Sue)}

Just as we made a graph of the relation of temperature to time, we can make a graph of the relation "is the bridge partner of," as shown on page 173. In this case, each point in the grid is associated with an ordered pair of persons rather than an ordered pair of numbers. Thus, the point in the grid that is directly above the point associated with Joe and directly to the right of the point associated with Sally is the point (Joe, Sally). There is a one-to-one correspondence between the points in the grid and the elements of M $\times$ W. As in the graph we presented earlier, we have encircled the points that are members of the relation "is the bridge partner of." The graph makes it quite clear why it makes sense to define a relation as a subset of a set of ordered pairs.

139 a A = {1, 2, 3}. Tabulate A × A.

b B = {a, b, c, d}. Tabulate B × B.

c A = {s}. Tabulate A × A.

d K = {cat, dog, rat}. Tabulate K × K.

e D = { }. Tabulate D × D.

f B = {2, 4, 6, 8}. C = {10}. Tabulate B × C. Tabulate C × B. Does C × B = B × C?

g A = {1, 3, 5}. B = {2, 4, 6}. Tabulate A × B. Tabulate B × A.

h A = {a, b}. B = { }. Does A × B = B × A?

140 Each member of set A, tabulated below, represents a number of apples that may be purchased, and each member of set C represents the possible cost of the apples purchased.

$$A = \{1, 2, 3, 4, 5, 6\}.$$
$$C = \{36, 12, 6, 18, 30, 24, 3, 9, 15\}.$$

a Tabulate the universe, A × C, and make a grid to represent A × C.

b If apples cost 6 cents each, encircle points in the grid to show the cost of 1, 2, 3, 4, 5, or 6 apples.

c If each apple costs 3 cents, draw squares around points to represent the cost of 1, 2, 3, 4, 5, or 6 apples.

141 Use sets X and Y, tabulated below, in connection with this exercise.

$$X = \{1, 2, 3, 4\}.$$
$$Y = \{1, 2, 3, 4, 5, 6\}.$$

a Tabulate the universe, X × Y, and make a grid to represent it.

b Consider the points (x, y). They are ordered pairs whose first components are members of X and whose second components are members of Y. Encircle the points in the grid for which the second component is twice the first component.

c Enclose with squares those points in the grid for which the second component is one-half the first. Notice that the relation of y to x is a subset of $X \times Y$.

142 K = {cat, dog, bird}.

M = {spider, cat, man, rat}.

a Tabulate M $\times$ K and make a grid to represent it.

b Encircle each point associated with a member of M $\times$ K in which the first component is a two-legged animal.

c Enclose with squares the points for which the second component is a two-legged animal.

d What is true of the point for which both components of the pair are two-legged animals?

143 Sets W and H tabulated below represent the weights and heights of the members of a certain family.

$$W = \{210, 190, 150, 120\}.$$
$$H = \{70, 66, 72, 61\}.$$

a Tabulate W $\times$ H and make a grid to represent it.

b Suppose that the following are the heights and weights of the members of the family:

	Weight	Height
Father	210	72
Mother	150	66
Son	190	70
Daughter	120	61

Graph the pairs (w, h) for the family. This subset is the relation of weight to height for this family.

c Tabulate the relation of weight to height as a set of ordered pairs.

Now that we have considered some specific examples, we can generalize our definition of a relation as follows:

Given two sets A and B, a relation from A to B is a non-empty subset of A $\times$ B.

Notice that, according to this definition, neither A nor B can be the empty set since the relation must be a non-empty subset.

In the examples of relations that we have already discussed, A and B were different sets. Let us now consider a relation that is a subset of A $\times$ A. Suppose that

$$A = \{1, 2, 3, 4\}.$$

Then,

$$A \times A = \{(1, 1), (1, 2), (1, 3), (1, 4),$$
$$(2, 1), (2, 2), (2, 3), (2, 4),$$
$$(3, 1), (3, 2), (3, 3), (3, 4),$$
$$(4, 1), (4, 2), (4, 3), (4, 4)\}.$$

The relation we are interested in consists of those ordered pairs in which the second component is 1 greater than the first component. This subset of $A \times A$ is the set, which we will call R, that is tabulated below.

$$R = \{(1, 2), (2, 3), (3, 4)\}.$$

Earlier, we defined a relation in terms of the Cartesian product of A and B. We can also define a relation in terms of the Cartesian product, $A \times A$:

A relation in A is a subset of $A \times A$.

The graph of the relation R, which was tabulated above, is shown below. The points in both the horizontal and the vertical axis are associated with the members of A, and the points in the grid are associated with the elements of $A \times A$. The encircled points are associated with the members of R and form the graph of the relation R.

Again, notice that, just as R is a subset of $A \times A$, the graph of R is a subset of the grid that is the graph of $A \times A$. Also note that all of the encircled points lie in a straight line. If, for example, we were to draw a line that contained both (1, 2) and (3, 4), the line would also contain (2, 3). For this reason, R is called a *linear relation* in A.

Not all relations are linear. For example, let us consider another relation in A. Suppose that we choose all of those members of $A \times A$ in which the second component is less than the first component. This relation, which we will call R*, is tabulated below.

$$R^* = \{(2, 1), (3, 1), (4, 1), (3, 2), (4, 2), (4, 3)\}.$$

The graph of R* is shown on page 176. R* is obviously not a linear relation because not all of the points in the graph of R* can be contained in a single line. We will call R* a *non-linear* relation.

```
4 ┤  ·   ·   ·   ·
3 ┤  ·   ·   · ⊙
2 ┤  ·   · ⊙ ⊙
1 ┤  · ⊙ ⊙ ⊙
   └─┼──┼──┼──┼─
     1  2  3  4
```

In all of the examples that we have given, we have used finite sets. A relation can also be a subset of an infinite Cartesian set. The relation itself may be either finite or infinite. Suppose that we now consider a relation in the set of natural numbers, N. For example, we can determine a subset of N × N that consists of all ordered pairs of natural numbers (x, y) whose second components are 1 less than their first components. This relation, L, is tabulated below; it should be evident that L is an infinite set.

Finite and infinite sets, page 30

$$L = \{(1, 0), (2, 1), (3, 2), (4, 3), \ldots, (n, n-1), \ldots \}.$$

We can also make an incomplete graph of the relation L. Obviously, we cannot illustrate a complete graph of either N × N or of relation L because these sets are infinite. But we can give an illustration that is sufficient to give us a good idea of what the entire graph would be like. The incomplete graphs of N × N and of L are shown on page 177. Note that we have used three small dots at the end of each axis to show that it extends on and on indefinitely.

These graphs also differ from earlier graphs in another important way. Because the graph of N × N includes the points associated with ordered pairs like (5, 0), (12, 0), (0, 6), and (0, 0), the points in the two axes serve a dual purpose. Consider, for example, point 3 in the horizontal axis. The natural number 3 is associated with this point, but so is the ordered pair of natural numbers (3, 0). Thus, this point may be thought of as either point 3 in the axis or point (3, 0) in the grid. Similarly, the point labeled with the numeral 6 in the horizontal axis may be thought of as either point 6 in the axis or point (6, 0) in the grid. The points in the vertical axis also play a dual rôle. Point 2 in the vertical axis is also point (0, 2) in the grid; point 5 in this axis is also point (0, 5) in the grid; and so on. The point in which the two axes intersect is point (0, 0) in the grid. This point is customarily called the *origin*. Thus, unlike our earlier graphs, which did not include ordered pairs either of whose components was 0, the points in the axes of this grid are a part of the graph of the universe, N × N.

The encircled points in this graph form an incomplete graph of the relation L. If we were to extend the graph of N × N, we could also extend the graph of L to include such members of L as (7, 6), (15, 14), (100, 99), and so on. However, from the portion of the graphs shown, it is fairly safe to conclude that L is a linear relation in N and that all of the points in the graph of L are included in the same line.

144 Consider the set A = {0, 1, 2, ... , 9}. Make a graph of A × A. How many members are in the set A × A? Let the relation W be a subset of A × A in which the first component of each element is less than the second component. Encircle the points in the graph of W. Is W a linear relation? How many members does W contain?

145 Consider the set B = {0, 1, 2, ... , 12}. Draw a graph of B × B. Let the relation X be the subset of B × B such that the first component is one greater than twice the second component. Indicate the graph of X by encircling the proper points. Is X linear? How many elements does X have?

146 Consider the set N = {0, 1, 2, ... }. Draw an incomplete graph of N × N. Let the relation Y be the subset of N × N such that the second component is one less than one-half of the first component. Indicate the graph of Y. Is Y a linear relation? How many members does Y have?

147 Consider the set N = {0, 1, 2, ...}. Draw an incomplete graph of N × N. Let the relation Z be the subset of N × N such that the second component is the square of the first component. Indicate the graph of Z. Is Z a linear relation? How many members does Z have?

Certain kinds of relations are of special interest because of their applicability to problem situations that are dealt with in the elementary school. Now that we have given you a basic idea of what linear and non-linear relations are, we will consider one very useful kind of linear relation.

Proportional relations

So far, we have established a relation as a subset of a Cartesian set. Thus, a relation is a set of ordered pairs. The relations that we intend to discuss in this section will be subsets of the Cartesian product C × C. Remember that C, often called the set of counting numbers, contains all the natural numbers except 0. We have chosen C × C as our universe for these relations to avoid certain difficulties that would arise if we were to use N × N.

Set of counting numbers, page 36

Let us now consider the relation in C whose members are of the form $(n, 2n)$, in other words, those elements of $C \times C$ in each of which the second component is twice the first component. This relation, which we will call S, is tabulated below. The dots to the right of (5, 10) indicate that the members of S go on and on and that each member is of the form $(n, 2n)$.

$$S = \{(1, 2), (2, 4), (3, 6), (4, 8), (5, 10), \ldots \}.$$

Obviously, S is a relation in C because S is a subset of $C \times C$. The incomplete graphs of $C \times C$ and of S are shown below. The points in the grid form a portion of the graph of $C \times C$, and the encircled points form a portion of the graph of S. Notice that, because 0 is not an element of C, no point that has 0 as either of its components is contained in the graph of $C \times C$. Note also that, because 0 is not an element of C, the points in the axes are not included in the graph of $C \times C$. From the portion of the graph of S that is shown, we can assume that S is a linear relation in C.

Relation S has one important characteristic that the relations you studied earlier do not have. This characteristic concerns the relationship between the members of S. Suppose that we take the first member of S, (1, 2), and multiply both of its components by 2. When we do this, we obtain (2, 4), which is another member of S. Next, suppose that we multiply both components of (1, 2) by 3; we then obtain (3, 6), which is another member of S. In fact, if we continue this process and multiply the components of (1, 2) by 4, by 5, by 6, and so on, we always obtain another member of S. If you choose any member of S, you can obtain other members of S by multiplying both components of the given element by 2, 3, 4, 5, and so on.

Because of their applicability to situations that involve rates and comparisons, such as 20 miles per hour, 3 pencils for 25¢, $3 to $4, and so on, the ordered pairs in a relation like S are called *rate pairs*. The relation S is called a *proportional relation*. We will give a better definition of a proportional relation after we have considered several more examples.

Consider all members of C $\times$ C of the form $(3n, 4n)$. By replacing n in $(3n, 4n)$ in turn by counting numbers, we obtain the following set of ordered pairs, which we will call set Q. Again, we have used the three dots to show that Q is an infinite set, each of whose members is of the form $(3n, 4n)$.

$$Q = \{(3, 4), (6, 8), (9, 12), (12, 16), \ldots\}.$$

Obviously, Q is a relation in C because it is a subset of C $\times$ C. As the incomplete graph of Q below shows, Q is a linear relation, and, since the members of Q are of the form $(3n, 4n)$, Q is a proportional relation.

We can use the same procedure for obtaining members of Q that we used for obtaining members of S above. Thus, if we multiply both of the components of the first member, (3, 4), by 2, by 3, by 4, and so on, we will always obtain another member of Q. In general, if you replace n in expressions like those shown below by counting numbers, you obtain proportional relations in C.

$$(n, 6n), (3n, 20n), (12n, 13n), (2n, n), (8n, 7n)$$

148 Using the set of counting numbers as the universe, tabulate the set of number pairs determined by the following forms. You need include only the names of the first 6 members of each set in your tabulation. Indicate whether or not each set is a proportional relation.

a $(n, 3n)$ **c** $(1, n)$ **e** $(2n, 5)$ **g** (n, n^2)

b $(2n, n - 1)$ **d** $(2n, 3n)$ **f** (n, n) **h** $(5n, 3n)$

149 Use each of the sets that you tabulated in exercise 148 to show by means of a graph that they are subsets of C × C.

150 In each of the exercises below, one element of a proportional relation is named. Write the names of at least six more elements that belong to the relation.

a (1, 3)   **c** (2, 3)   **e** (1, 1)   **g** (100, 500)
b (5, 1)   **d** (5, 2)   **f** (15, 25)   **h** (135, 170)

So far in this section, we have learned that a proportional relation is a relation whose members are of the form $(n, 2n)$, $(5n, 3n)$, or $(7n, 25n)$. Now we will develop further the concept of a proportional relation and give a precise definition of a proportional relation. First, we will examine an important characteristic of all rate pairs that are elements of the same proportional relation.

Consider proportional relation R tabulated below.

$$R = \{(4, 5), (8, 10), (12, 15), (16, 20), \ldots\}.$$

You already know that, because R is a proportional relation, you can determine elements of R by multiplying each component of (4, 5) by the same member of C. Thus, if you multiply both components of (4, 5) by 2, you obtain (8, 10); if you multiply both components by 3, you obtain (12, 15); and so on. In fact, you can see that any ordered pair of the form $(4n, 5n)$ is a member of R. Rate pairs that are members of the same proportional relation, that is, rate pairs that can be obtained from a numeral form like $(4n, 5n)$, are said to be *equivalent rate pairs*.

There is another way of determining whether or not two ordered pairs are equivalent. We can illustrate this method by choosing any two members of proportional relation R such as (8, 10) and (16, 20) and comparing the following two products: The product of the first component of (8, 10) and the second component of (16, 20) and the product of the first component of (16, 20) and the second component of (8, 10). The following diagram illustrates the two products we mean.

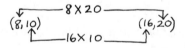

Because 8 × 20 and 16 × 10 are equal, the rate pairs (8, 10) and (16, 20) are equivalent and, hence, are elements of the same proportional relation. Similarly, the rate pair (4, 5) is an element of this proportional relation because 4 × 10 = 8 × 5. Also, (12, 15) is an element of proportional relation R because 12 × 10 = 8 × 15. If you were to find these two products in the same manner for every two members of proportional relation R, you would find that these two products are equal in each case. Thus, all of the elements of R are equivalent to each other.

As you might expect, if two rate pairs are not equivalent, then these two products are not equal. We see that (3, 2), for example, is not a member of R because it cannot be expressed in the form (4n, 5n). We can also decide that (3, 2) is not an element of R because the product of the first component of (4, 5) and the second component of (3, 2) is not equal to the product of the first component of (3, 2) and the second component of (4, 5); that is, $4 \times 2 \neq 3 \times 5$ and, therefore, (3, 2) is not equivalent to (4, 5). You can use this same procedure to show that other rate pairs, such as (7, 6), (33, 180), and (100, 200), are not elements of R.

We can now make the following generalization about equivalent rate pairs:

> Any two rate pairs represented by (a, b) and (c, d)
> are equivalent if $ad = cb$.
> Also, if (a, b) and (c, d) are equivalent,
> then $ad = cb$.

Traditionally, the rate pair (a, b) may be written in any of the forms, $a/b, \dfrac{a}{b},$ or $a\!:\!b$. In this book, we will use the form shown below. This symbol is read "a to b." Notice that, when a rate pair is expressed in the form a/b, it is not necessary to use parentheses. We will now restate the generalization given above, using this new notation.

$$\underline{a/\!b}$$

> Any two rate pairs a/b and c/d are equivalent if $ad = cb$.
> Also, if a/b and c/d are equivalent, then $ad = cb$.

The above generalization makes it very simple to decide immediately whether or not any two given rate pairs are equivalent. For example, we see that two such rate pairs as 5/6 and 10/12 are equivalent because $5 \times 12 = 10 \times 6$. Conversely, we know that 2/3 and 8/10 are not equivalent because $2 \times 10 \neq 8 \times 3$.

We can now use the idea of equivalent rate pairs in defining a proportional relation:

> A proportional relation is a set of equivalent rate pairs.
> That is, a proportional relation is a subset of C $\times$ C
> for which the following is true:

If a/b and c/d are elements
of the proportional relation, then $ad = cb$.
Also, if $ad = cb$, then a/b and c/d are elements
of the same proportional relation.

It is important to keep in mind that, although two rate pairs like 2/3 and 8/10 are not members of the *same* proportional relation, each of these rate pairs is contained in a proportional relation. Thus, 2/3 is an element of the proportional relation

$$\{2/3, 4/6, 6/9, 8/12, \ldots\};$$

while 8/10 is an element of the proportional relation

$$\{4/5, 8/10, 12/15, 16/20, \ldots\}.$$

In fact, every ordered pair of counting numbers is an element of exactly one proportional relation.

To show that a given rate pair cannot be contained in more than one proportional relation, let us suppose that there is an ordered pair of counting numbers a/b that does belong to two proportional relations. Suppose, for example, that a given rate pair a/b belongs to both $\{2/3, 4/6, 6/9, \ldots\}$ and $\{4/5, 8/10, 12/15, \ldots\}$. Then it must be true, according to the definition of a proportional relation, that $2b = 3a$ and that $4b = 5a$. However, by the multiplication property of equality, if $2b = 3a$, then $2 \cdot 2b = 2 \cdot 3a$, or $4b = 6a$. Thus, we have $4b = 5a$ and $4b = 6a$ and, by the transitive property of equality, $5a = 6a$. Hence, a must be equal to zero. But this is impossible, since a/b is a given ordered pair of *counting* numbers. Therefore, a/b is not contained in both proportional relations. Multiplicati property of equality, page 98 Transitive property of equality, page 98

Observe that, because each rate pair is an element of exactly one proportional relation, the Cartesian set $C \times C$ has been *partitioned* into disjoint subsets. We can illustrate this idea graphically. Consider the proportional relations that are tabulated below. Disjoint subsets, page 20

$$A = \{1/2, 2/4, 3/6, 4/8, \ldots\}.$$
$$B = \{2/1, 4/2, 6/3, 8/4, \ldots\}.$$
$$C = \{1/1, 2/2, 3/3, 4/4, \ldots\}.$$
$$D = \{2/3, 4/6, 6/9, 8/12, \ldots\}.$$

An incomplete graph of each of these relations is shown in the graph of $C \times C$ on page 183. The points in the graph of A are encircled; the points in the graph of B are enclosed by squares; the points in the graph of C are enclosed by triangles; and the points in the graph of D are enclosed by diamonds.

This graph shows clearly that every rate pair is an element of not more than one proportional relation. It should also be evident that the points that are not contained in the graphs of proportional relations A, B, C, or D would be contained in graphs of other proportional relations. For example, the point associated with 3/2 would be in the graph of {3/2, 6/4, 9/6, . . .}; the point associated with 1/5 would be in the graph of {1/5, 2/10, 3/15, . . .}; and so on.

Up to now in our study of proportional relations, it has been necessary for us to tabulate the proportional relation that we are considering because we have no other way of naming it. Tabulations of proportional relations such as those shown below are somewhat cumbersome to work with, so it would be convenient to have a better way of naming these proportional relations.

$$Q = \{4/7, 8/14, 12/21, 16/28, . . .\}.$$
$$R = \{3/2, 6/4, 9/6, 12/8, . . .\}.$$
$$S = \{11/5, 22/10, 33/15, 44/20, . . .\}.$$

We will now adopt a convention for naming proportional relations that is not unlike the kind of convention we might use in everyday conversation.

Suppose that the following sets represent two different basketball teams.

Team A = {Joey, Al, Harry, Sam, Clarence}.
Team B = {Paul, Henry, George, Eric, Ted}.

When referring to Team A, you might use the name of one of the members of the team to identify the team. For example, you might call Team A "Joey's team" or "Harry's team." Similarly, you might call Team B "Henry's team," "Eric's team," or "George's team." In each instance, it is assumed that the person to whom you are talking will know to which team you are referring and will know who the members of the team are.

We can use a similar technique in naming proportional relations like Q, R, and S, tabulated earlier. This means that the name of any element of Q, R, or S may be used as a name for the entire proportional relation. For example, the symbol 4/7, or the symbol 8/14, or the symbol 12/21 may be used to name proportional relation Q. We will call a symbol that names either a proportional relation or an element of the proportional relation a *ratio*. A ratio is a name of a proportional relation or of a rate pair in the same way that a numeral is a name of a number. Just as we use the symbol for equality between two numerals that name the same number, we can use the symbol for equality between two ratios that name the same proportional relation. Hence, because 4/7 and 8/14 both represent proportional relation Q, we can write

$$4/7 = 8/14.$$

For the same reason, we can also write

$$8/14 = 12/21,$$
$$4/7 = 12/21,$$
$$8/14 = 16/28.$$

The remarks that we have just made about naming proportional relation Q also apply to R, to S, and to any other proportional relation. Proportional relation R can be named by any ratio, such as 6/4, 12/8, 36/24, that is a name of a member of R. Similarly, the ratios 11/5, 33/15, 66/30, and so on, can be used to name proportional relation S.

You will recall that, earlier in this section, we expressed the following generalization concerning equivalent rate pairs.

Any two rate pairs a/b and c/d
are equivalent if $ad = cb$.
Also, if a/b and c/d are equivalent,
then $ad = cb$.

We can now express a similar generalization about proportional relations.

If a/b and c/d represent proportional relations,
then $a/b = c/d$ whenever $ad = cb$.
Also, if $a/b = c/d$, then $ad = cb$.

151 In an election in City A, 5 persons voted for every 8 persons eligible to vote. You can use the rate pair 5/8 to represent this rate. Tabulate the proportional relation of which 5/8 is a member. Include at least 10 other ratios in your tabulation. Make a graph of this proportional relation.

152 In a fund-raising campaign, Charity A and Charity B agree to share the proceeds in such a way that Charity A will receive $3 for each $2 that Charity B receives. What rate pair can you use to represent this rate? Name six other members of this proportional relation. Make a graph of this proportional relation.

153 Mr. Jones works on a commission of $2 for every $50 of merchandise sold. What rate pair can you use to represent this rate of commission? Name 5 other members of this proportional relation.

154 The Community Chest Drive in City A has collected $45 out of each $120 of its goal so far. Tabulate a set of rate pairs whose members can be used to represent this rate. Include six other ratios in your tabulation.

155 Tabulate a set of rate pairs that are members of the proportional relation 5/1. Make a graph of the proportional relation 5/1.

156 Use the definition of equal proportional relations to decide if the two ratios in each of the following exercises name the same proportional relation.

a 5/6, 10/13   **e** 1/51, 20/1010

b 115/245, 23/49   **f** 15/15, 4567/4566

c 45/495, 1/11   **g** 1/1, 55/55

d 82/24, 41/12   **h** 38/19, 342/171

157 Tabulate the proportional relation named by each of the following ratios. Then make a graph of each proportional relation.

a 5/2   **b** 90/100   **c** 3/4   **d** 4/3

158 Twelve inches is the same length as one foot. This fact can be represented by the rate pair 12/1. The graph of the proportional relation whose members are of the form $12n/n$ can be used to "convert" inches to feet. Show how this can be done.

159 Repeat exercise 158 for each of the following.

a 3 feet in 1 yard

b 2 pints in 1 quart

c 4 pecks in 1 bushel

d 3 gluz in 2 murds

160 Make graphs of the proportional relations of the form $(n, 2n)$ and of the form $(3n, 2n)$. Call these relations sets A and B, respectively. Use these graphs to argue that no element of A can be an element of B and no element of B can be an element of A.

Applications of proportional relations

We said earlier that proportional relations are of special interest because they are useful in solving many of the problems of the type that are introduced in the elementary school. It may be well at this time to consider some of the kinds of problems that can be solved by means of proportional relations.

Example A: Jim and Sam are business partners. Because of the amount of money each has invested in the business, they have agreed that the profits will be shared on the basis of $3 for Jim and $5 for Sam. We might ask questions like the following in connection with this example.

1) How much money should Sam receive when Jim receives $75?

2) How much money should Jim receive when Sam receives $300?

We can use the rate pair 3/5 to represent the rate at which the profits are to be shared by Jim and Sam. Note that the first component of 3/5 refers to the amount Jim is to receive, and the second component refers to the amount Sam is to receive.

One way to find the answers to the questions that are asked in Example A would be to tabulate the proportional relation of which 3/5 is a member. Then we could select the rate pairs that would enable us to answer the questions. Remember that we can obtain other elements of the proportional relation by multiplying the components of 3/5 by 2, by 3, by 4, by 5, and so on. Thus, we obtain

$$\{3/5,\ 6/10,\ 9/15,\ 12/20,\ 15/25,\ \ldots\}.$$

Note that the first question in Example A requires us to determine the second component of a rate pair that is equivalent to 3/5 whose first component is 75. The second question requires us to determine the first component of a rate pair that is equivalent to 3/5 whose second component is 300. From these observations, it is apparent that we would need to name a great many members of the proportional relation before we found the ones we want. For this reason, this would not be a very useful method of problem solving, so we will consider some other approaches.

A second method for solving the problem would be first to notice that each element of the proportional relation is of the form $3n/5n$. Hence, the rate pairs we wish to determine must also be of the form $3n/5n$.

To answer the first question in Example A, we note that, if n is replaced by 25, we obtain the rate pair whose first component is 75 and whose second component is 125—that is, 75/125. So we can conclude that Sam should receive $125 when Jim receives $75.

To answer the second question in Example A, we know that we must determine the first component of the rate pair whose second component is 300. Therefore, if we replace n in the form $3n/5n$ by 60, we obtain the rate pair whose second component is 300 and whose first component is 180—that is, 180/300. So we can conclude that Jim should receive $180 when Sam receives $300.

This second method is a reasonably satisfactory one for answering the questions asked in Example A. However, we could have chosen certain numbers that would make the replacement for n in $3n/5n$ far from obvious. Suppose, for example, we had asked you to find Sam's share when Jim's share is \$861. Then it would have required a little more work to find the proper replacement for n.

We can use the idea of equal proportional relations and of equivalent rate pairs to give us an even better method for finding the answer to questions like those in Example A. Remember that two proportional relations a/b and c/d are equal if $ad = cb$.

To answer the first question in Example A, we let y represent the amount of money Sam should receive. Now we want to find a replacement for y in the following open sentence so that it expresses a true statement. Keep in mind that the universe for y is C, the set of counting numbers.

$$3/5 = 75/y.$$

From the definition of equivalent rate pairs, we know that if $3/5$ and $75/y$ are equivalent, then

$$3y = 75 \times 5.$$

From this, we obtain

$$3y = 375.$$

In the discussion of the relation between multiplication and division in Chapter 5, we noted that $3y = 375$ can be written as

Division related to multiplication, page 103

$$y = 375 \div 3.$$

Hence, we obtain

$$y = 125.$$

From this last sentence, we know that the replacement for y in $3/5 = 75/y$ is 125; and we have determined the answer to the first question in Example A.

For the second question in Example A, we can use the following condition. In this condition, x represents the amount of money Jim should receive.

$$3/5 = x/300.$$

Notice that, in this case, we use x to represent the first component of the rate pair we wish to determine. We can use the definition of equivalent rate pairs to obtain

$$3 \times 300 = 5x.$$

From this, we obtain

$$900 = 5x.$$

Then, using the relation between multiplication and division, we write

$$900 \div 5 = x.$$

Finally, because $900 \div 5 = 180$, we obtain

$$180 = x.$$

From this, we know that the replacement for x in $3/5 = x/300$ is 180, and we have determined the answer to the second question in Example A.

Example B: On Monday, 42 of the 630 students who are enrolled at School A were absent. For each student who was absent, how many students are enrolled at School A?

From the information given in Example B, we know that the rate pair 42/630 represents a comparison of students who were absent to students enrolled. We also know that we want to find another rate pair that is a member of the same proportional relation and that has 1 as its first component.

Therefore, we can use the idea of equivalent rate pairs to obtain the following condition for this example.

$$42/630 = 1/n.$$

From this, we obtain

$$42n = 630,$$
$$n = 630 \div 42,$$
$$n = 15.$$

Thus, we know that 15 is the proper replacement for n in $42/630 = 1/n$. Therefore, for each student who was absent, 15 students are enrolled at School A.

Example C: Mr. Jones traveled 156 miles in 4 hours. At the same rate, how many miles can he travel in 6 hours?

The following conditions illustrate how the idea of equivalent rate pairs can be used to find the answer to Example C. You should be able to justify each of the steps.

$$156/4 = x/6.$$
$$6 \times 156 = 4x.$$
$$936 = 4x.$$
$$936 \div 4 = x.$$
$$234 = x.$$

From the last step, we know that x in $156/4 = x/6$ should be replaced by 234; therefore, Mr. Jones can travel 234 miles in 6 hours.

One use of proportional relations with which all of you are already familiar is their use in solving "per cent" problems. In fact, a per cent is nothing more than a rate pair whose second component is 100. Thus,

$$50\% = 50/100,$$
$$37\% = 37/100,$$
$$85\% = 85/100,$$
$$172\% = 172/100,$$
$$530\% = 530/100,$$

and so on. Now we will consider some examples involving rate pairs that represent per cents.

Example D: A high-school basketball team won 60% of its games last year. The team won 15 games. How many games did the team play last year?

In this example, to say that the team won 60% of its games means that, if the team had played 100 games, it would have won 60 of them. In other words, the rate of games won to games played can be represented by 60/100. Because 60% = 60/100, we can use the following steps to solve this problem.

$$60/100 = 15/p.$$
$$60p = 1500.$$
$$p = 1500 \div 60.$$
$$p = 25.$$

From the last step, we know that p in $60/100 = 15/p$ should be replaced by 25 and, therefore, the team played 25 games last year.

Example E: During one month, Mr. King found that 15% of the orders he received for a certain product were for \$500 or more. Mr. King received a total of 460 orders for the product that month. How many of these orders were for \$500 or more?

We know that, in this example, 15% means that 15 orders per 100 orders were for \$500 or more. Therefore, we can use the following steps to find the answer to this example.

$$15/100 = x/460.$$
$$100x = 460 \times 15.$$
$$100x = 6900.$$
$$x = 69.$$

From the last step, we know that x in $15/100 = x/460$ should be replaced by 69; therefore, Mr. King received 69 orders for \$500 or more for the product during that month.

Example F: Mr. King also found that, during the same month, 92 of the orders he received for the product were for $50 or less. What per cent of the 460 orders were for $50 or less?

We know that the per cent we are to find in this example names a rate pair whose second component is 100; therefore, we can use the following steps for this example.

$$92/460 = x/100.$$
$$9200 = 460x.$$
$$9200 \div 460 = x.$$
$$20 = x.$$

Thus, we know that the replacement for x in $92/460 = x/100$ is 20 and that $20/100 = 20\%$. So, 20% of Mr. King's orders during that month for the product were for $50 or less.

From the examples that we have given in this section, you can see that rate pairs and proportional relations are very useful in problem solving. Many kinds of problems that have been difficult for children in the past can be made quite simple when they are thought of in terms of proportional relations. Per cent problems are an especially good example of this kind of problem.

161 If apples sell at 3 for 15 cents, how much will 39 apples cost?

162 Of all the eggs Mr. Brown sells, he sells 30% of them directly to his neighbors. If he sells 210 dozen eggs monthly, how many dozen does he sell to his neighbors?

163 Beef loses 35% of its weight in dressing. How much did a steer weigh if the dressed meat weighs 611 lb.?

164 There are 35 boys and 15 girls in a given class. What per cent of the class is boys?

165 In a real-estate sale, Mr. Howard made a profit that was equal to 21% of his purchase price. Mr. Howard's profit was $840. What was his purchase price?

166 A rate of 60 miles per hour is the same as what rate in feet per minute?

167 A rate of 60 miles per hour would be the same as how many feet per second? [Hint: Use your answer to exercise 166.]

168 John received an increase of $12 per week in his salary. His original salary was $80 per week. What per cent of increase did he receive?

169 Mr. Brown buys a book for $4 and sells it for $5. His profit is what per cent of the purchase price?

170 An investment yields 5% interest annually. If the annual interest on the investment is 150 dollars, what is the principal?

171 In a certain pictorial graph, a picture of 1 cow represents 45,000 head of cattle. How many pictures of cows would be needed to represent 900,000 head of cattle? At this same rate, how many head of cattle are represented by 15 pictures of cows?

172 A store advertised a 20% discount sale. If a suit is purchased for $44, what was the original price? If the original price of an overcoat was $120, what is the sale price?

173 One dollar of American money is approximately the same as 4 Dutch guilders. About how many guilders are the same as 56 dollars?

*174 If 2 men can do a certain amount of work in 5 days, how many men would it take to do the same amount of work in 1 day?

*175 If 1 boy can see a distance of 5 miles from the top of a hill, how many miles can 3 boys see from the top of the hill?

Other kinds of relations

For the greater part of this chapter, we have been discussing a special kind of linear relation called a proportional relation. There are, of course, many other kinds of relations—both linear and non-linear—that are of interest in mathematics. In this section we will consider a few examples of some other kinds of relations.

You have probably used the following formula for "converting" centigrade temperature readings to Fahrenheit readings.

$$F = \tfrac{9}{5}C + 32.$$

We can use this formula to obtain ordered pairs of numbers of the form (c, f), where c represents the centigrade reading on a thermometer and f represents the Fahrenheit reading. Some of these number pairs are named in the chart below.

c	100	55	30	15	0
f	212	131	86	59	32

Note that we have restricted our replacements for c so that we obtain only ordered pairs of natural numbers. As a matter of fact, if we had not limited our replacements, we could also have obtained such pairs as $(-10, 14)$, $(36, 96\tfrac{4}{5})$, and $(-21, -5\tfrac{4}{5})$ from the formula. But, since we have not yet studied rational numbers, we have limited ourselves to that relation that is a subset of $N \times N$.

---

* Do not be too hasty in answering these exercises.

We can easily show that the relation obtained from the formula $F = \frac{9}{5}C + 32$ is not a proportional relation. Remember that we said that, if a relation is a proportional relation, then, for any two members of the relation represented by (a, b) and (c, d), $ad = cb$. If we choose the pairs $(100, 212)$ and $(55, 131)$, it is clear that

$$100 \times 131 \neq 55 \times 212.$$

Hence, we conclude that this relation is not a proportional relation. Although we need only one such example to decide that the relation is not a proportional relation, you might wish to choose other members of the relation to convince yourself of this fact.

An incomplete graph of the relation that we have been discussing is shown below.

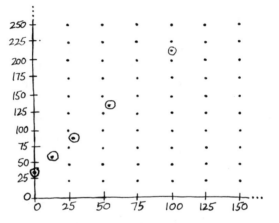

It is clear from the graph that the relation obtained from the formula $F = \frac{9}{5}C + 32$ is a linear relation, although we saw earlier that it is not a proportional relation.

As another example of a linear relation that is not a proportional relation, consider set Q, tabulated below.

$$Q = \{(0, 1), (1, 2), (2, 3), (3, 4), \ldots\}.$$

Certainly Q is a relation in N because it is a subset of N $\times$ N whose members are of the form $(n, n + 1)$. Q is also a linear relation as indicated by the incomplete graph shown on page 193. However, Q is not a proportional relation because it is not true that, for any two members of Q represented by (a, b) and (c, d), $ad = cb$. For example, for the pairs $(1, 2)$ and $(2, 3)$, $1 \times 3 \neq 2 \times 2$.

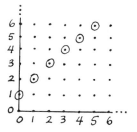

As a third example of a relation that is not a proportional relation, consider the members of N × N of the form (n, n^2). This relation, which we will call V, is tabulated below.

$$V = \{(0, 0), (1, 1), (2, 4), (3, 9), (4, 16), \ldots\}.$$

It should be evident that V is not a proportional relation; and, as the incomplete graph of V below indicates, neither is V a linear relation.

We can also obtain relations by using the ideas of "less than" or "greater than." Consider, for example, the relation in N whereby the sum of the components of each member is greater than 4. Some of the members of the relation are shown below.

$$(0, 5), (0, 6), (0, 7), \ldots$$
$$(1, 4), (1, 5), (1, 6), \ldots$$
$$(2, 3), (2, 4), (2, 5), \ldots$$
$$(3, 2), (3, 3), (3, 4), \ldots$$

An incomplete graph of this relation is shown on page 194. It should be apparent that this relation is not a linear relation and also that it is not a proportional relation.

176 Let P be a subset of N × N composed of (*a*, *b*) where *b* = 3*a* + 2. Make a graph of P. Is P a linear relation? Is P a proportional relation?

177 Let Q be the subset of N × N composed of (*a*, *b*) where the quotient of *b* and *a* is a natural number. Make a graph of Q. Is Q a linear relation? Is Q a proportional relation?

178 Let R be the subset of N × N composed of (*a*, *b*) where the product of *a* and *b* is an odd number. Make a graph of R. Is R a linear relation? Is R a proportional relation?

179 Let S be the subset of N × N composed of (*a*, *b*) where the sum of *a* and *b* is an even number. Is S a linear relation? Is S a proportional relation?

The examples that we have presented in this section should give you an idea of some of the kinds of relations that are of interest in mathematics. We conclude this chapter with a brief discussion of the properties that certain kinds of relations possess.

Properties of relations

Throughout this book we have used certain relations, such as equality, "is less than," and "is a subset of," without paying a great deal of attention to the properties of these relations. Equality is a relation in the sense that it "selects out" those ordered pairs of numbers whose first and second components are equal. Thus, set E, tabulated below, is a relation in N.

$$E = \{(0, 0), (1, 1), (2, 2), \ldots\}.$$

In Chapter 5, we did list five properties of equality. Among those properties were the three listed below. Properties equality, page 98

1) *Reflexive property:* For all *a*, *a* = *a*.
2) *Symmetric property:* For all *a* and *b*, if *a* = *b*, then *b* = *a*.
3) *Transitive property:* For all *a*, *b*, and *c*, if *a* = *b* and *b* = *c*, then *a* = *c*.

Thus, the relation of equality is reflexive, symmetric, and transitive. Any relation that has these three properties is called an *equivalence relation*. Hence, we conclude that equality is an equivalence relation.

In this chapter, we have used the relation "is equivalent to" in connection with rate pairs. We can now decide if this relation is an equivalence relation. For convenience, we will use the symbol $\sim$ to name the relation "is equivalent to." Thus, the sentence $6/4 \sim 9/6$ is read "$6/4$ is equivalent to $9/6$."

To decide if $\sim$ is an equivalence relation, we must check to see if it is reflexive, symmetric, and transitive. Certainly, each of the following is true about the members of C $\times$ C represented by a/b, c/d, and e/f.

1) For all a/b, it is true that $a/b \sim a/b$.

2) For all a/b and c/d, it is true that, if $a/b \sim c/d$, then $c/d \sim a/b$.

3) For all a/b, c/d, and e/f, it is true that, if $a/b \sim c/d$ and $c/d \sim e/f$, then $a/b \sim e/f$.

Hence, we conclude that "is equivalent to" is an equivalence relation because it has the properties of reflexivity, symmetry, and transitivity.

Another equivalence relation with which you are probably familiar is the geometric relation "is congruent to." Recall that the symbol $\cong$ is used to name the relation "is congruent to." For any given triangle ABC, certainly $\triangle ABC \cong \triangle ABC$; thus, congruence is reflexive. Further, if $\triangle ABC \cong \triangle DEF$, then $\triangle DEF \cong \triangle ABC$; thus, congruence is symmetric. Finally, if $\triangle ABC \cong \triangle DEF$ and $\triangle DEF \cong \triangle GHI$, then $\triangle ABC \cong \triangle GHI$; therefore, congruence is transitive. Because congruence has the three required properties, it is an equivalence relation.

Let us now consider some relations that are not equivalence relations. First we will examine the non-mathematical relation "is the father of." For convenience, we can assign a counting number to each person on earth. Hence, each person will have a numeral for a name. We can think of a finite subset of C $\times$ C as representing all possible pairings of people. For example, (6, 27) will represent the pair of persons who are named by the numerals 6 and 27; (5000, 1) will represent the pair named by the numerals 5000 and 1; and so on. The relation we are considering is a subset of C $\times$ C consisting of all those pairs of numbers such that the second component represents the father and the first component represents the offspring. Thus, if the pair (1, 5) is a member of this relation, this means that 5 is the father of 1. A partial tabulation of the relation "is the father of" is given below.

$$\{(1, 5), (5, 99), (55, 192), (6734, 10000), \ldots\}$$

If any pair represented by (a, b) is a member of this relation, then b is the father of a. Now we can see whether or not this relation is an equivalence relation; that is, we can see if "is the father of" is reflexive, symmetric, and transitive.

We will use a, b, and c to represent any three of the persons to whom we have assigned a number. First, it is obvious that this relation is not reflexive because any person a cannot be his own father; that is, a is the father of a is not true for any a. Next, we can determine if the relation is symmetric. The relation certainly is not symmetric because, if b is the father of a, then a is not the father of b. Finally, we see that the relation is not transitive because, if b is the father of a and c is the father of b, then c is not the father of a. Thus, because the relation "is the father of" does not have the properties of an equivalence relation—reflexivity, symmetry, and transitivity—it is not an equivalence relation.

Next let us consider the mathematical relation "is less than," which, like the equality relation, is a very important relation in elementary arithmetic. We already know that equality is an equivalence relation; we will now determine if "is less than" is an equivalence relation.

First of all, we know that "is less than" does not have the reflexive property because it is obviously not the case that, for all a, $a < a$. Secondly, "is less than" does not have the symmetric property because, if $a < b$, then it is not true that $b < a$. The relation "is less than" does, however, have the transitive property. It is true that, for all a, b, and c, if $a < b$ and $b < c$, then $a < c$.

We can conclude that, although the relation "is less than" is transitive, it is not an equivalence relation because it has neither the reflexive nor the symmetric property. Every equivalence relation must have all three of these properties; any relation that has only one or two of them is not an equivalence relation.

The relation "is less than" is called an *order* relation. We can use this relation to order the members of a set of numbers, such as the set of natural numbers. The natural-number line provides a useful geometric illustration of the order relation "is less than" in terms of "to the left of." The natural-number line pictured below shows that, if a first number is less than a second number, then the point associated with the first number is to the left of the point associated with the second number. Thus, $6 < 7$, and point 6 is to the left of point 7; $0 < 3$, and point 0 is to the left of point 3; $3 < 6$, and point 3 is to the left of point 6; and so on.

Certain other relations, such as "is a factor of" or "is a divisor of," are also of interest in arithmetic. You should be able to determine for yourself whether or not the relation "is a factor of" is an equivalence relation.

CONCLUSION

In this chapter, we considered sets of ordered pairs of numbers that have useful applications in problem solving. These sets of ordered pairs were relations in C or in N.

In the chapter that follows, we will discuss some ideas from elementary number theory. Our universe there will also be either C or N. Then, in Chapter 10, we will extend the natural-number system by including different elements in the set of numbers. But we will not find it necessary to introduce any new operations or relations.

CHAPTER QUIZ

1 Name at least ten members of the proportional relation named by each of the following ratios:

A 14%   C 8/3   E 1/11
B 6/25   D 100%   F 1/4

2 Each of the following ratios names a proportional relation. Find the per cent that belongs to the same proportional relation.

A 2/25   B 17/10   C 1/2   D 45/150   E 1/1

3 The formula for finding the area of a square is $A = s^2$. Use this formula to find some of the number pairs in C $\times$ C of the form (s, A). Then make a graph of this relation. Is this a linear relation? A proportional relation?

4 Use the form $(x, x - 1)$ to find a relation in C. Is this set a linear relation? A proportional relation? Make a graph of this relation.

5 A freely falling body will fall according to the formula $S = 16t^2$, where S represents the distance in feet that the body has fallen and t represents the time in seconds. Find how far a body will fall in one second, in two seconds, and so on up to 6 seconds. Make a graph of several numbers of this relation. Is it a linear relation?

6 The sum of two counting numbers is less than 10. Let (x, y) be the form of the number pairs whose sum is less than 10. Find all (x, y) that are contained in this relation. Then make a graph of the relation. Is this relation a subset of C $\times$ C? Is it a proportional relation?

7 Find the relations in C whose members have the following forms. Decide whether each is a linear relation and/or a proportional relation.

A (x, x) C $(x, 3)$ E $(x, x + 5)$
B $(x, 2x)$ D (x^2, x) F (x, x^2)

8 Make a graph of the set of ordered pairs of natural numbers whose sum is equal to 16.

SUPPLEMENTARY READINGS

Evenson, A. B., *Modern Mathematics: Introductory Concepts and Their Implications*. Pp. 75-110. A very complete discussion of relations from both an algebraic and a geometric point of view. Item 12 of Bibliography

May, K. O. and Van Engen, H., "Relations and Functions," *Twenty-Fourth Yearbook of NCTM*. Ch. 3, pp. 65-110. An excellent discussion of relations that emphasizes the place of number pairs in elementary and secondary school mathematics. Item 6 of Bibliography

Peterson, John and Hashisaki, J., *Theory of Arithmetic*. Pp. 37-58. A good discussion of equivalence relations and of relations as sets. Item 26 of Bibliography

The College Mathematics Staff, University of Chicago, *Concepts and Structure of Mathematics*. Chs. 6 and 7. Intended for a freshman general education course in mathematics; its discussion of relations is preceded by a treatment of sets and sentences. Item 20 of Bibliography

Van Engen, H., *et al.*, *Seeing Through Mathematics, Book 1*. Pp. 167-204. An elementary but complete treatment of proportional relations. Item 21 of Bibliography

Chapter nine

Elementary number theory

Square numbers and triangular numbers
Even numbers and odd numbers
Prime and composite numbers
The fundamental theorem of arithmetic
The greatest common divisor and the least common multiple

A study of the history of mathematics reveals that certain numbers and certain sequences of numbers have been of special interest since the beginnings of mathematics. The sources of fascination with numbers and sequences of numbers have ranged all the way from a belief in the magical properties of certain numbers to a fruitful curiosity about relationships between or among numbers. It is of interest to note that such numbers as 7 and 3 were thought to have magical significance in various cultures. For example, the ancient Greeks felt that it was by design and not by accident that there were 7 days in the week, 7 heavenly bodies, and 7 openings in the head for the eyes, ears, nose, and mouth. Similarly, the widespread belief that 3 is a magical number is probably the reason that folk tales deal with such topics as 3 bears or 3 pigs or 3 Graces.

However, it is not our purpose to discuss the mystical aspects of numbers, but rather to consider the more productive study of relationships among numbers that forms an important branch of mathematics called *number theory*. In this chapter, we will be concerned with a few of the elementary concepts of number theory. Some of the ideas will be discussed simply because they are interesting; others will be discussed not only because they are interesting, but also because they will be useful in later chapters.

In the discussion that follows, we will be working mainly with the set of natural numbers greater than 0, that is, with the set of counting numbers, set C.

Square numbers and triangular numbers

There is a considerable amount of literature that indicates that the mathematicians of ancient Greece were very much interested in number theory. In particular, they were interested in establishing relationships between number concepts and geometric concepts. This interest led to the study of "figurate" numbers. These included "square" numbers, "triangular" numbers, "rectangular" numbers, "cubic" numbers, and so on. In fact, our use of the term *square* for the second power of a number and of the term *cube* for the third power of a number stems from the Greek notion of figurate numbers. The illustration below shows some of the patterns that are associated with square numbers. Notice that each pattern has the same number of dots in each row as it has number of rows; the relationship between each of these patterns and the geometric concept of a square is obvious.

$$4 = 2^2 \qquad 9 = 3^2 \qquad 16 = 4^2 \qquad 25 = 5^2 \qquad 36 = 6^2$$

A few of the patterns associated with triangular numbers are illustrated below. Again, with the exception of the pattern for 1, the relationship between each of these patterns and the geometric concept of a triangle is evident.

$$1 \qquad 3 \qquad 6 \qquad 10 \qquad 15$$

The Greeks also developed other patterns for figurate numbers, but the examples of square numbers and triangular numbers are sufficient to illustrate the idea.

If we compare the successive patterns of the triangular numbers, we can observe an interesting relationship between the sequence of numbers and the sequence of patterns. For example, notice that the pattern for 6 contains one more row of dots than the pattern for 3 and that this additional row contains one more dot than the second row of the pattern for 3. Now let us express each of the numbers as a sum in terms of the number of dots in each row of dots, beginning with the top row. Thus, we express 3 and 6 as sums in the following way:

$$3 = 1 + 2.$$
$$6 = 1 + 2 + 3.$$

We can carry this correspondence between the sequence of patterns and the sequence of numbers further by observing that the pattern for 10 has one more row of dots, with one more dot in this row, than the pattern for 6. Thus, we can express the triangular number 10 as a sum in the following way:

$$10 = 1 + 2 + 3 + 4.$$

Similarly, on the basis of the pattern of dots, we can express 15 as a sum:

$$15 = 1 + 2 + 3 + 4 + 5.$$

Although none of the patterns beyond 15 is exhibited, you can assume that the patterns continue in the same fashion. In the table below, we have expressed each of the first 10 triangular numbers (except 1) as a sum in terms of its pattern of dots.

$$1 = 1.$$
$$1 + 2 = 3.$$
$$1 + 2 + 3 = 6.$$
$$1 + 2 + 3 + 4 = 10.$$
$$1 + 2 + 3 + 4 + 5 = 15.$$
$$1 + 2 + 3 + 4 + 5 + 6 = 21.$$
$$1 + 2 + 3 + 4 + 5 + 6 + 7 = 28.$$
$$1 + 2 + 3 + 4 + 5 + 6 + 7 + 8 = 36.$$
$$1 + 2 + 3 + 4 + 5 + 6 + 7 + 8 + 9 = 45.$$
$$1 + 2 + 3 + 4 + 5 + 6 + 7 + 8 + 9 + 10 = 55.$$

The information given in the table should suggest to you that the sum of the first n counting numbers will be a triangular number; that is, if you find the sum of the first seven, or the first fifteen, or the first one hundred counting numbers, you will obtain a triangular number. In fact, we can use the idea to give a "modern" or algebraic definition of a triangular number.

(We call this an algebraic definition to contrast it with the Greek definition, which was based upon the notion of a geometric pattern of dots.)

In the following illustration, we have again displayed some of the patterns for the triangular numbers. This time, however, we have combined pairs of consecutive patterns. In each case, we have "fitted" the pattern of the lesser triangular number with the pattern of the greater number so that the resulting pattern is a square.

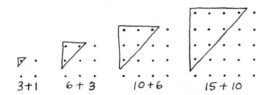

$$3+1 \qquad 6+3 \qquad 10+6 \qquad 15+10$$

This diagram suggests that the sum of any two consecutive triangular numbers is a square number. Let us see if the results we find when we consider the numbers themselves correspond with the results we obtained from the geometric patterns. In the statements expressed below, we have expressed each triangular number (except 1) as a sum as we did in the table on page 201.

$$1 + (1 + 2) = 4 = 2^2.$$
$$(1 + 2) + (1 + 2 + 3) = 9 = 3^2.$$
$$(1 + 2 + 3) + (1 + 2 + 3 + 4) = 16 = 4^2.$$
$$(1 + 2 + 3 + 4) + (1 + 2 + 3 + 4 + 5) = 25 = 5^2.$$
$$(1 + 2 + 3 + 4 + 5) + (1 + 2 + 3 + 4 + 5 + 6) = 36 = 6^2.$$

You should consider several more examples like those given in the table to convince yourself that the sum of any two consecutive triangular numbers is a square number. We can state this concept in another way: We can use the definition of a triangular number as the sum of the first n counting numbers. To do this, we can take the last statement expressed above and use some of the properties of the natural-number system to arrive at a slightly different way of expressing this sum. The sentence is repeated below.

$$(1 + 2 + 3 + 4 + 5) + (1 + 2 + 3 + 4 + 5 + 6) = 36 = 6^2.$$

From your knowledge of the associative property of addition, you know that the way in which the numbers are grouped does not affect the sum. Thus, we obtain Associative property of addition, page 87

$$(1 + 2 + 3 + 4 + 5) + (1 + 2 + 3 + 4 + 5) + 6 = 36 = 6^2.$$

Note that the two expressions within parentheses are the same, so we can use the distributive property to obtain $\quad$ Distributive property, page 95

$$2(1 + 2 + 3 + 4 + 5) + 6 = 36 = 6^2.$$

All of the statements about the sum of any two consecutive triangular numbers expressed on page 202 can be put in this form. So we can make the following generalization in terms of any counting number n. If you multiply the number that is the sum of the first n counting numbers by 2 and add $n + 1$ to this product, you obtain the square of $n + 1$; that is, $2(1 + 2 + \ldots + n) + (n + 1) = (n + 1)^2$. We will accept this property of counting numbers without proof. You should examine a few cases to convince yourself that the generalization given in this paragraph does hold.

We now know that the sum of any two consecutive triangular numbers is a square number. It would seem reasonable to ask, "Is the sum of any two consecutive square numbers a square number?" We can see immediately that the answer is "no" because $2^2 + 3^2 = 4 + 9 = 13$, and 13 is not a square number. From this observation, the question might now arise as to whether or not there are any cases in which the sum of two consecutive square numbers is a square number. We can easily find one case in which this is true. Thus,

$$3^2 + 4^2 = 9 + 16 = 25 = 5^2.$$

Next, we might ask if there is more than one case in which the sum of two consecutive square numbers is a square number.

Because of space limitations, we will not carry the discussion of triangular numbers and square numbers any further. So, we leave this last question unanswered. We raised the question simply to give you an idea of the kinds of questions that can be asked about sets of numbers such as the set of square numbers or the set of triangular numbers. This discussion should also indicate to you that the study of number theory is especially interesting because very often a satisfactory answer to one question may become the basis for another question so that, in solving one problem, you may be led to an even more interesting problem. In the next section, we will discuss some of the problems of number theory that are associated with even and odd numbers.

180 List the names of the first 20 triangular numbers.

181 Assume that the sum of the first n counting numbers may be represented as $\dfrac{n(n + 1)}{2}$. Find the 100th triangular number. Find the 123rd, the 1000th, and the 123lst triangular numbers.

182 Again assume that the expression $\dfrac{n(n+1)}{2}$ represents the sum of the first n counting numbers. Use expressions to show that the sum of any two consecutive triangular numbers is a square number.

183 The seventeenth-century French mathematician Fermat proved that every counting number greater than 1 can be expressed as the sum of at most three triangular numbers. Verify this for every counting number from 2 to 25.

184 If the numbers 0 and 1 are included in the set of square numbers, then it has been proved that every counting number can be expressed as the sum of exactly four square numbers. Verify this result for every counting number up to 25.

185 Besides the square and triangular numbers, there also are numbers that the Greeks called "rectangular numbers." The patterns for these numbers are formed by including one more dot in each row than there are numbers of rows. Some examples are shown below.

Determine the 1000th rectangular number. [There is a hard way and there is an easy way to do this!]

186 Determine the expression for the nth rectangular number, as defined in exercise 185.

187 If we admit the number zero as the first triangular number, T_1, and also as the first square number, S_1, then we can form the sequence of "pentagonal numbers" $T_1 + S_2$, $T_2 + S_3$, $T_3 + S_4$, $T_4 + S_5$, ... Find the first 20 members of this sequence.

188 Using the expressions for the nth triangular number and the $(n+1)$st square number, develop an expression for the nth pentagonal number. [Keep in mind that including zero in the set of triangular numbers and in the set of square numbers will make a difference in the expressions you use.]

189 If we admit the number zero as the first pentagonal number, then we might conjecture that every counting number may be expressed as the sum of exactly five pentagonal numbers. Test this conjecture for the counting numbers up to 20.

Even numbers and odd numbers

In the child's study of arithmetic, he first encounters elementary number theory when he studies some of the basic properties of even and odd counting numbers. You are already familiar with many of these properties. For example, you know that an even counting number is a number that is divisible by 2 so that the remainder is 0. Another way of saying this is to say that the counting number a is an even number if there is some other counting number b for which it is true that $a = 2b$. You also know that every counting number that is not an even number is an odd number. In general, you can use the expression $2n$ to represent any even number and the expression $2n + 1$ to represent any odd number. The universe for n in $2n$ is the set of counting numbers, and the universe for n in $2n + 1$ is the set of natural numbers. In other words, zero is not considered an even number in the following discussion.

From the preceding paragraph, it is apparent that every counting number is either an even number or an odd number; no counting number is a member of both the set of even numbers and the set of odd numbers. Hence, we can arrive at a conclusion concerning the set of even numbers and the set of odd numbers, both of which are tabulated below: These sets are a partition of the entire set of counting numbers into two disjoint subsets.

Partition, page 182

Disjoint sets, page 20

The set of even numbers is:

$$\{2, 4, 6, 8, 10, \ldots\}.$$

The set of odd numbers is:

$$\{1, 3, 5, 7, 9, \ldots\}.$$

We can ask many interesting questions about these two sets. For example, we might ask if the sum of two even numbers is always an even number, that is, if the set of even numbers is closed under the operation of addition. Certainly, if we consider specific pairs of even numbers, such as 2 and 6, or 8 and 24, or 100 and 48, we find that the sum is another even number. But we can show more generally that the sum of two even numbers is an even number by using $2a$ and $2b$ to represent any two even numbers. Remember that the universe for a and b is C, the set of counting numbers. We want to decide if the sum of $2a$ and $2b$ is an even number, no matter what replacements are used for a and b. This is very easy to show by using the distributive property of multiplication over addition. By using the distributive property, we know that

Closure of addition, page 87

$$2a + 2b = 2(a + b).$$

But we also know that $2(a + b)$ is an even number. This is the case because the product of 2 and the counting number $a + b$ is by definition an even number. Thus, we can conclude that the sum of any two even numbers is an even number.

Next, let us see what kind of generalization, if any, we can make about the sum of any two odd numbers. If we examine specific examples, such as $1 + 3$, $9 + 15$, $77 + 103$, and so on, it appears that the sum of two odd numbers is an even number. We can again use variables to show that this is indeed the case. Suppose that any two odd numbers are represented by $2m + 1$ and $2n + 1$, where m and n are natural numbers. We want to show that the sum of $2m + 1$ and $2n + 1$ is an even number. We can do this by using the closure, commutative, associative, and distributive properties. Properties of natural numbers, page 96

First we know that

$$(2m + 1) + (2n + 1) = 2m + 1 + 2n + 1.$$

By the commutative property, we obtain

$$2m + 1 + 2n + 1 = 2m + 2n + 1 + 1.$$

By the associative property, we obtain

$$2m + 2n + 1 + 1 = (2m + 2n) + (1 + 1).$$

Then, because $1 + 1 = 2 = 2 \cdot 1$, we can use the substitution property of equality to obtain Substitution property of equality, page 99

$$(2m + 2n) + (1 + 1) = 2(m + n) + 2 \cdot 1.$$

Again using the distributive property, we obtain

$$2(m + n) + 2 \cdot 1 = 2[(m + n) + 1].$$

Finally, since $(m + n) + 1$ is a counting number, we know that $2[(m + n) + 1]$ is even because it is the product of a counting number and 2. Hence, we know that the sum of any two odd numbers is an even number.

Many generalizations can be made about the sums and products of even and odd numbers. Since you will establish some of these generalizations in the exercises at the end of this section, we will consider now another important property of the set of odd numbers.

We have already established that the sum of any two odd numbers is an even number. Let us see what happens when we find the sum of the first two odd numbers, of the first three odd numbers, of the first four odd numbers, and so on. The table at the top of the next page shows the sums that are obtained for all of the odd numbers through 15.

$1 + 3 = 4 = 2^2.$
$1 + 3 + 5 = 9 = 3^2.$
$1 + 3 + 5 + 7 = 16 = 4^2.$
$1 + 3 + 5 + 7 + 9 = 25 = 5^2.$
$1 + 3 + 5 + 7 + 9 + 11 = 36 = 6^2.$
$1 + 3 + 5 + 7 + 9 + 11 + 13 = 49 = 7^2.$
$1 + 3 + 5 + 7 + 9 + 11 + 13 + 15 = 64 = 8^2.$

Note that, in each case, the sum is a square number. But also notice that the sum of the first *two* odd numbers is 2^2, the sum of the first *three* odd numbers is 3^2, the sum of the first *four* odd numbers is 4^2, and so on. We will accept, without proving it, the generalization that the sum of the first n odd numbers is equal to n^2, where n represents a counting number. We can easily establish that the even numbers do not share this property simply by noting that the sum of the first two even numbers $(2 + 4)$ is not the square of a counting number.

Many of the ideas presented in this section are easily discovered and understood by children in the elementary school. In fact, children are usually fascinated by such relationships among numbers, and their enjoyment of arithmetic can be enhanced by the inclusion of these and similar relationships in the arithmetic program.

190 Choose any square number, such as 64, and subtract the odd numbers in succession, beginning with 1; that is, first subtract 1 from 64, then 3 from 63, then 5 from 60, and so on. Continue this process until you obtain a difference that is less than the last odd number you subtracted. What is this last difference? Try several examples to see if the results are always the same.

191 Show that the sum of an odd and an even number is an odd number.

192 Show that the product of any two even numbers is an even number.

193 Show that the square of an odd number must be an odd number.

194 Show that the square of an even number plus one is an odd number.

195 Show that any number obtained from the expression $3n + 1$ when n is replaced with an even number must be an odd number.

Prime and composite numbers

Knowledge of prime numbers extends a long way back in the history of mathematics, and many mathematicians have been interested in discovering and establishing various properties of prime numbers. Before we can discuss these properties, we must agree upon precise definitions of prime and composite numbers; but, before we give these definitions, we will discuss what we mean when we talk about the divisors or factors of a number. The expressions "2 is a divisor of 6," "2 divides 6," "6 is divisible by 2," and "2 is a factor of 6" all refer to the same relation between the numbers 2 and 6. The first three expressions emphasize the fact that the *quotient* of 6 and 2 is a counting number, while the last expression emphasizes the fact that the *product* of 2 and some counting number is 6. The sentence below expresses the idea that 2 is a divisor of 6. This sentence is read "two divides six." Throughout this chapter, the symbol $a\,|\,b$ will be used to express the idea that the counting number a divides the counting number b, or a is a factor of b.

$$2\,|\,6.$$

From the preceding discussion, it follows that, for any two counting numbers represented by a and b, if $a\,|\,b$, then a is a factor of b. Also, if a is a factor of b, then $a\,|\,b$. We can define "divides," or "is a factor of," in the following way.

Let a and b be counting numbers. Then $a\,|\,b$ means
that there is a counting number n such that $a \cdot n = b$.

Next we can use some properties of the counting numbers, which are a subset of the natural numbers, to establish certain properties of "divides." The universe is the set of counting numbers. First, we want to establish that, if a given number a divides both the numbers b and c, then a also divides the sum of b and c.

We know that, if $a\,|\,b$, then, for some counting number n,

$$a \cdot n = b.$$

We also know that, if $a\,|\,c$, then, for some counting number m,

$$a \cdot m = c.$$

Next, we can use the addition property of equality to obtain

Addition property of equality, page 98

$$a \cdot n + a \cdot m = b + c.$$

Then, by the distributive property, we know that $a \cdot n + a \cdot m = a \cdot (n + m)$. Therefore, we obtain

$$a \cdot (n + m) = b + c.$$

But we know that n and m are both counting numbers. Thus, by the closure property of addition, $(n + m)$ is a counting number. So, from the statement $a \cdot (n + m) = b + c$, we know that $b + c$ is the product of a and the counting number $(n + m)$. Hence, from the definition of "divides"

Closure of addition, page 87

that was given earlier, we know that a divides $b + c$. We can use symbols to express the property that we have just established.

If $a|b$ and $a|c$, then $a|(b + c)$.

You should consider several specific examples to illustrate this property of "divides."

In proving another property of "divides" we will again use the definition we gave of $a|b$. We want to show that, if a divides b and if b divides c, then a divides c. First of all, from the definition of $a|b$, we know that, if $a|b$, then, for some counting number n,

$$a \cdot n = b.$$

Also, if $b|c$, then, for some counting number m,

$$b \cdot m = c.$$

We can now use the multiplication property of equality, together with the statement $a \cdot n = b$, to obtain

Multiplication property of equality, page 98

$$(a \cdot n) \cdot m = b \cdot m.$$

We know that $b \cdot m = c$, so, by the transitive property of equality, we obtain

Transitive property, page 98

$$(a \cdot n) \cdot m = c.$$

Then, by the associative property of multiplication, we obtain

Associative property of multiplication, page 92

$$a \cdot (n \cdot m) = c.$$

Because n and m are counting numbers, we know by the closure property of multiplication that $(n \cdot m)$ is also a counting number. Therefore, the statement $a \cdot (n \cdot m) = c$ means that c is equal to the product of a and the counting number $(n \cdot m)$. Hence, from the meaning of "divides," we know that a divides c. The property that we have just established may be expressed as follows.

Closure of multiplication, page 92

If $a|b$ and $b|c$, then $a|c$.

Again, you should consider some examples to test this generalization.

We will prove one more property of "divides" before we define prime and composite numbers. This property is an important one that enables us to conclude that, if a divides b and if b divides a, then a and b are equal.

From the meaning of "divides," we know that, if $a|b$, then, for some counting number n,

$$a \cdot n = b.$$

Also, if $b|a$, then, for some counting number m,

$$b \cdot m = a.$$

Next, by the multiplication property of equality, we know that, because $b \cdot m = a$,

$$(b \cdot m) \cdot n = a \cdot n.$$

Because $a \cdot n = b$, we can use the transitive property of equality to obtain

$$(b \cdot m) \cdot n = b.$$

Next, by the associative property of multiplication, we obtain

$$b \cdot (m \cdot n) = b.$$

From the identity-element property of multiplication, we know that, if the product of b and $(m \cdot n)$ is b, then $(m \cdot n)$ must be 1. If $m \cdot n = 1$, then both m and n must be 1 because, if the product of two counting numbers is 1, then each of the numbers must be 1. Thus, we can replace the n in $a \cdot n = b$ or the m in $b \cdot m = a$ by 1, to obtain

Identity element for multiplication, page 95

$$a \cdot 1 = b,$$
or
$$b \cdot 1 = a.$$

From either of these statements and the identity-element property of multiplication, we conclude that

$$a = b.$$

The generalization that we have just proved is expressed below.

If $a|b$ and $b|a$, then $a = b$.

By the identity-element property for multiplication, for every a,

$$1 \cdot a = a.$$

Using the definition that we gave for the "divides" relation, we know that this also means that, for every a,

$$1|a.$$

Thus, 1 is a divisor of, or a factor of, every counting number.

We can use the commutative property of multiplication to obtain the statement expressed below from $1 \cdot a = a$.

$$a \cdot 1 = a.$$

Again, we use the meaning of "divides" to obtain

$$a|a.$$

Hence, we can conclude that every counting number is a divisor of, or a factor of, itself.

Now that we have established the meaning of the terms "divides," "is a divisor of," and "is a factor of," we can define a *prime number* and a *composite number*.

A prime number is a counting number that has
exactly two divisors.

A composite number is a counting number that has
more than two divisors.

We can now use these definitions to determine whether or not any given counting number is a prime number or a composite number. Let us consider some examples. First, we will determine whether 6 is prime or composite. Each of the following is a true statement about 6.

$$1 \mid 6.$$
$$2 \mid 6.$$
$$3 \mid 6.$$
$$6 \mid 6.$$

Thus, we know that $\{1, 2, 3, 6\}$ is the set of divisors of 6. From this, we conclude that 6 is a composite number because it has more than two divisors. In the table below, we have named several counting numbers, tabulated the set of divisors of each number, and indicated whether the number is prime or composite.

Counting number	Set of divisors	Prime or composite
4	$\{1, 2, 4\}$	composite
5	$\{1, 5\}$	prime
9	$\{1, 3, 9\}$	composite
11	$\{1, 11\}$	prime
12	$\{1, 2, 3, 4, 6, 12\}$	composite
21	$\{1, 3, 7, 21\}$	composite
23	$\{1, 23\}$	prime

If you examine the sets of divisors of the prime numbers in the table, you should be able to determine what the two divisors of a prime number must be. First of all, every counting number—whether prime or composite—is divisible by itself and 1. Because every prime number has exactly two divisors, it follows that these two divisors will always be the number itself and 1.

It should also be apparent that every counting number greater than 1 is either a prime number or a composite number because either the number has exactly two divisors or it has more than two divisors. We make an exception of 1 because 1 has only one divisor—namely, 1. Thus, 1 is neither prime (because it does not have exactly two divisors) nor composite (because it does not have more than two divisors).

We can use the notion of prime and composite numbers to partition the set of counting numbers into these three disjoint subsets:

    a) The set whose member is 1
    b) The set of prime numbers
    c) The set of composite numbers.

One of the earliest references to prime numbers and to a method for determining which numbers are prime occurs in the work of the Greek scientist and mathematician Eratosthenes, who lived in the third century B.C. Eratosthenes devised a technique for finding primes, which is called the "Sieve of Eratosthenes." The diagram below illustrates how this method may be used to locate all of the primes between 1 and 100.

Note that the chart contains numerals for all of the counting numbers from 2, which is the first prime number, through 100. The numerals that have been crossed out represent composite numbers. They were determined by a simple procedure. First, every second numeral after the numeral 2 was crossed out because each of these numerals represents a number that is divisible by 2. Thus, each of these numbers is obviously a composite number because it has at least three factors—1, 2, and the number itself. Next, every third numeral after the numeral 3 was crossed out because each of these numerals represents a number that is divisible by 3 and is therefore composite. (Some of these numerals, such as 6 and 12, were already crossed out because they represent numbers that are also divisible by 2.)

The numeral 4 and all of the numerals for numbers that are divisible by 4 were already crossed out because every number that is divisible by 4 is also divisible by 2. Next, every fifth numeral after the numeral 5 was crossed out because each of these numerals represents a number that is divisible by 5. The numeral 6 and all the numerals for numbers that are divisible by 6 were already crossed out because every number divisible by 6 is also divisible by 2 and by 3. Next, every seventh numeral after 7 was crossed out because each of these numerals represents a number that is divisible by 7. This process was continued until all the numerals for numbers with 3 or more divisors had been crossed out. Thus, the numerals that have not been crossed out represent numbers that have exactly two factors; that is, they represent prime numbers.

There are two observations that can be made immediately from the chart. First, it is apparent that every even number greater than 2 is a composite number because it has at least 3 factors; thus, 2 is the only even number that is also a prime number. Second, although every prime greater than 2 is an odd number, it is certainly not true that every odd number is a prime number. The odd numbers that have other odd numbers as divisors are not prime, but composite.

The set of 25 prime numbers between 1 and 100, which are shown in the chart, is tabulated below.

{2, 3, 5, 7, 11, 13, 17, 19, 23, 29, 31, 37, 41, 43, 47,
53, 59, 61, 67, 71, 73, 79, 83, 89, 97}

One of the first questions that you might ask concerning the set of all prime numbers is whether the set is finite or infinite. Euclid, a Greek mathematician of the fourth century B.C., first proved that the set of all primes is infinite. This proof requires certain properties of prime and composite numbers not discussed here, so we will not present it.

We will now examine the set of primes between 1 and 100 more closely to see what relationships we can observe. Note that the primes 2 and 3 are the only consecutive counting numbers in the set. In fact, we can use our knowledge of even and odd numbers to show that 2 and 3 are the only consecutive counting numbers that are also primes in the entire set of counting numbers. This is true because, for any two consecutive counting numbers, one of the numbers must be even and the other must be odd. But we know that 2 is the only even prime; hence, we conclude that 2 and 3 must be the only two consecutive counting numbers that are both primes.

Notice that, in the set of primes between 1 and 100, there are several pairs of primes whose difference is 2. The primes of each of these pairs have exactly one counting number between them. A pair of primes whose

difference is 2 are called *twin primes*. Examples of twin primes are 3 and
5 and 5 and 7. You can find other examples of twin primes in the set tabulated on page 213. There are, of course, examples of twin primes beyond
100, such as 101 and 103, 137 and 139, 191 and 193; and it would seem
that the set of twin primes might be an infinite set. However, no one has
yet proved either that this set is infinite or that it is finite.

So far we have observed that there is only one pair of primes whose
difference is 1 and that there are a number of pairs of primes whose
difference is 2. We can also find consecutive pairs of primes, with no
primes between them, whose difference is very great. We will now develop
a method for finding a sequence of counting numbers that contains a great
many members and that does not contain a prime number.

To find a sequence of counting numbers that does not contain a prime,
we need to introduce a new symbol that is widely used in mathematics.
This symbol is an exclamation point. When this symbol is used with a
numeral, it represents the product of the number named and every counting number less than the given number. It is called the *factorial symbol*. For
example, the symbol 4!, shown below, which is read "four factorial,"
represents the product $4 \cdot 3 \cdot 2 \cdot 1$. Similarly, $6! = 6 \cdot 5 \cdot 4 \cdot 3 \cdot 2 \cdot 1$,

$$4!$$

and 10! is equal to the product of the first 10 counting numbers. We can
use this new notation to develop a sequence of 99 consecutive counting
numbers that does not contain a prime number.

To help us construct this sequence of numbers, we will use the symbol
100! to represent the number that is the product of the first 100 counting
numbers. The first number in our sequence is the sum of 100! and 2; that
is, the sum of the product of the first 100 counting numbers and 2. The
second number in the sequence is the sum of 100! and 3, the third is the
sum of 100! and 4, and so on. The sequence that we have in mind is indicated below:

$$100! + 2, \ 100! + 3, \ 100! + 4, \ 100! + 5, \ \ldots, \ 100! + 100$$

This is a sequence of 99 consecutive counting numbers, none of which is
prime. We can show that none of these numbers is prime in the following
way: The first number in the sequence is divisible by 2 because both 100!
(which contains 2 as one of its factors) and 2 are divisible by 2. We established earlier in this chapter the generalization that, if $a \mid b$ and $a \mid c$, then
$a \mid b + c$; thus, we know that 2 divides $100! + 2$ because it divides both
100! and 2. Similarly, 3 divides both 100! (which contains 3 as one of its
factors) and 3; therefore, by the same generalization, 3 divides $100! + 3$.

100! + 4 is divisible by 4 by the same reasoning, 100! + 5 is divisible by 5, and so on, throughout the entire sequence. Thus we know that each number in the sequence has at least 3 divisors, and that we have constructed a sequence of 99 consecutive counting numbers that does not contain a prime number. You should be able to construct a sequence of 999 numbers, none of which is prime, by using 1000!. The first number in this sequence would be 1000! + 2, and the last would be 1000! + 1000. In this manner, we can determine very large "gaps" in the set of counting numbers between any two prime numbers. However, this does not mean that we can ever determine a counting number so great that no prime number greater than the given number exists.

Another interesting question concerning prime numbers that has not yet been answered satisfactorily is the question, "Can every even number greater than 2 be expressed as the sum of 2 primes?" This question was first posed by a Russian mathematician named Goldbach in 1742, and is known as Goldbach's Conjecture. If we consider a few examples, it does seem to be the case that every even number greater than 2 can be expressed as the sum of 2 primes; for example $4 = 2 + 2$, $6 = 3 + 3$, $8 = 3 + 5$, $36 = 31 + 5$, $96 = 83 + 13$, and so on. No one has yet been able to determine an even number that cannot be expressed in this way, but neither has anyone been able to prove that this will always be the case.

We often have discussed a property of natural numbers or of prime numbers in terms of specific examples. We have shown that the generalization holds true for several specific cases and then have *accepted* the property without giving a formal proof of it. However, it seems appropriate at this time to warn you that the fact that a generalization holds true for specific examples by no means constitutes a *proof* of the generalization. We can use an example of a generalization concerning the set of prime numbers to illustrate this point.

Suppose that, on the basis of several examples, we assume that every odd number greater than 1 can be expressed as the sum of a prime number and a power of 2. We might then check several more examples to test our assumption; thus, $3 = 2^0 + 2$, $5 = 2^1 + 3$, $7 = 2^2 + 3$, $9 = 2^2 + 5$, $13 = 2^3 + 5$, $39 = 2^5 + 7$, and so on. If we find satisfactory results for enough examples, we might be tempted to conclude that our assumption was correct and thus to decide that we have "proved" that every odd number greater than 1 can be expressed as the sum of a power of 2 and a prime number. However, it is not the case that 149 can be expressed in this way. Whether or not there are other odd numbers for which the generalization is not valid is not important. One example for which the assumption does not hold (called a "counter-example") is sufficient to show that the generalization is not a valid one. Thus, the fact that we can cite many examples for which a generalization holds true does not guarantee that the generalization holds true for *all* examples. Many generalizations that would appear to be easily proved because they are "reasonable" are often very difficult to prove—and, indeed, are not always as reasonable as they first appear.*

196 Show that 149 cannot be expressed as the sum of a power of 2 and a prime number.

197 Determine 10 even numbers between 50 and 150 that can be expressed as the sum of two prime numbers.

198 Construct a sequence of 12 consecutive counting numbers that does not contain a prime number.

199 Replace n in the expression $2n^2 + 29$ by 1, 2, 3, 4, 5, and 6. What counting numbers do you obtain? What conjecture might you make about the numbers obtained from this expression? Give a counter-example to show that this conjecture is not true.

The fundamental theorem of arithmetic

Closely related to the idea of determining the divisors of a number is the notion of determining ways of expressing a number as a product of a subset of its set of divisors. Below, we have shown several ways of expressing 60 as a product of two or more members of its set of divisors, or factors.

$$60 = 2 \cdot 30.$$
$$60 = 15 \cdot 4.$$
$$60 = 12 \cdot 5.$$
$$60 = 10 \cdot 3 \cdot 2.$$
$$60 = 2 \cdot 2 \cdot 5 \cdot 3.$$

You should be able to think of several ways, other than those given above, of expressing 60 as a product of a subset of its set of divisors. Notice that, in the last sentence above, 60 is expressed as a product in terms of its *prime* factors. In each of the other sentences, at least one of the factors is not a prime factor.

It has been established that every composite number can be expressed as a product of two or more prime numbers. The question in which we are

---

* "The Remarkable Lore of Prime Numbers," Martin Gardner, *Scientific American*, March, 1964, pages 120-128. This article contains some fascinating recent discoveries about prime numbers. Item 40 of Bibliography

now interested is whether or not any composite number can be expressed as the product of primes in more than one way. In the example that we have been considering, the question would be to determine if there is some combination of prime numbers, other than 2, 2, 5, and 3, whose product is equal to 60.

In this discussion, we are not concerned with the order in which the factors are named; this means that we would not consider $2 \cdot 5 \cdot 2 \cdot 3$ to be a different way of expressing 60 as the product of primes. It would seem likely that, for every composite number, there is just one way of expressing the number as the product of primes. But, as we cautioned earlier in this chapter, some generalizations that "seem likely" may be false. In fact, it is possible to construct sets of numbers containing "prime" and "composite" numbers for which it is not true that every composite number in the set can be expressed as the product of primes in just one way. We will now proceed to construct such a set.

Consider the following set of numbers as the universe for this discussion:

$$\{1, 4, 7, 10, 13, 16, 19, 22, 25, 28, 31, 34, 37, 40, 43, 46, 49,$$
$$52, 55, 58, 61, 64, 67, 70, 73, 76, 79, 82, 85, 88, 91, 94, 97,$$
$$100, 103, \ldots\}$$

This set is an infinite set of numbers that includes every third member of the set of counting numbers, beginning with 1. For the sake of the discussion, we are going to assume that such numbers as 2, 3, 5, 6, 8, and so on, do not exist—at least, they are not in our universe. Note that, because 2 is not contained in the set, 4 now fits the definition of a prime number, with divisors 1 and 4. Similarly, 22 is a prime number, with divisors 1 and 22. In the table below and on the next page, we have classified each number in the set, from 4 through 103, according to whether it is prime or composite. In this set, just as in the set of counting numbers, 1 is neither prime nor composite because it has only one divisor. For each composite number, we have named the divisors in parentheses.

4 prime	28 composite (1, 4, 7, 28)
7 prime	31 prime
10 prime	34 prime
13 prime	37 prime
16 composite (1, 4, 16)	40 composite (1, 4, 10, 40)
19 prime	43 prime
22 prime	46 prime
25 prime	49 composite (1, 7, 49)

52 composite (1, 4, 13, 52)	79 prime
55 prime	82 prime
58 prime	85 prime
61 prime	88 composite (1, 4, 22, 88)
64 composite (1, 4, 16, 64)	91 composite (1, 7, 13, 91)
67 prime	94 prime
70 composite (1, 7, 10, 70)	97 prime
73 prime	100 composite (1, 4, 10, 25, 100)
76 composite (1, 4, 19, 76)	103 prime

Of course, the members of this set go on indefinitely, but we have classified enough of the members for the purpose we have in mind. Remember that our original objective was to construct a set of numbers in which a composite number could be expressed as the product of primes in more than one way. Note that the divisors of the composite number 100 are 1, 4, 10, 25, and 100. Thus, 100 can be expressed as a product in the following three ways:

$$100 = 1 \times 100.$$
$$100 = 4 \times 25.$$
$$100 = 10 \times 10.$$

In the first statement, 100 has not been expressed as the product of primes because neither 1 nor 100 is prime. In the second statement, 100 has been expressed as the product of primes because both 4 and 25 are prime numbers in the set with which we are working. Similarly, in the third statement, 100 has been expressed as the product of primes because 10 is a prime number in the set. Thus, in the set of numbers tabulated on page 217, the number 100 can be expressed as the product of prime numbers in two ways, as 4×25 and as 10×10.

At the beginning of this section, we remarked that it might seem obvious that every composite number in the set of counting numbers can be expressed as the product of primes in just one way. We then proceeded to develop a set of numbers for which it is not true that every composite number in the set can be expressed as the product of primes in just one way. We did this to show that some ideas that seem "obvious" on the surface are perhaps more complex or more far-reaching than they first appear to be. However, it is true that every composite number in the set of counting numbers can be expressed as the product of primes in just one way. There are several rather complicated proofs of this property, which we will not present in this text. Instead, we will accept without proof this property, which is known as the *fundamental theorem of arithmetic*. It can be expressed as shown at the top of the next page.

If the order of the factors is disregarded,
every composite number in the set of counting numbers
can be expressed as the product of prime numbers
in just one way.

We often use the fundamental theorem of arithmetic without really being aware that we are using it. We will make use of it in later chapters of this book. Note that this theorem emphasizes the importance of the prime numbers in the set of natural numbers because it establishes the idea that every number that is not prime can be expressed in terms of primes.

200 Find the prime factors of the following counting numbers.

a 54	**d** 75	**g** 363	**j** 168	**m** 432
b 120	**e** 225	**h** 343	**k** 963	**n** 504
c 576	**f** 840	**i** 1009	**l** 3564	**o** 8619

201 Consider the following subset of the counting numbers

$$S = \{1, 5, 9, 13, 17, 21, 25, 29, 33, \ldots\}.$$

Name 4 numbers that are prime in set S, but are not prime in the set of counting numbers.

202 In set S, described in exercise 201, find pairs of factors for 225. Find a prime factorization for 225. Is this prime factorization unique?

203 Find a prime factorization in set S of each of the following numbers.

    a 105   **b** 81   **c** 189   **d** 441

204 Is prime factorization unique in S?

The greatest common divisor and the least common multiple

We now turn our attention to two other important ideas in number theory that concern the fundamental theorem of arithmetic. Both of these ideas were once included in the arithmetic program of the elementary school. However, they were eliminated from the arithmetic program in the 1920's because they were thought to be unnecessary and difficult concepts. But they are very useful concepts, and, if properly presented, they are not too difficult for children to understand.

One of these ideas is the *greatest common divisor* of two or more numbers. As the name indicates, the greatest common divisor is the greatest number that is a divisor of each of the numbers. Often, the initials "gcd" are used in mathematical literature as an abbreviated name for the greatest common divisor. We will discuss several methods of determining the greatest common divisor of two or more numbers.

One method of finding the gcd is to tabulate the set of divisors of each number and to observe what number or numbers the sets have in common. The greatest number that is a member of all the sets is the gcd of the numbers. Suppose, for example, you want to find the gcd of 12 and 18. The set of divisors of each of these numbers is tabulated below.

$$12: \{1, 2, 3, 4, 6, 12\}$$
$$18: \{1, 2, 3, 6, 9, 18\}$$

The intersection of the set of divisors of 12 and the set of divisors of 18 is the set of common divisors of the two numbers. The set tabulated below is the set of common divisors of 12 and 18.

Intersection of sets, page 21

$$\{1, 2, 3, 6\}$$

Because 6 is the greatest member of the set of common divisors of 12 and 18, the gcd of these two numbers is 6.

You can also find the greatest common divisor of two or more numbers by first expressing each number as the product of its prime divisors. For example, suppose that we want to find the gcd of 84, 126, and 210. Below, we have expressed each of these numbers as the product of prime factors.

$$84 = 2 \cdot 2 \cdot 3 \cdot 7.$$
$$126 = 2 \cdot 3 \cdot 3 \cdot 7.$$
$$210 = 2 \cdot 3 \cdot 5 \cdot 7.$$

Now we can compare the products expressed at the right above to determine the common prime divisors of the numbers. Each of the products contains 2 as a factor; therefore, 2 is a common prime factor of the three numbers. (The first product contains 2 more than once, but neither of the other products does; hence, the gcd will contain only one 2 among its prime factors.) Similarly, each of the products contains 3 as a factor, and each contains 7 as a factor. Thus, 2, 3, and 7 are the common prime factors of 84, 126, and 210. The greatest common divisor of the three numbers is equal to the product of the common prime factors; so $2 \cdot 3 \cdot 7$, or 42, is the gcd of 84, 126, and 210.

Next, we will use the method involving prime factors to find the greatest common divisor of 35 and 27. Each of these numbers is expressed below as a product of its prime factors.

$$35 = 5 \cdot 7.$$
$$27 = 3 \cdot 3 \cdot 3.$$

Note that neither of the prime factors of 35 is also a prime factor of 27; thus, the two numbers have no common prime factors. From this, we conclude that 1 is the gcd of 35 and 27. Numbers whose greatest common divisor is one—that is, numbers that have no common prime factors—are said to be *relatively prime* numbers. Neither 35 nor 27 is itself a prime number; but, because they have no common divisors other than 1, they can be thought of as *prime with respect to each other*.

We will now discuss a third method of finding the greatest common divisor of two numbers. In this method, we will make use of another theorem of arithmetic that involves an important relationship between any two members of the set of natural numbers. This theorem, which is stated below, is found in Euclid's writings.

For any two natural numbers a and b, if $b > 0$,
then there are two other natural numbers, q and r,
such that $a = q \cdot b + r$, where $r < b$.

This theorem may be easier for you to understand if you think of it in terms of the usual division terminology. In the statement of the theorem, you can think of a as representing the dividend, b the divisor, q the quotient, and r the remainder. Thus, the theorem can be interpreted as follows: The dividend is equal to the product of the quotient and the divisor plus the remainder, which must be less than the divisor. Suppose, for example, that a is replaced by 74 and b is replaced by 7. This means that q must be replaced by 10 and r must be replaced by 4 because $74 = 10 \cdot 7 + 4$. You should be able to explain why it would not be sensible to have a remainder greater than the divisor. If $r = 0$, then b is a member of the set of divisors of a.

Now let us use this theorem in finding the greatest common divisor of two numbers. Suppose that we want to find the gcd of 72 and 60. In this method, we begin by finding the quotient of 72 and 60. The following sentence expresses the fact that the quotient of 72 and 60 is equal to 1, with remainder 12.

$$72 = 1 \cdot 60 + 12.$$

Next, we find the quotient of 60 and the remainder 12. The sentence below expresses the fact that the quotient of 60 and 12 is 5, with remainder 0.

$$60 = 5 \cdot 12 + 0.$$

From this second sentence, we know that 12 is a divisor of 60 because the remainder is 0 when we divide 60 by 12. Now we can use this information in connection with the expression at the right of the "equals" sign in the sentence $72 = 1 \cdot 60 + 12$. Since 12 is a divisor of 60, it is certainly a divisor of $1 \cdot 60$; also 12 is obviously a divisor of 12. Earlier in the chapter, we proved the property that, if $a \mid b$ and $a \mid c$, then $a \mid b + c$. From this property, we know that 12 is a divisor of $1 \cdot 60 + 12$ because it is a divisor of $1 \cdot 60$ and of 12. But $1 \cdot 60 + 12 = 72$; thus we can conclude that 12 is a divisor of 72. We have now established that 12 is a common divisor of 72 and 60. 12 is the *greatest* common divisor of 72 and 60 because any common divisor of these two numbers must also be a divisor of 12. This follows from the equation $72 = 1 \cdot 60 + 12$, or $12 = 72 - 1 \cdot 60$.

This method may seem a bit cumbersome to you by comparison with the two methods discussed earlier. However, we will now consider another example to show the power of the method. Suppose that we want to find the gcd of 1155 and 553. It is not so easy to determine the factors of either of these numbers, so that the methods described earlier are not appropriate for this example. As in the preceding example, we begin by finding the quotient of the two numbers whose gcd we are trying to find, and we express the result in the following way:

$$1155 = 2 \cdot 553 + 49.$$

Next we find the quotient of 553 and the remainder, 49.

$$553 = 11 \cdot 49 + 14.$$

We must carry the process farther because we have not yet obtained a remainder of 0. This time, we find the quotient of 49 and 14, the second remainder.

$$49 = 3 \cdot 14 + 7.$$

We still do not have a remainder of 0, so we find the quotient of 14 and the third remainder, 7.

$$14 = 2 \cdot 7 + 0.$$

Because, in the last sentence, the remainder is 0, we know that 7 is a common divisor of 14 and 7. It is the gcd of 14 and 7 because no number greater than 7 is a divisor of 7. Now we work backward through each example to see what conclusion we can reach about the gcd of 1155 and 553. First, we will consider the expression $3 \cdot 14 + 7$. Because 7 is a divisor of 14, it is a divisor of $3 \cdot 14$. 7 is also a divisor of 7; hence, 7 is a divisor of $3 \cdot 14 + 7$. From this, it follows that 7 is a divisor of 49, which is equal to $3 \cdot 14 + 7$. Further, 7 is the gcd of 49 and 14 because any common divisor of 49 and 14 must be a divisor of 7.

Next, we know that 7 is a divisor of $11 \cdot 49 + 14$ because we have already established that it is a divisor of 49 and of 14. Therefore, 7 must be a divisor of 553, which is equal to $11 \cdot 49 + 14$. Thus, 7 is the gcd of 553 and 49.

Now 7 is also a divisor of $2 \cdot 553 + 49$. Finally, we can conclude that 7 is a divisor of 1155, which is equal to $2 \cdot 553 + 49$. Thus, we know that 7 is the gcd of 1155 and 553.

It should be apparent that, in this method, if the two numbers whose greatest common divisor you are trying to find are relatively prime, then you will obtain a remainder of 0 only when the last divisor you use is 1. Suppose for example, that we do not know that 220 and 159 are relatively prime and that we use this method to find the gcd of the two numbers. First, we find the quotient of 220 and 159 and express the result as follows.

$$220 = 1 \cdot 159 + 61.$$

Then we continue the process in the same manner as with the preceding examples:

$$159 = 2 \cdot 61 + 37.$$
$$61 = 1 \cdot 37 + 24.$$
$$37 = 1 \cdot 24 + 13.$$
$$24 = 1 \cdot 13 + 11.$$
$$13 = 1 \cdot 11 + 2.$$
$$11 = 5 \cdot 2 + 1.$$
$$2 = 2 \cdot 1 + 0.$$

You should be able to use the last sentence in the series and work backward through each step to explain why 1 is the gcd of 220 and 159.

We can now generalize this method for finding the gcd of any two natural numbers, a and b. We will use $q_1, q_2, q_3, \ldots, q_n$ for the quotients we obtain and $r_1, r_2, r_3, \ldots, r_n$ for the remainders. When the last remainder, r_n, is 0, the preceding remainder, r_{n-1}, is the gcd of a and b. Thus,

$$a = q_1 \cdot b + r_1.$$
$$b = q_2 \cdot r_1 + r_2.$$
$$r_1 = q_3 \cdot r_2 + r_3.$$
$$\vdots \qquad \vdots \qquad \vdots$$
$$r_{n-2} = q_n \cdot r_{n-1} + r_n.$$

If $r_n = 0$, it is possible to show, by working backward through all of the steps, that r_{n-1} is the gcd of a and b.

The last idea we will discuss in this chapter is a relation between counting numbers that is, in a sense, the reverse of the idea of the greatest common divisor. This is the idea of the *least common multiple* of two or more counting numbers, often abbreviated to "lcm" in mathematical literature. The least common multiple of two or more numbers is the least number that has each of the numbers as a factor, or divisor.

One method of finding the least common multiple of two numbers is to tabulate the set of multiples of each number and then to compare these two sets. For example, you can find the least common multiple of 12 and 18 in the following way. The first set tabulated below is the set of multiples of 12. The second set is the set of multiples of 18. The multiples of any counting number are found by multiplying the given number by each counting number in turn.

$$12: \{12,\ 24,\ \textcircled{36},\ 48,\ 60,\ \textcircled{72},\ \ldots\}$$
$$18: \{18,\ \textcircled{36},\ 54,\ \textcircled{72},\ 90,\ 108,\ \ldots\}$$

Obviously, we have not named all of the multiples of either 12 or 18 because each of these numbers has infinitely many multiples. However, from the multiples that we have named, we can see that the encircled numerals, 36 and 72, represent common multiples of 12 and 18. Because 36 is the least number that has both 12 and 18 as divisors, 36 is the *least* common multiple of the two numbers.

There is a second method of finding the least common multiple of two numbers that is related to the method just presented. In this method, we tabulate the set of multiples of the greater of the two numbers as in the preceding method. Next, however, instead of determining multiples of the lesser number, we test each successive multiple of the greater number to determine if it is also a multiple of the lesser number. Let us demonstrate this method by finding the lcm of 14 and 6.

First, we tabulate the set of multiples of 14, the greater number.

$$\{14,\ 28,\ 42,\ 56,\ 70,\ \ldots\}$$

Now we determine which of these multiples of 14 is also a multiple of the lesser number, 6. 6 is not a factor of 14, nor of 28; but 6 is a factor of 42. We know that 42 is the least multiple of 14 that is also a multiple of 6; therefore, 42 is the lcm of 14 and 6.

Another method of finding the lcm of two or more numbers is to use the fundamental theorem of arithmetic and to express each number as the product of prime factors. Suppose, for example, we want to find the lcm of 8, 9, and 10.

We first express each number as the product of its prime factors. Thus,

$$8 = 2 \cdot 2 \cdot 2.$$
$$9 = 3 \cdot 3.$$
$$10 = 2 \cdot 5.$$

We can find the prime factors of the lcm by combining prime factors of all three numbers in a product in such a way that we have the minimum number of factors required. First of all, the product must include three 2's for the lcm to be a multiple of 8. Secondly, the product must include two 3's for the lcm to be a multiple of 9. Finally, the product must include 5 for the lcm to be a multiple of 10. We need not concern ourselves with including the 2 that is a prime factor of 10 because we have already included three 2's in the product. Thus, we know that the prime factors of the least common multiple of 8, 9, and 10 are 2, 2, 2, 3, 3, and 5, and the lcm is the product of these prime factors. Hence, the lcm of 8, 9, and 10 is equal to 360 because

$$2 \cdot 2 \cdot 2 \cdot 3 \cdot 3 \cdot 5 = 360.$$

We will give one further example to illustrate this method. Suppose that we want to find the lcm of 30 and 45. First, we express each number as the product of its prime factors. Thus,

$$30 = 2 \cdot 3 \cdot 5.$$
$$45 = 3 \cdot 3 \cdot 5.$$

It should be apparent that the lcm of 30 and 45 is the product of 2, 3, 3, and 5. Thus, 90 is the lcm of 30 and 45 because

$$2 \cdot 3 \cdot 3 \cdot 5 = 90.$$

205 Find the greatest common divisor of the numbers named in each of the following exercises.

a 48 and 120   **c** 64, 80, and 144   **e** 126, 210, and 252
b 84, 150, and 308   **d** 105, 210, and 280   **f** 63, 189, and 315

206 Use the method described on pages 221-223 to find the greatest common divisor of the following pairs of numbers.

a 10200 and 16380   **b** 3071 and 7553

207 Find the least common multiple of the numbers named in each of the following exercises.

a 5 and 12   **c** 8 and 30   **e** 10, 20, and 25   **g** 15, 40, and 80
b 4 and 20   **d** 18 and 45   **f** 36, 48, and 72

CONCLUSION

The material presented in this chapter is just a sample—we hope an interesting one—of the kinds of ideas that are studied in number theory. Many of the ideas presented in this chapter, such as prime number, relatively prime numbers, least common multiple, and greatest common divisor, will be of use to us in subsequent chapters when we are working with fractions and rational numbers.

CHAPTER QUIZ

1 Tell whether each of the following sentences expresses a true or a false statement.

   A $72 \mid 144$.   C $6 \mid 0$.   E $1 \mid 546$.   G $38 \mid 148$.

   B $18 \mid 186$.   D $0 \mid 6$.   F $546 \mid 1$.   H $146 \mid 1606$.

2 Use the Sieve of Eratosthenes to indicate the primes between 100 and 200.

3 Use the counting numbers from 25 through 45 to make replacements for n in $n^2 - n + 41$. Examine each result to see if the number is prime or composite. Is it true that, for *every* replacement of n, $n^2 - n + 41$ represents a prime number?

4 Do you obtain a prime number for every replacement of n by a counting number in $4n^2 + 1$?

5 Prove that the product of two or more natural numbers is even unless all of the numbers are odd.

6 Under what conditions is the sum of two or more natural numbers even?

7 Find at least one pair of twin primes not named in the text. Twin primes, pages 213-214

8 Express each of the numbers named below as the product of prime numbers.

   A 144   C 978   E 1014

   B 138   D 143   F 24560

9 Prove that any number whose digit in the ones' place represents an even number is divisible by 2.

10 Prove that any number whose digit in the ones' place is either 0 or 5 is divisible by 5.

11 A number is divisible by 4 if the number represented by its last two digits is divisible by 4. Show that this is true.

12 Could two consecutive natural numbers greater than 2 both be prime numbers?

13 Some primes are one greater than a power of 2. For example, $5 = 2^2 + 1$ and $17 = 2^4 + 1$. Find at least two other such primes.

14 For certain replacements of n, the number $n^2 + 1$ is a prime. Name at least six members of this set.

15 If n is a counting number greater than 1, there is always a prime number between n and $2n$. Check this for several replacements of n.

16 Check Goldbach's Conjecture by expressing each of the even numbers named below as the sum of two primes. Goldbach's conjecture, page 215

   A 18   B 144   C 98

17 Find a number expressible in the form $n! + 1$ that is prime. Show that $n! + 2$ is composite for every replacement of n greater than or equal to 2.

18 Find the gcd of the following pairs of numbers.

A 146, 28   D 16, 480

B 765, 135   E 125, 32

C 1000, 155   F 17, 23

19 Find the lcm of the numbers named in each of the following exercises.

A 12, 14   D 144, 884

B 8, 12   E 290, 9, 81

C 16, 32, 44   F 45, 135

20 Show that the sum of the divisors of 6, other than 6 itself, is 6. Find another counting number that is equal to the sum of the divisors that are less than the number itself. [The Greeks called such numbers as these *perfect numbers*. It is not known whether there is an odd perfect number or not. Neither is it known whether the set of perfect numbers is finite or infinite.]

21 If one of two numbers is a divisor of the other, what do you know about the lcm of the two numbers? What do you know about the gcd of the two numbers?

22 Describe a method for finding the lcm of two numbers that are relatively prime to each other.

23 Below are given pairs of natural numbers of the form (a, b). Find two other natural numbers q and r, where $r < b$, for which it is true that $a = q \cdot b + r$.

A (45, 6)   C (45670, 432)

B (166, 15)   D (100, 10)

24 Prove that, if a, b, c, and d are counting numbers such that $a = b + c$ where $d \mid a$ and $d \mid b$, then $d \mid c$.

SUPPLEMENTARY READINGS

Barnett, I. A., *Some Ideas About Number Theory*, NCTM, 1961. This pamphlet contains a brief and elementary treatment of some of the more interesting topics in number theory. Item 41 of Bibliography

Bowers, Henry and Joan, *Arithmetical Excursions: An Enrichment of Elementary Mathematics*. This book contains several topics from number theory. Chapter 18 contains some interesting information on figurate, perfect, and amicable numbers. Item 42 of Bibliography

Essays on Number Theory, Vols. I and II, SMSG. These booklets contain a careful treatment of number theory topics and require at least high-school mathematics as a foundation. Item 43 of Bibliography

Ore, Oystein, *Number Theory and Its History*. This text contains an excellent account of the historical origins of many topics in number theory as well as a clear exposition of the topics themselves. Item 44 of Bibliography

Peterson and Hashisaki, *Theory of Arithmetic*, pp. 124-136. Contains information and exercises on primes, fundamental theorem of arithmetic, gcd, and lcm. Item 26 of Bibliography

Swain, Robert, *Understanding Arithmetic*, pp. 113-134. Contains a good chapter on number theory from an elementary point of view. Includes some material on divisibility. Item 39 of Bibliography

Chapter ten

Rational numbers of arithmetic

The concept of a fraction
Sets of equivalent fractions
Addition of rational numbers of arithmetic
Multiplication of rational numbers of arithmetic
Ordering the rational numbers of arithmetic
The system of rational numbers of arithmetic
Subtraction and division of rational numbers of arithmetic
The number line and density

You will recall that addition and multiplication are the fundamental operations of the system of natural numbers and that each of these operations is closed in that system. However, neither subtraction, which is defined in terms of addition, nor division, which is defined in terms of multiplication, is closed in the natural-number system. The following two questions are examples of problems that have no solutions when we are dealing with natural numbers:

Closure of addition and multiplication, pages 87 and 92

a) 6 must be added to what number to obtain 4 as the sum?
b) By what number must 3 be multiplied to obtain 5 as the product?

The first of these questions will be answered in Chapter 12, when we consider the system of positive and negative rational numbers. In this chapter, we will develop the system of rational numbers of arithmetic. This system enables us to find a satisfactory answer to the second question. First, however, we will discuss briefly the intuitive concepts that underlie the rational numbers of arithmetic.*

---

* Often, the set of numbers that we call "the rational numbers of arithmetic" is identified with the set that includes the positive rational numbers and 0, that is, the set of non-negative rational numbers. In this chapter, we will sometimes refer to the rational numbers of arithmetic simply as the rational numbers. You should keep in mind, however, that here we are dealing only with the set of numbers that correspond to the positive rational numbers and 0.

The concept of a fraction

The need for numbers other than natural numbers—for numbers that are "between" the natural numbers—probably first arose when ancient man began to measure the lengths of objects. Basic to the process of measurement is the concept of a unit of measure. We might note in passing that early units of measure were frequently associated with parts of the anatomy. For example, a cubit, which was used as a unit of measure by the ancient Egyptians and Babylonians, was the distance from the tip of the middle finger to the elbow of the outstretched arm. In England, King Henry I standardized the yard as a unit of measure by taking the distance from the tip of the middle finger of his outstretched arm to the tip of his nose.

The problem that early man encountered was that of expressing a length that did not correspond to an exact number of the units he was using for the measurement. If the length of an object corresponded fairly well to an exact number of units of measure, then the natural numbers were adequate for describing such lengths. But suppose that the length of an object turned out to be "between 3 and 4 feet" or "about 7 yards." Such measurements lack precision, and the Babylonians and Egyptians found it necessary to invent other numbers to express these measurements.

Let us construct an imaginary situation that might have occurred in ancient times. Suppose that two Babylonian merchants have agreed upon a certain cost per unit for some cloth. This situation is shown in the illustration below. The sticks in the illustration are of equal length, and 1 "stick" represents the unit of measure being used. Notice that the cloth is more than 5 sticks, or units, but less than 6 units long. The merchants must decide what the price will be for the piece of the cloth that extends beyond the fifth stick, as well as the price for the 5-unit piece.

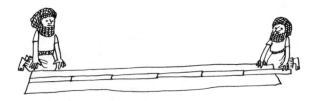

Let us assume that, eventually, the two merchants hit upon the idea of marking off the last stick into 4 parts of equal length. The illustration at the top of the next page shows an enlarged view of the end of the piece of cloth and of the last stick, now marked off into 4 equal parts. Note that the end of the cloth is very nearly aligned with the third mark on the stick.

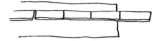

The merchants agree that this measure is precise enough for their purposes, and they agree that the merchant who is buying the cloth will pay for 5 whole units, plus a certain amount for the part of the unit. The buyer determines the price for the part of the unit by separating the unit price into four equal amounts and paying three of the four amounts.

From our knowledge of history, it seems likely that people did solve their measurement problems in some manner similar to the one just described. The important point to be noted in this imaginary situation is that they found it necessary to use a *pair* of natural numbers to find an answer to their problem. They found that a single natural number was not adequate for the situation.

You are aware, of course, that our fictitious merchants were working with the *fraction* $\frac{3}{4}$. In this fraction, the *denominator* 4 represents the number of parts of equal length into which the unit of measure was divided. The *numerator* 3 represents the number of these parts that correspond to the length of the piece of the cloth.

In Chapter 8, you dealt with sets of number pairs, called rate pairs. However, the number pairs we are considering in this chapter are not rate pairs. Later in the chapter we will define a set of number pairs as a single number. The reasons for defining sets of number pairs in this way will become apparent as we proceed. It is important that you, as a teacher, become aware of the mathematical justification for considering these sets of pairs of numbers as single numbers and for defining the operations of addition and multiplication on such numbers.

In the rest of this section, we will discuss some physical situations in which number pairs that we call fractions might be used. You have already seen that the process of measurement is one source of fraction ideas. There are many other physical situations in which fractions are useful. The diagram below is illustrative of the way in which a pair of natural numbers can be used in describing a physical situation. All of the rectangular pieces of cardboard pictured in the diagram are of the same size. In each picture,

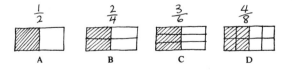

the piece of cardboard has been marked off into a certain number of parts of the same size. Thus, in picture A, the cardboard has been marked off into 2 parts of the same size; in picture B, the cardboard has been marked off into 4 parts of the same size; and so on.

For each picture, a pair of natural numbers called a fraction is named to indicate what part of the piece of cardboard is shaded. Like rate pairs, fractions can be symbolized in any of the forms a/b, $\frac{a}{b}$, (a, b), etc. We have chosen to use a/b for ratios and $\frac{a}{b}$ for fraction numerals. A fraction numeral is usually read differently from a ratio. For example, the fraction numeral $\frac{3}{4}$ is read "three fourths," while the ratio 3/4 is read "three to four." In picture A, $\frac{1}{2}$ represents the idea that 1 of the 2 parts is shaded. The numerator of $\frac{1}{2}$ is 1, and the denominator of $\frac{1}{2}$ is 2. In picture B, the fraction numeral $\frac{2}{4}$ expresses the idea that 2 of the 4 parts are shaded. The numerator of $\frac{2}{4}$ is 2, and the denominator is 4.

Note that, in each picture, the same amount of the entire piece of cardboard is shaded. This suggests that, even though a different fraction is associated with each picture, these fractions are related to each other in some way. We can also think of other fractions, such as $\frac{5}{10}$, $\frac{33}{66}$, and $\frac{50}{100}$, that represent the shaded portion of the piece of cardboard. It makes sense to think of all the fractions that can be used to represent the shaded portion of the cardboard as elements of the same set. This set, which we will temporarily call set S, is tabulated below.

$$S = \{\tfrac{1}{2}, \tfrac{2}{4}, \tfrac{3}{6}, \tfrac{4}{8}, \ldots\}.$$

The illustration below provides another example of the physical meaning of fractions. All of the circular pieces of cardboard are of the same size. In each picture, the piece of cardboard has been marked off into a certain

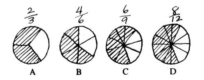

number of parts of the same size. Thus, in picture A, the cardboard has been marked off into 3 parts of the same size; in picture B, the cardboard has been marked off into 6 parts of the same size; and so on.

For each picture, the fraction named indicates what part of the cardboard is shaded. Notice that, in each picture, the same part of the entire piece of cardboard is shaded. As in the previous example, this suggests that all of the fractions named in this illustration are related to each other. We can also think of other fractions that might be used in describing this situation, such as $\frac{10}{15}$, $\frac{40}{60}$, $\frac{200}{300}$, etc. Again, we can think of all the fractions that can be used to represent the shaded portion of the cardboard as elements of the same set. This set, which we will call set T, is tabulated below.

$$T = \{\tfrac{2}{3}, \tfrac{4}{6}, \tfrac{6}{9}, \tfrac{8}{12}, \ldots\}.$$

You will recall that, in our discussion of proportional relations in Chapter 8, we established a rule for deciding whether or not two rate pairs belong to the same proportional relation. Let us now see if an analogous rule can be applied to fractions that are elements of the same set. Suppose that we choose $\tfrac{1}{2}$ and $\tfrac{3}{6}$ from set S, tabulated on page 232, to see if the rule we established for elements of a proportional relation also holds for fractions that are elements of S. Equivalent rate pairs, page 181

The above diagram shows that the product of the numerator of $\tfrac{1}{2}$ and the denominator of $\tfrac{3}{6}$ is equal to the product of the numerator of $\tfrac{3}{6}$ and the denominator of $\tfrac{1}{2}$; that is, $1 \times 6 = 3 \times 2$. You can show that this is true for any two elements of S or for any two elements of T. Fractions that are related in the way that $\tfrac{1}{2}$ and $\tfrac{3}{6}$ are related are said to be *equivalent fractions*. Thus, any two members of S or of T are equivalent. You can also show that, if two fractions are not equivalent, then the products secured in the manner indicated in the diagram above will not be the same. For example, suppose that we choose the fraction $\tfrac{4}{8}$ from S and the fraction $\tfrac{6}{9}$ from T. We can see that $4 \times 9 \neq 6 \times 8$; therefore, we conclude that these two fractions are not equivalent.

It would seem evident that, for any physical situation that involves a part-to-whole relationship, we can use a number pair, or fraction, to represent it. It is also apparent that each such fraction is an element of an infinite set of equivalent fractions that can be determined by the following rule.

If two fractions $\tfrac{a}{b}$ and $\tfrac{c}{d}$ are equivalent,
then $ad = cb$.
Also, if $ad = cb$
for natural numbers a, b, c, d where b, $d \neq 0$,
then $\tfrac{a}{b}$ and $\tfrac{c}{d}$ are equivalent.

The sets of equivalent fractions that are determined by the rule just given are disjoint subsets of $N \times C$. Notice that any pair of natural numbers of the form $\tfrac{a}{0}$ is not a fraction. This is a reasonable restriction, since Disjoint subsets, page 20 it does not make much sense to think of "dividing" an object into zero parts of the same size. Thus, in the above rule, neither b nor d can be replaced by 0.

Several sets of fractions are tabulated below. You should use the rule that we have just given to verify for yourself that the fractions named in each set are equivalent.

$$A = \{\tfrac{8}{5}, \tfrac{16}{10}, \tfrac{24}{15}, \tfrac{32}{20}, \ldots\}.$$

$$B = \{\tfrac{2}{1}, \tfrac{4}{2}, \tfrac{6}{3}, \tfrac{8}{4}, \ldots\}.$$

$$D = \{\tfrac{0}{1}, \tfrac{0}{2}, \tfrac{0}{3}, \tfrac{0}{4}, \ldots\}.$$

$$E = \{\tfrac{1}{1}, \tfrac{2}{2}, \tfrac{3}{3}, \tfrac{4}{4}, \ldots\}.$$

The illustration below shows a physical interpretation of certain of the fractions in set B. Notice that we have not included a picture to illustrate the fraction $\tfrac{2}{1}$ (read as "two ones"), although it is possible to think of "dividing" an object into ones, and then taking 2 of them. In any event, we do know that the fraction $\tfrac{2}{1}$ is equivalent to the other elements of B, and, hence, is an element of set B.

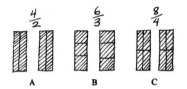

You could use the method that we used for set B to give physical interpretations for sets A and E, tabulated above. If you examine set D, you can see that an explanation of the elements of D, in terms of a part-to-whole physical relationship is possible, although it does not make a great deal of sense. The fractions in set D are, however, equivalent to each other, and D certainly contains ordered pairs whose first components are natural numbers and whose second components are counting numbers. Thus, we must, for the sake of completeness, include set D among our sets of equivalent fractions.

So far, it seems that, although a set of equivalent fractions is different from a proportional relation in terms of physical meaning, it has some of the same properties as a proportional relation. Later on you will find that there are ways, other than the purely physical, in which sets of fractions differ from sets of rate pairs. For the present, we can give you only an intuitive idea of how these two concepts differ. When we described the physical interpretation of rate pairs, we talked about situations like 2 pencils for 5¢, 25 miles in 2 hours, and so on. In giving a physical basis for fractions, we talked about parts of a whole, that is, $\frac{1}{2}$ of a piece of cardboard, or $\frac{6}{8}$ of a piece of cardboard. From this, we see that the physical situation that is represented by a fraction is quite different from the physical situation represented by a rate pair. For the time being, the difference in the physical situations from which the ideas are abstracted is the way in which you can distinguish between rate pairs and fractions.

208 Draw 4 rectangles of the same size. Mark off the first rectangle into 4 parts of the same size, the second into 8, the third into 12, and the fourth into 16. Shade $\frac{1}{4}$ of the first rectangle. Next shade a portion of each of the other rectangles so that the shaded portion has the same size as the shaded portion of the first rectangle. Then use a fraction to represent the part of the whole that is shaded in each rectangle. Do all of these fractions belong to the same set?

209 Repeat exercise 208. This time, mark off and shade $\frac{1}{5}$ of the first rectangle, $\frac{2}{10}$ of the second, $\frac{6}{30}$ of the third, and $\frac{10}{50}$ of the fourth. Are these fractions equivalent?

210 For each fraction named below, write the names of 6 fractions that are elements of the same set.

a $\frac{5}{6}$ b $\frac{15}{34}$ c $\frac{2}{7}$ d $\frac{4}{5}$ e $\frac{0}{6}$

211 In each expression below, replace the variable by several non-zero natural numbers in turn. For which of the expressions do you obtain sets of equivalent fractions?

a $\frac{a}{2a}$ b $\frac{1}{b}$ c $\frac{n+1}{2n+2}$ d $\frac{n-1}{n+1}$

Sets of equivalent fractions

Now that we have arrived at an intuitive notion of what a fraction is in terms of a physical situation, we can go on to a discussion of the mathematical meaning of sets of equivalent fractions.

In Chapter 8, we defined a set of rate pairs, like the one tabulated below, as a proportional relation. We also agreed to use the name of any rate pair in the set as a name for the entire proportional relation.

$$\{5/6, 10/12, 15/18, 20/24, \ldots\}$$

Thus, the set tabulated above may be called the proportional relation 5/6, the proportional relation 15/18, and so on.

A set of fractions, like the one tabulated at the top of the next page, will be a number in the system developed in this chapter. Such a number will be called a *rational number of arithmetic*, or, simply, a *rational number*. The properties of these numbers will be developed in the subsequent sections of this chapter.

$$\left(\tfrac{7}{8}, \tfrac{14}{16}, \tfrac{21}{24}, \tfrac{28}{32}, \ldots\right)$$

We will use the same method for naming a rational number of arithmetic as we used for naming a proportional relation. This means that any fraction numeral that names an element of a rational number is also a name of the number itself. Each of the following sentences expresses a true statement about the rational number tabulated above.

$$\tfrac{7}{8} = \left(\tfrac{7}{8}, \tfrac{14}{16}, \tfrac{21}{24}, \ldots\right).$$
$$\tfrac{14}{16} = \left(\tfrac{7}{8}, \tfrac{14}{16}, \tfrac{21}{24}, \ldots\right).$$
$$\tfrac{28}{32} = \left(\tfrac{7}{8}, \tfrac{14}{16}, \tfrac{21}{24}, \ldots\right).$$
$$\tfrac{56}{64} = \left(\tfrac{7}{8}, \tfrac{14}{16}, \tfrac{21}{24}, \ldots\right).$$

Because $\tfrac{7}{8}, \tfrac{14}{16}, \tfrac{28}{32}$, and so on, are all names for the same number, we can write the following:

$$\tfrac{7}{8} = \tfrac{14}{16}.$$
$$\tfrac{14}{16} = \tfrac{28}{32}.$$
$$\tfrac{7}{8} = \tfrac{28}{32}.$$
$$\tfrac{14}{16} = \tfrac{420}{480}.$$

You will recall that a ratio like 6/12, 7/100, or 3/1 can be used to name either a rate pair or a proportional relation, which is an infinite set of equivalent rate pairs. Similarly, a fraction numeral like $\tfrac{7}{8}$ or $\tfrac{3}{4}$ or $\tfrac{12}{5}$ can be used to name either a fraction or a rational number of arithmetic, which is an infinite set of equivalent fractions.

We can now make the following generalization:

For any two rational numbers of arithmetic $\tfrac{a}{b}$ and $\tfrac{c}{d}$,
if $ad = cb$, then $\tfrac{a}{b} = \tfrac{c}{d}$.
Also, if $\tfrac{a}{b} = \tfrac{c}{d}$, then $ad = cb$.

Notice that the above generalization includes two concepts. The first is that, if the product of the numerator of $\tfrac{a}{b}$ and the denominator of $\tfrac{c}{d}$ is equal to the product of the numerator of $\tfrac{c}{d}$ and the denominator of $\tfrac{a}{b}$, then the numbers $\tfrac{a}{b}$ and $\tfrac{c}{d}$ are equal.* The second idea is that, if the two numbers

---

* Technically, of course, a rational number of arithmetic, which involves an infinite set of equivalent fractions, does not have a numerator or a denominator; the fraction that indicates the number does have a numerator and a denominator. To simplify our language, however, we will agree to talk about the numerator and denominator of a rational number.

are equal, then these two products are also equal. Many of the generalizations with which the mathematician is concerned are of this kind, and he customarily uses the expression "if and only if" in stating such generalizations. The generalization on page 236 can be expressed more briefly in the following way.

For any two rational numbers of arithmetic $\frac{a}{b}$ and $\frac{c}{d}$,
$\frac{a}{b} = \frac{c}{d}$ if and only if $ad = cb$.

As a consequence of this definition, we see that, if the numerator and the denominator of a number are multiplied by the same counting number n, then an equal number is obtained. That is, $\frac{a}{b} = \frac{an}{bn}$, where a is a natural number and b and n are counting numbers. This is so because multiplica- Commutative and tion is commutative and associative in the set of natural numbers; and, associative properties of hence, $a \cdot bn = an \cdot b$ for all a, b, and n. multiplication, page 92

Because a rational number of arithmetic is an infinite set of fractions and the name of any element of the set may be used to name the entire set, a rational number has infinitely many names. You will recall that natural numbers can also be named in many different ways. For example, symbols like $3 + 2, 5 + 0, 85 - 80$, and $75 \div 15$ are all names for the natural number whose standard name is 5. For each rational number of arithmetic, there is also a name that may be thought of as the standard name of that number. Every number contains one fraction whose numerator and denominator are relatively prime. Remember that two numbers are Relatively prime relatively prime if their greatest common divisor is 1. We will call a fraction numbers, page 221 whose numerator and denominator are relatively prime a *basic fraction*. Thus, $\frac{2}{3}$, $\frac{5}{8}$, $\frac{12}{7}$, $\frac{5}{1}$, and $\frac{20}{21}$ are examples of basic fractions because their numerators and denominators are relatively prime; while $\frac{18}{2}$, $\frac{6}{8}$, $\frac{12}{15}$, and $\frac{7}{21}$ are not basic fractions because their numerators and denominators are not relatively prime.

The numeral for the basic fraction that is contained in a rational number of arithmetic is the *standard name* of that number. In the chart below, we have listed several rational numbers of arithmetic and given the standard name of each number.

Rational number	Standard name
$\{\frac{1}{3}, \frac{2}{6}, \frac{3}{9}, \ldots\}$	$\frac{1}{3}$
$\{\frac{8}{9}, \frac{16}{18}, \frac{24}{27}, \ldots\}$	$\frac{8}{9}$
$\{\frac{0}{1}, \frac{0}{2}, \frac{0}{3}, \ldots\}$	$\frac{0}{1}$
$\{\frac{5}{2}, \frac{10}{4}, \frac{15}{6}, \ldots\}$	$\frac{5}{2}$
$\{\frac{8}{1}, \frac{16}{2}, \frac{24}{3}, \ldots\}$	$\frac{8}{1}$

Certain rational numbers are closely associated with natural numbers in terms of their physical interpretations and in terms of their properties. For example, the rational number $\frac{2}{1}$ is related to the natural number 2. It should be apparent that the physical quantity represented by the fraction $\frac{2}{1}$ is the same as the quantity represented by the natural number 2 (although the numbers are usually used in connection with quite different situations).

Later you will see that, when you are adding or multiplying rational numbers, $\frac{2}{1}$ and 2 behave in the same way. In fact, every natural number can be associated with a rational number, as we have indicated in the following diagram.

Because of this association, we say that every natural number has a *mate* that is a rational number; thus, $\frac{3}{1}$ is the mate of 3, $\frac{4}{1}$ is the mate of 4, $\frac{55}{1}$ is the mate of 55, and so on. Also, because $\frac{6}{2} = \frac{3}{1}$, $\frac{6}{2}$ is the mate of 3; because $\frac{24}{4} = \frac{6}{1}$, $\frac{24}{4}$ is the mate of 6, and so on. Note that not every rational number has a natural-number mate. For example, such numbers as $\frac{2}{3}, \frac{11}{12}, \frac{25}{8}$, etc., do not correspond to natural numbers.

We have spent considerable time in developing a few basic concepts about fractions and rational numbers of arithmetic. Now we can proceed to discuss such ideas as the sum of two rational numbers and the product of two such numbers.

212 Give the standard name of each of the following rational numbers.

    a $\frac{10}{15}$ **b** $\frac{24}{40}$ **c** $\frac{4}{12}$ **d** $\frac{6}{20}$ **e** $\frac{18}{4}$ **f** $\frac{27}{9}$

213 Find three fractions that are equivalent to each of the following.

    a $\frac{4}{7}$ **b** $\frac{9}{12}$ **c** $\frac{10}{16}$ **d** $\frac{2}{9}$ **e** $\frac{18}{3}$

214 Give the standard name of the rational number to which each of the fractions named in exercise 213 belongs.

Addition of rational numbers of arithmetic

You learned how to add, subtract, multiply, and divide rational numbers of arithmetic (although you probably called them fractions) in elementary school. However, we wish to give you a more systematic and precise understanding of operations with these numbers. We also want to help you understand that the way in which these operations are defined is important in terms of mathematical and logical consistency. For these reasons, we will proceed as though you had no—or at least very little—knowledge of operations with rational numbers.

The system of natural numbers, which we developed and used in the preceding chapters of this book, is an example of a mathematical system. The natural-number system includes (a) the set of natural numbers as elements and (b) the operations of addition and multiplication, together with certain properties of these operations.

We now want to establish another mathematical system, one that contains the rational numbers of arithmetic as elements. We must define the two operations, addition and multiplication, in such a way that they have the essential properties to complete the new number system.

We would like to define operations with rational numbers of arithmetic in such a way that these operations will have the properties of the analogous operations with natural numbers. This means, for example, that we want two rational numbers that are mates of natural numbers to have a sum that is the mate of the sum of the natural numbers. In other words, we want the sum of $\frac{2}{1}$ and $\frac{3}{1}$ to be the mate of the sum of 2 and 3. We would also like the product of two rational numbers that are mates of natural numbers to be the mate of the product of the two natural numbers. That is, we want the product of $\frac{2}{1}$ and $\frac{3}{1}$ to be the mate of the product of 2 and 3.

Along with the idea that we do not want the results of operations with rational numbers of arithmetic to conflict with the results we obtain when operating with natural numbers, there is another requirement we would like our definitions to meet. We would like the sum that we obtain when we add two rational numbers of arithmetic to "make sense" in the physical world.

For example, $\frac{6}{3}$ is the mate of 2, and $\frac{9}{3}$ is the mate of 3. Now suppose that the fraction $\frac{6}{3}$ represents the amount of one kind of pie and that the fraction $\frac{9}{3}$ represents the amount of another kind of pie, as shown in the illustration below. If we combine the two kinds of pie, we can see that $\frac{15}{3}$ represents the total amount of pie. Hence, we would expect the sum of $\frac{6}{3}$ and $\frac{9}{3}$ to be $\frac{15}{3}$, which is the mate of 5.

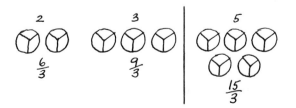

So far, we have decided that the sum of two rational numbers should be defined in such a way that each of the following is true.

$$\tfrac{2}{1} + \tfrac{3}{1} = \tfrac{5}{1}.$$
$$\tfrac{6}{3} + \tfrac{9}{3} = \tfrac{15}{3}.$$

Note that, in the first example, all the numbers named have the same—that is, a common—denominator, and that the numerator of $\tfrac{5}{1}$ is equal to the sum of the numerators of $\tfrac{2}{1}$ and $\tfrac{3}{1}$. This is also true of the numbers named in the second example.

It seems reasonable that, if two rational numbers have a common denominator, then the sum will be as follows: The denominator of the sum will be the same as the denominator of the given numbers, and the numerator of the sum will be equal to the sum of the numerators of the given numbers.*

We can state this idea more succinctly if we use $\tfrac{a}{c}$ and $\tfrac{b}{c}$ to represent two numbers whose sum we are finding.

For any two rational numbers of arithmetic $\tfrac{a}{c}$ and $\tfrac{b}{c}$,
$$\tfrac{a}{c} + \tfrac{b}{c} = \tfrac{a+b}{c}.$$

The above statement is a basic definition of the *sum of two rational numbers of arithmetic*. It may occur to you that we have defined the sum of two numbers in terms of numbers that have a common denominator and that our definition is limited in this respect. Thus, we need to determine how to obtain sums when the numbers have different denominators. To find the sum of $\tfrac{a}{b}$ and $\tfrac{c}{d}$ when $b \neq d$, we replace $\tfrac{a}{b}$ and $\tfrac{c}{d}$ by equal rational numbers that do have a common denominator.

But how do we know that we will obtain the same sum if we replace one or both rational numbers by equal numbers? In the examples given above, we saw that $\tfrac{2}{1} + \tfrac{3}{1} = \tfrac{5}{1}$ and that $\tfrac{6}{3} + \tfrac{9}{3} = \tfrac{15}{3}$. Because $\tfrac{2}{1} = \tfrac{6}{3}$, $\tfrac{3}{1} = \tfrac{9}{3}$, and $\tfrac{5}{1} = \tfrac{15}{3}$, it seems that, if the rational numbers are replaced by equal numbers, the sums obtained are also equal.

Let us consider another example to see if we obtain similar results. According to the definition of the sum of two rational numbers, we know that

$$\tfrac{3}{5} + \tfrac{4}{5} = \tfrac{3+4}{5} = \tfrac{7}{5}.$$

Now let us replace $\tfrac{3}{5}$ and $\tfrac{4}{5}$ by equal numbers and see what sum we obtain. For convenience, the three numbers $\tfrac{3}{5}$, $\tfrac{4}{5}$, and $\tfrac{7}{5}$ are tabulated at the top of the next page.

---

* To be more precise, the fraction that indicates the sum has the same denominator as the fractions that indicate the two given numbers; and the numerator of the fraction that indicates the sum is the sum of the numerators of the fractions that indicate the given numbers.

$$\tfrac{3}{5} = (\tfrac{3}{5}, \tfrac{6}{10}, \tfrac{9}{15}, \tfrac{12}{20}, \ldots).$$

$$\tfrac{4}{5} = (\tfrac{4}{5}, \tfrac{8}{10}, \tfrac{12}{15}, \tfrac{16}{20}, \ldots).$$

$$\tfrac{7}{5} = (\tfrac{7}{5}, \tfrac{14}{10}, \tfrac{21}{15}, \tfrac{28}{20}, \ldots).$$

From these tabulations, we see that $\tfrac{3}{5} = \tfrac{9}{15}$ and that $\tfrac{4}{5} = \tfrac{12}{15}$; so we can expect the sum of $\tfrac{9}{15}$ and $\tfrac{12}{15}$ to be the same as the sum of $\tfrac{3}{5}$ and $\tfrac{4}{5}$. Again using the definition of sum given on page 240, we obtain

$$\tfrac{9}{15} + \tfrac{12}{15} = \tfrac{21}{15}.$$

We note that $\tfrac{21}{15} = \tfrac{7}{5}$; so we have seen in a second example that replacing two rational numbers by equal numbers does not affect their sum.

These results should not surprise you, since they are analogous to the results we obtain with natural numbers. Thus, we will accept without proof the following property for rational numbers of arithmetic.

Addition property of equality, page 98

Given the rational numbers of arithmetic

$$\tfrac{a}{c}, \tfrac{b}{c}, \tfrac{x}{y}, \text{ and } \tfrac{z}{y},$$

if $\tfrac{a}{c} = \tfrac{x}{y}$ and $\tfrac{b}{c} = \tfrac{z}{y}$, then $\tfrac{a}{c} + \tfrac{b}{c} = \tfrac{x}{y} + \tfrac{z}{y}$.

Later in this chapter, we will find a special case of this property quite useful. This different version is given below.

If $\tfrac{a}{c} = \tfrac{b}{c}$, then $\tfrac{a}{c} + \tfrac{d}{c} = \tfrac{b}{c} + \tfrac{d}{c}$.

When you studied algebra, you may have learned this property as the rule "If equals are added to equals, then the sums are equal." We can now use this property to show how to determine the sum of two rational numbers with different denominators.

Suppose, for example, that we want to find the sum of $\tfrac{3}{4}$ and $\tfrac{2}{3}$. So far, we have a definition for the sum of two rational numbers that have a common denominator. However, we also know that we can replace $\tfrac{3}{4}$ and $\tfrac{2}{3}$ by equal numbers without affecting their sum. Thus, if we choose equal rational numbers for $\tfrac{3}{4}$ and $\tfrac{2}{3}$ that have a common denominator, then we can find the sum of these two numbers.

We know that

$$\tfrac{3}{4} = (\tfrac{3}{4}, \tfrac{6}{8}, \tfrac{9}{12}, \tfrac{12}{16}, \ldots).$$

We also know that

$$\tfrac{2}{3} = (\tfrac{2}{3}, \tfrac{4}{6}, \tfrac{6}{9}, \tfrac{8}{12}, \ldots).$$

Now suppose that we replace $\tfrac{3}{4}$ by $\tfrac{9}{12}$ and $\tfrac{2}{3}$ by $\tfrac{8}{12}$. Because of the property just discussed, we know that

$$\tfrac{9}{12} + \tfrac{8}{12} = \tfrac{3}{4} + \tfrac{2}{3}.$$

Since $\frac{9}{12}$ and $\frac{8}{12}$ have a common denominator, we can use the definition of sum to obtain

$$\frac{9}{12} + \frac{8}{12} = \frac{17}{12}.$$

Finally, because $\frac{9}{12} + \frac{8}{12} = \frac{3}{4} + \frac{2}{3}$, we know that

$$\frac{3}{4} + \frac{2}{3} = \frac{17}{12}.$$

Whenever two fractions have different denominators, we need not always tabulate the rational number of arithmetic that contains each of the fractions to determine replacements with a common denominator. Instead, we can multiply the numerator and denominator of the first number by the denominator of the second and multiply the numerator and denominator of the second number by the denominator of the first. For example, we can find replacements for $\frac{3}{4}$ and $\frac{2}{3}$ that have a common denominator in the following way:

$$\frac{3 \times 3}{4 \times 3} = \frac{9}{12}.$$

$$\frac{2 \times 4}{3 \times 4} = \frac{8}{12}.$$

You will recall that, as a consequence of the definition of equal rational numbers of arithmetic, $\frac{a}{b} = \frac{an}{bn}$. Thus, for any two numbers $\frac{a}{b}$ and $\frac{c}{d}$, if we multiply a and b by d, $\frac{ad}{bd} = \frac{a}{b}$; and if we multiply c and d by b, $\frac{bc}{bd} = \frac{c}{d}$. Note that $\frac{ad}{bd}$ and $\frac{bc}{bd}$, which are equal to $\frac{a}{b}$ and $\frac{c}{d}$ respectively, have bd as a common denominator. Equal rational numbers of arithmetic, page 236

Now we can give a general method for finding the sum of any two rational numbers $\frac{a}{b}$ and $\frac{c}{d}$. By the definition of equal rational numbers, we know that

$$\frac{a}{b} = \frac{ad}{bd},$$

and that

$$\frac{c}{d} = \frac{bc}{bd}.$$

Therefore,

$$\frac{a}{b} + \frac{c}{d} = \frac{ad}{bd} + \frac{bc}{bd}.$$

Next, by the definition of sum, we know that

$$\frac{ad}{bd} + \frac{bc}{bd} = \frac{ad + bc}{bd}.$$

Hence, we conclude that, for any two rational numbers $\frac{a}{b}$ and $\frac{c}{d}$,

$$\frac{a}{b} + \frac{c}{d} = \frac{ad + bc}{bd}.$$

This statement concerning the sum of two rational numbers enables us to find the sum of two numbers, no matter what the denominators are. From now on, when we want to find the sum of two rational numbers of arithmetic, we will be using either $\frac{a}{c} + \frac{b}{c} = \frac{a+b}{c}$ or $\frac{a}{b} + \frac{c}{d} = \frac{ad+bc}{bd}$, whichever is appropriate in the given situation.

Now that we have defined the sum of two rational numbers of arithmetic, we will consider some properties of this operation. First, we will decide if the sum of two rational numbers is always a rational number; that is, we will determine whether or not the set of rational numbers of arithmetic is closed under addition. You learned earlier that the sum of any two natural numbers is a natural number and that the product of any two natural numbers is a natural number; so addition and multiplication of natural numbers are closed. We can use closure of addition and multiplication of natural numbers to help us prove that addition of rational numbers of arithmetic is also closed. It is important to keep in mind that every fraction has a natural number as its numerator and a non-zero natural number (a counting number) as its denominator.

We know that the sum of any two numbers $\frac{a}{b}$ and $\frac{c}{d}$ can be expressed as follows:

$$\frac{a}{b} + \frac{c}{d} = \frac{ad+bc}{bd}.$$

Now consider the sum $\frac{ad+bc}{bd}$. We know that a and c are natural numbers because they are the numerators of the fractions $\frac{a}{b}$ and $\frac{c}{d}$. Similarly, b and d are non-zero natural numbers. Because multiplication is closed in the set of natural numbers, ad and bc are likewise natural numbers. Furthermore, since the sum of any two natural numbers is a natural number, we know that $ad + bc$ is a natural number. We also know that bd is a counting number because it is the product of two counting numbers. Thus, because $ad + bc$ is a natural number and bd is a non-zero natural number, $\frac{ad+bc}{bd}$ is a rational number of arithmetic. Thus, we have established that the sum of any two rational numbers is a rational number. This *closure property* is expressed below.

For any two rational numbers of arithmetic $\frac{a}{b}$ and $\frac{c}{d}$, $\frac{a}{b} + \frac{c}{d}$ is a rational number of arithmetic.

As you might expect, addition of rational numbers of arithmetic is also commutative and associative. The *commutative property* is expressed as follows:

For any two rational numbers of arithmetic $\frac{a}{b}$ and $\frac{c}{d}$, $\frac{a}{b} + \frac{c}{d} = \frac{c}{d} + \frac{a}{b}.$

You should be able to prove commutativity by using the definition of Commutative properties of addition and multiplication, pages 87 and 9 the sum of two rational numbers and commutativity of addition and multiplication of natural numbers.

The *associative property* of addition of rational numbers may be expressed as follows:

For any three rational numbers of arithmetic

$$\frac{a}{b}, \frac{c}{d}, \text{ and } \frac{e}{f},$$

$$(\frac{a}{b} + \frac{c}{d}) + \frac{e}{f} = \frac{a}{b} + (\frac{c}{d} + \frac{e}{f}).$$

Again, we will leave the proof of this property as an exercise for you.

So far, we have seen that addition of rational numbers is closed, commutative, and associative. In these respects, it is like addition of natural numbers. We will discuss one other property in this section that is analogous to a property of addition of natural numbers. This is the rôle of the number $\frac{0}{1}$ in addition. We have already noted that $\frac{0}{1}$ is the mate of the natural number 0; so we would expect $\frac{0}{1}$ to behave like 0. You know that 0 is the identity element for addition of natural numbers; that is, Identity element for addition, page 95 the sum of a given natural number and 0 is the given natural number.

Now we want to see if the sum of a given rational number and $\frac{0}{1}$ is equal to the given number. Certainly, if we examine specific examples, we can see that this is the case.

$$\frac{7}{8} + \frac{0}{1} = \frac{7 \cdot 1 + 8 \cdot 0}{8 \cdot 1} = \frac{7}{8}.$$

$$\frac{25}{4} + \frac{0}{1} = \frac{25 \cdot 1 + 4 \cdot 0}{4 \cdot 1} = \frac{25}{4}.$$

$$\frac{6}{1} + \frac{0}{1} = \frac{6 + 0}{1} = \frac{6}{1}.$$

We can also show very easily that the sum of any number $\frac{a}{b}$ and $\frac{0}{1}$ is $\frac{a}{b}$. From the definition of sum, we know that

$$\frac{a}{b} + \frac{0}{1} = \frac{a \cdot 1 + b \cdot 0}{b \cdot 1}.$$

From the properties of multiplication of natural numbers, we know that Properties o multiplicatic of natural numbers, pages 92 an $a \cdot 1 = a$, that $b \cdot 1 = b$, and that $b \cdot 0 = 0$. Hence,

$$\frac{a}{b} + \frac{0}{1} = \frac{a + 0}{1}.$$

Because 0 is the identity element for addition of natural numbers, we also know that $a + 0 = a$. Therefore, we conclude that

$$\frac{a}{b} + \frac{0}{1} = \frac{a}{b}.$$

Thus, we have established that $\frac{0}{1}$ is the *identity element* for addition of rational numbers. This property can be expressed as follows:

For any rational number of arithmetic $\frac{a}{b}, \frac{a}{b} + \frac{0}{1} = \frac{a}{b}.$

215 Use the addition property of equality for natural numbers to prove the following: For any three rational numbers $\frac{a}{c}$, $\frac{b}{c}$, and $\frac{d}{c}$, if $\frac{a}{c} = \frac{b}{c}$, then $\frac{a}{c} + \frac{d}{c} = \frac{b}{c} + \frac{d}{c}$.

Addition property of equality, page 98

216 Prove that, if $\frac{a}{b}$ and $\frac{c}{d}$ are rational numbers, then $\frac{a}{b} + \frac{c}{d} = \frac{c}{d} + \frac{a}{b}$.

217 Prove that, if $\frac{a}{b}$, $\frac{c}{d}$, and $\frac{e}{f}$ are rational numbers, then
$(\frac{a}{b} + \frac{c}{d}) + \frac{e}{f} = \frac{a}{b} + (\frac{c}{d} + \frac{e}{f})$.

218 Determine the standard name of each of the following sums.

a $\frac{2}{3} + \frac{7}{3}$ c $\frac{15}{9} + \frac{1}{9}$ e $\frac{2}{3} + \frac{9}{5}$ g $\frac{14}{9} + \frac{8}{15}$

b $\frac{9}{5} + \frac{2}{5}$ d $\frac{7}{8} + \frac{5}{8}$ f $7 + \frac{5}{2}$ h $\frac{1}{9} + 4$

219 For each sum named in exercise 218, replace both addends by equal numbers and determine the standard name of the sum.

Multiplication of rational numbers of arithmetic

In the preceding section, we developed a definition of sum so that the sum of two numbers that are mates of natural numbers is the mate of the sum of the natural numbers. We also found that addition of rational numbers of arithmetic has certain properties that we want the operation to have. We would now like to define the product of two rational numbers of arithmetic so that the product of two numbers that are mates of natural numbers is the mate of the product of the natural numbers. Also, there are certain properties that it is desirable for the operation of multiplication to have.

We will again use the natural numbers 2 and 3 and their mates $\frac{2}{1}$ and $\frac{3}{1}$ to illustrate the objective we have in mind. The sentence below expresses a true statement about the product of the natural numbers 2 and 3.

$$2 \times 3 = 6.$$

It is important to define the product of two rational numbers so that the following statement is also true.

$$\frac{2}{1} \times \frac{3}{1} = \frac{6}{1}.$$

From this example, we can see that the numerator of $\frac{6}{1}$ is equal to the product of the numerators of $\frac{2}{1}$ and $\frac{3}{1}$. However, we must be cautious about making any generalizations about the way the denominator of $\frac{6}{1}$ was obtained. It is possible that the denominator is 1 because $\frac{2}{1}$ and $\frac{3}{1}$ have 1 as a common denominator; or it is possible that the denominator of $\frac{6}{1}$ is 1 because 1 is the product of the denominators of $\frac{2}{1}$ and $\frac{3}{1}$. Let us see if we can determine the correct alternative by now using $\frac{6}{3}$ as the mate for 2 and $\frac{9}{3}$ as the mate for 3. As before, we would like the product of $\frac{6}{3}$ and $\frac{9}{3}$ to be the mate of 6.

In the previous example we decided that the numerator of the product is obtained by finding the product of the numerators. Thus, we expect the numerator of the product of $\frac{6}{3}$ and $\frac{9}{3}$ to be 6×9, or 54. Now we want to determine the denominator. Remember that we want the product to be equal to $\frac{6}{1}$ because we want the product of $\frac{6}{3}$ and $\frac{9}{3}$ to be the mate of 6. If we choose 3 as the denominator of the product because it is the common denominator of $\frac{6}{3}$ and $\frac{9}{3}$, we obtain $\frac{54}{3}$. However, this is not a satisfactory result because $\frac{54}{3} \neq \frac{6}{1}$. If we choose 9 as the denominator because it is the product of the denominators of $\frac{6}{3}$ and $\frac{9}{3}$, we obtain $\frac{54}{9}$. This is a satisfactory result because we can use the definition of equal rational numbers of arithmetic to show that $\frac{54}{9} = \frac{6}{1}$; that is, $54 \times 1 = 6 \times 9$.

Thus, we want to define product in such a way that the following statement is true.

$$\tfrac{6}{3} \times \tfrac{9}{3} = \tfrac{54}{9}.$$

We want this to be a true statement because we want the product of $\frac{6}{3}$ and $\frac{9}{3}$ to be the mate of 6, and we know that $\frac{54}{9}$ is the mate of 6.

On the basis of the two examples that we have considered so far, we can make a tentative decision about the way we ought to define the product of two rational numbers of arithmetic. It seems reasonable that we can find the product of two such numbers by finding the product of the numerators and the product of the denominators of the fractions that are used to represent the given numbers.

We have used this procedure in the examples shown below. Note that in each example the two numbers whose product we are finding are mates of natural numbers and that the product is the mate of the product of the natural numbers.

$$\tfrac{25}{5} \times \tfrac{10}{5} = \tfrac{250}{25}.$$
$$\tfrac{6}{2} \times \tfrac{14}{7} = \tfrac{84}{14}.$$
$$\tfrac{12}{3} \times \tfrac{30}{5} = \tfrac{360}{15}.$$
$$\tfrac{0}{7} \times \tfrac{48}{3} = \tfrac{0}{21}.$$
$$\tfrac{3}{3} \times \tfrac{20}{5} = \tfrac{60}{15}.$$

We can now give a general definition for finding the product of any two rational numbers of arithmetic. Of course, this definition is not based solely upon the few examples we have given in the text; but, as you will see later, the definition is satisfactory in terms of the properties that we want the operation of multiplication to have.

For any two rational numbers of arithmetic $\frac{a}{b}$ and $\frac{c}{d}$,
$$\tfrac{a}{b} \cdot \tfrac{c}{d} = \tfrac{ac}{bd}.$$

Notice that this definition applies to all rational numbers of arithmetic; it is irrelevant whether or not the fractions involved have a common denominator. Now we can use the definition of product to investigate various properties of multiplication of rational numbers.

First of all, we can use this definition and the fact that multiplication of natural numbers is closed to show that the product of any two rational numbers is a rational number.

First, by the definition of product, we know that

$$\frac{a}{b} \cdot \frac{c}{d} = \frac{ac}{bd}.$$

Because a and c are natural numbers, we know that ac is a natural number. By the same reasoning, we know that bd is a natural number that is not 0. Therefore, $\frac{ac}{bd}$ is a rational number of arithmetic.

Thus, we have established that the product of any two rational numbers is a rational number. This *closure property of multiplication* is stated below.

> For any two rational numbers of arithmetic $\frac{a}{b}$ and $\frac{c}{d}$,
> $\frac{a}{b} \cdot \frac{c}{d}$ is a rational number of arithmetic.

Next we show that either or both the numbers in a product can be replaced by equal numbers without affecting the product. We have already seen that this is true in one case. In the examples we used earlier, we saw that $\frac{2}{1} \times \frac{3}{1} = \frac{6}{1}$ and that $\frac{6}{3} \times \frac{9}{3} = \frac{54}{9}$. Thus, replacing $\frac{2}{1}$ by $\frac{6}{3}$ and $\frac{3}{1}$ by $\frac{9}{3}$ did not affect the product, since $\frac{54}{9} = \frac{6}{1}$. It can be established that this is true for all rational numbers. We will accept without proof the following property of multiplication.

> For any rational numbers of arithmetic $\frac{a}{b}, \frac{c}{d}, \frac{e}{f}$, and $\frac{g}{h}$,
> if $\frac{a}{b} = \frac{e}{f}$ and if $\frac{c}{d} = \frac{g}{h}$,
> then $\frac{a}{b} \cdot \frac{c}{d} = \frac{e}{f} \cdot \frac{g}{h}$.

A special case of this property, which is also quite useful, is stated below.

> For any rational numbers of arithmetic $\frac{a}{b}, \frac{c}{d}$, and $\frac{e}{f}$,
> if $\frac{a}{b} = \frac{c}{d}$, then $\frac{a}{b} \cdot \frac{e}{f} = \frac{c}{d} \cdot \frac{e}{f}$.

You may remember this property as a rule you learned in algebra that, "if equals are multiplied by equals, then the products are equal." This property is analogous to the multiplication property of equality that was given for natural numbers. Multiplication property of equality, page 98

We can also show that multiplication of rational numbers is commutative and associative. After all, we would find it quite unsatisfactory if the product of $\frac{1}{2}$ and $\frac{3}{4}$ were not equal to the product of $\frac{3}{4}$ and $\frac{1}{2}$. We would also expect that, if we found the product of $(\frac{4}{5} \cdot \frac{7}{2})$ and $\frac{5}{1}$, this product would be equal to the product of $\frac{4}{5}$ and $(\frac{7}{2} \cdot \frac{5}{1})$.

Both commutativity and associativity of multiplication are easily proved by using the definition of product and certain properties of multiplication of natural numbers. We will simply state the properties and leave the proofs as exercises.

The *commutative property* of multiplication is expressed below.

For any two rational numbers of arithmetic $\frac{a}{b}$ and $\frac{c}{d}$,
$$\frac{a}{b} \cdot \frac{c}{d} = \frac{c}{d} \cdot \frac{a}{b}.$$

The *associative property* of multiplication is expressed below.

For any three rational numbers of arithmetic $\frac{a}{b}, \frac{c}{d},$ and $\frac{e}{f}$,
$$(\frac{a}{b} \cdot \frac{c}{d}) \cdot \frac{e}{f} = \frac{a}{b} \cdot (\frac{c}{d} \cdot \frac{e}{f}).$$

220 Use the multiplication property of equality for natural numbers to prove the following: For any numbers $\frac{a}{b}, \frac{c}{d},$ and $\frac{e}{f}$, if $\frac{a}{b} = \frac{c}{d}$, then $\frac{a}{b} \cdot \frac{e}{f} = \frac{c}{d} \cdot \frac{e}{f}$.

221 Prove that, if $\frac{a}{b}$ and $\frac{c}{d}$ are rational numbers, then $\frac{a}{b} \cdot \frac{c}{d} = \frac{c}{d} \cdot \frac{a}{b}$.

222 Prove that, if $\frac{a}{b}, \frac{c}{d},$ and $\frac{e}{f}$ are rational numbers, then $(\frac{a}{b} \cdot \frac{c}{d}) \cdot \frac{e}{f} = \frac{a}{b} \cdot (\frac{c}{d} \cdot \frac{e}{f})$.

223 Find the standard name of each of the following products.

a $\frac{2}{5} \cdot \frac{3}{4}$ **b** $\frac{6}{5} \cdot \frac{3}{8}$ **c** $\frac{9}{2} \cdot \frac{11}{12}$ **d** $\frac{6}{13} \cdot \frac{5}{8}$ **e** $12 \cdot \frac{1}{3}$

By now it should be apparent that the properties of addition and multiplication of rational numbers of arithmetic are very much like those of addition and multiplication of natural numbers. We have already established an identity element for addition—namely, $\frac{0}{1}$—that is the mate of 0, the identity element for addition of natural numbers. On the basis of the similarities explored thus far, we would expect $\frac{1}{1}$ to be the identity element for multiplication of rational numbers, since 1 serves this function in the system of natural numbers. In fact, $\frac{1}{1}$ is the identity element, as we can easily demonstrate.

Identity element for multiplicati of natural numbers, page 95

Suppose that $\frac{a}{b}$ is any given number. Then, by the definition of product, we obtain

$$\frac{1}{1} \cdot \frac{a}{b} = \frac{1 \cdot a}{1 \cdot b}.$$

Since 1 is the identity element for multiplication of natural numbers, we know that $1 \cdot a = a$ and that $1 \cdot b = b$. Therefore,

$$\frac{1 \cdot a}{1 \cdot b} = \frac{a}{b},$$

and, by the transitive property of equality,

Transitive property of equality, page 98

$$\frac{1}{1} \cdot \frac{a}{b} = \frac{a}{b}.$$

Hence, we have shown that the product of $\frac{1}{1}$ and a given rational number is equal to the given number. The fact that $\frac{1}{1}$ is the *identity element* for multiplication is expressed below.

For any rational number of arithmetic $\frac{a}{b}$,
$$\frac{1}{1} \cdot \frac{a}{b} = \frac{a}{b}.$$

You know that the product of every natural number and zero is zero. Similarly, the product of every rational number and $\frac{0}{1}$ is $\frac{0}{1}$. This property may be expressed as follows:

Zero property of multiplication, page 76

For any rational number of arithmetic $\frac{a}{b}$,
$$\frac{0}{1} \cdot \frac{a}{b} = \frac{0}{1}.$$

The proof of this property is quite simple and is left as an exercise.

We have seen that the rational numbers that are mates of the natural numbers behave in the way the natural numbers do with respect to addition and multiplication. Because this is so, we will sometimes use the names of natural numbers for such numbers as $\frac{0}{1}, \frac{1}{1}, \frac{2}{1}$, and so on. For example, we may say that 1, rather than $\frac{1}{1}$, is the identity element for multiplication of rational numbers or that 0, rather than $\frac{0}{1}$, is the identity element for addition. Similarly, we may write

$$2 + \frac{3}{2} = \frac{7}{2}$$

to express the same true statement as

$$\frac{2}{1} + \frac{3}{2} = \frac{7}{2}.$$

Or, again, we may write

$$5 \times \frac{7}{8} = \frac{35}{8}$$

instead of

$$\frac{5}{1} \times \frac{7}{8} = \frac{35}{8}.$$

Multiplication of rational numbers does have one important property that multiplication of natural numbers does not have. In the set of natural numbers, the only pair of numbers whose product is equal to 1 is (1, 1). Thus, in the following sentences, there are no natural-number replacements that will result in true statements.

$$6 \times n = 1.$$
$$15 \times x = 1.$$
$$7 \times a = 1.$$
$$100 \times y = 1.$$

The situation is different, however, in the set of rational numbers. The following sentences illustrate the fact that there are many pairs of numbers other than $(\frac{1}{1}, \frac{1}{1})$ whose product is $\frac{1}{1}$, or 1.

$$\frac{5}{6} \times \frac{6}{5} = \frac{30}{30}, \text{ or } 1.$$
$$\frac{10}{3} \times \frac{3}{10} = 1.$$
$$9 \times \frac{1}{9} = 1.$$
$$\frac{4}{7} \times \frac{7}{4} = 1.$$
$$\frac{17}{35} \times \frac{35}{17} = 1.$$

If the product of two rational numbers is $\frac{1}{1}$, or 1, then each number is called the *multiplicative inverse* (or *reciprocal*) of the other. For example, $\frac{5}{6}$ is the multiplicative inverse of $\frac{6}{5}$, and $\frac{6}{5}$ is the multiplicative inverse of $\frac{5}{6}$. In fact, every rational number except $\frac{0}{1}$ has a multiplicative inverse. It is obvious that $\frac{0}{1}$ cannot have a multiplicative inverse because the product of $\frac{0}{1}$ and every number is $\frac{0}{1}$; hence, it would be impossible for the product of $\frac{0}{1}$ and any number to be $\frac{1}{1}$.

From the examples that we have given, it seems apparent that the multiplicative inverse of $\frac{a}{b}$ is $\frac{b}{a}$. We can show that this is the case. Keep in mind that neither a nor b may be replaced by 0.

By the definition of product, we know that

$$\frac{a}{b} \cdot \frac{b}{a} = \frac{ab}{ba}.$$

Now we can easily show that $\frac{ab}{ba} = \frac{1}{1}$ by using the definition of equal rational numbers of arithmetic and the fact that multiplication of natural numbers is commutative. That is, $ab \times 1 = ab$ and $ba \times 1 = ba$, and $ba = ab$. Hence, $\frac{ab}{ba} = \frac{1}{1}$. Thus, since $\frac{a}{b} \cdot \frac{b}{a} = \frac{ab}{ba}$ and $\frac{ab}{ba} = \frac{1}{1}$, it follows that

$$\frac{a}{b} \cdot \frac{b}{a} = \frac{1}{1}.$$

We have just established that every rational number except $\frac{0}{1}$ has a multiplicative inverse. This property, which we will find very useful in our discussion of division, is expressed below.

For each rational number of arithmetic $\frac{a}{b}$, if $\frac{a}{b} \neq \frac{0}{1}$, then $\frac{b}{a}$ is the multiplicative inverse (reciprocal) of $\frac{a}{b}$.

You will recall that, in the system of natural numbers, multiplication distributes over addition. We will now establish a similar property that relates addition and multiplication of rational numbers. First, we will consider some examples. Suppose that we want to verify that the following is a true statement.

Distributive property, page 95

$$\frac{1}{2}(\frac{3}{4} + \frac{7}{6}) = \frac{1}{2}(\frac{3}{4}) + \frac{1}{2}(\frac{7}{6}).$$

First we will find a standard name for the number expressed at the left of the "equals" sign. $(\frac{3}{4} + \frac{7}{6}) = \frac{46}{24}$, or $\frac{23}{12}$; and $\frac{1}{2}(\frac{23}{12}) = \frac{23}{24}$. Therefore,

$$\tfrac{1}{2}(\tfrac{3}{4} + \tfrac{7}{6}) = \tfrac{23}{24}.$$

Next we will find a standard name for $\frac{1}{2}(\frac{3}{4}) + \frac{1}{2}(\frac{7}{6})$. $\frac{1}{2}(\frac{3}{4}) = \frac{3}{8}$, and $\frac{1}{2}(\frac{7}{6}) = \frac{7}{12}$; so $\frac{1}{2}(\frac{3}{4}) + \frac{1}{2}(\frac{7}{6}) = \frac{3}{8} + \frac{7}{12}$. But $\frac{3}{8} + \frac{7}{12} = \frac{92}{96}$, or $\frac{23}{24}$. Therefore,

$$\tfrac{1}{2}(\tfrac{3}{4}) + \tfrac{1}{2}(\tfrac{7}{6}) = \tfrac{23}{24}.$$

Obviously, $\frac{23}{24} = \frac{23}{24}$; therefore,

$$\tfrac{1}{2}(\tfrac{3}{4} + \tfrac{7}{6}) = \tfrac{1}{2}(\tfrac{3}{4}) + \tfrac{1}{2}(\tfrac{7}{6}).$$

You should use a similar procedure to verify that each of the following is true.

$$3(\tfrac{2}{3} + \tfrac{3}{2}) = 3(\tfrac{2}{3}) + 3(\tfrac{3}{2}).$$
$$\tfrac{1}{4}(\tfrac{7}{10} + 4) = \tfrac{1}{4}(\tfrac{7}{10}) + \tfrac{1}{4}(4).$$
$$\tfrac{0}{3}(2 + \tfrac{5}{8}) = \tfrac{0}{3}(2) + \tfrac{0}{3}(\tfrac{5}{8}).$$

Each of these true statements shows that multiplication distributes over addition of rational numbers.

We will now prove that the rational numbers do have a distributive property by using $\frac{a}{b}$, $\frac{c}{d}$, and $\frac{e}{f}$ to represent any three numbers. We want to establish that

$$\tfrac{a}{b}(\tfrac{c}{d} + \tfrac{e}{f}) = \tfrac{a}{b}(\tfrac{c}{d}) + \tfrac{a}{b}(\tfrac{e}{f}).$$

First we will work with the expression at the left. We know that $(\frac{c}{d} + \frac{e}{f}) = (\frac{cf + de}{df})$; so

Sum of two rational numbers, page 242

$$\tfrac{a}{b}(\tfrac{c}{d} + \tfrac{e}{f}) = \tfrac{a}{b}(\tfrac{cf + de}{df}).$$

Next, by the definition of product, we know that $\frac{a}{b}(\frac{cf + de}{df}) = \frac{a(cf + de)}{bdf}$. Because multiplication distributes over addition of natural numbers, we know that $a(cf + de) = acf + ade$. So we can conclude that

Definition of product, page 246

$$\tfrac{a}{b}(\tfrac{c}{d} + \tfrac{e}{f}) = \tfrac{acf + ade}{bdf}.$$

Now we want to show that $\frac{a}{b}(\frac{c}{d}) + \frac{a}{b}(\frac{e}{f})$ is also equal to $\frac{acf + ade}{bdf}$. First we know that $\frac{a}{b}(\frac{c}{d}) = \frac{ac}{bd}$ and that $\frac{a}{b}(\frac{e}{f}) = \frac{ae}{bf}$. Therefore,

$$\tfrac{a}{b}(\tfrac{c}{d}) + \tfrac{a}{b}(\tfrac{e}{f}) = \tfrac{ac}{bd} + \tfrac{ae}{bf}.$$

Next we obtain

$$\tfrac{a}{b}(\tfrac{c}{d}) + \tfrac{a}{b}(\tfrac{e}{f}) = \tfrac{acbf + aebd}{bdbf}.$$

Since multiplication of natural numbers is commutative and associative, we know that $acbf = b(acf)$, that $aebd = b(ade)$, and that $bdbf = b(bdf)$. Therefore,

$$\frac{a}{b}\left(\frac{c}{d}\right) + \frac{a}{b}\left(\frac{e}{f}\right) = \frac{b(acf) + b(ade)}{b(bdf)}.$$

By the definition of product and the distributive property of natural numbers, we know that $\frac{b(acf) + b(ade)}{b(bdf)} = \frac{b}{b} \times \frac{acf + ade}{bdf}$. But $\frac{b}{b} = \frac{1}{1}$. So, since $\frac{1}{1}$ is the identity element for multiplication, $\frac{b(acf) + b(ade)}{b(bdf)} = \frac{acf + ade}{bdf}$. Hence,

$$\frac{a}{b}\left(\frac{c}{d}\right) + \frac{a}{b}\left(\frac{e}{f}\right) = \frac{acf + ade}{bdf}.$$

Thus, we have shown that both $\frac{a}{b}\left(\frac{c}{d} + \frac{e}{f}\right)$ and $\frac{a}{b}\left(\frac{c}{d}\right) + \frac{a}{b}\left(\frac{e}{f}\right)$ are equal to $\frac{acf + ade}{bdf}$, and we have demonstrated that multiplication distributes over addition of rational numbers. This property is expressed below.

For any rational numbers of arithmetic $\frac{a}{b}$, $\frac{c}{d}$, and $\frac{e}{f}$,

$$\frac{a}{b}\left(\frac{c}{d} + \frac{e}{f}\right) = \frac{a}{b}\left(\frac{c}{d}\right) + \frac{a}{b}\left(\frac{e}{f}\right).$$

224 Prove that, if $\frac{a}{b}$ is a rational number, then $\frac{0}{1} \cdot \frac{a}{b} = \frac{0}{1}$.

225 Find the multiplicative inverse for each of the following numbers.

   a $\frac{5}{9}$ **b** $\frac{2}{1} + \frac{1}{3}$ **c** $\frac{37}{11}$ **d** $\frac{2}{3} + \frac{1}{5}$ **e** $\frac{4}{7} \cdot \frac{5}{6}$ **f** 3

226 Verify that the distributive property of multiplication over addition of rational numbers holds for each of the following examples.

   a $\frac{2}{3}\left(\frac{1}{5} + \frac{5}{6}\right) = \frac{2}{3} \cdot \frac{1}{5} + \frac{2}{3} \cdot \frac{5}{6}$.   **b** $\frac{6}{1}\left(\frac{1}{2} + \frac{2}{3}\right) = \frac{6}{1} \cdot \frac{1}{2} + \frac{6}{1} \cdot \frac{2}{3}$.

Now that we have shown that multiplication distributes over addition of rational numbers, we have all the properties of these two operations that are needed to develop the system of rational numbers of arithmetic. However, before we describe this number system, we will determine how rational numbers of arithmetic are ordered.

Ordering the rational numbers of arithmetic

In connection with the natural numbers, we used the idea of the successor set to order the natural numbers. It will now be useful to develop a general method for deciding when one rational number of arithmetic is greater than or less than another. Order of natural numbers, pages 34-3$

If we consider the fractions that are elements of a rational number of arithmetic, we can determine which fraction represents the greater quantity in a given physical situation. The illustration on page 253 shows that $\frac{5}{6}$ is greater than $\frac{1}{2}$ because $\frac{5}{6}$ of the "pie" is a greater amount than $\frac{1}{2}$ of the "pie." From this it follows that the number $\frac{5}{6}$ is greater than the number $\frac{1}{2}$; that is, $\frac{5}{6} > \frac{1}{2}$.

$$\frac{5}{6} \qquad \frac{1}{2}$$

The problem, however, is to establish a *general* method of determining whether one rational number of arithmetic is greater than or less than another without resorting to a comparison of physical objects. This is desirable because the comparison of two numbers in a physical situation is not always convenient or obvious. Suppose, for example, that we want to know which is the greater, $\frac{7}{56}$ or $\frac{22}{178}$. It would be quite difficult to construct a physical model that would enable us to decide which of the numbers, $\frac{7}{56}$ or $\frac{22}{178}$, represents the greater quantity. Instead, it is necessary to establish some general mathematical basis for determining the order of rational numbers.

We have already established a definition of equal rational numbers of arithmetic; perhaps we can use this definition to help us define a "greater than" relation between two numbers. We know that any two numbers $\frac{a}{b}$ and $\frac{c}{d}$ are equal if $ad = cb$. Let us examine some specific examples to see what relation exists between ad and cb if $\frac{a}{b}$ is greater than $\frac{c}{d}$. Each of the following is a true statement about two rational numbers. We have chosen examples in which it is obvious that the first number is greater than the second.

Equality of rational numbers of arithmetic, page 236

$$\frac{3}{5} > \frac{1}{8}.$$
$$\frac{3}{1} > \frac{2}{1}.$$
$$\frac{7}{2} > \frac{2}{3}.$$
$$\frac{8}{10} > \frac{1}{5}.$$
$$\frac{5}{4} > \frac{1}{4}.$$

In each of these examples, we can think of the first number as $\frac{a}{b}$ and the second number as $\frac{c}{d}$. Each of the following is a true statement about the numbers that are replacements for a, b, c, and d in the products ad and cb.

$$3 \cdot 8 > 1 \cdot 5.$$
$$3 \cdot 1 > 2 \cdot 1.$$
$$7 \cdot 3 > 2 \cdot 2.$$
$$8 \cdot 5 > 1 \cdot 10.$$
$$5 \cdot 4 > 1 \cdot 4.$$

From these examples, it seems that, if $\frac{a}{b}$ is greater than $\frac{c}{d}$, then ad is greater than cb. We use this as a basis for our definition. It is also true that, if the product ad is greater than the product cb, then $\frac{a}{b}$ is greater than $\frac{c}{d}$. Hence, the "greater than" relation for rational numbers of arithmetic may be defined as follows:

For any two rational numbers of arithmetic $\frac{a}{b}$ and $\frac{c}{d}$,
$\frac{a}{b} > \frac{c}{d}$ if and only if $ad > cb$.

You should use the definition of "greater than" and the definition of an equivalence relation to determine if this relation is reflexive, symmetric, or transitive. Also notice that, from the definition of equal rational numbers of arithmetic and the definition of "greater than," it is possible to make the following generalization.

Equivalence relation, page 194

For any two rational numbers of arithmetic $\frac{a}{b}$ and $\frac{c}{d}$,
just one of the following is true:
$\frac{a}{b} = \frac{c}{d}, \frac{a}{b} > \frac{c}{d}$, or $\frac{c}{d} > \frac{a}{b}$.

The two properties of the relation of "greater than" that are expressed below are useful in finding solutions of conditions that involve addition or multiplication of rational numbers.

For the rational numbers of arithmetic $\frac{a}{b}, \frac{c}{d}, \frac{e}{f}$, and $\frac{g}{h}$,
if $\frac{a}{b} > \frac{e}{f}$ and if $\frac{c}{d} = \frac{g}{h}$, then $\frac{a}{b} + \frac{c}{d} > \frac{e}{f} + \frac{g}{h}$.

For the rational numbers of arithmetic $\frac{a}{b}, \frac{c}{d}, \frac{e}{f}$, and $\frac{g}{h}$,
where $\frac{c}{d}$ and $\frac{g}{h}$ are non-zero,
if $\frac{a}{b} > \frac{e}{f}$ and if $\frac{c}{d} = \frac{g}{h}$, then $\frac{a}{b} \cdot \frac{c}{d} > \frac{e}{f} \cdot \frac{g}{h}$.

The first of these two properties assures us that, if $\frac{a}{b}$ is greater than $\frac{e}{f}$ and if $\frac{c}{d} = \frac{g}{h}$, then the sum of $\frac{a}{b}$ and $\frac{c}{d}$ is greater than the sum of $\frac{e}{f}$ and $\frac{g}{h}$; the second property assures us that, under the given conditions, the product of $\frac{a}{b}$ and $\frac{c}{d}$ is greater than the product of $\frac{e}{f}$ and $\frac{g}{h}$.

You should be able to develop a proof of the first property by using the definition of sum and the definition of "greater than." The second property can be proved by using the definition of product and the definition of "greater than."

227 Give three examples of each of the following properties of "greater than."
a If $\frac{a}{b} > \frac{e}{f}$ and $\frac{c}{d} = \frac{g}{h}$, then $\frac{a}{b} + \frac{c}{d} > \frac{e}{f} + \frac{g}{h}$ for the rational numbers of arithmetic $\frac{a}{b}, \frac{c}{d}, \frac{e}{f}$, and $\frac{g}{h}$.
b If $\frac{a}{b} > \frac{e}{f}$ and $\frac{c}{d} = \frac{g}{h}$, then $\frac{a}{b} \cdot \frac{c}{d} > \frac{e}{f} \cdot \frac{g}{h}$ for the rational numbers of arithmetic $\frac{a}{b}, \frac{c}{d}, \frac{e}{f}$, and $\frac{g}{h}$, where $\frac{c}{d}$ and $\frac{g}{h}$ are non-zero.

228 For the rational numbers $\frac{a}{b}$ and $\frac{c}{d}$, we define $\frac{a}{b} < \frac{c}{d}$ if and only if $\frac{c}{d} > \frac{a}{b}$. An ordered pair of rational numbers of arithmetic is named in each of the eight exercises at the top of page 255. Decide if "=," ">," or "<" should be used to express the relation between the first and second components of each ordered pair.

a $(\frac{1}{3}, \frac{1}{2})$ c $(\frac{1}{4}, 4)$ e $(\frac{18}{2}, \frac{27}{3})$ g $(8\frac{1}{2}, \frac{33}{4})$

b $(\frac{6}{1}, \frac{2}{3})$ d $(\frac{3}{5}, \frac{5}{3})$ f $(\frac{6}{10}, \frac{5}{10})$ h $(\frac{1}{8}, \frac{5}{40})$

229 For any number $\frac{a}{b}$, if $\frac{a}{b} > \frac{1}{1}$, what can you conclude about the multiplicative inverse of $\frac{a}{b}$? If $\frac{a}{b} < \frac{1}{1}$, what can you conclude about its multiplicative inverse?

230 a Suppose that $\frac{463}{198} \times \frac{581}{580} = \frac{a}{b}$. Decide, without computing, whether $\frac{a}{b} > \frac{463}{198}$, $\frac{a}{b} < \frac{463}{198}$, or $\frac{a}{b} = \frac{463}{198}$.

b Suppose that $\frac{a}{b} \cdot \frac{c}{d} = \frac{x}{y}$, where a, b, c, and d are counting numbers, and that $a = b + 1$ and $c = d + 1$. Is $\frac{x}{y} > \frac{1}{1}$, is $\frac{x}{y} = \frac{1}{1}$, or is $\frac{x}{z} < \frac{1}{1}$?

c If $\frac{a}{b} \cdot \frac{c}{d} = \frac{a}{b}$, what must be true of $\frac{c}{d}$?

d If $\frac{a}{b} \cdot \frac{c}{d} > \frac{a}{b}$, what must be true of $\frac{c}{d}$?

e If $\frac{a}{b} \cdot \frac{c}{d} < \frac{a}{b}$, what must be true of $\frac{c}{d}$?

The system of rational numbers of arithmetic

We are now in a position to say why it is possible to call a set of equivalent fractions a number. We have defined sums and products involving such numbers as $\frac{1}{2}$, $\frac{5}{38}$, and $\frac{0}{1}$. We have also shown that addition and multiplication are closed, commutative, and associative and that multiplication distributes over addition. Thus, because sets of equivalent fractions, together with the operations and their properties, do satisfy the definition of a number system, we are justified in calling them numbers. This was not the case with the sets of ordered pairs we called proportional relations in Chapter 8.

Number system, page 96

We have not talked about the relation of equality in connection with the set of rational numbers of arithmetic because equality has the same properties with respect to rational numbers of arithmetic as it has with respect to natural numbers. We will simply state that, with respect to the system of rational numbers of arithmetic, the relation of equality is reflexive, symmetric, and transitive and that the addition and multiplication properties of equality hold for rational numbers as well as for naturals.

Properties of equality, page 98

The chart on the next page summarizes the properties of the system of rational numbers of arithmetic and of the relations of equality and "greater than." The multiplicative-inverse property is not shared by the natural-number system; so we have "boxed it in" to show that it is a special property of this system. You may wish to compare this chart with the one for the natural-number system that appears on page 96.

The system of rational numbers of arithmetic

	Addition	Multiplication
Closure $\longrightarrow$	$\frac{a}{b} + \frac{c}{d}$ is a rational number of arithmetic.	$\frac{a}{b} \cdot \frac{c}{d}$ is a rational number of arithmetic.
Commutativity $\longrightarrow$	$\frac{a}{b} + \frac{c}{d} = \frac{c}{d} + \frac{a}{b}.$	$\frac{a}{b} \cdot \frac{c}{d} = \frac{c}{d} \cdot \frac{a}{b}.$
Associativity $\longrightarrow$	$(\frac{a}{b} + \frac{c}{d}) + \frac{e}{f} =$ $\frac{a}{b} + (\frac{c}{d} + \frac{e}{f}).$	$(\frac{a}{b} \cdot \frac{c}{d})\frac{e}{f} = \frac{a}{b}(\frac{c}{d} \cdot \frac{e}{f}).$
Distributivity $\longrightarrow$		$\frac{a}{b}(\frac{c}{d} + \frac{e}{f}) = \frac{a}{b}(\frac{c}{d}) + \frac{a}{b}(\frac{e}{f}).$

Special properties of addition and multiplication

Identity element $\longrightarrow$	$\frac{a}{b} + \frac{0}{1} = \frac{a}{b}.$	$\frac{a}{b} \cdot \frac{1}{1} = \frac{a}{b}.$
Zero $\longrightarrow$		$\frac{a}{b} \cdot \frac{0}{1} = 0.$
Inverse $\longrightarrow$		$\boxed{\frac{a}{b} \cdot \frac{b}{a} = \frac{1}{1}}$

Properties of equality

Reflexive $\longrightarrow$	$\frac{a}{b} = \frac{a}{b}.$
Symmetric $\longrightarrow$	If $\frac{a}{b} = \frac{c}{d}$, then $\frac{c}{d} = \frac{a}{b}.$
Transitive $\longrightarrow$	If $\frac{a}{b} = \frac{c}{d}$ and $\frac{c}{d} = \frac{e}{f}$, then $\frac{a}{b} = \frac{e}{f}.$
Addition $\longrightarrow$	If $\frac{a}{b} = \frac{c}{d}$, then $\frac{a}{b} + \frac{e}{f} = \frac{c}{d} + \frac{e}{f}.$
Multiplication $\longrightarrow$	If $\frac{a}{b} = \frac{c}{d}$, then $\frac{a}{b} \cdot \frac{e}{f} = \frac{c}{d} \cdot \frac{e}{f}.$

Properties of "greater than"

Transitive $\longrightarrow$	If $\frac{a}{b} > \frac{c}{d}$ and $\frac{c}{d} > \frac{e}{f}$, then $\frac{a}{b} > \frac{e}{f}.$
Addition $\longrightarrow$	If $\frac{a}{b} > \frac{e}{f}$ and $\frac{c}{d} = \frac{g}{h}$, then $\frac{a}{b} + \frac{c}{d} > \frac{e}{f} + \frac{g}{h}.$
Multiplication $\longrightarrow$	If $\frac{a}{b} > \frac{e}{f}$ and $\frac{c}{d} = \frac{g}{h}$, then $\frac{a}{b} \cdot \frac{c}{d} > \frac{e}{f} \cdot \frac{g}{h}.$

Use the pairs of fraction numerals given below in connection with exercises 231, 232, and 233.

a $\frac{1}{2}, \frac{1}{3}$ **b** $\frac{3}{4}, \frac{1}{7}$ **c** $\frac{5}{7}, \frac{3}{11}$ **d** $\frac{1}{2}, \frac{2}{4}$

231 Tabulate the rational number of arithmetic that is named by each numeral in each pair. Name at least 6 fractions in your tabulation.

232 Tabulate the rational number of arithmetic equal to the sum of each pair.

233 Tabulate the rational number equal to the product of each pair.

234 Find each sum or product named below.

a $\frac{2}{3} + 1$ **b** $\frac{2}{3} \times \frac{0}{5}$ **c** $\frac{5}{16} + \frac{4}{4}$ **d** $\frac{456}{678} \times \frac{567}{567}$ **e** $\frac{45}{139} \times \frac{49}{49}$

235 Give examples to illustrate the reflexive, symmetric, and transitive properties of equality in the system of rational numbers.

236 Prove that there is exactly one identity element for addition of rational numbers. You can do this by first assuming that there are two identity elements, 0 and 0′, such that $\frac{a}{b} + 0 = \frac{a}{b}$ and $\frac{a}{b} + 0' = \frac{a}{b}$.

Subtraction and division of rational numbers of arithmetic

As in the natural-number system, subtraction and division are not essential to the system of rational numbers of arithmetic because subtraction can be defined in terms of addition and division can be defined in terms of multiplication. You will recall that, in Chapter 5, when we studied subtraction of natural numbers, we talked about subtraction in connection with sentences like

Subtraction related to addition, page 102

$$n + 5 = 8.$$

If n is replaced by 3, the above sentence expresses a true statement. However, we agreed that the replacement for n that satisfies $n + 5 = 8$ also satisfies

$$n = 8 - 5.$$

Thus, because the *sum* of 3 and 5 is 8, the *difference* of 8 and 5 is 3.

We can analyze subtraction of rational numbers of arithmetic in much the same way. For example, because

$$\tfrac{1}{4} + \tfrac{1}{2} = \tfrac{3}{4},$$

we know that

$$\tfrac{3}{4} - \tfrac{1}{2} = \tfrac{1}{4}.$$

Again, suppose that the sum of $\frac{a}{b}$ and $\frac{2}{3}$ is equal to $\frac{7}{8}$. We can express this idea in either of the two ways shown below.

$$\tfrac{a}{b} + \tfrac{2}{3} = \tfrac{7}{8}$$

or

$$\tfrac{7}{8} - \tfrac{2}{3} = \tfrac{a}{b}.$$

Now let us imagine that we do not know how to obtain the difference of $\frac{7}{8}$ and $\frac{2}{3}$, and must use the first sentence above to determine $\frac{a}{b}$.

The following exposition shows that we can, in fact, find the difference of $\frac{7}{8}$ and $\frac{2}{3}$ by using our knowledge of addition and certain properties of natural numbers and of rational numbers of arithmetic. From $\frac{a}{b} + \frac{2}{3} = \frac{7}{8}$, we first obtain

$$\frac{3a + 2b}{3b} = \frac{7}{8}.$$

Next we use the definition of equal rational numbers of arithmetic to obtain

$$8(3a + 2b) = 21b.$$

Since multiplication is distributive over addition of natural numbers, $8(3a + 2b) = 24a + 16b$; so

$$24a + 16b = 21b.$$

Similarly, $21b = 16b + 5b$; therefore,

$$24a + 16b = 16b + 5b.$$

By the cancellation property of addition of natural numbers, we obtain

$$24a = 5b.$$

Cancellation property of addition, page 95

Because multiplication of natural numbers is commutative, we know that $24a = a \cdot 24$. Thus,

$$a \cdot 24 = 5b.$$

From the definition of equal rational numbers of arithmetic, we know that if $ad = cb$, then $\frac{a}{b} = \frac{c}{d}$. So, from $a \cdot 24 = 5b$, we obtain

$$\frac{a}{b} = \frac{5}{24}.$$

Thus, we have shown that the difference of $\frac{7}{8}$ and $\frac{2}{3}$ is $\frac{5}{24}$ because the sum of $\frac{5}{24}$ and $\frac{2}{3}$ is $\frac{7}{8}$.

Obviously, the procedure we just went through is a lengthy one and is not a very practical method for finding the difference of two numbers. It was presented to show that subtraction is not essential because we can find the difference of two rational numbers of arithmetic by using our knowledge of sums. Certainly, this kind of approach to subtraction is not a wise one to use with elementary school children. Instead, we make use of our knowledge of subtraction of natural numbers to define the difference of two rational numbers of arithmetic. The difference of two rational numbers of arithmetic is defined as follows:

For any two rational numbers of arithmetic $\frac{a}{b}$ and $\frac{c}{d}$,
if $\frac{a}{b} \geq \frac{c}{d}$,
then $\frac{a}{b} - \frac{c}{d} = \frac{ad - bc}{bd}$.

Note that, in this definition, we must stipulate that the first number be greater than or equal to the second number. This is necessary because subtraction is not closed in the set of rational numbers of arithmetic, just as it is not closed in the set of natural numbers. This means that, if the

universe is the set of rational numbers of arithmetic, there is no replacement for n that satisfies any of the following conditions.

$$n + 6\tfrac{3}{4} = 5\tfrac{1}{2}.$$
$$\tfrac{2}{3} - \tfrac{7}{8} = n.$$
$$3 - 4 = n.$$

Thus, it is apparent that subtraction is not closed in the set of rational
numbers of arithmetic. You should be able to give examples to demonstrate that subtraction of rational numbers has neither a commutative nor
an associative property.

237 Is subtraction of rational numbers of arithmetic a commutative operation?
Give an example to support your answer.

238 Is subtraction of rational numbers of arithmetic an associative operation?
Give an example to support your answer.

239 Use the method described on pages 257 and 258 to determine $\tfrac{a}{b}$ without
subtracting if $\tfrac{a}{b} + \tfrac{4}{5} = \tfrac{8}{3}$.

240 Find the standard name of each of the following differences.
 a $\tfrac{5}{8} - \tfrac{1}{3}$ **b** $\tfrac{7}{12} - \tfrac{2}{5}$ **c** $\tfrac{9}{4} - \tfrac{4}{3}$ **d** $2 - \tfrac{9}{10}$

241 a Find a rational number of arithmetic $\tfrac{x}{y}$ such that $\tfrac{3}{4} - \tfrac{x}{y} < \tfrac{1}{1000}$.
 b Find a rational number of arithmetic $\tfrac{x}{y}$ such that $\tfrac{3}{4} - \tfrac{x}{y} < \tfrac{1}{444}$.

Now we will relate division of rational numbers to multiplication in
much the same way that we related division to multiplication in the set of
natural numbers. There are, however, some important differences between
division in the set of rational numbers and division in the set of natural
numbers that will be discussed.

In our discussion of division of natural numbers, we related

Division
related to
multiplication,
page 103

$$n \times 2 = 6$$

to the condition

$$n = 6 \div 2.$$

We said that the replacement for n that satisfies $n \times 2 = 6$ also satisfies
$n = 6 \div 2$. In other words, because the *product* of 3 and 2 is 6, the *quotient*
of 6 and 2 is 3.

Similarly, when we are working with rational numbers, we agree that,
because the product of $\tfrac{2}{1}$ and $\tfrac{1}{2}$ is $\tfrac{1}{1}$, the quotient of $\tfrac{1}{1}$ and $\tfrac{2}{1}$ is $\tfrac{1}{2}$. Thus,

$$\tfrac{2}{1} \times \tfrac{1}{2} = \tfrac{1}{1}$$

also means

$$\tfrac{1}{2} = \tfrac{1}{1} \div \tfrac{2}{1}.$$

Because of the relationship between multiplication and division, we can find the number that satisfies

$$\tfrac{5}{8} \div \tfrac{1}{3} = \tfrac{a}{b}$$

by using

$$\tfrac{a}{b} \times \tfrac{1}{3} = \tfrac{5}{8}.$$

Let us use our definition of product to see how this can be done. First, by the definition of product, we obtain

$$\tfrac{a \cdot 1}{b \cdot 3} = \tfrac{5}{8}$$

from $\tfrac{a}{b} \times \tfrac{1}{3} = \tfrac{5}{8}$. Now we know that $a \cdot 1 = a$ and that $b \cdot 3 = 3b$, so we can write

$$\tfrac{a}{3b} = \tfrac{5}{8}.$$

Next, by using the definition of equal rational numbers of arithmetic, we obtain

$$a \cdot 8 = 15 \cdot b.$$

But, again using the definition of equal rational numbers of arithmetic, we know that

$$\tfrac{a}{b} = \tfrac{15}{8}.$$

Hence, $\tfrac{15}{8} \times \tfrac{1}{3} = \tfrac{5}{8}$ also means $\tfrac{5}{8} \div \tfrac{1}{3} = \tfrac{15}{8}$.

From this example, it should be apparent that, because of the way in which division is related to multiplication, it is not absolutely necessary to establish a separate method for finding the quotient of two rational numbers. However, it is useful to have a shorter method for finding quotients.

In the past, children in the elementary school were taught that, "to divide fractions, you invert the divisor and multiply." They used this procedure without really understanding why it was possible to find quotients in this way. When we "invert the divisor and multiply," we make use of two important properties of division. First we use the idea that the quotient of a given number and 1 is the given number. This is a property of division, no matter what set of numbers you are using. Because we are now interested in using this property in connection with division of rational numbers, we will state the property in terms of such numbers.

For any rational number of arithmetic, $\tfrac{a}{b} \div \tfrac{1}{1} = \tfrac{a}{b}$.

This follows from the fact that $\tfrac{a}{b} \cdot \tfrac{1}{1} = \tfrac{a}{b}$ for any rational number of arithmetic $\tfrac{a}{b}$.

The second property of division that we use is the property that the quotient of two numbers is not affected if both the dividend and the divisor are multiplied by the same non-zero number. This property, which also holds for any set of numbers, is stated below in terms of rational numbers of arithmetic.

For any three rational numbers of arithmetic $\frac{a}{b}$, $\frac{c}{d}$, and $\frac{e}{f}$,
if $\frac{c}{d} \neq 0$ and if $\frac{e}{f} \neq 0$, then $\frac{a}{b} \div \frac{c}{d} = (\frac{a}{b} \cdot \frac{e}{f}) \div (\frac{c}{d} \cdot \frac{e}{f})$.

When we divide rational numbers, we choose a number by which to multiply both dividend and divisor so that the divisor becomes 1. For example, suppose that we want to find the replacement for $\frac{x}{y}$ that satisfies the following condition.

$$\frac{9}{2} \div \frac{6}{5} = \frac{x}{y}.$$

Our problem is to multiply both $\frac{9}{2}$ and $\frac{6}{5}$ by some number so that the product of $\frac{6}{5}$ and the number is 1. We can now make use of the multiplicative-inverse property, which we established earlier. We know that $\frac{5}{6}$ is the multiplicative inverse, or reciprocal, of $\frac{6}{5}$ because $\frac{6}{5} \times \frac{5}{6} = 1$. The property that we just stated concerning multiplying both dividend and divisor by the same number enables us to write

Multiplicative inverse, page 250

$$\frac{9}{2} \div \frac{6}{5} = (\frac{9}{2} \cdot \frac{5}{6}) \div (\frac{6}{5} \cdot \frac{5}{6}).$$

Thus, from this statement and from $\frac{9}{2} \div \frac{6}{5} = \frac{x}{y}$, we obtain

$$(\frac{9}{2} \cdot \frac{5}{6}) \div (\frac{6}{5} \cdot \frac{5}{6}) = \frac{x}{y}.$$

But $(\frac{6}{5} \cdot \frac{5}{6}) = 1$, so we obtain

$$(\frac{9}{2} \cdot \frac{5}{6}) \div 1 = \frac{x}{y}.$$

Next, by the property concerning the division of a given number by 1, we know that

$$(\frac{9}{2} \cdot \frac{5}{6}) \div 1 = \frac{9}{2} \cdot \frac{5}{6}.$$

So we obtain

$$\frac{9}{2} \cdot \frac{5}{6} = \frac{x}{y}.$$

This condition has the same solution as $\frac{9}{2} \div \frac{6}{5} = \frac{x}{y}$. This means that

$$\frac{9}{2} \div \frac{6}{5} = \frac{9}{2} \cdot \frac{5}{6}.$$

We have gone through this procedure to give you an explanation of why you find the quotient of two rational numbers by "inverting the divisor and multiplying." Another way of saying this is to say that, to find the quotient of two rational numbers, you find the product of the dividend and the multiplicative inverse, or reciprocal, of the divisor. Thus, we can define the quotient of two rational numbers of arithmetic in this way:

For any two rational numbers of arithmetic $\frac{a}{b}$ and $\frac{c}{d}$,
if $\frac{c}{d} \neq 0$, then $\frac{a}{b} \div \frac{c}{d} = \frac{a}{b} \cdot \frac{d}{c}$.

Note that $\frac{c}{d}$ cannot be equal to 0. This limitation is necessary because 0 does not have a multiplicative inverse; and, if $\frac{c}{d}$ were equal to 0, then $\frac{d}{c}$ could not represent the multiplicative inverse of $\frac{c}{d}$.

The explanation of division just given represents the approach that we think ought to be used for teaching division of rationals of arithmetic in the elementary school. However, there is another method of defining division by using the relation between multiplication and division. This approach to division is based entirely upon the definitions and properties of rational numbers already developed.

We begin again with the condition

$$\frac{9}{2} \div \frac{6}{5} = \frac{x}{y}.$$

Because of the way division is defined in terms of multiplication, this is the same as

$$\frac{9}{2} = \frac{x}{y} \times \frac{6}{5}.$$

One of the properties of multiplication that we discussed earlier establishes that, if $\frac{a}{b} = \frac{c}{d}$ and $\frac{e}{f} = \frac{g}{h}$, then $\frac{a}{b} \cdot \frac{e}{f} = \frac{c}{d} \cdot \frac{g}{h}$. We now use this property to multiply both $\frac{9}{2}$ and $\frac{x}{y} \times \frac{6}{5}$ by $\frac{5}{6}$, the multiplicative inverse of $\frac{6}{5}$. Thus,

$$\frac{9}{2} \times \frac{5}{6} = (\frac{x}{y} \times \frac{6}{5}) \times \frac{5}{6}.$$

Because multiplication is associative, $(\frac{x}{y} \times \frac{6}{5}) \times \frac{5}{6} = \frac{x}{y} \times (\frac{6}{5} \times \frac{5}{6})$. Therefore,

$$\frac{9}{2} \times \frac{5}{6} = \frac{x}{y} \times (\frac{6}{5} \times \frac{5}{6}).$$

It should now be apparent why we chose to multiply both sides of the condition by the multiplicative inverse of $\frac{6}{5}$. Since $\frac{6}{5} \times \frac{5}{6} = \frac{1}{1}$ and $\frac{x}{y} \times \frac{1}{1} = \frac{x}{y}$, we obtain

$$\frac{9}{2} \times \frac{5}{6} = \frac{x}{y}.$$

Thus, we have again shown that $\frac{9}{2} \div \frac{6}{5} = \frac{9}{2} \times \frac{5}{6}$.

We now generalize this method by using $\frac{a}{b}, \frac{c}{d}$, and $\frac{x}{y}$ to represent three given numbers when $\frac{c}{d}$ is non-zero. The series of conditions on the next page is obtained just as were the steps in the example already discussed; hence, the justification for each step here is the same as for the corresponding step in the example.

$$\frac{a}{b} \div \frac{c}{d} = \frac{x}{y}.$$

$$\frac{a}{b} = \frac{x}{y} \times \frac{c}{d}.$$

$$\frac{a}{b} \times \frac{d}{c} = \left(\frac{x}{y} \times \frac{c}{d}\right) \times \frac{d}{c}.$$

$$\frac{a}{b} \times \frac{d}{c} = \frac{x}{y} \times \left(\frac{c}{d} \times \frac{d}{c}\right).$$

$$\frac{a}{b} \times \frac{d}{c} = \frac{x}{y} \times \frac{1}{1}.$$

$$\frac{a}{b} \times \frac{d}{c} = \frac{x}{y}.$$

$$\frac{a}{b} \times \frac{d}{c} = \frac{a}{b} \div \frac{c}{d}.$$

Thus, we have shown in two different ways that the quotient of two rational numbers is equal to the product of the dividend and the multiplicative inverse of the divisor. We feel that the first method presented in this section, which is more intuitive and less subtle than the second, is more appropriate for elementary school children who are just learning how to divide rational numbers.

We will now use our definition of quotient to see what properties division of rational numbers has. To find the quotient of two rational numbers, we find the product of two numbers—namely, the dividend and the reciprocal of the divisor. We know that the product of any two such numbers is a rational number of arithmetic. Because every number except 0 has a multiplicative inverse and because multiplication is closed in the set of rational numbers, the quotient of any two non-zero rational numbers is also a rational number. Thus, unlike division of natural numbers, division of non-zero rational numbers has a closure property.

We have just seen that division does have one property in the set of rational numbers that it does not have in the set of natural numbers. You should be able to give examples to show that division of rational numbers of arithmetic does not have either a commutative or an associative property, just as division of natural numbers does not have these properties.

Often it is convenient to think of a rational number as the quotient of two natural numbers. In the discussion that follows, we will show why it is possible to think of these numbers in this way. Earlier, when we discussed addition and multiplication, we wanted numbers like $\frac{3}{1}, \frac{8}{1}, \frac{10}{1}$, and so on, to behave in the way their natural-number mates do. We developed definitions for sums and products that did assure satisfactory results for the mates of natural numbers. We can easily show that the difference of two numbers that are mates of natural numbers is the mate of the difference of the two natural numbers. Thus,

$$\frac{6}{1} - \frac{5}{1} = \frac{1}{1}.$$

corresponds to $6 - 5 = 1$, and

$$\frac{12}{3} - \frac{10}{5} = \frac{30}{15}$$

corresponds to $4 - 2 = 2$.

We can carry this even further to show that no rational number of arithmetic satisfies

$$\frac{3}{1} - \frac{9}{1} = \frac{a}{b},$$

just as no natural number satisfies

$$3 - 9 = n.$$

Now let us see what happens when we consider division. First of all, it is apparent that, if the quotient of two natural numbers is a natural number, then the quotient of the two rational numbers of arithmetic that are mates of the natural numbers is the mate of the quotient of the two natural numbers. For example,

$$\frac{8}{1} \div \frac{2}{1} = \frac{8}{1} \times \frac{1}{2} = \frac{8}{2}$$

corresponds to $8 \div 2 = 4$, and

$$\frac{12}{1} \div \frac{6}{2} = \frac{12}{1} \times \frac{2}{6} = \frac{24}{6}$$

corresponds to $12 \div 3 = 4$.

Now suppose we consider a case in which the quotient of the two natural numbers is not a natural number. For example, there is no natural number a that satisfies

$$2 \div 3 = a.$$

However, the numbers that are mates of 2 and 3 *do* have a quotient that is a rational number of arithmetic. Thus,

$$\frac{2}{1} \div \frac{3}{1} = \frac{2}{1} \times \frac{1}{3} = \frac{2}{3}.$$

In the following sentences, we have shown more examples of pairs of rational numbers that are mates of pairs of natural numbers whose quotient is not a natural number. Note that, in each example, the quotient is a rational number, but it is not a mate of a natural number.

$$\frac{6}{1} \div \frac{5}{1} = \frac{6}{1} \times \frac{1}{5} = \frac{6}{5}.$$
$$\frac{12}{1} \div \frac{25}{1} = \frac{12}{25}.$$
$$\frac{7}{1} \div \frac{8}{1} = \frac{7}{8}.$$
$$\frac{4}{1} \div \frac{3}{1} = \frac{4}{3}.$$
$$\frac{10}{1} \div \frac{15}{1} = \frac{10}{15}.$$

Consequently, in solving a problem involving natural numbers for which the solution is not a natural number, like $6 \div 5 = n$ or $7 \div 100 = x$, we can first replace the natural numbers by their mates in the set of rational numbers. Then we obtain a quotient that is a rational number that can be considered as the quotient of the given natural numbers. In this way, we obtain results that are both mathematically consistent and useful in solving practical problems.

242 Use the method described on page 260 to determine $\frac{a}{b}$ without dividing if $\frac{a}{b} \cdot \frac{3}{4} = \frac{9}{5}$.

243 Prove that, if $\frac{a}{b}$, $\frac{c}{d}$, and $\frac{e}{f}$ are rational numbers of arithmetic, where $\frac{c}{d}$ and $\frac{e}{f}$ are non-zero, then $\frac{a}{b} \div \frac{c}{d} = (\frac{a}{b} \cdot \frac{e}{f}) \div (\frac{c}{d} \cdot \frac{e}{f})$. [Hint: Let $\frac{a}{b} \div \frac{c}{d} = \frac{x}{y}$ and let $(\frac{a}{b} \cdot \frac{e}{f}) \div (\frac{c}{d} \cdot \frac{e}{f}) = \frac{u}{v}$. Then show that $\frac{x}{y} = \frac{u}{v}$.]

244 Find a standard name for each of the following quotients.
 a $\frac{3}{4} \div \frac{9}{5}$ **b** $\frac{7}{12} \div \frac{8}{3}$ **c** $4\frac{1}{2} \div \frac{5}{6}$ **d** $\frac{2}{3} \div \frac{8}{21}$ **e** $6 \div 15$

We have now investigated the fundamental properties of addition and multiplication of rational numbers of arithmetic, the relations of equality and "greater than," the system of rational numbers of arithmetic, and subtraction and division involving these numbers. In the final section of this chapter, we will consider several other properties of rational numbers of arithmetic.

The number line and density

The properties of rational numbers of arithmetic that we want to discuss in this section can best be explained in connection with a number line. We will begin by considering how natural numbers can be associated with points in a line to develop a natural-number line.

We start by representing a line like the one pictured below and by choosing any one arbitrary point to which we assign the number 0. Then we choose some convenient unit of length and use this unit to locate a point that is one unit to the right of point 0. To this point, we assign the number 1. To the next point, which is located 1 unit to the right of 1 and, hence, 2 units to the right of 0, we assign the number 2. We can continue this process indefinitely and thereby locate a point in the line for each natural number.

Because of the way in which points and numbers correspond to each other, we can use the names of the numbers to name the points. Thus, the point in the line that corresponds to the number 0 may be called point 0, the point that corresponds to 1 may be called point 1, and so on. Note that the order of the points in the number line is the same as the order of the natural numbers. For example, because $0 < 1$, point 0 is to the left of point 1; because $3 < 7$, point 3 is to the left of point 7. In connection with the number line, we can think of the relation "to the left of" as corresponding to the relation "less than" as defined for numbers. This means that a point in the number line is to the left of another point in the line if and only if the number that corresponds to the first point is less than the number that corresponds to the second point.

Another important observation that we can make in connection with the natural-number line concerns the relation of *betweenness*. Notice, for example, that point 6 is between point 5 and point 7. This is the case because of the way in which the numbers are related; that is, the number 6 is between the numbers 5 and 7 because 5 is less than 6 and 6 is less than 7. We can express this in mathematical notation in the following way:

$$5 < 6 < 7.$$

By contrast, we can observe that point 3 in the number line is not between points 0 and 1. This is so because it is not the case that $0 < 3 < 1$. Thus, the relation of betweenness for points in the line corresponds to the relation of betweenness for natural numbers.

Except for 0, every natural number is between two other natural numbers. For example,

$$0 < 1 < 2.$$
$$1 < 2 < 3.$$
$$8 < 9 < 10.$$
$$36 < 37 < 38.$$
$$7000 < 7001 < 7002.$$

It is not the case, however, that between any two natural numbers, there is another natural number. For example, there is no natural number that satisfies any of the conditions expressed below.

$$6 < n < 7.$$
$$8 < n < 9.$$
$$16 < n < 17.$$
$$200 < n < 201.$$

If we think of a line as a continuous set of points without "gaps" or "holes," it seems reasonable to conclude that, between any two points in a line, there is another point in the line. From this it follows that, although every natural number corresponds to a point in the number line, it is not true that every point in the line corresponds to a natural number. For example, assuming that there is at least one point in the line between the point labeled 0 and the point labeled 1, we know that this point does not correspond to a natural number because there is no natural number between 0 and 1.

We can also see that it is possible to name both the least member and the greatest member of a set of natural numbers that are between two natural numbers. Consider the set of points in the number line that are between point 25 and point 38. (When we say "between," we exclude points 25 and 38.) The least member of this set is 26 and the greatest is 37. This is true because every natural number a other than 26 that satisfies

$$25 < a < 38$$

is greater than 26; thus, 26 is the least member of this set of numbers. Similarly, every natural number a other than 37 that satisfies $25 < a < 38$ is less than 37; thus, 37 is the greatest member of this set.

Next we will construct a number line for the rational numbers of arithmetic and see what relationships we can observe. In the number line pictured below, some of the rational numbers of arithmetic have been made to correspond to points in the line. Because of physical limitations, we have not located the points that correspond to such numbers as $\frac{1}{5}, \frac{5}{6}, \frac{7}{9}, \frac{16}{15}$, and so on. We will simply assume that, because a line is an infinite and continuous set of points, it would be possible, at least theoretically, to locate a point that corresponds to any rational number of arithmetic that you could name.

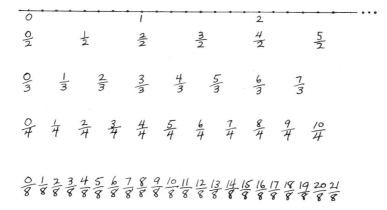

The first thing that we can observe is that, as with the natural-number line, the relation "to the left of" for points corresponds to the relation "less than" for numbers. For example, $\frac{3}{4} < \frac{5}{3}$, and point $\frac{3}{4}$ is to the left of point $\frac{5}{3}$; $\frac{6}{8} < \frac{13}{8}$, and point $\frac{6}{8}$ is to the left of point $\frac{13}{8}$. On the other hand, because $\frac{2}{2}$ is not less than $\frac{2}{3}$, point $\frac{2}{2}$ is not to the left of point $\frac{2}{3}$.

Now let us examine the relation of betweenness in connection with this number line. First of all, we see that every rational number of arithmetic except 0 is between two other rational numbers of arithmetic, just as any natural number except 0 is between two other natural numbers. For natural numbers, we showed that the converse of this is not true; that is, there is not a natural number between every pair of natural numbers. The case is different, however, with rational numbers. Between any two rational numbers of arithmetic, there is a rational number of arithmetic.

First we will consider some specific examples to show that this is true. Suppose that we want to determine a number that is between $\frac{1}{3}$ and $\frac{1}{2}$. This number will satisfy

$$\frac{1}{3} < \frac{a}{b} < \frac{1}{2}.$$

There is more than one number that will satisfy $\frac{1}{3} < \frac{a}{b} < \frac{1}{2}$; but we are now interested in determining just one of the numbers that is between $\frac{1}{3}$ and $\frac{1}{2}$. From your study of arithmetic, you may recall that you can find a number between two numbers by finding the sum and then dividing the sum by 2. We will use this idea to determine $\frac{a}{b}$. First

$$\frac{1}{3} + \frac{1}{2} = \frac{5}{6}.$$

Then

$$\frac{5}{6} \div \frac{2}{1} = \frac{5}{6} \times \frac{1}{2} = \frac{5}{12}.$$

Therefore, $\frac{a}{b} = \frac{5}{12}$, and

$$\frac{1}{3} < \frac{5}{12} < \frac{1}{2}.$$

You can easily verify that $\frac{5}{12}$ is between $\frac{1}{3}$ and $\frac{1}{2}$ by noting that $\frac{1}{3} = \frac{4}{12}$ and $\frac{1}{2} = \frac{6}{12}$. Obviously, $\frac{5}{12}$ is between $\frac{4}{12}$ and $\frac{6}{12}$.

We have discovered one number—namely, $\frac{5}{12}$—that is between $\frac{1}{3}$ and $\frac{1}{2}$, but we might now wonder whether or not there is a number between $\frac{1}{3}$, or $\frac{4}{12}$, and $\frac{5}{12}$. We want now to find a number that satisfies

$$\frac{4}{12} < \frac{c}{d} < \frac{5}{12}.$$

Again we find the sum of the two numbers $\frac{4}{12}$ and $\frac{5}{12}$ and divide by 2.

$$\frac{4}{12} + \frac{5}{12} = \frac{9}{12}.$$
$$\frac{9}{12} \div \frac{2}{1} = \frac{9}{12} \times \frac{1}{2} = \frac{9}{24}.$$

Thus, $\frac{c}{d} = \frac{9}{24}$ and

$$\frac{4}{12} < \frac{9}{24} < \frac{5}{12}.$$

$\frac{9}{24}$ is obviously between $\frac{4}{12}$ and $\frac{5}{12}$ because $\frac{4}{12} = \frac{8}{24}$ and $\frac{5}{12} = \frac{10}{24}$.

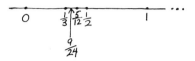

In the two examples just discussed, we used the method of finding the average of two numbers to find a number between them. The fact that this process can be continued indefinitely shows that there is an infinite set of rational numbers between any two given numbers. We have already determined two numbers between $\frac{1}{3}$ and $\frac{1}{2}$—namely, $\frac{5}{12}$ and $\frac{9}{24}$. In the same way, many others, such as $\frac{11}{24}, \frac{19}{48}, \frac{21}{48}, \frac{39}{96}$, and so on, can be determined.

We will now consider the general case to show that there exists at least one rational number between two given numbers. Suppose that we are given any two numbers $\frac{a}{b}$ and $\frac{c}{d}$ for which we know that either $\frac{a}{b} < \frac{c}{d}$ or $\frac{c}{d} < \frac{a}{b}$. In other words, we know that $\frac{a}{b} \neq \frac{c}{d}$; therefore, one of the two numbers is less than the other.

We know that, if we find the average of $\frac{a}{b}$ and $\frac{c}{d}$, then this number is between $\frac{a}{b}$ and $\frac{c}{d}$. We also know that the average is a rational number of arithmetic because both addition and division are closed in the set of non-zero rational numbers of arithmetic. To explain more fully, we find the average of $\frac{a}{b}$ and $\frac{c}{d}$ by first finding the sum $\frac{ad+bc}{bd}$, which we know is a rational number of arithmetic because addition is closed. Then we find the quotient of this sum and $\frac{2}{1}$, which is $\frac{ad+bc}{2bd}$. We also know that the number $\frac{ad+bc}{2bd}$ is a rational number because division is closed in the set of non-zero rational numbers of arithmetic. So we have determined at least one number, $\frac{ad+bc}{2bd}$, that is between any two given numbers $\frac{a}{b}$ and $\frac{c}{d}$. If $\frac{a}{b} < \frac{c}{d}$, then $\frac{a}{b} < \frac{ad+bc}{2bd} < \frac{c}{d}$. Similarly, if $\frac{c}{d} < \frac{a}{b}$, then $\frac{c}{d} < \frac{ad+bc}{2bd} < \frac{a}{b}$.

Because there exists at least one rational number of arithmetic between two given rational numbers of arithmetic, the set of rational numbers of arithmetic is said to be *dense*. Thus, unlike the set of natural numbers, the set of rational numbers of arithmetic has a *density property*. Because of this property, you might be tempted to think that there is a rational number of arithmetic that corresponds to every point in the line. However, this is *not* the case, as you will learn when you study the set of real numbers in Chapter 13.

In connection with the natural-number line, we said that it is possible to name the least and the greatest member of any set of natural numbers that are between two given numbers. As an example, we used the set of natural numbers between 25 and 38. Let us now see if we can name the least and the greatest member of the set of rational numbers that are between $\frac{25}{1}$ and $\frac{38}{1}$. We know that the rational numbers $\frac{x}{y}$ between $\frac{25}{1}$ and $\frac{38}{1}$ satisfy

$$\frac{25}{1} < \frac{x}{y} < \frac{38}{1}.$$

We know that 26 is the least natural number between 25 and 38. However, $\frac{26}{1}$ is *not* the least rational number between $\frac{25}{1}$ and $\frac{38}{1}$; for example, $25\frac{1}{2}$, or $\frac{51}{2}$, is less than $\frac{26}{1}$ and is between $\frac{25}{1}$ and $\frac{38}{1}$. Suppose that, as a first attempt, we select $25\frac{1}{4}$, or $\frac{101}{4}$, as the least member of the set of rational numbers between $\frac{25}{1}$ and $\frac{38}{1}$. But, by the density property, we know that there is at least one number between $\frac{25}{1}$ and $\frac{101}{4}$. This number, which must be less than $\frac{101}{4}$ and greater than $\frac{25}{1}$, is also between $\frac{25}{1}$ and $\frac{38}{1}$. We can show that $\frac{201}{8}$ is between $\frac{25}{1}$ and $\frac{101}{4}$. Hence, we know that $\frac{101}{4}$ is not the least number between $\frac{25}{1}$ and $\frac{38}{1}$ because $\frac{201}{8}$ is less than $\frac{101}{4}$ and is also between $\frac{25}{1}$ and $\frac{38}{1}$. By the density property, we can conclude that there is no least member of the set of numbers between $\frac{25}{1}$ and $\frac{38}{1}$. The same line of reasoning would show that neither is there a greatest member of the set.

Because the set of rational numbers is dense, there is at least one member of this set that is between any two given members. When we tabulate the set of natural numbers, we simply begin with 0 and name the succeeding numbers in order, as follows:

$$\{0, 1, 2, 3, 4, 5, 6, 7, \ldots\}.$$

We can immediately see that none of the numerals for natural numbers have been omitted in this tabulation, since there is no natural number between any two successive natural numbers. However, this method cannot be used for the rational numbers because of the density property.

Instead, we tabulate the set of rational numbers of arithmetic as follows:

$$\{\frac{0}{1}, \frac{1}{1}, \frac{1}{2}, \frac{2}{1}, \frac{1}{3}, \frac{3}{1}, \frac{1}{4}, \frac{2}{3}, \frac{3}{2}, \frac{1}{5}, \frac{5}{1}, \frac{1}{6}, \frac{6}{1}, \frac{2}{5}, \frac{5}{2}, \frac{3}{4}, \frac{4}{3}, \ldots\}.$$

In this tabulation, only the names of basic fractions are used so that no number is named more than once. For example, since $\frac{1}{1}$ is named, none of the other names for this number, such as $\frac{2}{2}$ or $\frac{8}{8}$, is included. Furthermore, every rational number of arithmetic is named in this tabulation. This is achieved by first naming all numbers $\frac{a}{b}$ for which $a + b = 1$ (there is only one); then all numbers $\frac{a}{b}$ for which $a + b = 2$ (there is only one); next all numbers $\frac{a}{b}$ for which $a + b = 3$ (there are two); and so on. You might extend the tabulation given above to include all rational numbers of arithmetic $\frac{a}{b}$ for which $a + b = 8$, $a + b = 9$, and $a + b = 10$.

Basic fraction, page 237

245 Determine three numbers that are between the two numbers named in each of the following exercises. Draw a number line to illustrate your answer.

a $\frac{5}{8}, \frac{3}{4}$ **b** $\frac{1}{10}, \frac{1}{11}$ **c** $\frac{0}{1}, \frac{3}{1}$ **d** $\frac{1}{4}, \frac{1}{5}$

246 Without computing, find a natural number n that satisfies each of the following conditions.

a $\frac{3}{16} \times \frac{n}{25} = \frac{3}{16}$.

c $\frac{56}{83} \div \frac{5}{n} = \frac{56}{83}$.

b $\frac{156}{314} + \frac{40}{n} = 1\frac{156}{314}$.

d $\frac{n}{8} \times \frac{8}{56} = \frac{3}{3}$.

CONCLUSION

In this chapter, we have developed the system of rational numbers of arithmetic. We have found that many of the properties of this system are similar to those of the natural-number system. However, we have also found that rational numbers of arithmetic have certain properties that are not shared by the natural numbers. Among them are the multiplicative-inverse, closure for division, and the density properties.

In the following chapter, we will study decimal names for rational numbers of arithmetic and will discuss computation with decimals.

CHAPTER QUIZ

1 Explain why such numbers as $\frac{3}{1}, \frac{5}{1}$, and $\frac{10}{1}$ are often replaced by their mates 3, 5, and 10 in computation.

2 Why is a symbol like $\frac{5}{0}$ meaningless?

3 What is the multiplicative inverse of each number named below?

A $\frac{1}{2}$ B $\frac{3}{5}$ C $\frac{10}{3}$ D $\frac{5}{1}$ E 12   F $\frac{7}{100}$

4 Which rational number has no multiplicative inverse? Why?

5 Prove that, for any rational number $\frac{a}{b}$ and any natural number n, if $n \neq 0$, then $\frac{a}{b} = \frac{an}{bn}$.

6 How many rational numbers of arithmetic $\frac{a}{b}$ satisfy $\frac{5}{6} > \frac{a}{b} > \frac{3}{4}$ if b is replaced by 240 and a is replaced by a natural number greater than or equal to 0?

7 Whenever possible, name the greatest and the least member of each set of numbers described below.

A All natural numbers that satisfy $1 < n < 1000$

B All rational numbers that satisfy $\frac{1}{2} < n < \frac{5}{2}$

C All natural numbers

D The numbers obtained by replacing n in $\frac{1}{n}$ by a natural number greater than 0

E The numbers obtained by replacing n in $\frac{n}{n+1}$ by a natural number

8 Show that, if two fractions have the same denominator, then the fraction that represents the greater number has the greater numerator.

9 Show that there is no least rational number that is a member of the set determined by each of the following:

   A $0 < \frac{a}{b}$.   B $100 < \frac{a}{b} < 200$.   C $\frac{1}{2} < \frac{a}{b} < \frac{3}{4}$.

10 Find six numbers between each pair of numbers named below.

   A $2, 3$ B $\frac{1}{2}, \frac{3}{4}$ C $\frac{9}{100}, \frac{1}{10}$ D $\frac{56}{83}, \frac{56}{84}$

11 By making proper replacements for a, b, c, and d from the set of natural numbers, demonstrate that

$$\frac{a}{b} < \frac{a+c}{b+d} < \frac{c}{d}.$$

What care must be taken in making replacements?

12 Notice that $\frac{1}{1} - \frac{99}{100} = \frac{1}{100}$, $\frac{1}{1} - \frac{574}{575} = \frac{1}{575}$, and $\frac{1}{1} - \frac{999}{1000} = \frac{1}{1000}$. What replacement should be made for a so that $\frac{1}{1} - \frac{a}{830}$ is as small as possible? So that $\frac{1}{1} - \frac{a}{1,000,000}$ is as small as possible? What expression could be used to represent any rational number of arithmetic so that the difference between the given number and 1 is as small as possible?

13 Show that, if the product of two rational numbers is 0, then at least one of the numbers must be 0. In mathematical terminology, show that, if $\frac{a}{b} \cdot \frac{c}{d} = 0$, then $\frac{a}{b} = 0$ or $\frac{c}{d} = 0$.

14 Determine the standard name of each product named below.

   A $\frac{3}{4} \times \frac{5}{6} \times \frac{10}{13} \times \frac{0}{5} \times \frac{1}{3}$ B $\frac{0}{6} \times \frac{1}{57} \times \frac{57}{41} \times \frac{16}{15}$

SUPPLEMENTARY READINGS

National Council of Teachers of Mathematics, *Topics in Mathematics for Elementary School Teachers: Twenty-ninth Yearbook*, "The Rational Numbers," Ch. 6. This explanation has slightly different terminology from that used in this chapter, but the basic approach to fractions is similar to the one we have given. An intuitive development of ordered pairs of natural numbers to represent a part-to-whole relationship is given. Item 45 of Bibliography

Smith, David Eugene, *History of Mathematics, Vol. II*, pp. 208-250. This section contains an interesting discussion of the background of common and decimal fractions. The development of the symbolism used for fractions is traced through the past. Item 46 of Bibliography

Van Engen, *et al.*, *Seeing Through Mathematics, Book 1*, Unit 7. This book contains a careful development of the system of rational numbers of arithmetic in terms of ordered pairs of natural numbers. Many good sets of exercises are included, as well as applications to problem solving. Item 21 of Bibliography

Chapter eleven

Computation involving
rational numbers of arithmetic

Computing with fraction numerals
Terminating decimals
Computing with decimals
Decimals used for ordering rational numbers of arithmetic
Scientific notation

For many years, the elementary schools emphasized almost exclusively computational skills for both natural numbers and rational numbers. The important properties of the number systems were frequently ignored, and the child spent most of his time learning how to process numerals and use short cuts in computation. One of the goals of the revolution in mathematics and arithmetic has been to provide a better balance between the teaching of computational skills and an understanding of the basic properties of numbers.

Of course, the ability to compute is essential, but computational skill *per se* should not be the main goal of arithmetic instruction. And, in fact, many of the computational techniques are better remembered and better applied if the child understands the principles underlying such techniques.

In Chapter 10, we presented the important theoretical considerations that enable us to develop the system of rational numbers of arithmetic. In this chapter, we will first discuss some of the more important computational procedures involving these numbers. Then we will extend the decimal numeration system to include names for rational numbers, and we will consider computation with decimals.

Computing with fraction numerals

As you learned in the previous chapter, the name of the basic fraction for a rational number of arithmetic is the standard name of that number. When we are computing, we usually use the standard name to express the results of the computation. For example, when we find the sum of $\frac{1}{4}$ and $\frac{1}{4}$, we usually give the sum as $\frac{1}{2}$ rather than as $\frac{2}{4}$.

Basic fraction and standard name, page 237

Often, when we find the sum of two rational numbers, we do not obtain a basic fraction. Thus, when we find the sum of $\frac{7}{8}$ and $\frac{5}{6}$, we obtain

$$\frac{7}{8} + \frac{5}{6} = \frac{7 \cdot 6 + 8 \cdot 5}{8 \cdot 6} = \frac{82}{48}.$$

Because 82 and 48 are not relatively prime, we know that $\frac{82}{48}$ is not a basic fraction. We can use our knowledge of equivalent fractions to find the basic fraction that is equivalent to $\frac{82}{48}$. One way to determine the equivalent fractions in a set like the one tabulated below is to multiply the numerator and the denominator of the basic fraction by each counting number in turn. Thus, in

Relatively prime numbers, page 221

$$\{\tfrac{1}{2}, \tfrac{2}{4}, \tfrac{3}{6}, \tfrac{4}{8}, \ldots\},$$

$\frac{2}{4}$ is obtained by multiplying 1 and 2 by 2; $\frac{3}{6}$ is obtained by multiplying 1 and 2 by 3; etc. We can find the basic fraction for a given fraction like $\frac{82}{48}$ by the opposite procedure of "removing" common factors from the numerator and denominator. Thus, when we divide both 82 and 48 by 2, we obtain $\frac{41}{24}$, which is the basic fraction for $\frac{82}{48}$. Hence, $\frac{7}{8} + \frac{5}{6} = \frac{41}{24}$.

Our objective now is to develop a short cut in computation that will enable us to find the standard name of the sum more quickly. To do this, we can make use of the idea of the least common multiple of two numbers, which we discussed in Chapter 9.

Least common multiple, page 223

We can use the least common multiple (lcm) of 8 and 6 as the *least common denominator* (lcd) of the fractions $\frac{7}{8}$ and $\frac{5}{6}$. 24 is the least common denominator of $\frac{7}{8}$ and $\frac{5}{6}$ because it is the least common multiple of 8 and 6. Thus, if we express $\frac{7}{8}$ as $\frac{21}{24}$ and $\frac{5}{6}$ as $\frac{20}{24}$, we know that the sum of $\frac{21}{24}$ and $\frac{20}{24}$ is equal to the sum of $\frac{7}{8}$ and $\frac{5}{6}$ because $\frac{7}{8} = \frac{21}{24}$, and $\frac{5}{6} = \frac{20}{24}$. Therefore, we can replace $\frac{7}{8}$ by $\frac{21}{24}$ and $\frac{5}{6}$ by $\frac{20}{24}$ to obtain

$$\frac{7}{8} + \frac{5}{6} = \frac{21}{24} + \frac{20}{24} = \frac{41}{24}.$$

By expressing $\frac{7}{8}$ as $\frac{21}{24}$ and $\frac{5}{6}$ as $\frac{20}{24}$, before we find the sum of these two numbers, we obtain the basic fraction $\frac{41}{24}$.

The description of the method that we have just given makes it appear much more complicated than it really is. It is less complicated than it appears because, after having worked with a great many examples, we go through these steps very quickly without thinking about them or attempting to justify them. Several more examples that involve this procedure are shown below.

$$\frac{3}{4} + \frac{1}{2} = \frac{3}{4} + \frac{2}{4} = \frac{5}{4}.$$

$$\frac{5}{8} + \frac{7}{12} = \frac{15}{24} + \frac{14}{24} = \frac{29}{24}.$$

$$\frac{3}{5} + \frac{1}{10} = \frac{6}{10} + \frac{1}{10} = \frac{7}{10}.$$

$$\frac{2}{9} + \frac{1}{6} = \frac{4}{18} + \frac{3}{18} = \frac{7}{18}.$$

Note that in some examples the least common denominator happens to be the denominator of one of the two given numbers.

The procedure of choosing numbers that have the least common multiple of the given denominators as the common denominator does not necessarily enable you to obtain the standard name of the sum immediately. For example, if you use this method to find the sum of $\frac{1}{2}$ and $\frac{1}{6}$, you obtain $\frac{4}{6}$, which is not a basic fraction. However, this procedure will often enable you to obtain the basic fraction for the sum immediately.

We wish to emphasize that this method and the other computational techniques that will be discussed here are simply convenient short cuts. It is not absolutely essential that children be taught such techniques and, in fact, it is quite unwise to introduce them until the child has a firm understanding of the concepts involved.

From what we know about the relationship between addition and subtraction, it should be obvious that the procedure just described for addition can also be used for subtraction. The following example illustrates this procedure for subtraction. Suppose that we want to find the difference of $\frac{5}{6}$ and $\frac{3}{4}$. If we use the definition of the difference of two rational numbers of arithmetic, we obtain

Definition of difference, page 258

$$\frac{5}{6} - \frac{3}{4} = \frac{5 \cdot 4 - 6 \cdot 3}{24} = \frac{2}{24}.$$

To obtain the standard name of $\frac{5}{6} - \frac{3}{4}$, we must then find the basic fraction that is equivalent to $\frac{2}{24}$. This fraction is $\frac{1}{12}$; therefore, the standard name that expresses the difference of $\frac{5}{6}$ and $\frac{3}{4}$ is the fraction numeral $\frac{1}{12}$. If, instead, we use the idea of the least common denominator, we obtain

$$\frac{5}{6} - \frac{3}{4} = \frac{10}{12} - \frac{9}{12} = \frac{1}{12}.$$

When we use the short cut just described for subtraction, we assume that the numbers $\frac{5}{6}$ and $\frac{3}{4}$ may be replaced by equal numbers without affecting the difference. In other words, we assume that, because $\frac{5}{6} = \frac{10}{12}$ and $\frac{3}{4} = \frac{9}{12}$,

$$\frac{5}{6} - \frac{3}{4} = \frac{10}{12} - \frac{9}{12}.$$

Subtraction of rational numbers does have the property described above, and it is true that the difference of two numbers is not affected if either or both of them are replaced by equal numbers. For this reason, it is permissible to use this short cut for examples that involve subtraction.

Next we will develop a computational short cut that will enable us to find more quickly a basic fraction for a product or a quotient. Suppose that you want to find the product of $\frac{9}{10}$ and $\frac{2}{3}$. By the definition of product, you know that

Definition of product, page 246

$$\frac{9}{10} \times \frac{2}{3} = \frac{9 \cdot 2}{10 \cdot 3} = \frac{18}{30}.$$

$\frac{18}{30}$, however, is not a basic fraction; so the numeral $\frac{18}{30}$ is not the standard name of the product of $\frac{9}{10}$ and $\frac{2}{3}$. We can use the usual method of dividing 18 and 30 by their greatest common divisor, 6, to obtain

Greatest common divisor, page 219

$$\frac{18}{30} = \frac{3}{5}.$$

$\frac{3}{5}$ is a basic fraction; so we know that the numeral $\frac{3}{5}$ is the standard name of $\frac{9}{10} \times \frac{2}{3}$.

In elementary school you probably learned to "cancel" common factors whenever possible before you found the product of two rational numbers. For example, you probably found the product $\frac{9}{10} \times \frac{2}{3}$ in the following way.

$$\frac{\overset{3}{\cancel{9}}}{\underset{5}{\cancel{10}}} \times \frac{\overset{1}{\cancel{2}}}{\underset{1}{\cancel{3}}} = \frac{3}{5}.$$

This procedure can seem very mysterious to a child, because it appears as though $\frac{9}{10}$ has been replaced by $\frac{3}{5}$ and $\frac{2}{3}$ has been replaced by $\frac{1}{1}$ without any explanation of why this is possible. Actually, we make use of several important properties when we use this short cut. We will go through each step of the process and show what properties are used.

First, by the definition of product, we know that

$$\frac{9}{10} \times \frac{2}{3} = \frac{9 \cdot 2}{10 \cdot 3}.$$

Also, $9 \cdot 2 = 3 \cdot 3 \cdot 2$, and $10 \cdot 3 = 5 \cdot 2 \cdot 3$. Therefore, $\frac{9 \cdot 2}{10 \cdot 3} = \frac{3 \cdot 3 \cdot 2}{5 \cdot 2 \cdot 3}$. Hence,

$$\frac{9}{10} \times \frac{2}{3} = \frac{3 \cdot 3 \cdot 2}{5 \cdot 2 \cdot 3}.$$

We see now that 3 and 2 are common factors of the numerator and the denominator of $\frac{3 \cdot 3 \cdot 2}{5 \cdot 2 \cdot 3}$. We can divide both the numerator and the denominator by these common factors to find the basic fraction for the product. Thus,

$$\frac{3 \cdot \overset{1}{\cancel{3}} \cdot \overset{1}{\cancel{2}}}{5 \cdot \underset{1}{\cancel{2}} \cdot \underset{1}{\cancel{3}}} = \frac{3}{5},$$

and, since equality is transitive,

Transitive
property of
equality,
page 98

$$\frac{9}{10} \times \frac{2}{3} = \frac{3}{5}.$$

Obviously, this same short cut can be applied to the division process, since we find the quotient of two numbers by finding the product of the dividend and the multiplicative inverse of the divisor. The following example illustrates the use of cancellation in division.

Definition of
division,
page 262

$$7 \div \frac{7}{2} = \frac{\overset{1}{\cancel{7}}}{1} \times \frac{2}{\underset{1}{\cancel{7}}} = \frac{2}{1} = 2.$$

You should be able to explain what properties are involved when cancellation is used in division.

Traditionally, a great deal of emphasis has been given to computation involving so-called "improper fractions" and "mixed numbers." As you know, a fraction is called improper if it is greater than or equal to $\frac{1}{1}$. Because such numbers as $\frac{8}{3}$ or $\frac{6}{2}$ or $\frac{72}{10}$ do not behave any differently from other rational numbers, we will not use such terms as "proper fractions" or "improper fractions" and will not give any special consideration to these terms.

Numerals of the form $3\frac{1}{2}$ or $8\frac{2}{3}$ have traditionally been called "mixed numbers" because they were thought of as a combination of a natural number and a rational number of arithmetic. Actually, a numeral like $3\frac{1}{2}$ is simply another name for $\frac{7}{2}$. The fraction numeral $\frac{21}{6}$ is another name for the number $3\frac{1}{2}$, as are the numerals $\frac{14}{4}$ or $\frac{42}{12}$. We can also think of $3\frac{1}{2}$ as the sum of $\frac{3}{1}$ and $\frac{1}{2}$. Thus,

$$\frac{3}{1} + \frac{1}{2} = \frac{7}{2} = 3\frac{1}{2}.$$

Because $\frac{3}{1}$ is the mate of 3, we frequently write

$$3 + \frac{1}{2} = 3\frac{1}{2}.$$

Children often are given special techniques for finding the sum of such numbers. They are told that they can "add the 'whole numbers' and the 'fractions' separately." For example, they learn to find the sum of $2\frac{1}{3}$ and $6\frac{1}{4}$ by first finding the sum of $\frac{1}{3}$ and $\frac{1}{4}$ and then the sum of $\frac{6}{1}$ and $\frac{2}{1}$ to obtain $8\frac{7}{12}$. Involved in this short cut is the idea that each of the numbers $2\frac{1}{3}$ and $6\frac{1}{4}$ is thought of as a sum. Thus,

$$2\frac{1}{3} + 6\frac{1}{4} = (\tfrac{2}{1} + \tfrac{1}{3}) + (\tfrac{6}{1} + \tfrac{1}{4}).$$

Next, because addition is associative and commutative, we know that

Associative
and
commutative
properties
of addition,
pages 243-244

$$(\tfrac{2}{1} + \tfrac{1}{3}) + (\tfrac{6}{1} + \tfrac{1}{4}) = (\tfrac{2}{1} + \tfrac{6}{1}) + (\tfrac{1}{3} + \tfrac{1}{4}).$$

Then, since equality is transitive,

$$2\tfrac{1}{3} + 6\tfrac{1}{4} = (\tfrac{2}{1} + \tfrac{6}{1}) + (\tfrac{1}{3} + \tfrac{1}{4}).$$

But $\tfrac{2}{1} + \tfrac{6}{1} = \tfrac{8}{1}$ and $\tfrac{1}{3} + \tfrac{1}{4} = \tfrac{7}{12}$; therefore,

$$2\tfrac{1}{3} + 6\tfrac{1}{4} = \tfrac{8}{1} + \tfrac{7}{12} = 8\tfrac{7}{12}.$$

In practice, it is common to use the mates of $\tfrac{2}{1}$ and $\tfrac{6}{1}$ and, thus, to work with such expressions as

$$2\tfrac{1}{3} + 6\tfrac{1}{4} = (2 + \tfrac{1}{3}) + (6 + \tfrac{1}{4}).$$

The steps would then follow as in the example above. Hence, when we find the sum of two numbers like $2\tfrac{1}{3}$ and $6\tfrac{1}{4}$ by "adding the 'whole numbers' and the 'fractions' separately," we are making use of several properties of the system of rational numbers of arithmetic.

We have not included in this section all of the computational short cuts that have been a part of the traditional arithmetic program. Instead, we have taken several examples of these short cuts and given the mathematical justifications for them. Part of our motive for presenting these short cuts, as we stated earlier, is to give you an idea of how short cuts, unless thoroughly understood, can obscure understanding and to advise against their use in a mechanical way.

247 Find the standard name for each sum, difference, product, or quotient named below.

a $\tfrac{3}{5} + \tfrac{1}{6}$ e $8\tfrac{1}{3} - 5\tfrac{4}{5}$ i $\tfrac{12}{5} \div \tfrac{21}{40}$

b $\tfrac{7}{10} + \tfrac{11}{24}$ f $\tfrac{16}{5} \cdot \tfrac{1}{4}$ j $5\tfrac{13}{15} \div 2\tfrac{2}{9}$

c $6\tfrac{3}{4} + 3\tfrac{5}{8}$ g $4\tfrac{1}{12} \cdot 2\tfrac{11}{14}$

d $\tfrac{23}{18} - \tfrac{9}{14}$ h $6\tfrac{2}{3} \cdot \tfrac{9}{10}$

Terminating decimals

Now that we have discussed some of the methods of computation involving rational numbers of arithmetic, we will discuss the use of decimals to name such numbers. When the term "decimal" is used, people often think only of numerals that include a decimal point, such as 45.25 or 6.8 or .03. As we pointed out in Chapter 6, however, any numeral in our system of numeration is a decimal because it is a base-ten numeral. Such decimals as 45.25, 6.8, and so on, represent an *extension* of the decimal numeration system to include names for all of the rational numbers of arithmetic. Obviously, the rational numbers that are mates of natural

Decimal numeration system, page 127

numbers can be named by the same decimals as the natural numbers. For example, the decimal 675 names $\frac{675}{1}$ as well as the natural number 675; the decimal 18 names $\frac{18}{1}$ as well as the natural number 18; and so on. Decimals like 45.25 or 6.8 are used to name the rational numbers of arithmetic that are not mates of natural numbers.

Decimals for rational numbers were originally introduced to make computation easier. In 1585 a Belgian surveyor named Simon Stevin published his ideas on extending the decimal numeration system to include names for rational numbers. He emphasized that the computational methods that apply to decimals for natural numbers would also apply to decimals for rational numbers. In this way, it would be possible to avoid computing with numerals of the form $\frac{a}{b}$. He proposed several ways of writing these numerals, including the following ways of expressing 5.46.

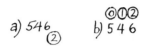

Although his methods of notation did not survive, his idea for such a system of notation was an important contribution to mathematics.

As you know, when we express a number like $\frac{3}{4}$ in decimal notation, we use a fraction numeral whose denominator expresses a power of 10, like 10, 100, or 1000. Then, instead of writing the fraction numeral in its usual form, we use a decimal point to indicate the denominator. For example,

Power of number, page 129

$$\frac{3}{4} = \frac{75}{100} = \frac{75}{10^2} = .75.$$
$$\frac{4}{5} = \frac{8}{10} = \frac{8}{10^1} = .8.$$
$$\frac{3}{2} = \frac{15}{10} = \frac{15}{10^1} = 1.5.$$
$$6\frac{7}{8} = \frac{55}{8} = \frac{6875}{1000} = \frac{6875}{10^3} = 6.875.$$

Note that the position of the decimal point is determined by the power of 10 that is expressed in the denominator. For example, there are 2 digits to the right of the point in the decimal .75 because the denominator of $\frac{75}{100}$ is the second power of 10; there is 1 digit to the right of the point in the decimal 1.5 because the denominator of $\frac{15}{10}$ is the first power of 10; and so on.

Decimals like those in the above examples are called *terminating decimals*, or *finite decimals*, because these decimals have a finite number of non-zero digits. Certain numbers, such as $\frac{1}{3}$, $\frac{5}{6}$, or $\frac{3}{7}$ cannot be named by terminating decimals, but are named by decimals with infinitely many non-zero digits. We will consider non-terminating decimals in Chapter 13; for now, we will restrict ourselves to computation with terminating decimals.

When we discussed the decimal numeration system in Chapter 6, we showed how each digit in a decimal is associated with a power of 10. You

Decimall Arithmetick.

computation is found by the confideration of fuch tenth or difme progreffion; that is, that it confifteth therein entirely, as fhall hereafter appeare: Wee call this Treatife fitly by the name of Difme, whereby all accounts happning in the affayres of man, may be wrought and effected without fractions or broken numbers, as hereafter appeareth.

The fecond Definition.

Every number propounded, is called Comencement, whofe figne is thus (°).

Explication.

By example, a certaine number is propounded of three hundred fixty foure: we call the 364 Comencements, defcribed thus 364 (°) and fo of all other like.

The third Definition.

And each tenth part of the unity of the Comencement, wee call the Prime, whofe figne is thus ('), and each tenth part of ẙ unity of the Prime, we call the Second, whofe figne is (²), and fo of ẙ other : each tenth part of the unity of the precedent figne, alwayes in order, one further.

Explication.

As 3 (¹) 7 (²) 5 (³) 9 (⁴) that is to fay, 3 Primes, 7 Seconds, 5 Thirds, 9 Fourths, and fo proceeding infinitly: but to fpeake of their value, you may note, that according to this definition, the faid numbers are $\frac{3}{10}$ $\frac{7}{100}$ $\frac{5}{1000}$ $\frac{9}{10000}$, together $\frac{3759}{10000}$ and likewife 8 (⁰) 9 (¹) 3 (²) 7 (³) are worth 8 $\frac{9}{10}$ $\frac{3}{100}$ $\frac{7}{1000}$ together 8 $\frac{937}{1000}$ and fo of other like. Alfo you may underftand, that in this Difme we ufe no fractions,

C 2

This page from the 1608 English edition of
The Art of Tenths: *Decimall Arithmetick* by Simon Stevin shows his
attempts to introduce decimal notation for rational numbers.

The Bettman Archive, Inc.

will recall that we used this idea to write decimals in expanded form. Expanded form, page 132 The expanded form of the decimal 98,562 is shown below to help you remember how this was done.

$$98{,}562 = 9 \cdot 10^4 + 8 \cdot 10^3 + 5 \cdot 10^2 + 6 \cdot 10^1 + 2 \cdot 10^0.$$

From the expanded form for 98,562 you can tell at a glance what number each digit in the numeral represents. Because the digit 9 is associated with 10^4, it represents 90,000; because the digit 8 is associated with 10^3, it represents 8000; and so on. Remember that the zero power of 10—that Zero power of a number, page 131 is, 10^0—is equal to 1; therefore, $2(10^0) = 2(1) = 2$.

We said earlier that it is possible to extend the decimal numeration system to include names for rational numbers. If this is the case, we should be able to write a numeral like 75.32 in expanded form. We know that the digit 7 in 75.32 is associated with 10^1 and that the digit 5 is associated with 10^0. The question now is to determine the powers of 10 that are associated with the digits to the right of the decimal point.

We know that the numeral $75\frac{32}{100}$ names the same number as 75.32. Thus, we can express 75.32 as a sum in the following way.

$$75.32 = 70 + 5 + \tfrac{32}{100}.$$

But $\frac{32}{100}$ can be expressed as the sum of $\frac{3}{10}$ and $\frac{2}{100}$. Therefore,

$$75.32 = 70 + 5 + \tfrac{3}{10} + \tfrac{2}{100}.$$

Further, we know that $70 = 7 \cdot 10^1$, that $5 = 5 \cdot 10^0$, that $\frac{3}{10} = 3 \cdot \frac{1}{10} = 3 \cdot \frac{1}{10^1}$, and that $\frac{2}{100} = 2 \cdot \frac{1}{100} = 2 \cdot \frac{1}{10^2}$. Thus, we can write

$$75.32 = 7 \cdot 10^1 + 5 \cdot 10^0 + 3 \cdot \tfrac{1}{10^1} + 2 \cdot \tfrac{1}{10^2}.$$

The expression at the right of the symbol for equality in the sentence above is one way of writing the numeral 75.32 in expanded form.

However, this is not altogether satisfactory because we have said that, when a number is expressed in expanded form, each digit is associated with a power of 10 and that the exponents of the powers of 10 occur in decreasing order from left to right.

The expanded form of the numeral 75.32 given above does not seem to conform to the pattern we have in mind. We can eliminate this inconsistency by introducing some new definitions concerning power notation. We will not consider negative numbers until the next chapter, but we will assume that you already have some knowledge of negative numbers and will introduce the definition of a negative exponent. Thus, for $\frac{1}{10^1}$ we agree to use 10^{-1}. Accordingly, $\frac{1}{12^2}$ is equal to 12^{-2}; $\frac{1}{2^4}$ is equal to 2^{-4}; and so on. In general, for any non-zero whole numbers m and n, $\frac{1}{n^m} = n^{-m}$. This agreement concerning negative exponents, of course, has broader implications than its use in expanded form notation. However, our present concern is with expanded form, and we can now write the expanded form of the numeral 75.32, using the idea of negative exponents.

Because $\frac{1}{10^1} = 10^{-1}$ and $\frac{1}{10^2} = 10^{-2}$, we can rewrite

$$75.32 = 7 \cdot 10^1 + 5 \cdot 10^0 + 3 \cdot \frac{1}{10^1} + 2 \cdot \frac{1}{10^2}$$

as

$$75.32 = 7 \cdot 10^1 + 5 \cdot 10^0 + 3 \cdot 10^{-1} + 2 \cdot 10^{-2}.$$

Notice that each digit in the numeral 75.32 is associated with a power of 10. Furthermore, because -1 is one less than 0 and -2 is one less than -1, the exponents of the powers of 10 occur in decreasing order from left to right. Several more examples of decimals in expanded form are shown below so that you can study the pattern that applies to all decimals for rational numbers of arithmetic.

$$.45 = .40 + .05 = 4 \cdot 10^{-1} + 5 \cdot 10^{-2}.$$
$$8.835 = 8 \cdot 10^0 + 8 \cdot 10^{-1} + 3 \cdot 10^{-2} + 5 \cdot 10^{-3}.$$
$$603.002 = 6 \cdot 10^2 + 0 \cdot 10^1 + 3 \cdot 10^0 + 0 \cdot 10^{-1} + 0 \cdot 10^{-2} + 2 \cdot 10^{-3}.$$
$$.1004 = 1 \cdot 10^{-1} + 0 \cdot 10^{-2} + 0 \cdot 10^{-3} + 4 \cdot 10^{-4}.$$

We can give a general pattern for the expanded form of any decimal by using letters of the alphabet as placeholders for the digits. Thus, suppose that we use the letters $a, b, c, \ldots x, y, z$ to represent the digits in a decimal. The expanded form may be obtained by replacing each letter by one of the digits from 0 through 9. The expanded form of any decimal then will have the following pattern:

$$\ldots a \cdot 10^3 + b \cdot 10^2 + c \cdot 10^1 + d \cdot 10^0 + x \cdot 10^{-1} + y \cdot 10^{-2} + z \cdot 10^{-3} \ldots$$

248 Each of the following numerals is given in expanded form. For each numeral, give the decimal that names the same number.

a $4 \cdot 10^1 + 9 \cdot 10^0 + 6 \cdot 10^{-1} + 3 \cdot 10^{-2} + 0 \cdot 10^{-3} + 1 \cdot 10^{-4}$

b $5 \cdot 10^2 + 0 \cdot 10^1 + 0 \cdot 10^0 + 0 \cdot 10^{-1} + 6 \cdot 10^{-2}$

c $6 \cdot 10^{-3} + 0 \cdot 10^{-4} + 8 \cdot 10^{-5}$

d $5 \cdot 10^2 + 0 \cdot 10^1 + 0 \cdot 10^0 + 3 \cdot 10^{-1} + 8 \cdot 10^{-2}$

e $9 \cdot 10^3 + 0 \cdot 10^2 + 0 \cdot 10^1 + 9 \cdot 10^0 + 0 \cdot 10^{-1} + 9 \cdot 10^{-2}$

f $4 \cdot 10^4 + 0 \cdot 10^3 + 0 \cdot 10^2 + 3 \cdot 10^1 + 0 \cdot 10^0 + 0 \cdot 10^{-1} + 0 \cdot 10^{-2}$

249 Rewrite each of the six numerals at the top of the next page in two ways. First, without using exponents, show the power of 10 that is associated with each digit. Then use exponents in writing the expanded form of each numeral. For example, 6.04 would first be written as $6 \cdot 1 + 0 \cdot \frac{1}{10} + 4 \cdot \frac{1}{100}$ and then as $6 \cdot 10^0 + 0 \cdot 10^{-1} + 4 \cdot 10^{-2}$.

a 4.623   **c** 9.005   **e** .5

b 580.04   **d** .005   **f** 100.001

250 Express each of the following fraction numerals as a decimal.

    a $\frac{4}{10}$ **d** $\frac{132}{10}$ **g** $\frac{182}{100}$

    b $\frac{56}{100}$ **e** $\frac{1463}{1000}$ **h** $\frac{36}{50}$

    c $\frac{56}{10}$ **f** $\frac{15}{1000}$ **i** $\frac{19}{20}$

251 Express each of the following in the form $\frac{a}{1} + \frac{b}{c}$, where $\frac{a}{1}$ represents a rational number that is the mate of a natural number and $\frac{b}{c}$ represents a rational number between $\frac{0}{1}$ and $\frac{1}{1}$. Also express each number as a decimal numeral.

    a $4\frac{1}{2}$ **c** $20\frac{3}{8}$ **e** $\frac{15}{8}$

    b $\frac{129}{4}$ **d** $\frac{14}{4}$ **f** $4\frac{35}{16}$

    In this discussion of decimals we have not given you techniques for expressing rational numbers as decimals or for "converting" decimals to fraction numerals. We have assumed that you already know how to do this. We have considered, instead, the extension of the decimal numeration system to include decimals for rational numbers of arithmetic. With this background, we will discuss computation with decimals in the following section.

Computing with decimals

    As we stated earlier, decimals for rational numbers were devised primarily to simplify computation. When we compute with decimals, we use all of the procedures that we use in computing with numerals for natural numbers. This means that we make use of our knowledge of the basic facts, our methods for "carrying" and "borrowing," and so on. In a sense, we can say that we compute with decimals as though they were natural numbers until it comes time to interpret the results of the computation.

    Let us now consider several examples to help us analyze the addition process with decimals. When we discussed computation involving natural numbers in Chapter 7, we showed how the expanded forms of decimals could be used to explain our computational procedures. We can use the same idea in connection with decimals. Suppose, for example, that we want to find the sum of 2.4 and 6.3. Of course, you know that $2.4 + 6.3 = 8.7$, but let us see how we can justify the methods we use to obtain this sum. First, we can express the numbers in expanded form as shown in the sentence below.

Expanded forms in computation, page 146

$$2.4 + 6.3 = (2 \cdot 10^0 + 4 \cdot 10^{-1}) + (6 \cdot 10^0 + 3 \cdot 10^{-1}).$$

Next, because addition is associative and commutative, we regroup and rearrange the addends to obtain

Associative and commutative properties of addition, pages 243-244

$$(2 \cdot 10^0 + 4 \cdot 10^{-1}) + (6 \cdot 10^0 + 3 \cdot 10^{-1}) =$$
$$(2 \cdot 10^0 + 6 \cdot 10^0) + (4 \cdot 10^{-1} + 3 \cdot 10^{-1}).$$

Then, because multiplication distributes over addition, we obtain

Distributive property, page 252

$$(2 \cdot 10^0 + 6 \cdot 10^0) + (4 \cdot 10^{-1} + 3 \cdot 10^{-1}) =$$
$$((2 + 6)10^0) + ((4 + 3)10^{-1}).$$

Since $(2 + 6) = 8$ and $(4 + 3) = 7$,
$$((2 + 6)10^0) + ((4 + 3)10^{-1}) = 8 \cdot 10^0 + 7 \cdot 10^{-1}.$$

But $8 \cdot 10^0 + 7 \cdot 10^{-1}$ is the expanded form of 8.7. Therefore,

$$8 \cdot 10^0 + 7 \cdot 10^{-1} = 8.7.$$

And, finally,

$$2.4 + 6.3 = 8.7.$$

We have used a rather simple example to illustrate this idea; but it should be apparent that, no matter how complicated the computation might be, the method that we have used in this example could always be used to justify the computational procedure for decimals. Although many more steps would be required, we could use similar reasoning to show, for example, that $75.342 + 128.088 = 203.430$.

We use the same algorism for addition of numbers represented by decimals as we use for addition of natural numbers. Thus, when we write our numerals for computing, we have already made use of associativity and commutativity by the way we arrange the numerals. The algorism below shows how the digits associated with each power of 10 are aligned so that we need to use only basic facts when we compute.

$$
\begin{aligned}
16.57 &= 1 \cdot 10^1 + 6 \cdot 10^0 + 5 \cdot 10^{-1} + 7 \cdot 10^{-2} \\
8.19 &= 8 \cdot 10^0 + 1 \cdot 10^{-1} + 9 \cdot 10^{-2} \\
\hline
24.76 &= 2 \cdot 10^1 + 4 \cdot 10^0 + 7 \cdot 10^{-1} + 6 \cdot 10^{-2}
\end{aligned}
$$

After we have performed a great many computations, we use the addition algorism mechanically without really concerning ourselves about the justification for the algorism. We know that, if we write the numerals in the proper way, then the decimal point in the numeral for the sum "automatically" occurs in the same place as it occurs in the numerals for the addends.

Too often in the past, children were taught only the mechanical procedures for computing with decimals. However, instead of giving them rules to be memorized, it is best to explain the addition process with decimals in terms of the work with rational numbers that are named by the decimals. To illustrate this, we can again consider the sum of 2.4 and 6.3.

Because $2.4 = \frac{24}{10}$ and $6.3 = \frac{63}{10}$, we know that

$$2.4 + 6.3 = \frac{24}{10} + \frac{63}{10}.$$

By the definition of the sum of two rational numbers of arithmetic, we obtain

$$\frac{24}{10} + \frac{63}{10} = \frac{87}{10}.$$

Because $\frac{87}{10} = 8.7$, we conclude that

$$2.4 + 6.3 = 8.7.$$

Let us consider another example of how rational numbers of the form $\frac{a}{b}$ can be used to explain addition involving decimals. Suppose that we want to find the sum of 75.606 and 8.724. Since $75.606 = \frac{75606}{1000}$ and $8.724 = \frac{8724}{1000}$, we know that

$$75.606 + 8.724 = \frac{75606}{1000} + \frac{8724}{1000}.$$

Hence,

$$\frac{75606}{1000} + \frac{8724}{1000} = \frac{84330}{1000}.$$

Because $\frac{84330}{1000} = 84.330$, we conclude that

$$75.606 + 8.724 = 84.330.$$

After children have considered many examples of this kind, they will then begin to observe the correspondence between the position of the point in the numeral for the sum and that in each numeral for the addends.

The remarks that we have made concerning addition also apply to subtraction involving decimals. We can justify the computational process for subtraction in terms of the expanded forms of the numerals in the same way that we did for addition. The following example shows both the usual subtraction algorism and the computation with the expanded forms.

$$
\begin{array}{ll}
57.97 = & 5 \cdot 10^1 + 7 \cdot 10^0 + 9 \cdot 10^{-1} + 7 \cdot 10^{-2} \\
8.65 = & 8 \cdot 10^0 + 6 \cdot 10^{-1} + 5 \cdot 10^{-2} \\
\hline
49.32 = & 4 \cdot 10^1 + 9 \cdot 10^0 + 3 \cdot 10^{-1} + 2 \cdot 10^{-2}
\end{array}
$$

As we said in connection with addition, subtraction involving decimals can best be understood by comparing it with subtraction of rational numbers of arithmetic in the form $\frac{a}{b}$. Suppose, for example, that we want to explain why the difference of 8.34 and 2.29 is 6.05 in terms of the numbers named by these decimals. First of all, we know that $8.34 = \frac{834}{100}$ and that $2.29 = \frac{229}{100}$. Therefore,

$$8.34 - 2.29 = \tfrac{834}{100} - \tfrac{229}{100}.$$

From our knowledge of subtraction of rational numbers of arithmetic, we know that

$$\tfrac{834}{100} - \tfrac{229}{100} = \tfrac{605}{100}.$$

Because $\frac{605}{100} = 6.05$, we conclude that

$$8.34 - 2.29 = 6.05.$$

After children have considered many such examples, they are ready to make certain observations about the position of the decimal point in the numeral for the difference. They should soon see that, if the denominator of each number in a difference is ten, then the difference is also expressed as tenths; or, if the denominator of each number is one hundred, then the difference is expressed as hundredths, and so on.

252 For each of the following sums or differences, first use fractions to find a decimal for the sum or difference. Then compute with the given decimals.
a $3.79 + 12.45$ **c** $4.582 - .916$ **e** $81.700 + 4.593$
b $6.7180 + .0549$ **d** $34.83 - 19.74$ **f** $54.12 - 19.86$

We can use the expanded forms of numbers to explain multiplication involving decimals just as we did for addition. Before we do this, however, we should remind you of what you learned in Chapter 6 concerning the product of two numbers expressed in power notation. There, you learned that, to find the product of two numbers such as 5^3 and 5^5, you find the sum of the exponents. Thus, $5^3 \cdot 5^5 = 5^{3+5} = 5^8$. Because we will be working with numbers that have negative exponents, such as 10^{-1} or 10^{-3}, we must also assume that you know how to find the sum of two negative numbers, such as -2 and -4. We will assume that you know, for example, that the sum of two negative numbers is negative, and that $-2 + (-4) = -6$.

Product of powers, page 130

Now we will use the expanded forms of the numbers to show how to find the product of 2.2 and .4. We have chosen an easy example so that it is possible to explain the principle involved without having to go through too many steps. First, we express each of the numbers in expanded form.

$$.4 \times 2.2 = 4 \cdot 10^{-1} \times (2 \cdot 10^0 + 2 \cdot 10^{-1}).$$

Then, because multiplication distributes over addition, we obtain

Distributive property, page 252

$$4 \cdot 10^{-1} \times (2 \cdot 10^0 + 2 \cdot 10^{-1}) =$$
$$(4 \cdot 10^{-1} \times 2 \cdot 10^0) + (4 \cdot 10^{-1} \times 2 \cdot 10^{-1}).$$

By the associative and commutative properties of multiplication, we can show that $(4 \cdot 10^{-1} \times 2 \cdot 10^0) = (4 \cdot 2 \times 10^{-1} \cdot 10^0)$ and also that $(4 \cdot 10^{-1} \times 2 \cdot 10^{-1}) = (4 \cdot 2 \times 10^{-1} \cdot 10^{-1})$. Therefore, $(4 \cdot 10^{-1} \times 2 \cdot 10^0) + (4 \cdot 10^{-1} \times 2 \cdot 10^{-1}) =$

Associative and commutative properties of multiplication, page 248

$$(4 \cdot 2 \times 10^{-1} \cdot 10^0) + (4 \cdot 2 \times 10^{-1} \cdot 10^{-1}).$$

From the definition of the product of two powers we obtain

$$10^{-1} \cdot 10^0 = 10^{-1+0} = 10^{-1}$$

and

$$10^{-1} \cdot 10^{-1} = 10^{-1+(-1)} = 10^{-2}.$$

Therefore, since $4 \cdot 2 = 8$,

$$(4 \cdot 2 \times 10^{-1} \cdot 10^0) + (4 \cdot 2 \times 10^{-1} \cdot 10^{-1}) = 8 \cdot 10^{-1} + 8 \cdot 10^{-2}.$$

But $8 \cdot 10^{-1} + 8 \cdot 10^{-2}$ is the expanded form of .88. Therefore,

$$.4 \times 2.2 = .88.$$

The following example shows both the work with the expanded forms of the numerals and the usual multiplication algorism.

$$
\begin{array}{rl}
.023 = & 0 \cdot 10^{-1} + 2 \cdot 10^{-2} + 3 \cdot 10^{-3} \\
3.1 = & 3 \cdot 10^0 + 1 \cdot 10^{-1} \\
\hline
23 = & 0 \cdot 10^{-2} + 2 \cdot 10^{-3} + 3 \cdot 10^{-4} \\
690 = & 0 \cdot 10^{-1} + 6 \cdot 10^{-2} + 9 \cdot 10^{-3} \\
\hline
.0713 = & 0 \cdot 10^{-1} + 7 \cdot 10^{-2} + 1 \cdot 10^{-3} + 3 \cdot 10^{-4}
\end{array}
$$

Note that in the example at the left no decimal points appear in the numerals that represent the partial products. This is true because, when we compute with decimals like .023 and 3.1, we use the same process as the one we use with the numerals 23 and 31. We locate the point in the numeral for the product only *after* we have completed the computation and have decided that the product of a number expressed to thousandths and a number expressed to tenths should be expressed to ten-thousandths.

We will now consider some examples to illustrate the use of fractions to explain multiplication involving decimals. First, suppose that we want to find the product of 7.6 and .8. Because $7.6 = \frac{76}{10}$ and $.8 = \frac{8}{10}$, we know that

$$7.6 \times .8 = \frac{76}{10} \times \frac{8}{10}.$$

Also,

$$\frac{76}{10} \times \frac{8}{10} = \frac{76 \cdot 8}{10 \cdot 10} = \frac{608}{100}.$$

Because $\frac{608}{100} = 6.08$, we conclude that

$$7.6 \times .8 = 6.08.$$

Now suppose that we want to find the product of .0015 and 12. We know that $.0015 = \frac{15}{10000}$ and that $12 = \frac{12}{1}$; therefore, we obtain

$$.0015 \times 12 = \frac{15}{10000} \times \frac{12}{1}.$$

Next,

$$\frac{15}{10000} \times \frac{12}{1} = \frac{15 \cdot 12}{10000 \cdot 1} = \frac{180}{10000}.$$

Because $\frac{180}{10000} = .0180$, we conclude that

$$.0015 \times 12 = .0180.$$

After children have seen what the results are for many such examples, they are *then* ready to make certain generalizations about the product of two numbers expressed as decimals. At first, they should always work with fractions until they see that the product of two numbers expressed to tenths is expressed to hundredths, because the product of the denominators is 10×10, or 100; that the product of a number expressed to tenths and a number expressed to hundredths is expressed to thousandths, because the product of the denominators is 10×100, or 1000; and so on.

Because division is defined in terms of multiplication, the computational procedures we use for division involving decimals can be justified by using the expanded forms of the numerals in somewhat the same way as was done for multiplication. We will not take the time or the space to give an example, but will merely take for granted that this is true. We will show, however, how the use of fractions helps children understand division involving decimals. First, we will consider examples in which we need not be concerned about the remainder because the dividend is exactly divisible by the divisor.

In Chapter 10, we established as a property of division that the quo- Division of rational numbers arithmetic page 261 tient of two numbers is not affected if both dividend and divisor are multiplied by the same non-zero number. We make use of this property when we divide numbers expressed as decimals. In computing with decimals, we multiply both dividend and divisor by a power of 10 so that the resulting divisor is the mate of a natural number. Suppose, for example, that we want to find the quotient $1.014 \div 7.8$. If we multiply 7.8 by 10, we obtain 78.0, which can also be expressed as $\frac{78}{1}$, whose mate is 78. Remember that we must also multiply 1.014 by 10. When we do this, we obtain 10.14. Once we have multiplied both 1.014 and 7.8 by 10, we know that the quotient of the numbers we obtain is the same as the quotient of 1.014 and 7.8. Therefore, we can write

$$1.014 \div 7.8 = 10.14 \div 78.0.$$

Now, because $10.14 = \frac{1014}{100}$ and $78.0 = \frac{78}{1}$, we know that

$$10.14 \div 78.0 = \frac{1014}{100} \div \frac{78}{1}.$$

Next, since the quotient of two rational numbers is equal to the product of the dividend and the multiplicative inverse of the divisor, we obtain

$$\frac{1014}{100} \div \frac{78}{1} = \frac{1014}{100} \times \frac{1}{78}.$$

By the definition of product,

$$\frac{1014}{100} \times \frac{1}{78} = \frac{1014 \times 1}{100 \times 78}.$$

Since multiplication is commutative,

$$\frac{1014 \times 1}{100 \times 78} = \frac{1014 \times 1}{78 \times 100}.$$

But $\frac{1014 \times 1}{78 \times 100} = \frac{1014}{78} \times \frac{1}{100}$. Since $\frac{1014}{78} = \frac{13}{1}$, we obtain

$$\frac{1014}{78} \times \frac{1}{100} = \frac{13}{1} \times \frac{1}{100} = \frac{13}{100}.$$

Because $\frac{13}{100} = .13$, we conclude that

$$1.014 \div 7.8 = .13.$$

Thus, we have found the quotient of 1.014 and 7.8 by using our knowledge of division of rational numbers and division of natural numbers. Now we will work the same example again, using the usual division algorism. We will find the quotient of 10.14 and 78 because we know that $1.014 \div 7.8 = 10.14 \div \frac{78}{1}$.

```
        _____
   78 )10. 14      | 10
      7 80         |
      _____       |
       234         | 3
       234         |
      _____       |___
         0         | 13
                   | .13
```

Notice that we ignore the decimal point in the numeral 10.14 and compute just as though we were finding the quotient of 1014 and 78. After we have completed the computation, we determine where the point should be in the decimal for the quotient by noting that the denominator of $\frac{1014}{100}$ is 100. If we always use the technique of rewriting the example so that the divisor is the mate of a natural number, then we need only notice how the dividend is expressed in deciding how to express the quotient. Thus, if the dividend is expressed to hundredths, then the quotient is also expressed to hundredths; if the dividend is expressed to thousandths, then the quotient is also expressed to thousandths; and so on.

Another example of the division algorism is given below.

$$.12\overline{)3.912}$$

We can multiply both .12 and 3.912 by 100. Therefore, this example may be rewritten as shown below. We then compute just as though we were working with natural numbers.

Once we have completed the computation, we observe that the dividend is expressed to tenths. So we conclude that the quotient should be expressed to tenths because $\frac{3912}{10} \div \frac{12}{1} = \frac{3912 \times 1}{10 \times 12} = \frac{3912}{12} \times \frac{1}{10}$.

Although division is closed in the set of non-zero rational numbers of arithmetic, sometimes the quotient of two numbers cannot be expressed by a terminating decimal. For example, the quotient of 1 and 3 is certainly a rational number (namely, $\frac{1}{3}$); but $\frac{1}{3}$ cannot be expressed by a terminating decimal. This means that, in such cases, the division process would have to be carried on indefinitely. So, we decide in advance that we want the quotient to be expressed to the nearer hundredth, or the nearer tenth, or the nearer thousandth. Then, if we want the quotient expressed to tenths, we must first express the dividend to tenths; if we want the quotient expressed to hundredths, we must first express the dividend to hundredths; and so on.

For example, suppose that we want to find the quotient of 19.2 and 3.4 and that we want the quotient expressed to the nearer hundredth. First of all, we know that $19.2 \div 3.4 = \frac{192}{1} \div \frac{34}{1}$; so we will find the quotient of 192 and 34. However, we want the quotient to be expressed to hundredths; so we know that the dividend should be expressed to hundredths. As you know, any number, such as $\frac{192}{1}$, can be named by many different decimals because it is possible to write any number of digits for 0 to the right of the decimal point and still obtain another decimal for the same number. Thus, because $\frac{192}{1} = \frac{1920}{10}, \frac{192}{1} = 192.0$; and because $\frac{192}{1} = \frac{19200}{100}, \frac{192}{1} = 192.00$, and so on. (In Chapter 13, we will use this idea to show why terminating decimals may be thought of as non-terminating decimals.) Since we want to express the quotient to the nearer hundredth, we will choose 192.00 as the dividend. Then we divide as though we were working with natural numbers.

$$
\begin{array}{r|l}
34\overline{)192.00} & 500 \\
\quad 170\ 00 & \\
\hline
\quad\ 22\ 00 & 60 \\
\quad\ 20\ 40 & \\
\hline
\quad\quad 1\ 60 & 4 \\
\quad\quad 1\ 36 & \\
\hline
\quad\quad\ \ \cancel{24} & \cancel{564} \\
& 5.65
\end{array}
$$

When we compute, we obtain a quotient of 564 with remainder 24. Because 24 is greater than $\frac{1}{2}$ of the divisor, we round the quotient up to 565. To find the decimal for the quotient, we finally divide 565 by 100 to obtain 5.65. So we know that the quotient, to the nearer hundredth, is 5.65. If the remainder had been less than $\frac{1}{2}$ of the divisor, we would have rounded the quotient down to 5.64. If the remainder had been equal to $\frac{1}{2}$ of the divisor, then we would have rounded the quotient to 5.64, which is the nearer even hundredth.

From our discussion of computation with decimals, it should be evident that the use of decimals for rational numbers does indeed simplify computation. Once a child has learned how to interpret the results of his computation, he can use his knowledge of computation involving natural numbers without regard for decimal points. Then he uses his knowledge of rational numbers and of the particular algorism with which he is working to interpret his results.

253 Find the standard name of each sum named below. Use the method of choosing the least common denominator for all the numbers.

a $\frac{2}{3} + \frac{5}{6}$ d $\frac{2}{5} + (\frac{1}{2} + \frac{1}{3})$ g $\frac{5}{2} + \frac{3}{1}$

b $\frac{1}{2} + \frac{5}{8}$ e $(\frac{2}{5} + \frac{1}{2}) + \frac{1}{3}$ h $\frac{9}{5} + \frac{9}{4}$

c $\frac{5}{1} + \frac{3}{11}$ f $\frac{11}{3} + \frac{5}{9}$ i $\frac{3}{8} + \frac{2}{8}$

254 Find the standard name of each product expressed below. Use cancellation wherever possible.

a $\frac{3}{4} \times \frac{6}{5}$ d $\frac{14}{5} \times \frac{15}{6}$ g $\frac{7}{2} \times \frac{12}{21}$

b $6\frac{1}{2} \times 2$ e $3\frac{2}{3} \times \frac{4}{11}$ h $\frac{5}{8} \times \frac{3}{10}$

c $\frac{8}{3} \times \frac{3}{8}$ f $6 \times \frac{1}{3}$ i $\frac{2}{3} \times \frac{1}{2}$

255 Write each of the following numerals in expanded form.

a 14,562   d 56,902,005   g .000 005 009
b 1,900.002   e .459   h 4500.00056
c 5005   f .000409   i 15.67

256 Write each of the following in the form $\frac{a}{b}$, where a and b represent natural numbers.

a 56   d 45,666.666   g 5.006
b .098   e 400.001   h .000809
c 1.5   f 145.145   i .00040

257 Find the sum, product, difference, and quotient of each pair of numbers named below. For subtraction, subtract the second number from the first. For division, use the first number as the dividend and the second number as the divisor. For exercise c, find the quotient to the nearer hundredth.

a 1.7, .34   c 150, 15.66   e 4545, 45.45
b 5.44, .2   d 4545, .009   f .3, .0003

258 Express each pair of numbers named below in the form $\frac{a}{b}$, where a is a natural number and b is a power of 10. Then find the product of the two numbers. Finally, express the product as a decimal.

a 15.5, .34   c 99.9, .111   e 456.7, 150.55
b 7.34, 9.6   d .101, .005   f .441, .00051

Decimals used for ordering rational numbers of arithmetic

Aside from their value in computation, decimals that express rational numbers of arithmetic are also useful for ordering these numbers. In Chapter 10, we stated the following order property for rational numbers of arithmetic:

> For any two rational numbers of arithmetic $\frac{a}{b}$ and $\frac{c}{d}$, $\frac{a}{b} > \frac{c}{d}$ if and only if $ad > cb$.

Definition "greater than," page 254

Of course, we often know immediately if one number is greater than another. For example, we need not use the order property as expressed above to decide that $\frac{1}{2} > \frac{1}{4}$, that $\frac{1}{3} < \frac{7}{8}$, that $\frac{6}{5} > 1$, or that $\frac{2}{3} < \frac{3}{4}$.

When rational numbers are expressed as decimals, we need only compare the two decimals to decide which one names the greater number. For example, suppose that you want to decide which of the two decimals, 5.671 or 5.672, names the greater number. First, we could write the numerals in expanded form, as shown below.

$$5.671 = 5 \cdot 10^0 + 6 \cdot 10^{-1} + 7 \cdot 10^{-2} + 1 \cdot 10^{-3}.$$
$$5.672 = 5 \cdot 10^0 + 6 \cdot 10^{-1} + 7 \cdot 10^{-2} + 2 \cdot 10^{-3}.$$

Notice that, in the sums expressed at the right in each sentence, all of the addends are the same except the last. If we compare these addends, we see that $2 \cdot 10^{-3}$ is a greater number than $1 \cdot 10^{-3}$. Therefore, we conclude that $5.672 > 5.671$.

Of course, we need not write the numerals in expanded form to reach this conclusion. We simply compare the digits in the two numerals, note that the final digits are different, observe that $.002 > .001$, and decide that $5.672 > 5.671$.

Similarly, we can decide by inspection that $6.8432 < 68.432$ because the digit 6 in 6.8432 is associated with 10^0; while the digit 6 in 68.432 is associated with 10^1. Thus, because $6 \cdot 10^0$, or 6, is less than $6 \cdot 10^1$, or 60, we know that 6.8432 is the lesser number.

259 Be prepared to explain why each of the following sentences expresses a true statement.

a $.003 > .0003$.
b $7.45 > 7.44$.
c $.1 < 1$.
d $956.0 > 95.60$.
e $.36 < .38$.
f $.0001 < .001$.

Scientific notation

Astronomers, physicists, chemists, and engineers often work with numbers that represent very large quantities and also with numbers that represent very small quantities. For example, light travels approximately 6,000,000,000,000 miles per year. Scientists use this number as a unit of measure that is called a light-year. Physicists might use a number like .000 000 000 000 000 000 000 000 000 9 to represent the mass of an electron. We could give many other examples of such numbers used in the sciences.

Since numerals like these are somewhat unwieldy for purposes of recording data and computing, a special way of naming such numbers has been developed. If a number is expressed as the product of a number that is greater than or equal to 1 but less than 10 and a power of 10, then the number is said to be expressed in *scientific notation*. The first factor in the product is usually expressed as a decimal and the second factor is expressed in power notation.

Some examples should make clear how a number may be expressed in scientific notation. For example, suppose that we want to express 732,800 as the product of a number between 1 and 10 and a power of 10. First of all, we will divide 732,800 by a power of 10 so that we obtain a quotient that is between 1 and 10. Then, the quotient and the divisor can be used to express 732,800 in scientific notation. Now notice that if we divide 732,800 by 100,000, we obtain 7.32800, or 7.328. This means that $732,800 = 7.328 \times 100,000$. 7.328 is a number between 1 and 10, and $100,000 = 10^5$. Therefore, 7.328×10^5 is scientific notation for 732,800.

Next let us consider a number that is less than one, like .039. Obviously, we would not divide to obtain a number between 1 and 10 in this case; instead, we should multiply .039 by some power of 10. If we multiply .039 by 100, we obtain 3.9. This means that $.039 = 3.9 \div 100$. But $3.9 \div 100 = 3.9 \times \frac{1}{100} = 3.9 \times 10^{-2}$. This last product has a number between 1 and 10 as its first factor and a power of 10 as its second factor. Thus, 3.9×10^{-2} is scientific notation for .039.

The following table lists several more numbers expressed in scientific notation. The expressions in parentheses show the intermediate step that was used in obtaining the scientific notation for each number.

	Decimal notation		Scientific notation
A	1345	(1.345×1000)	1.345×10^3
B	11	(1.1×10)	1.1×10^1
C	1,567,902	$(1.567902 \times 1,000,000)$	1.567902×10^6
D	.5	$(5 \times \frac{1}{10})$	5×10^{-1}
E	3.4	(3.4×1)	3.4×10^0
F	.567	$(5.67 \times \frac{1}{10})$	5.67×10^{-1}
G	.0056	$(5.6 \times \frac{1}{1000})$	5.6×10^{-3}
H	.000 000 51	$(5.1 \times \frac{1}{10,000,000})$	5.1×10^{-7}

Note that in example E the number 3.4 is already a number between 1 and 10. When we express such a number in scientific notation, we simply use 10^0 as the factor that is a power of 10, since $10^0 = 1$.

260 Write each of the numbers named below in scientific notation.

a 456,456

b .000 000 090 009

c .150 008 3

d 12,340,890.00045

e $6\frac{1}{2}$

f $\frac{1}{10000}$

CONCLUSION

In this chapter, we have introduced finite decimals for those rational numbers of arithmetic that can be named by terminating decimals. We have also extended the decimal numeration system to include terminating decimals by showing how these numerals can be written in expanded form. We have discussed some of the computational techniques that may be used when we compute with names for rational numbers, including "mixed" numerals and decimals. There are a number of short cuts for computing that we did not discuss because we feel that such methods should not be overemphasized. Children, of course, should learn how to compute well, but they should not be required to learn meaningless and mechanical procedures that will only impair their understanding and soon be forgotten.

CHAPTER QUIZ

1 List ten different names for the multiplicative identity element.
2 List ten different names for the additive identity element.
3 Determine each sum, product, difference, and quotient given below. In most of these exercises, the computation will be simplified if you recognize certain relationships among the numbers and if you use the properties of the system of rational numbers of arithmetic.

A $\frac{46}{13} + \frac{55}{55} = \frac{x}{y}.$ E $\frac{51}{16} \times \frac{52}{31} \times \frac{16}{51} = \frac{x}{y}.$

B $\frac{2}{3} \times \frac{16}{3} \times \frac{14}{15} \times \frac{0}{8} \times \frac{11}{5} = \frac{x}{y}.$ F $\frac{35}{72} \times (\frac{72}{35} + \frac{19}{19}) = \frac{x}{y}.$

C $\frac{26}{45} \div \frac{202}{101} = \frac{x}{y}.$ G $(\frac{44}{17} + \frac{56}{56}) \div \frac{19}{19} = \frac{x}{y}.$

D $\frac{x}{y} \times \frac{46}{15} = \frac{46}{15}.$ H $\frac{7}{60} - \frac{1}{36} = \frac{x}{y}.$

4 A "unit fraction" is a number of the form $\frac{1}{a}, \frac{1}{b}, \frac{1}{c}$, and so on, where the denominators are non-zero natural numbers. What formula can be used to determine the sum $\frac{1}{a} + \frac{1}{b}$ for any two unit fractions?

5 Write the following numerals in expanded form in three ways. For example, 56.9 can be written as $50 + 6 + \frac{9}{10}$, as $5 \cdot 10 + 6 \cdot 1 + 9 \cdot \frac{1}{10}$, or as $5 \cdot 10^1 + 6 \cdot 10^0 + 9 \cdot 10^{-1}$.
A 23,456.21 B 5.0651 C .0000934 D 1.5005

6 Write each of the following decimals in the form $\frac{a}{b}$, where a and b are natural numbers that are relatively prime.
A .5601 B 45.44 C .0034 D 100.001 E 200.06

7 Write each of the following as a decimal.
A $\frac{1}{2}$ B $\frac{3}{4}$ C $\frac{56}{100}$ D $\frac{4}{25}$ E $\frac{78}{250}$ F $\frac{3}{2}$

8 Explain why you cannot make use of the property $\frac{a}{b} = \frac{an}{bn}$ to convert $\frac{2}{3}$ to a decimal. List five other rational numbers of arithmetic that cannot be written as decimals by using this property.

9 Explain why all of the following are names for the same rational number: .7, .70, .700, .7000.

10 Without computing, decide whether each product expressed below is greater than both factors, less than both factors, or greater than one factor but less than the other. What generalization can you make?
A 45.9023 × .00056 D .105 × .956
B 1.11 × .909 E 1.56078 × 2.569752
C 3 × .0101099 F .0568201 × .9956

11 Estimate each of the following.

    A .99 + 1.999   B 46.0001 × .9999   C 38 ÷ 19.001

12 Children are often taught the "caret" method for division illustrated below. Tell what property of rational numbers is involved.

$$3.64_\wedge \overline{)\,.42_\wedge 11}$$

13 Choose the proper symbol, $<$, $>$, or $=$, to express the relation between the first and second number of each pair named below.

    A .00462, .00463   D .000 034 62, .000 034 621

    B 5.2891, 5.2991   E .0366, .03660

    C 36.42891, 36.42885   F 3.04, 3.004

14 $5 < 7$; therefore, $.5 < .7$. What property can we use to justify this?

15 Write each of the numbers named below in scientific notation.

    A 1456.092   E .44

    B 1,000,000,000   F 45.00056

    C 1,000,923,000   G 45,000.56

    D .000 000 000 000 000 49   H 156.32×10^{-4}

16 In each of the following exercises, use the four numbers that are named to make replacements for a, b, c, and d in the form $a < b < c < d$ so that a true statement results.

    A 5.00, 5.01, 4.9995, 5.005

    B .0045, .00445, .00451, .004501

    C $6.5 \cdot 10^{-6}$, $6.50 \cdot 10^{-5}$, $6.501 \cdot 10^{-6}$, $6.4909 \cdot 10^{-5}$

    D $7.34 \cdot 10^{8}$, $7.34 \cdot 10^{9}$, $7.334 \cdot 10^{8}$, $7.3401 \cdot 10^{9}$

    E $9.45 \cdot 10^{-3}$, $9.451 \cdot 10^{-3}$, $9.4401 \cdot 10^{-3}$, $9.44999 \cdot 10^{-3}$

    F .000 045, .000 45, .000 044 01, .000 004 4

SUPPLEMENTARY READINGS

"Numeration Systems for the Rational Numbers," *Twenty-ninth Yearbook of the National Council of Teachers of Mathematics*, Ch. 7. Despite minor differences in terminology, the approach to computation presented here is like the one in this chapter. Item 45 of Bibliography

Sawyer, W. W., *Introducing Mathematics, Vol. I: Vision in Elementary Mathematics*, Chapter 13. This book contains some very interesting ideas about fractions. The material is not developed along the same lines as the material in this chapter, but a number of interesting enrichment topics are provided. Item 47 of Bibliography

Van Engen, *et al.*, *Seeing Through Mathematics, Book 1*, Unit 7. This book is perhaps the best source of information and exercises to supplement the material in this chapter. Item 21 of Bibliography

Chapter twelve

Rational numbers

Positive and negative numbers
Operations on rational numbers
Subtraction and division of rational numbers

In previous chapters of this book, we discussed the natural numbers and the rational numbers of arithmetic. We observed certain similarities between the naturals and the rationals of arithmetic. These sets of numbers are alike insofar as both sets, together with addition and multiplication and certain properties of these operations, do satisfy the basic require- Requirements for number ments for a number system. However, the rational numbers of arithmetic system, page 96 have certain properties that the natural numbers do not have. For example, every rational number except 0 has a multiplicative inverse. In each case the Multiplicative product of the given number and its multiplicative inverse is $\frac{1}{1}$. Further, inverse, page 250 the rational numbers of arithmetic are dense; that is, between any two Density given numbers, there exists another rational number of arithmetic. The property, page 269 natural numbers have neither the multiplicative inverse nor the density property.

When we began our discussion of the rational numbers of arithmetic, we posed two questions of the kind that cannot be answered when one is dealing only with the natural numbers. These questions were: (a) 6 must be added to what number to obtain 4 as the sum? (b) By what number must 3 be multiplied to obtain 5 as the product? With the development of the rational numbers of arithmetic, we found that we were able to answer questions like Question b by using the rational numbers that are the mates of 3 and 5. Remember that the non-zero rational numbers of arithmetic are closed with respect to division. Thus, in answer to Question b, we know that the solution of $x \times \frac{3}{1} = \frac{5}{1}$ is the same as the solution of $x = \frac{5}{1} \div \frac{3}{1}$ and that $\frac{5}{1} \div \frac{3}{1} = \frac{5}{1} \times \frac{1}{3} = \frac{5}{3}$; hence, $\frac{5}{3}$ satisfies $x \times \frac{3}{1} = \frac{5}{1}$. There is no natural number by which 3 can be multiplied to get 5; but there is a rational number by which $\frac{3}{1}$ can be multiplied to get $\frac{5}{1}$.

Closure with respect to division, page 263

However, even with the introduction of the rational numbers of arithmetic, we still have no answer for Question a. In this chapter we will consider a set of numbers—the set of positive and negative rational numbers and zero, or, more simply, the set of all rational numbers—that will enable us to answer questions like Question a above.

Positive and negative numbers

Our approach to the rational numbers will be quite different from our development of the naturals and of the rational numbers of arithmetic. If time and space permitted, we could develop the rational numbers from the rational numbers of arithmetic just as we developed those numbers from the natural numbers.* Instead, we will make use of your intuition about numbers and rely in part upon what you already know about positive and negative numbers from algebra. With the idea of a number line and a certain amount of imagination, we can very easily develop the set of rational numbers and their properties.

In Chapter 10, we constructed a number line for the rational numbers of arithmetic like the one pictured below. In constructing such a line, we first choose an arbitrary point with which we associate the number 0. Then, using some arbitrary unit, we locate points to correspond to certain members of the set of rational numbers of arithmetic. Of course, physical limitations prevent us from locating the points that correspond to more than just a few numbers; but it seems quite reasonable that it would be theoretically possible to locate points to which we could assign every conceivable rational number of arithmetic.

Number line page 267

Because of the way in which the number line is constructed and because of the way in which we have defined "less than," the relation "less than"

---

* For a development of rational numbers in terms of infinite sets of ordered pairs of rational numbers of arithmetic, see *Seeing Through Mathematics*, Book 2, Van Engen, *et al.* Item 48 of Bibliography

corresponds to the relation "to the left of." This means that $\frac{1}{2}$ is less than 1 and point $\frac{1}{2}$ is to the left of point 1; $\frac{1}{4}$ is less than $\frac{1}{2}$ and point $\frac{1}{4}$ is to the left of point $\frac{1}{2}$. Similarly, 0 is less than all other rational numbers of arithmetic, and point 0 is to the left of all other points in the line to which numbers have been assigned.

Now, however, suppose that we think of the number line as being analogous to the scale on a thermometer. Suppose also that we consider points in the line to the left of point 0, just as we consider points below 0 on the thermometer scale. In the number line pictured below, we have located and labeled certain points to the left of 0. Point A is the same distance to the left of 0 as $\frac{1}{4}$ is to the right of 0; point B is the same distance

to the left of 0 as $\frac{1}{2}$ is to the right of 0; C is the same distance from 0 as is $\frac{3}{4}$; D is the same distance from 0 as is 1; and E is the same distance from 0 as is 2. Thus, we can think of point A as the "opposite" of point $\frac{1}{4}$, B as the opposite of $\frac{1}{2}$, and so on.

For every point in the line to the right of point 0 to which a number has been assigned, there is a second point in the line that is the same distance to the left of point 0 and that can be thought of as the opposite of the given point. With each of these opposite points, we can also associate a number that is in a sense the "opposite" of the number assigned to the given point.

In general, every number that is assigned to a given point to the right of point 0 can be thought of as representing a directed distance (to the right) from point 0 to the given point. Further, every number that is assigned to a point to the left of point 0 can be thought of as representing a directed distance (to the left) from point 0 to the given point. We can now adopt the conventional mathematical terminology and notation in calling the numbers that represent distances to the right of 0 *positive rational numbers* and the numbers that represent distances to the left of 0 *negative rational numbers*.

In the number line shown below, we have associated rational numbers with certain points in the line. Notice that all of the numbers greater than zero are positive numbers, symbolized as $+\frac{1}{3}$, $+\frac{1}{2}$, $+\frac{3}{4}$, and so on. All of the numbers less than zero are negative numbers, symbolized as $-\frac{1}{3}$, $-\frac{1}{2}$, $-\frac{3}{4}$, and so on. The number assigned to the first point to the right of point 0 is read "positive $\frac{1}{3}$" (note that it represents a distance of $\frac{1}{3}$ to the *right* of point 0); the number assigned to the second point to the right of 0 is read "positive $\frac{1}{2}$"; and so on. The number assigned to the first point to the left of 0 is read "negative $\frac{1}{3}$" (note that it represents a distance of $\frac{1}{3}$ to the *left* of point 0); the number assigned to the second point to the left of 0 is read "negative $\frac{1}{2}$"; and so on. Note that 0 is neither positive nor negative and, consequently, we see that the *set of rational numbers* is the union of the following three sets:

1) The set of positive rational numbers
2) The set of negative rational numbers
3) The set whose member is 0

Just as the natural numbers and the rational numbers of arithmetic can be ordered in terms of "less than" or "greater than," so can the rational numbers be ordered. In the rational-number line shown on page 299, the relation "less than" corresponds to the relation "to the left of." For example, point $-\frac{1}{3}$ is to the left of point 0, and $-\frac{1}{3}$ is less than 0; point -1 is to the left of point $-\frac{1}{2}$, and -1 is less than $-\frac{1}{2}$; point $+1$ is to the left of point $+\frac{3}{2}$, and $+1$ is less than $+\frac{3}{2}$. From the number line, you can see that every negative rational number is less than every positive rational number. You can also see that every negative number is less than 0, because every point to which a negative number is assigned is to the left of point 0 and also to the left of every point to which a positive number is assigned.

The positive rational numbers and 0 comprise one subset of the set of rational numbers that is of interest to us. This subset corresponds to the set of numbers that we have been calling the rational numbers of arithmetic. Because the positive numbers and 0 behave in the same way as the rational numbers of arithmetic do, they may be called the *mates* of the rational numbers of arithmetic. Since these sets of numbers are mates, we often omit the symbol "$+$" when we name the positive rational numbers. This means, for example, that we will usually express $+\frac{1}{3}$ simply as $\frac{1}{3}$ unless we have some special reason for emphasizing the fact that we are considering *positive* $\frac{1}{3}$.

There are certain other subsets of the set of rational numbers that are also interesting and useful. One such subset is the set of positive numbers 1, 2, 3, and so on, that correspond to the counting numbers. This set is called the *positive integers*. As you might expect, the set of negative numbers that are the opposites of the positive integers (-1, -2, -3, and so on) is called the *negative integers*. The union of the set of positive integers, the set of negative integers, and the set whose member is 0 is called the *integers.**

261 Order the following rational numbers, beginning with the least number.

$$+5, \; -6, \; -\tfrac{12}{5}, \; +\tfrac{5}{12}, \; -\tfrac{22}{7}, \; +\tfrac{13}{3}, \; +\tfrac{27}{5}, \; -3, \; +\tfrac{2}{5}, \; -\tfrac{7}{3}$$

Operations on rational numbers

Earlier we said that the positive rational numbers and 0 "behave" like the rational numbers of arithmetic. By this we mean that, when we find sums and products of pairs of positive numbers, we get results that correspond to the results we obtain when we find sums and products of pairs of rational numbers of arithmetic.

For example, suppose that the temperature at 7 A.M. one day is 16° above zero, or $+16°$, and that by noon the temperature has risen 10°, or $+10°$. Then we find the temperature at noon by adding $+16$ and $+10$. Thus,

$$+16 + (+10) = +26.$$

Also, when we multiply two positive rational numbers, we find that the results correspond to the results with rational numbers of arithmetic. For example,

$$+3 \cdot (+8) = +24.$$

Several other examples of this correspondence between positive rational numbers and rational numbers of arithmetic are given below.

$$+\tfrac{1}{2} + (+1) = +1\tfrac{1}{2}.$$
$$+5 \cdot (+3\tfrac{1}{2}) = +17\tfrac{1}{2}.$$
$$+12 + (+4) = +16.$$
$$+8 \cdot (+6\tfrac{1}{4}) = +50.$$

262 Use your knowledge of addition and multiplication of rational numbers of arithmetic to find the standard name of each of the following.

a $+\tfrac{3}{5} + (+\tfrac{4}{3})$ **b** $+\tfrac{4}{9} + (+\tfrac{5}{12})$ **c** $+\tfrac{7}{2} \cdot (+\tfrac{8}{21})$ **d** $+\tfrac{12}{25} \cdot (+\tfrac{35}{18})$

Now, however, we need to decide what the results will be when the sums and products involve negative numbers. Suppose, for example, that

---

* *Set Theory and the Structure of Arithmetic*, by Norman Hamilton and Joseph Landin, contains a precise development of the rational numbers in terms of ordered pairs of integers. Item 13 of Bibliography

the temperature at 7 A.M. one morning is 15° below zero, or $-15°$, and that by noon the temperature has risen 7°, or $+7°$. Of course, we know that the temperature at noon is $-8°$. That is, we know that

$$-15 + (+7) = -8.$$

But how do we know this? Similarly, how do we determine the rational number that satisfies each of the following conditions?

$$-6 + (-8) = n.$$
$$-\tfrac{3}{4} \cdot (+4) = n.$$
$$-1\tfrac{7}{8} + (+5) = n.$$
$$-6 \cdot (-11) = n.$$

Before we can find solutions of conditions like those just expressed, we need to consider certain properties of the rational numbers. One important and useful property of the rational numbers that is not shared by the natural numbers or rational numbers of arithmetic is expressed as follows:

For every rational number a,
there exists another rational number $-a$,
called the *additive inverse* of a,
such that the sum of a and its additive inverse
is equal to 0; that is, $a + (-a) = 0$.

In $a + (-a) = 0$, $-a$ may represent either a positive or a negative number, depending upon what replacement has been made for a. For example, if a is replaced by $+1$, then $-a$ represents -1, since $+1 + (-1) = 0$. If, however, a is replaced by a negative number, such as -5, then $-a$ represents $+5$, because $-5 + (+5) = 0$. Thus, the symbol $-a$ does not necessarily name a negative number, but names the additive inverse of a given number.

The statements expressed below give examples of the additive inverses of several rational numbers.

$$+3 + (-3) = 0.$$
$$+\tfrac{13}{2} + (-\tfrac{13}{2}) = 0.$$
$$-4\tfrac{2}{3} + (+4\tfrac{2}{3}) = 0.$$
$$-33\tfrac{4}{5} + (+33\tfrac{4}{5}) = 0.$$

From these examples, you can see that the additive inverse of a given rational number corresponds to the notion of the "opposite" of a point that we used in connection with the number line on page 299. Furthermore, the fact that the sum of 3 and -3 is 0 seems quite natural in the sense that winning 3 points ($+3$) in one game and losing 3 points (-3) in a second game leaves a player with a combined score of 0 points. Similarly, a surplus of $6\frac{1}{2}$ dollars one week, combined with a deficit of $6\frac{1}{2}$ dollars the next week, leaves one with a balance of 0 dollars. Thus, it is possible to think of situations that fit examples like those given on page 302.

263 Is the additive inverse of a rational number always less than the given number?

264 Give the additive inverse for each of the following rational numbers.

    a $+6$ **b** $+\frac{3}{5}$ **c** $-\frac{5}{4}$ **d** -4 **e** $+\frac{10}{3}$ **f** $-\frac{2}{7}$ **g** 0

The chart below summarizes the important properties of the set of rational numbers under the operations of addition and multiplication. You should compare this chart with the one given in Chapter 10 for the rational numbers of arithmetic.

Properties of rational numbers of arithmetic, page 256

Since the properties of the rational numbers—with the exception of the additive-inverse property—are analogous to the properties developed for the rational numbers of arithmetic, they should be easy for you to understand and accept. We will not prove these properties.

Properties of rational numbers

	Addition	Multiplication
Closure $\longrightarrow$	For each x and y, $x + y$ is a rational number.	For each x and y, xy is a rational number.
Commutativity $\longrightarrow$	For each x and y, $x + y = y + x$.	For each x and y, $xy = yx$.
Associativity $\longrightarrow$	For each x, y, and z, $(x + y) + z = x + (y + z)$.	For each x, y, and z, $(xy)z = x(yz)$.
Distributivity $\longrightarrow$	For each x, y, and z, $x(y + z) = xy + xz$.	
Identity-element $\longrightarrow$	For each x, $x + 0 = x$.	For each x, $x \cdot 1 = x$.
Inverse $\longrightarrow$	For each x, $x + (-x) = 0$.	For each x, if x is non-zero, then $x \cdot \dfrac{1}{x} = 1$.
Zero $\longrightarrow$		For each x, $x \cdot 0 = 0$.
Cancellation $\longrightarrow$	For each x, y, and z, if $x + z = y + z$, then $x = y$.	For each x, y, and z, if z is non-zero and if $xz = yz$, then $x = y$.

In the chart, we have used x, y, and z as variables, rather than variables like $\frac{a}{b}$ or $\frac{c}{d}$. Because the universe for each variable is the set of rational numbers, each variable is to be replaced by a number such as $-\frac{1}{3}$, $\frac{3}{8}$, $\frac{2}{1}$, $\frac{0}{1}$, $-1\frac{1}{5}$, and so on. Also note that, in the statement of the multiplicative-inverse property, we have used $\frac{1}{x}$ to represent the inverse of x. Thus, if x is replaced by $\frac{5}{8}$, for example, then $\frac{1}{x}$ must be replaced by $\frac{8}{5}$, the multiplicative inverse of $\frac{5}{8}$.

Now we return to the problem of determining the sum of two rational numbers if either or both numbers are negative. We can use the properties of rational numbers expressed in the chart and the properties of equality to help us determine the sum in such cases. Properties of equality, page 98

In the following examples, we will use integers, just to simplify the computation. The methods that are used here for integers can also be used for any other rational numbers. Let us first consider an example in which one addend is positive and the other is negative. Suppose that we want to find the sum of 6 and -4. First of all, because $6 = 2 + 4$, we know that

$$6 + (-4) = (2 + 4) + (-4).$$

Then, because addition is associative,

$$(2 + 4) + (-4) = 2 + \left(4 + (-4)\right).$$

But, since $a + (-a) = 0$, we know that $4 + (-4) = 0$, and

$$2 + \left(4 + (-4)\right) = 2 + 0.$$

Finally, because 0 is the identity element for addition,

$$2 + 0 = 2.$$

Therefore, by the transitive property of equality,

$$6 + (-4) = 2.$$

Now let us consider an example in which both addends are negative. Keep in mind that we are *assuming* that the properties summarized in the chart on page 303 hold for the entire set of rational numbers. We are demonstrating how these assumed properties, along with a bit of ingenuity, can be used to determine sums; we are *not* establishing rules for computation involving rational numbers. Suppose that we want to find the sum of -5 and -8. First of all, let us consider another example in which we find the sum of -5, -8, *and* the additive inverses of these two numbers. That is, let us consider the sum

$$\bigl(-5 + (-8)\bigr) + (8 + 5).$$

Because addition is assumed to be associative, we can obtain

$$\bigl(-5 + (-8)\bigr) + (8 + 5) = \bigl(-5 + (-8 + 8)\bigr) + 5.$$

But, we know that $-8 + 8 = 0$; therefore,

$$\bigl(-5 + (-8 + 8)\bigr) + 5 = (-5 + 0) + 5.$$

Because 0 is the identity element for addition, $-5 + 0 = -5$; so

$$(-5 + 0) + 5 = -5 + 5.$$

But $-5 + 5 = 0$; therefore, by the transitive property,

$$\bigl(-5 + (-8)\bigr) + (8 + 5) = 0.$$

Since $8 + 5 = 13$, we can obtain

$$\bigl(-5 + (-8)\bigr) + 13 = 0.$$

By the addition property of equality, we know that, if $a = b$, then $a + c = b + c$; hence,

Addition property of equality, page 98

$$\bigl([-5 + (-8)] + 13\bigr) + (-13) = 0 + (-13).$$

By the associative property,

$$\bigl([-5 + (-8)] + 13\bigr) + (-13) = \bigl(-5 + (-8)\bigr) + \bigl(13 + (-13)\bigr).$$

Also, $0 + (-13) = -13$. Thus,

$$\bigl(-5 + (-8)\bigr) + \bigl(13 + (-13)\bigr) = -13.$$

We know that $13 + (-13) = 0$ and that

$$\bigl(-5 + (-8)\bigr) + 0 = -5 + (-8);$$

so we conclude that

$$-5 + (-8) = -13.$$

We will consider one more example in which we find the sum of a positive and a negative number. Suppose that we want to find the sum of -7 and 3. We can begin, as in the previous example, by finding the sum of -7 and 3 and the additive inverses of these two numbers. You should be able to justify each step given below and on the next page.

$$(-7 + 3) + \bigl(7 + (-3)\bigr) = (-7 + 7) + \bigl(3 + (-3)\bigr).$$
$$(-7 + 7) + \bigl(3 + (-3)\bigr) = 0.$$

$$(-7 + 3) + (7 + (-3)) = 0.$$
$$(-7 + 3) + ([4 + 3] + (-3)) = 0.$$
$$(-7 + 3) + (4 + [3 + (-3)]) = 0.$$
$$(-7 + 3) + 4 = 0.$$
$$(-7 + 3) + (4 + (-4)) = 0 + (-4).$$
$$-7 + 3 = -4.$$

265 What similarity do you notice between the additive-inverse property and the multiplicative-inverse property?

266 Use the method illustrated in the examples just discussed to find each of the sums named below.

a $15 + (-6)$ **d** $18 + (-8)$
b $-18 + 16$ **e** $(14 + (-3)) + 26$
c $-7 + (-3)$ **f** $-9 + (-10 + 9)$

267 Is the additive inverse of a negative number positive, or is it negative?

We can also use the properties of rational numbers to determine the product of a pair of rational numbers. We already know that the product of two positive numbers is positive because the positive numbers behave like the rational numbers of arithmetic. Now let us consider an example in which one of the numbers is positive and the other is negative. For example, we will now find the product of 5 and -4.

First, consider the following product:

$$5 \cdot (-4 + 4).$$

We know that $-4 + 4 = 0$ and that $5 \times 0 = 0$; therefore,

$$5 \cdot (-4 + 4) = 0.$$

Because we have assumed that multiplication distributes over addition, we can express the product $5 \cdot (-4 + 4)$ as a sum in the following way.

$$5 \cdot (-4 + 4) = 5 \cdot (-4) + 5 \cdot 4.$$

Hence, by the transitive property,

$$5 \cdot (-4) + 5 \cdot 4 = 0.$$

We already know that $5 \cdot 4 = 20$; so

$$5 \cdot (-4) + 20 = 0.$$

Since the sum of $5 \cdot (-4)$ and 20 is equal to 0, $5 \cdot (-4)$ must be equal to the additive inverse of 20, or -20. Thus, we conclude that

$$5 \cdot (-4) = -20.$$

Next let us consider an example in which both factors are negative. This time, suppose that we want to find the product of -5 and -4. To do this, we will first consider the product

$$-5 \cdot (-4 + 4).$$

Because $-4 + 4 = 0$ and $-5 \cdot 0 = 0$,

$$-5 \cdot (-4 + 4) = 0.$$

By the distributive property,

$$-5 \cdot (-4 + 4) = -5 \cdot (-4) + (-5) \cdot 4.$$

Thus,

$$-5 \cdot (-4) + (-5) \cdot 4 = 0.$$

From the previous example, we know that $-5 \cdot 4 = -20$; so

$$-5 \cdot (-4) + (-20) = 0.$$

Since the sum of $-5 \cdot (-4)$ and -20 is equal to 0, $-5 \cdot (-4)$ must be equal to the additive inverse of -20, or 20. Therefore,

$$-5 \cdot (-4) = 20.$$

268 Use the method illustrated in the preceding examples to find the product named in each of the following exercises.

a $-5 \cdot 2$ **c** $14 \cdot (-21)$
b $-8 \cdot (-9)$ **d** $(-3) \cdot (-4) \cdot (-2)$

269 Is the multiplicative inverse of a positive number positive, or is it negative?

270 Is the multiplicative inverse of a negative number positive, or is it negative?

Subtraction and division of rational numbers

Now that we have summarized the basic properties of the rational-number system, we shall discuss subtraction and division of rational numbers. We will consider division first because the discussion of it can be very brief.

In Chapter 10, we defined the quotient of two rational numbers of arithmetic to be the product of the dividend and the multiplicative inverse of the divisor. The quotient of two rational numbers is defined in the same way:

Quotient of two rational numbers of arithmetic, page 262

> For any two rational numbers x and y,
> if y is non-zero, then $x \div y = x \cdot \frac{1}{y}$,
> where $\frac{1}{y}$ represents the multiplicative inverse of y.

From this definition, you should be able to explain why the set of non-zero rational numbers is closed under division. Keep in mind that the set of non-zero rational numbers contains all of the positive and all of the negative rational numbers; in fact, it contains every rational number except zero.

271 Find the standard name of each of the following quotients.

a $+\frac{3}{5} \div (-\frac{4}{15})$ **b** $-\frac{8}{27} \div (-\frac{35}{18})$ **c** $-\frac{10}{63} \div (+\frac{25}{28})$

272 Explain why the set of non-zero rational numbers is closed under division.

273 Is there an identity element for division of rational numbers?

Now let us consider subtraction of rational numbers. In earlier discussions of natural numbers and rational numbers of arithmetic, we have said that subtraction is defined in terms of addition. For example, we know that $x + 3 = 8$ has the same solution as $x = 8 - 3$. That is, because the *sum* of x and 3 is 8, it follows that the *difference* of 8 and 3 is also x. Hence, we know that 5 satisfies both of these conditions; therefore, $8 - 3 = 5$. But, from our discussion of addition of rational numbers, we know that the sum of 8 and the additive inverse of 3 is also equal to 5. That is,

Subtraction related to addition, pages 102 and 257

$$8 + (-3) = (5 + 3) + (-3).$$
$$(5 + 3) + (-3) = 5 + (3 + (-3)).$$
$$5 + (3 + (-3)) = 5 + 0.$$
$$5 + 0 = 5.$$

Hence,

$$8 + (-3) = 5.$$

Thus, because $8 - 3$ and $8 + (-3)$ are both equal to 5,

$$8 - 3 = 8 + (-3).$$

In other words, the difference of 8 and 3 is equal to the sum of 8 and the additive inverse of 3. This specific example illustrates the following definition of subtraction for all rational numbers.

For any two rational numbers x and y,
$$x - y = x + (-y),$$
where $-y$ is the additive inverse of y.

Notice the similarity between the definition of the difference of two rational numbers and the definition of the quotient of two rational numbers. The quotient of any two rational numbers x and y is equal to the product of x and the *multiplicative* inverse of y. The difference of any two rational numbers x and y is equal to the sum of x and the *additive* inverse of y. Thus, we can say that subtraction and division are "secondary" operations because they can be defined in terms of addition and multiplication respectively.

At the beginning of this chapter we said that, once we had discussed operations on rational numbers, we would be able to determine a number that satisfies a condition like $x + 6 = 4$. First of all, we know that the condition $x = 4 - 6$ has the same solution as $x + 6 = 4$. But, using the definition of the difference of two rational numbers, we know that $4 - 6 = 4 + (-6)$. Hence, $x = 4 + (-6)$. Now, if we use steps similar to those given on page 308 for the difference of 8 and 3, we can show that $4 + (-6) = -2$. Therefore, we know that -2 satisfies both $x = 4 - 6$ and $x + 6 = 4$.

From the way we have defined the difference of two rational numbers, along with the fact that every rational number has an additive inverse and the fact that the rational numbers are closed under addition, we conclude that the rational numbers are closed under subtraction.

274 Find the standard name for each of the following differences.

    a $+\frac{3}{5} - (+\frac{4}{3})$ **b** $-\frac{4}{9} - (+\frac{5}{12})$ **c** $+\frac{17}{30} - (-\frac{11}{24})$ **d** $-\frac{25}{14} - (-\frac{10}{49})$

275 Is there an identity element for subtraction of rational numbers?

CONCLUSION

In this chapter we have given a rather sketchy outline of the rational numbers, the operations with these numbers, and the important properties of the operations. Our intention was to give you some acquaintance with the system of rational numbers and to strengthen your understanding of what a number system is. You should also realize that the extension from the rational numbers of arithmetic to the rational numbers has resulted in a more useful set of numbers for problem-solving purposes, since subtraction is closed in the set of rational numbers.

CHAPTER QUIZ

1 Construct a number line that shows the locations of the following points.

     A $\frac{3}{4}$ C -2 E $\frac{2}{3} + (-\frac{1}{3})$ G $-\frac{1}{2} \cdot \frac{2}{3}$

     B $\frac{5}{2}$ D $-\frac{1}{4}$ F $-1\frac{1}{2}$ H $-\frac{3}{5} \cdot (-\frac{5}{3})$

2 Does the set of integers have the density property?

3 Does the set of rational numbers have the density property?

Density property, page 269

4 Find the additive inverse and the multiplicative inverse for each of the following rational numbers.

A $\frac{1}{2}$ D $-\frac{1}{10}$ G $\frac{7}{8}$

B $-\frac{3}{4}$ E $6\frac{1}{2}$ H $-\frac{11}{2}$

C -2 F $-3\frac{2}{3}$ I $-\frac{5}{4}$

5 Is the multiplicative inverse of a negative number positive or negative? Is the additive inverse of a negative number positive or negative?

6 For each of the following pairs of numbers, find the sum and the difference of the two numbers. In finding the difference, use the first number of each pair as the subtrahend.

A $5\frac{1}{2}, \frac{7}{8}$ C $\frac{3}{5}, -\frac{6}{10}$ E $0, -\frac{1}{3}$

B $-2, -3$ D $-2, 1\frac{1}{5}$ F $-\frac{1}{3}, 0$

7 Find the product and the quotient of each of the following pairs of numbers. In finding the quotient, use the first number of each pair as the dividend.

A $\frac{3}{4}, \frac{5}{8}$ C $3\frac{1}{5}, -2\frac{1}{2}$ E $-2, \frac{4}{5}$

B $-\frac{1}{2}, -2$ D $-\frac{9}{10}, -1$ F $1, -1$

8 Determine the rational number that satisfies each of the following conditions.

A $-3 + x = -4.$ E $x + 4 = -8.$

B $\frac{1}{2} \cdot x = \frac{7}{2}.$ F $\frac{7}{3} \div (-2) = x.$

C $-\frac{3}{4} \cdot (-\frac{2}{3}) = x.$ G $x \cdot \frac{5}{4} = -\frac{3}{4}.$

D $6 + (-4\frac{1}{2}) = x.$ H $-x + (-4) = 6\frac{1}{2}.$

SUPPLEMENTARY READINGS

Niven, Ivan, *Numbers: Rational and Irrational*, Chapter 2. The material in this chapter bridges the gap between the content of Chapter 12 of this book and the content of Chapter 13, which deals with the real numbers. Item 49 of Bibliography

Peterson and Hashisaki, *Theory of Arithmetic*. This book develops the rational numbers from sets of ordered pairs of integers. It shows very nicely how the idea of ordered pairs can take on many meanings as rational numbers, fractions, rate pairs, or quotients. Item 26 of Bibliography

Chapter thirteen

Real numbers

Rational numbers expressed as decimals
Irrational numbers and the set of real numbers
Rational approximations
The real-number line and the completeness property

When we studied the set of natural numbers and operations on these numbers, we observed that the natural numbers are closed only under the operations of addition and multiplication. Subsequently we found that the set of non-zero rational numbers of arithmetic is closed under division as well and that the set of rational numbers is closed under subtraction, along with addition, multiplication, and division.

Since the set of rational numbers is closed under the four fundamental operations of arithmetic, it would seem that our study of numbers would be complete. In terms of the traditional content of elementary arithmetic, it is true that the rational numbers form an adequate set of numbers. However, if we consider an operation like determining the square root of a number, or if we consider certain ideas relating to measurement—such as the circumference and area of a circle or the measure of the hypotenuse of a right triangle—we find that the set of rational numbers is no longer adequate.

In this chapter we will consider in an informal and intuitive way the set of real numbers; with the set of real numbers, we will conclude our study of number systems. Because we will discuss real numbers in terms of their decimal representations, we will first consider decimals for rational numbers in some detail.

Rational numbers expressed as decimals

No doubt you learned long ago that each rational number can be expressed in the form $\frac{a}{b}$, where a represents an integer and b represents a non-zero Integers, page 300 integer. You also learned that the decimal for a rational number can be determined by using the division process. For example, the decimal for $\frac{1}{2}$ is found by dividing $\frac{10}{10}$ by 2 and then using a decimal point to show that the quotient is $\frac{5}{10}$; the decimal for $\frac{7}{5}$ is found by dividing $\frac{70}{10}$ by 5 and then inserting a decimal point to show that the quotient is $\frac{14}{10}$; and so on. In fact, you probably committed to memory the decimals for certain of the more commonly used rational numbers like the following.

$$\frac{1}{2} = .5. \qquad \frac{2}{3} = .666\ldots$$
$$\frac{1}{3} = .333\ldots \qquad \frac{3}{4} = .75.$$
$$\frac{1}{4} = .25. \qquad \frac{3}{8} = .375.$$
$$\frac{1}{5} = .2. \qquad \frac{1}{6} = .1666\ldots$$

The three dots to the right of the last digit in the decimal for $\frac{1}{3}$ indicate that the digit 3 is repeated endlessly. The same is true of the digit 6 in the decimals for $\frac{2}{3}$ and $\frac{1}{6}$.

Although we have named only positive numbers in these examples, it should be apparent that it is possible to express negative rational numbers as decimals. In fact, the decimal for the additive inverse of each positive rational number has exactly the same digits as the decimal for the positive number. Thus, $-\frac{1}{2} = -.5$, $-\frac{1}{3} = -.333\ldots$, $-\frac{1}{4} = -.25$, and so on. For the sake of convenience, we will usually consider decimals for positive numbers with the understanding that the generalizations we make about the positive rational numbers are valid for negative numbers as well.

Note that there are two kinds of decimals in the examples given above. There are decimals like .5 and .375 that, as you learned in Chapter 11, are called terminating decimals. By contrast, there are decimals like .33 . . . Terminating decimals, page 279 and .1666 . . . that are called *repeating decimals*. In a repeating decimal, the same non-zero digit or group of digits may be repeated endlessly. We will now examine both kinds of decimals more carefully.

First, let us consider terminating decimals and see if we can decide what kind of rational number can be named by such a decimal. Keep in mind that a decimal is simply another way of expressing a number whose denominator is a power of 10. For example, $.5 = \frac{5}{10}$ and $.375 = \frac{375}{1000}$. This means that the denominator of a rational number that can be expressed by a terminating decimal must be 1, or the denominator must have the same prime factors as 10; that is, the denominator must have only 2 or only 5 or both 2 and 5 as its prime factors. Hence, because $8 = 2^3$, the decimal for $\frac{3}{8}$ is a terminating decimal; because $4 = 2^2$, the decimal for $\frac{1}{4}$ is terminating. Similarly, the decimal for $\frac{1}{2}$ or $\frac{3}{5}$ or $\frac{1}{20}$ or $\frac{7}{25}$ is terminating. By contrast, $\frac{1}{3}$ cannot be named by a terminating decimal because the prime factor of 3 is 3; $\frac{1}{6}$ cannot be named by a terminating decimal because the prime factors of 6 include 3; and $\frac{1}{70}$ cannot be named by a terminating decimal because the prime factors of 70 include 7. This generalization applies only to rational numbers whose numerator and denominator are relatively prime. For example, the decimal for the rational number $\frac{7}{14}$ is terminating, even though 7 is a prime factor of 14. This is so because $\frac{7}{14} = \frac{1}{2}$.

Prime factors, page 216

Relatively prime numbers, page 221

276 Find a decimal for each of the following rational numbers.

a $\frac{5}{6}$ b $\frac{32}{100}$ c $-\frac{1}{9}$ d $6\frac{2}{5}$ e $\frac{1}{11}$ f $-\frac{31416}{10000}$

277 Which of the following rational numbers can be expressed as terminating decimals?

a $\frac{5}{16}$ c $\frac{9}{40}$ e $-\frac{6}{75}$ g $\frac{4}{15}$ i $\frac{13}{60}$

b $\frac{6}{125}$ d $\frac{5}{12}$ f $\frac{19}{70}$ h $-\frac{7}{18}$ j $\frac{9}{50}$

Although such numbers as $\frac{1}{6}$, $\frac{2}{7}$, and $\frac{5}{11}$ are named by non-terminating rather than terminating decimals, these decimals do have interesting patterns, which we shall now investigate. We noted earlier that the digit 3 in the decimal for $\frac{1}{3}$ can be thought of as repeating endlessly and that the digit 6 in the decimal for $\frac{1}{6}$ may be repeated endlessly. Any rational number that is named by a non-terminating decimal is named by a *repeating decimal* in which a digit or group of digits repeats endlessly. The group of repeating digits is called the *repetend* of the decimal. In the examples given below, we have used dots above the first and last digits (or the only digit) of the repetend. For example, in the decimal for $\frac{13}{7}$, 1.857142, the dots indicate that the repetend consists of the six digits 8, 5, 7, 1, 4, and 2 and that these six digits are to be thought of as repeating in the given order endlessly. We will use this method of writing repeating decimals from now on.*

$$\frac{2}{3} = .\dot{6}. \qquad \frac{5}{6} = .8\dot{3}. \qquad \frac{2}{9} = .\dot{2}.$$
$$\frac{7}{11} = .\dot{6}\dot{3}. \qquad \frac{13}{7} = 1.\dot{8}5714\dot{2}. \qquad \frac{15}{26} = .5\dot{7}692\dot{3}.$$

* Another common method for writing repeating decimals is to put a bar above all the digits in the repetend. Thus, .6̇3̇ might also be written as .6̄3̄, .5̇7692̇3 as .5̄7̄6̄9̄2̄3̄, and so on.

If we examine the division process whereby we obtain a decimal for a rational number like $\frac{7}{11}$, we can see why the digits in the decimal repeat. The computation necessary for finding the decimal for $\frac{7}{11}$ is shown below.

$$
\begin{array}{r|r}
11\overline{)7.0000} & 6000 \\
\underline{6\ 6000} & \\
4000 & 300 \\
\underline{3300} & \\
700 & 60 \\
\underline{660} & \\
40 & 3 \\
\underline{33} & \\
7 & \overline{6363} \\
& .6363
\end{array}
$$

Note that the first digits in the numerals that express the remainders are, alternately, 4 and 7 and that the digits in the decimal are, alternately, 6 and 3. As you can see, the last remainder is 7, and, if the division process had been carried one step farther, the next digit in the decimal would again be 6 and the next remainder would again be 4. Thus, it should be apparent that, no matter how far you carry the division process, the first digits in the numerals for the remainders will continue to alternate between 4 and 7 and the digits in the numeral for the quotient will continue to alternate between 6 and 3. Hence, we conclude that $\frac{7}{11} = .\overset{..}{6}\overset{}{3}$.

In the division algorism that we used above, the number named by the first digit in the numeral for the remainder at every step of the process must be less than the divisor. This means that the number of possible first digits in the numerals for the remainders (including 0 as a possible remainder) is equal to the number that is the divisor. It follows that the remainders must begin to repeat at some stage in the division process. Once the remainders begin to repeat, then the digits in the decimal for the quotient begin to repeat. This implies that any non-zero repetend in a decimal for a given rational number $\frac{a}{b}$ can have at most $b - 1$ digits because there are $b - 1$ possible non-zero remainders.

To return to the specific example given above, when any number that is not a multiple of 11 is divided by 11, we will obtain one of ten possible remainders. These ten possible remainders are the natural numbers 1 through 10. When we divided 7 by 11, we actually obtained only two of the possible remainders, 4 and 7. Hence, the decimal for the quotient has only two digits, 6 and 3, that will repeat endlessly.

Two more examples are shown on the next page. In the first example we have found the repetend of the decimal for $\frac{3}{7}$, and in the second example we have found the repetend of the decimal for $\frac{5}{11}$. We will not discuss these examples in detail; but if you study the pattern of remainders in each example, you should be able to see why the decimal is necessarily a repeating decimal.

```
  7)3.000000 │ 400000        11)5.00 │ 40
  2 800000   │                  4 40 │
    200000   │ 20000             60   │ 5
    140000   │                   55   │
     60000   │ 8000               5   │ 45
     56000   │                         .45
      4000   │ 500
      3500   │
       500   │ 70
       490   │
        10   │ 1
         7   │
         3   │ 428571
             │ .428571
```

The preceding discussion should convince you that every rational number $\frac{a}{b}$ can be thought of as either a terminating (finite) decimal or a repeating (infinite) decimal. In fact, since a terminating decimal like .5 can be written as .50 or .5000 or .50000000, we can think of the decimal .5 as having a repetend of 0. Hence, we can write

$$.5 = .5\dot{0}.$$

Similarly, because every terminating decimal can be thought of as having 0 as its repetend, we can write the following.

$$.25 = .25\dot{0}.$$
$$.375 = .375\dot{0}.$$
$$.18 = .18\dot{0}.$$

Thus, every terminating decimal can be thought of as a repeating decimal with repetend 0, and we can make the following generalization concerning rational numbers.

Every rational number can be expressed by a repeating decimal.

The chart on the next page shows the repeating decimals for several rational numbers. Notice that, in several of the examples, the repetend has as many digits as there are possible non-zero remainders.

$\frac{1}{7} = .\dot{1}4285\dot{7}.$ $\qquad$ $\frac{1}{19} = .\dot{0}526315789473684 2\dot{1}.$

$\frac{1}{13} = .\dot{0}7692\dot{3}.$ $\qquad$ $\frac{1}{23} = .\dot{0}434782608695652173913.$

$\frac{1}{17} = .\dot{0}58823529411764\dot{7}.$ $\qquad$ $\frac{1}{29} = .\dot{0}3448275862068965517241379 3\dot{1}.$

---

278 Find the repeating decimal that names each of the following rational numbers. Use dots above the proper digits to indicate the repetend in each case. What do you notice about the repetends?

   a $\frac{1}{7}$ **b** $\frac{2}{7}$ **c** $\frac{3}{7}$ **d** $\frac{4}{7}$ **e** $\frac{5}{7}$ **f** $\frac{6}{7}$

279 How many possible remainders are there when 1 is divided by each of the following numbers?

   a 5   **b** 12   **c** 23   **d** 25   **e** 31

280 Find a decimal for each of the following numbers.

   a $\frac{1}{5}$ **b** $\frac{4}{9}$ **c** $-\frac{1}{25}$ **d** $-\frac{1}{31}$

We have seen that every rational number can be expressed by a repeating decimal; we would also like to see if the converse is true. That is, we want to know if every repeating decimal names a rational number. We will now consider some specific examples to decide if this assumption is reasonable.

Suppose that we are given the repeating decimal .56. Suppose also that we assume that this decimal does name some rational number x. Another way of saying this is to say that we want to find the rational number x that satisfies the condition

$$x = .\dot{5}\dot{6}.$$

Although we have not established any rules for computing with repeating decimals like .56, we can assume that certain results we obtain when we compute with terminating decimals are also valid for repeating decimals. Thus, it seems reasonable that, if $x = .\dot{5}\dot{6}$ (which can also be written as .5656), then

$$100x = 56.\dot{5}\dot{6}.$$

Now we can use certain rules that you learned in high-school algebra, and "subtract" in the following way.

$$\begin{array}{r} 100x = 56.\dot{5}\dot{6}. \\ \underline{x = \quad .\dot{5}\dot{6}.} \\ 99x = 56. \end{array}$$

From this last condition, we can easily obtain

$$x = \tfrac{56}{99}.$$

Hence, we conclude that

$$\tfrac{56}{99} = .\dot{5}\dot{6}.$$

You can verify this result by computing to find the quotient of 56 and 99.

We can use much the same method to find the rational number that is equal to the repeating decimal 7.901. In other words, we want to find the rational number y that satisfies

$$y = 7.\dot{9}0\dot{1}.$$

Because the repetend consists of 3 digits, we will multiply both y and $7.\dot{9}0\dot{1}$ (thought of as $7.901\dot{9}0\dot{1}$) by 10^3, or 1000. When we do this, we obtain

$$1000y = 7901.\dot{9}0\dot{1}.$$

Then, if we subtract as we did in the previous example, we find that

$$999y = 7894.$$

Thus,

$$y = \tfrac{7894}{999}.$$

Since $\tfrac{7894}{999} = 7\tfrac{901}{999}$,

$$7\tfrac{901}{999} = 7.\dot{9}0\dot{1}.$$

Again, you can use the division process to verify this result.

On the basis of these examples, it seems reasonable to say that every repeating decimal does name a rational number. In fact, you should be able to use these examples to help you describe a general method for determining the rational number that is named by a given repeating decimal.

In the following examples, we will establish an interesting and rather surprising relationship between certain repeating decimals and the rational numbers they name. First let us use the method developed in the preceding examples to determine the rational number named by the decimal .9. As before, we begin with the condition

$$x = .\dot{9}.$$

Then we multiply x and $.9\dot{9}$ by 10 to obtain

$$10x = 9.\dot{9}.$$

Again, we subtract as in the previous examples.

$$
\begin{array}{r}
10x = 9.\dot{9}. \\
x = .\dot{9}. \\
\hline
9x = 9.
\end{array}
$$

From the condition $9x = 9$, we obtain $x = \frac{9}{9}$ or $x = \frac{1}{1}$. (Since $\frac{1}{1}$ is the mate of 1, we will usually omit the denominator and write $x = 1$.) Therefore,

$$1 = .\dot{9}.$$

Because 1.0 is also a decimal for 1, it follows that

$$1.0 = .\dot{9}.$$

Let us consider another example to see if we obtain analogous results. Suppose that we want to find the rational number that satisfies the following condition.

$$a = .4\dot{9}.$$

First we multiply both a and .49 by 10 to obtain

$$10a = 4.\dot{9}, \text{ or } 4.9\dot{9}.$$

Next we subtract to obtain

$$
\begin{array}{r}
10a = 4.9\dot{9}. \\
a = .4\dot{9}. \\
\hline
9a = 4.5.
\end{array}
$$

From $9a = 4.5$, we know that

$$a = .5, \text{ or } .5\dot{0}.$$

Hence, we conclude that

$$.4\dot{9} = .5\dot{0}.$$

Because $.5\dot{0} = \frac{1}{2}$, we also know that

$$.4\dot{9} = \frac{1}{2}.$$

If you consider other examples of this kind, you should see that the following generalization is a reasonable one.

> Every rational number that can be named
> by a repeating decimal whose repetend is 0
> can also be named by another repeating decimal
> whose repetend is 9.

In this section, we have seen that every rational number can be named by a repeating decimal* and that, conversely, every repeating decimal

---

* *Arithmetical Excursions* by Bowers and Bowers contains some interesting material, in Chapter 14, on the patterns found in repeating decimals. Item 42 of Bibliography

names a rational number. The questions now arise as to whether or not there are *nonrepeating* decimals and, if so, what kind of numbers are named by such decimals. Certainly we can conceive of decimals like those shown below that, if we were to continue the exhibited sequence of digits, would not be repeating decimals. In the next section of this chapter, we will consider the following question: What kind of numbers do such decimals represent?

A .101 001 000 100 001 000 001 000 000 1 . . .
B .363 366 333 666 333 366 663 333 366 666 . . .
C .012 345 678 910 111 213 141 516 . . .

281 Determine the rational number $\frac{a}{b}$ that is named by each of the following decimals.

a $6.\dot{9}$ c $16.1\dot{6}$ e $.\dot{1}0\dot{1}$
b $5.\dot{5}$ d $16.\dot{1}\dot{6}$ f $.\dot{1}00\dot{1}$

282 Use a decimal whose repetend is 0 and another decimal whose repetend is 9 to name each of the following rational numbers.

a $\frac{5}{8}$ b 4   c $\frac{1}{25}$ d $\frac{3}{16}$ e $\frac{4}{5}$

Irrational numbers and the set of real numbers

At the end of the preceding section, we suggested that there are certain numbers that can be expressed by nonrepeating decimals. We gave several examples of decimals that do not have repetends. Other examples of nonrepeating decimals are obtained when we consider the square roots of certain rational numbers.

As you may recall, each positive number has two square roots—a positive, or principal, square root and a negative square root. In the following discussion we will consider only principal square roots, although the remarks we make concerning them will also be valid for negative square roots.

The square root of a given positive number is the number whose square is equal to the given number. For example, because $2^2 = 4$, the square root of 4 is 2. In mathematical notation, we write

$$\sqrt{4} = 2.$$

The symbol $\sqrt{4}$ is read "the square root of 4."

If a and b are positive numbers and $a = b^2$, then a is called a *perfect square*. For example, because $1 = 1^2$, 1 is a perfect square; because $4 = 2^2$, 4 is a perfect square; because $9 = 3^2$, 9 is a perfect square; because $\frac{9}{4} = (\frac{3}{2})^2$, $\frac{9}{4}$ is a perfect square; and so on. It is apparent that the square root of a rational number that is a perfect square is a rational number.

Each of the following sentences expresses a true statement about the square root of an integer that is a perfect square.

$$\sqrt{1} = 1. \qquad \sqrt{16} = 4. \qquad \sqrt{49} = 7.$$
$$\sqrt{4} = 2. \qquad \sqrt{25} = 5. \qquad \sqrt{64} = 8.$$
$$\sqrt{9} = 3. \qquad \sqrt{36} = 6. \qquad \sqrt{81} = 9.$$

We could extend this list to include decimals for such numbers as $\sqrt{100}$, $\sqrt{121}$, $\sqrt{144}$, and for such numbers as $\sqrt{\frac{16}{9}}$, $\sqrt{\frac{49}{4}}$, and $\sqrt{\frac{25}{36}}$. Now, however, let us consider the square roots of certain numbers that are not perfect squares, such as $\sqrt{2}$ or $\sqrt{3}$ or $\sqrt{5}$. What can we say about such numbers?

First of all, let us see if we can determine a decimal for $\sqrt{5}$. We will use a process of successive estimations. We know that $\sqrt{5}$ must be greater than 2 and less than 3, since $2^2 = 4$ and $3^2 = 9$. Thus, we can write

$$2 < \sqrt{5} < 3.$$

Remember that the sentence "$2 < \sqrt{5} < 3$" is read "2 is less than $\sqrt{5}$, and $\sqrt{5}$ is less than 3." Remember also that the sentence means that $\sqrt{5}$ is between 2 and 3. Since 2^2 is nearer to $(\sqrt{5})^2$ than is 3^2, we might next choose 2.3 as a reasonable estimate of $\sqrt{5}$. But $2.3^2 = 5.29$; so we know that $\sqrt{5}$ is less than 2.3. Suppose that we now use 2.2 as an estimate. $2.2^2 = 4.84$; so we know that $\sqrt{5}$ is greater than 2.2. From these two estimates, 2.3 and 2.2, we know that

$$2.2 < \sqrt{5} < 2.3.$$

Our next estimate of $\sqrt{5}$ should be between 2.2 and 2.3. We might reasonably choose 2.23 or 2.24 as our next estimate. If you square each of these numbers, you will see that the following statement is true.

$$2.23 < \sqrt{5} < 2.24.$$

We can continue this procedure indefinitely, and the following statements summarize the results concerning two more successive estimates of $\sqrt{5}$.

$$2.236 < \sqrt{5} < 2.237.$$
$$2.2360 < \sqrt{5} < 2.2361.$$

On the basis of the above procedure, we cannot say whether or not the decimal for $\sqrt{5}$ is a repeating decimal. We can only say that, for the first five digits in the decimal for $\sqrt{5}$, the digits do not repeat in any regular pattern. But we do not know what might be true for the first ten or the first fifty or the first thousand digits.

We must use other means to prove that $\sqrt{5}$ cannot be named by a repeating decimal. In our proof we will show that $\sqrt{5}$ cannot be a rational number of the form $\frac{a}{b}$. We know that every rational number $\frac{a}{b}$ can be named by a repeating decimal and that each repeating decimal names a rational number $\frac{a}{b}$. Thus, once we have shown that $\sqrt{5}$ is not a rational number $\frac{a}{b}$, then we will be able to conclude that $\sqrt{5}$ cannot be named by a repeating decimal.

We begin our proof that $\sqrt{5}$ is not a rational number by first assuming that it *is* a rational number and that we can find two integers a and b, with b not equal to zero, for which it is true that

$$\frac{a}{b} = \sqrt{\frac{5}{1}}.$$

If $\frac{a}{b} = \sqrt{\frac{5}{1}}$, then it follows that

$$\frac{5}{1} = \frac{a^2}{b^2}.$$

Therefore,

$$5b^2 = a^2.$$

From this last condition, we know that $5b^2$ is to be equal to a^2. If we consider the prime factorization of a^2, we know that a^2 has an even number of prime factors because it has twice as many factors as a. This means that, if a has 3 prime factors, then a^2 has 6; if a has 4 prime factors, then a^2 has 8; and so on. The same reasoning applies to b^2. But because b^2 has an even number of factors, $5b^2$ has an odd number of prime factors, since $5b^2$ has a factor of 5 in addition to the prime factors of b^2. Thus, a^2 and $5b^2$ represent two different ways of factoring the same number into the product of primes, since in one case we have an even number of factors and in the other case we have an odd number of factors.

Prime factors of a number, page 216

But this contradicts the fundamental theorem of arithmetic to the effect that every integer can be expressed as the product of prime factors in just one way. Thus, by assuming that $\sqrt{5}$ is a rational number $\frac{a}{b}$, we have arrived at a conclusion that contradicts the fundamental theorem of arithmetic. Therefore, we reject the assumption that $\sqrt{5}$ is a rational number, and we must conclude that it is not a rational number. Thus, we have established the following theorem.

Fundamental theorem of arithmetic, pages 218-219

$\sqrt{5}$ is not a rational number.

From this theorem it follows that $\sqrt{5}$ cannot be expressed by a repeating decimal. Hence, we assume that it is expressed by a nonrepeating decimal.

A proof similar to the one we just gave for $\sqrt{5}$ not being a rational number can also be used to show that such numbers as $\sqrt{2}$, $\sqrt{3}$, $\sqrt{6}$, and $\sqrt{7}$ are not rational. We assume that each such number is named by a nonrepeating decimal; numbers that are named by nonrepeating decimals are *irrational numbers*. We also assume that each nonrepeating decimal names an irrational number. Note that the word *irrational* means "not rational" and that irrational numbers are numbers that cannot be expressed as the quotient (or "ratio") of two integers.

The square root of any positive number that is not a perfect square is an irrational number. There are other irrational numbers, also. You are probably familiar with the irrational number π that is used in determining the circumference and area of a circle. Similarly, the nonrepeating decimals listed on page 319 express irrational numbers.

Now that we have given you some understanding of what an irrational number is, along with some examples of these numbers, we can define the set called the *real numbers*. The set of real numbers is the union of the following two sets.

1 The set of all irrational numbers
2 The set of all rational numbers

Keep in mind that each rational number can be named by a repeating decimal and that each irrational number can be named by a nonrepeating decimal. Since repeating and nonrepeating decimals are non-terminating and can be thought of as having an infinite sequence of digits, they are called *infinite decimals*. Thus, the set of real numbers can be defined as follows:

The set of real numbers is the set of all numbers that
are named by infinite decimals.

283 Develop a proof like the one given in the text for $\sqrt{5}$ to show that $\sqrt{3}$ is not a rational number.

284 What happens when you attempt to show that $\sqrt{4}$ is an irrational number by a proof similar to that of exercise 283?

285 Does the failure of the "proof" in exercise 284 prove that $\sqrt{4}$ is a rational number?

286 Which of the following real numbers can be expressed by a repeating decimal?

a $\frac{4}{5}$ **b** $\frac{3}{7}$ **c** $\sqrt{2}$ **d** $\sqrt{\frac{4}{9}}$ **e** $-\frac{5}{9}$ **f** $-\sqrt{7}$ **g** $\sqrt{16}$ **h** $-\sqrt{9}$

287 Is the set of irrational numbers closed under addition? Give an example to justify your answer.

288 Is the set of irrational numbers closed under multiplication? Give an example to justify your answer.

Rational approximations

We do not intend to discuss computation involving real numbers in any great detail, but we will make several observations about such computation. The computational methods that we use for rational numbers apply to these numbers when they are considered as real numbers. For example, the statements below are true both when we think of the numbers expressed as rational numbers and when we think of them as real numbers.

$$3\frac{1}{2} + 6 = 9\frac{1}{2}.$$
$$7\frac{2}{3} + (-8) = -\frac{1}{3}.$$
$$\frac{1}{5} \times \frac{1}{2} = \frac{1}{10}.$$
$$-2 \times \frac{7}{8} = -\frac{7}{4}.$$
$$-5 - 3 = -8.$$
$$-\frac{2}{3} \div (-\frac{2}{3}) = 1.$$

Now, however, let us consider some examples in which one or both numbers are irrational. From a mathematical point of view, $6 + \sqrt{3}$ is the sum of 6 and $\sqrt{3}$ and $8 + \pi$ is the sum of 8 and π. Similarly, $5\sqrt{10}$ is the product of 5 and $\sqrt{10}$ and 9π is the product of 9 and π. From a practical point of view, however, such irrational numbers as 9π and $8 + \pi$ are not always useful, since it is difficult for us to interpret them or compare them with the more commonly used rationals. Suppose, for example, that we wish to know whether the sum $5 + \sqrt{13}$ is greater than or less than the product 2.5π. Certainly, it is not immediately obvious which of these numbers is greater; consequently, we must develop some method for comparing them.

When we are working with irrationals like $\sqrt{13}$ and π, we often use *rational approximations* for these numbers. Thus, we can use the method of successive estimations described earlier in this chapter to determine that Successive estimations, page 320

$$\sqrt{13} = 3.6055 \ldots .$$

If we round the decimal for $\sqrt{13}$ to the nearer tenth, hundredth, or thousandth, we obtain a rational number that is *approximately equal* to $\sqrt{13}$. Such a number is a rational approximation of $\sqrt{13}$. We know that $\sqrt{13}$ is not equal to 3.606 or 3.6 or 3.61, since it is an irrational number, but we do know that $\sqrt{13}$ is approximately equal to each of these numbers. Thus, we can make the true statements about $\sqrt{13}$ that are expressed below. The symbol $\approx$, which is used in each of these sentences, is read "is approximately equal to."

$$\sqrt{13} \approx 3.6.$$
$$\sqrt{13} \approx 3.61.$$
$$\sqrt{13} \approx 3.606.$$

The nonrepeating decimal for the irrational number π has been determined to more than 10,000 places. Since this decimal is obtained by methods that are beyond the scope of this book, we will simply give the decimal without attempting to compute it. The decimal for the number π is given below to 8 places.

$$\pi = 3.14159265\ldots.$$

In each of the following sentences, we have given a rational approximation for π.

$$\pi \approx 3.1.$$
$$\pi \approx 3.14.$$
$$\pi \approx 3.142.$$
$$\pi \approx 3.1416.$$

For most practical purposes, a rational approximation of an irrational number to the nearer thousandth or ten-thousandth is quite adequate.

We can now use rational approximations to answer the question we raised earlier as to which is the greater, $5 + \sqrt{13}$ or 2.5π. Suppose that we use decimals to the nearer hundredth to express approximations both for $\sqrt{13}$ and for π. Because $\sqrt{13} \approx 3.61$ we know that

$$5 + \sqrt{13} \approx 8.61.$$

Because $\pi \approx 3.14$, we know that

$$2.5\pi \approx 7.85.$$

Since 8.61 is greater than 7.85, we conclude that

$$(5 + \sqrt{13}) > 2.5\pi.$$

Notice that, during the course of this discussion, we have used the relation "approximately equal to" rather loosely. We have named several numbers that are approximately equal to $\sqrt{13}$ and several that are approximately equal to π. In fact, "approximately equal to" should be qualified whenever it is used. Under certain circumstances an approximation to the nearer tenth might be satisfactory, while at other times an approximation to the nearer billionth might be required.

289 Find a rational approximation for $\sqrt{10}$ to the nearer ten-thousandth.

290 Which is greater, 3π or $3\sqrt{10}$?

291 Which is greater, $\sqrt{10} - 1.4$ or $\sqrt{10} \div 2$?

292 Explain how you know, without using rational approximations, that $\sqrt{6} > \sqrt{2}$. How do you know that $7 < \sqrt{50}$? How do you know that $2\sqrt{3} > \sqrt{3}$?

The real-number line and the completeness property

For each set of numbers that we have studied thus far in this book, we have developed a number line by assigning members of the given set of numbers to points in the line. A rational-number line is pictured below to help you recall how this was done. <small>Rational-number line, page 299</small>

Because the rational numbers, like the rational numbers of arithmetic, are dense, it might seem to you that a rational number can be assigned to each point in the line and that there is a one-to-one correspondence between the set of rational numbers and the set of points that make up the line. However, this is not the case; it is only with the real numbers—that is, the union of the rational and irrational numbers—that we can establish a one-to-one correspondence between the set of numbers and the line. <small>Density property, page 269</small>

In constructing a real-number line, we locate points associated with the rational numbers just as we did in the rational-number line. Then we use rational approximations to locate points associated with irrational numbers. For example, suppose that we want to determine the approximate location of $\sqrt{10}$ in the real-number line. First, we determine a sequence of approximations for $\sqrt{10}$, just as we did earlier for $\sqrt{5}$ and $\sqrt{13}$. The following statements summarize the results of several steps of this procedure.

$$3 < \sqrt{10} < 4.$$
$$3.1 < \sqrt{10} < 3.2.$$
$$3.16 < \sqrt{10} < 3.17.$$
$$3.162 < \sqrt{10} < 3.163.$$
$$3.1622 < \sqrt{10} < 3.1623.$$

A portion of the real-number line between point 3 and point 4 is represented on page 326. There we have used the sequences of decimal approximations to give an approximate location of $\sqrt{10}$. From the statements given on page 325, we know that $\sqrt{10}$ is associated with a point in the line between 3.162 and 3.163. We also know from these statements that point $\sqrt{10}$ is between point 3.1622 and point 3.1623, but physical limitations prevent us from giving a better picture of the location of $\sqrt{10}$. Theoretically, however, we could locate point $\sqrt{10}$ more and more precisely by using more and more precise rational approximations. The irrational number $\sqrt{10}$, then, is that number that is greater than any number in the sequence 3, 3.1, 3.16, 3.162, 3.1622, ... and less than any number in the sequence 4, 3.2, 3.17, 3.163, 3.1623 . . ..

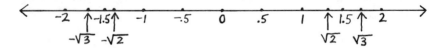

In the real-number line represented below, we have located certain points associated with irrational numbers as well as points associated with rational numbers. In locating the points associated with irrational numbers, we used decimal approximations, although it is possible to locate irrational points exactly by geometric methods. Notice that we have included two points in the number line that are associated with *negative* irrational numbers. These two points are the points associated with the negative square root of 2 and the negative square root of 3. It should be apparent that every positive irrational number can be paired with a negative irrational number so that the members of each pair are additive inverses. In this number line, as with earlier ones, the relation "to the left of" corresponds to the relation "less than." Thus, by inspecting the number line, we can see that $\sqrt{2} < 1.5$, $1.5 < \sqrt{3}$, $-2 < -\sqrt{3}$, and so on. This is true because the points associated with $\sqrt{2}$, 1.5, and -2 are to the left of the points that are associated with 1.5, $\sqrt{3}$, and $-\sqrt{3}$, respectively.

Additive inverse, page 302

The real numbers, together with the operations of addition and multiplication, form a number system. This means that the properties we summarized for the rational numbers in the preceding chapter also apply to the real numbers. However, the real numbers do have one important property that the rational numbers do not have. This property, the *completeness property* of real numbers, is related to the fact that we can establish a one-to-one correspondence between the set of real numbers and

Properties rational numbers, page 303

the set of points in a line, while we cannot do so with the set of rational numbers.

To help you understand the completeness property of the reals, we need to discuss what is meant by the upper and lower bounds of a set of numbers. Suppose, for example, that we wish to consider the set of real numbers between 1 and 2. "Between 1 and 2" means greater than 1 and less than 2. Because the set of real numbers, as well as the set of rational numbers, is dense, we cannot name either the least member or the greatest member of the set of real numbers between 1 and 2. Instead, we must talk in terms of *lower* and *upper bounds* (sometimes called *limits*) of such a set. We can define the lower and upper bounds of a set of real numbers as follows.

A set of real numbers has a lower bound if,

for each number a of the set,

there exists a number b such that

$a \geq b$ (read "a is greater than or equal to b").

A set of real numbers has an upper bound if,

for each number a of the set,

there exists a number c such that

$a \leq c$ (read "a is less than or equal to c").

In the example that we were considering earlier, it is easy to determine several lower and upper bounds for the set of real numbers between 1 and 2. Such numbers as -1, 0, $\frac{1}{2}$, $\frac{3}{4}$, and 1 are lower bounds of this set, since every real number a between 1 and 2 is greater than each of these numbers. Similarly, such numbers as 2, $2\frac{1}{2}$, 3, and $\sqrt{10}$ are upper bounds of this set, since every real number a between 1 and 2 is less than each of these numbers. The number line below shows that every number less than or equal to 1 is a lower bound of the set of numbers between 1 and 2 and shows also that every number greater than or equal to 2 is an upper bound of this set.

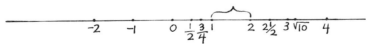

We can carry this idea a bit further and consider the number that is the *greatest lower bound* (glb) and the number that is the *least upper bound* (lub) of a set of numbers. The greatest lower bound of the set of real numbers between 1 and 2 is 1, since all other lower bounds, such as $\frac{1}{2}$, 0, -1, and so on, are less than 1. Also, the least upper bound of the set of reals between 1 and 2 is 2, since all other upper bounds, such as $2\frac{1}{2}$, 3, 10, and so on, are greater than 2. We can define the least upper bound of a set of real numbers in the following way.

A number s is a least upper bound
of a set of real numbers
if $s \leq n$ for all numbers n
that are upper bounds of the set.

You should be able to construct an analogous definition of the greatest lower bound of a set of real numbers.

293 Define the greatest lower bound of a set of real numbers.
294 Find four successive rational approximations for $\sqrt{6}$.
295 Find four successive rational approximations for $\sqrt{12}$.

We can now explain the completeness property of the real numbers. If we consider the set of real numbers x such that $x < .3$, we know that .3 is the least upper bound of this set because every number x that satisfies this condition is less than .3 and all other upper bounds of this set are greater than .3. Thus, the set of real numbers x that satisfy the condition $x < .3$ has as its least upper bound the rational number .3.

Now, however, consider the set of all real numbers y that satisfy the condition $y < \sqrt{5}$. Does this set have a least upper bound that is a rational number? In an earlier section of this chapter we showed that such rational numbers as 3, 2.3, 2.24, 2.237, and 2.2361 are upper bounds of this set. This is so because every number y that satisfies $y < \sqrt{5}$ is less than each of these numbers. But we also know that it is possible to find rational numbers between 2.2361 and $\sqrt{5}$ that are upper bounds of this set. In fact, it is impossible to determine a rational number that is the *least* upper bound of this set. By contrast, we can very easily determine the irrational number that is the least upper bound of this set. The irrational number $\sqrt{5}$ is the least upper bound of this set, since every member of the set of numbers that satisfy $y < \sqrt{5}$ is less than $\sqrt{5}$ and all other upper bounds of this set are greater than $\sqrt{5}$.

We could give many more such examples to suggest that, for any set of real numbers that has an upper bound, it is always possible to find a real number—either rational or irrational—that is the least upper bound of that set. It is not, however, always possible to find a rational number that is a least upper bound of such a set. We can state the completeness property of real numbers in the following way.

For every set of real numbers that has an upper bound,
there exists a real number
that is the least upper bound of the set.

You can see that the completeness property and the notion that there is a one-to-one correspondence between the set of reals and the line are related ideas. From the intuitive notion that there are no "gaps" in the real-number line, it seems to follow naturally that every non-empty set of real numbers that has an upper bound has a least upper bound.

296 Find the least upper bound of the set of real numbers that satisfy each of the following conditions. Tell whether the least upper bound is rational or irrational.

a $x^2 < 2$.　**b** $x^2 < \frac{9}{4}$.　**c** $x^2 < 10$.　**d** $x^2 < \frac{2}{3}$.

CONCLUSION

With this brief and informal discussion of the set of real numbers, we have completed our study of numbers and number systems. The set of real numbers is an extremely powerful and useful set of numbers. All of the ideas and properties that we discussed in connection with earlier sets of numbers can be applied to various subsets of the real numbers. For example, all the properties of the natural numbers correspond to properties of the non-negative integers (the positive integers and zero), which are a subset of the real numbers; and, similarly, all the properties of the rational numbers of arithmetic correspond to properties of the non-negative rational numbers.

In this chapter, we found that the real numbers have a completeness property that is not shared by the rational numbers and that, consequently, we can establish a one-to-one correspondence between the set of real numbers and the set of points in a line. In Chapter 14, we will assume the completeness property of real numbers in our discussion of measurement.

CHAPTER QUIZ

1 Determine a decimal for each of the following rational numbers.

　A $6\frac{3}{4}$　C $\frac{7}{12}$　E $-\frac{2}{3}$　G $4\frac{4}{5}$

　B $-\frac{5}{8}$　D $6\frac{1}{2} - 3\frac{3}{10}$　F $-\frac{6}{7}$　H $\frac{8}{12}$

2 Explain why the decimal for the rational number $\frac{9}{12}$ is a terminating decimal, even though 3 is a prime factor of 12.

3 Determine the rational number $\frac{a}{b}$ that is named by each of the following decimals.

　A $.208\dot{0}$　C $2.0\dot{3}\dot{9}$　E $7.2\dot{0}$　G $6.23\dot{0}$

　B $3.4\dot{5}$　D $7.1\dot{9}$　F $-.1\dot{6}$　H $.\dot{3}23\dot{5}$

4 Find two decimals for each of the following numbers, one with 0 as its repetend and one with 9 as its repetend.

    A $\frac{3}{4}$ B $2\frac{2}{5}$ C $-6\frac{1}{2}$ D 7

5 Which of the following real numbers are named by nonrepeating decimals?

    A $-\frac{3}{7}$ C $\sqrt{169}$ E $\sqrt{2}\cdot\sqrt{2}$ G $\sqrt{81}$

    B $\sqrt{14}$ D $-\sqrt{11}$ F $\sqrt{18}$ H $-\sqrt{12}$

6 Find a rational approximation for $\sqrt{2}$ to the nearer ten-thousandth.

7 Find a rational approximation for $\sqrt{8}$ to the nearer ten-thousandth.

8 On the basis of your answers to exercises 6 and 7, is $\sqrt{8} = 2\sqrt{2}$?

9 Is the relation "approximately equal to" an equivalence relation?

10 Which of the following statements are true?

    A $4 > \sqrt{4}$.   D $\sqrt{2} \approx 1.414$.   G $\sqrt{6}\cdot\sqrt{7} > \sqrt{5}\cdot\sqrt{7}$.

    B $6 < \sqrt{36}$.   E $3\sqrt{5} > 2\sqrt{5}$.   H $\pi \cdot \frac{1}{\pi} = 1$.

    C $\frac{\pi}{2} > -\pi$.   F $-3 < \sqrt{3}$.   I $\sqrt{3} + (-\sqrt{3}) = 0$.

11 Determine if the set of real numbers that satisfies each of the following conditions has a least upper bound or a greatest lower bound. Tell whether the bound is a rational or an irrational number.

    A $3x < 6\frac{1}{2}$.   C $x > \sqrt{8}$.   E $x > \sqrt{16}$.

    B $x < \sqrt{8}$.   D $6x > 25$.   F $x^2 < 12$.

12 Make a chart in which you list the properties of the real-number system.

SUPPLEMENTARY READINGS

Adler, Irving and Ruth, *The New Mathematics*, Chapter 5. This book is a good source for an intuitive development of the real numbers through several sources. Item 50 of Bibliography

Niven, Ivan, *Numbers: Rational and Irrational*, Chapter 3. This book presents the real numbers from both a geometric viewpoint and a decimal approach. Item 49 of Bibliography

Peterson and Hashisaki, *Theory of Arithmetic*, Chapter 8. This book contains a wide variety of excellent information on the real numbers. Item 26 of Bibliography

Van Engen, *et al.*, *Seeing Through Mathematics, Book 2*, Unit 11 and *Seeing Through Mathematics, Book 3*, Unit 18. The content of these units provides an intuitive development of the real-number system. Items 48 and 51 of Bibliography

Chapter fourteen

Measurement

Man's achievements in science are often based upon progress in his ability to measure. As the instruments of measurement are improved and measures become more and more precise, the scientist finds more and more answers to his questions concerning our universe.

Because of the importance of measurement to science and to our everyday activities, measurement concepts have always been a part of the elementary-school arithmetic program. Since measurement is included in the study of arithmetic in the elementary school—even though it is not strictly a part of arithmetic—we feel that this book would not be complete without a discussion of some of the basic concepts of measurement.

Development of standards for measuring

Measurement is a process whereby a number is assigned to a mathematical object, such as a segment, or to a physical object, such as a cardboard carton; this number is used to answer quantitative questions like "How much?", "How far?", "How long?", and "How heavy?" Often we use measurement when we compare physical objects; then we use the numbers that are the measures of objects to help us decide which is longer, which holds more, which is heavier, and so on. For the comparison of two measures to be meaningful, it is important that both measurements be obtained by using the same *unit* of measure. We will discuss standard units of measure in a later section of this chapter; for the moment, we will discuss a few of the attempts that man has made to establish standards for measuring.

The units of measure used by ancient and non-scientific societies were often first derived from the lengths of certain parts of the human body. For example, units like the width of the hand, the length of the arm, and the length of the step or pace served the same purpose as standard units serve today.

In Biblical times, the cubit was a common unit of measure throughout the Middle East. The cubit is the distance from the tip of the middle finger to the elbow, as shown in the illustration below. Obviously, such a measure provided only a very rough standard unit, since the distance would vary

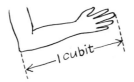

from person to person. The following quotation from the Bible is of interest both because it is concerned with the use of the cubit as a unit of measure and because it gives us a clue to the numerical value of π at that time.

> Also he made a molten sea of ten cubits from brim to brim, round in compass, and five cubits the height thereof; and a line of thirty cubits did compass it round about.
>
> (II Chronicles, 4, 2)

Since the circumference of a circle is equal to the product of π and the measure of the diameter of the circle, it is apparent that 3 was used as the numerical value of π at the time.

The Romans introduced the unit of length called the pace, which was originally equal to the distance covered in two steps. From the pace, the Romans later developed the mile, which was at that time the same distance as 1000 paces. The foot and the inch are also of Roman origin.

The hand, the span, and the yard are English measures. The hand, which has now been standardized as a length of 4 inches, was originally the breadth of a man's hand, as shown in the illustration at the top of page 333. The span, also shown in the same illustration, is the distance

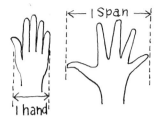

between the tip of the thumb and the little finger when a man's fingers are spread apart as far as possible. The yard was formerly a unit of length equivalent to the distance from the tip of a man's nose to the end of his thumb when his arm was outstretched. The breadth of the thumb, which was also used as a unit of measure, is approximately the same as one inch.

We may think of the units of measure that we have been discussing as rather crude and imprecise. But we still use certain of these measures, such as the pace, and even others that are just as imprecise, such as a "pinch" of salt or a "dash" of pepper or a "ten-minute" drive.

Not only were the units of measure used in a particular community somewhat imprecise, but neighboring communities frequently would use quite different units. For example, the original 13 colonies in America did not have uniform measures when they declared their independence from England. In fact, one of the first problems faced by Congress was the establishment of a system of standard measures for the United States.

The growth of commerce between communities and nations made standard units of measure necessary. As early as 1215, England was concerned with the establishment of standard units, and the Magna Carta contains the following provision concerning standard units of measure.

> There shall be one measure of wine throughout our entire kingdom, and one measure of ale; also one measure of grain, namely, the quarter of London; and one width of dyed cloth, that is, namely, two yards between the borders; with weights, moreover, it shall be as with measures.

In 1795, the metric system was officially adopted as the established system of measure of all of France. Many years of discussion preceded the adoption of the metric system, and many years passed after its adoption before the system was actually used throughout France.

From this brief discussion of the efforts of communities and nations to establish uniform standards of measure, we can see that difficulties might arise when we consider precision and accuracy and when we "convert" from one unit of measure to another. Before we discuss these problems, however, we will need to consider some of the basic notions involved in measurement and in the establishment of standard units.

Linear measure

Linear measurement is the process whereby a number called distance is assigned to the pair of points that are endpoints of a segment. The number that is assigned to the segment is the *measure* of the segment. (The ideas of segment, "betweenness," endpoints of a segment, etc., will be discussed more thoroughly in the chapter on geometry. For the time being, your intuitive understanding of these ideas will suffice.) For the most part, we will be talking about measurement in terms of such mathematical objects as segments, rectangles and their interiors, cubes and their interiors, and so on, in this chapter. But we could apply the ideas discussed here to measurement of physical objects as well. We usually call the linear measure of a segment or of an object its *length*.

Measurement ordinarily involves a comparison of two or more objects. If, for example, we want to compare the lengths of two segments, we might assign the number 1 as the measure of the shorter segment (assuming the two segments have different lengths). We would then use the shorter segment as the "unit of length" and determine the measure of the longer segment in terms of this "unit."

Thus, to determine the measure of a segment, like segment AB pictured below, we may first choose another segment as an arbitrary unit of measure. We then determine the number of these segments—called *unit segments*—contained in segment AB. The dotted lines in the illustration indicate the unit segments that have been "laid off" on segment AB. Notice that 6 of the units are included within AB and that the end of the seventh unit extends beyond point B. Because 7 unit segments are required to include segment AB, we say that 7 is the *outer measure* of segment AB. The outer measure of a segment or other object is the number of units that are required to include the object that is being measured. The number 6 is the

inner measure of segment AB because 6 units are completely included in segment AB. The inner measure of a segment or other object is the number of units that are completely included in the object being measured.

If a segment happens to contain an exact number of the units that are being used, then the outer and inner measure of the segment are equal.

In this case, we say that the number that is the inner measure and at the same time the outer measure of the segment is *the* measure of the segment.

It should be clear that the measure of a segment depends upon the length of the unit segment that is used to obtain the measure. In the illustration below, we have again found the inner and outer measures of segment AB. This time, however, we have used a longer unit segment, and

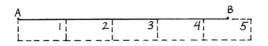

we find that the outer measure of segment AB is 5, while the inner measure is 4.

Finally, in the following illustration, we have chosen a third unit of measure that is shorter than either of the unit segments we used earlier to find the measure of segment AB. Notice that, in this case, the endpoint

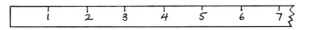

of the fifteenth unit segment coincides with point B. Thus, the inner and outer measure of segment AB are both equal to 15 because exactly 15 of the given units include segment AB. In this case, we say that 15 is the measure of segment AB.

From the examples that we have been discussing, you can see that the number that is the linear measure of a segment is dependent upon the unit of measure. Hence, we ordinarily use *standard units* of linear measure, such as the inch, the foot, the mile, and so on. However, before we discuss standard units of measure, there are several other ideas relating to linear measure that should be thought about.

Each time we measured segment AB, we laid off the given unit segment as many times as necessary to determine the number of these units included in segment AB. In physical measurement, instead of doing this every time we want to measure an object, we can construct a *scale* like the one pictured below. On this scale, or rule, an arbitrary unit segment has already been laid off, and the numeral under each mark indicates the number of units required to "cover" the scale up to the mark.

In the following illustration, we have shown how the rule pictured above can be used to measure segment AB. Note that the left edge of the rule is aligned with the dot representing the left endpoint of segment AB. When the rule is used in this way, the measure of the segment is determined simply by noticing the location of the other endpoint of the segment with respect to the marks on the rule. Thus, we can see that, when we use the arbitrary unit represented on this rule, the inner measure of segment AB is 5, while the outer measure is 6.

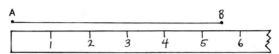

Obviously, the scale on a rule is determined by the unit used in constructing the rule. If we had used either a longer or a shorter unit for the rule pictured above, we would have obtained different numbers as the inner and outer measures of segment AB. The rules that we use from now on will have different scales, depending upon the lengths of the units we use to construct the rules.

In the pictures below, we have used rules A, B, and C, each having a different scale, to measure segment PQ. If you compare the scales on rules

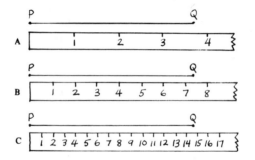

A, B, and C, you can see that the unit used for rule A is twice as long as the unit used for rule B and that the unit used for rule B is twice as long as the unit used for rule C. For convenience, we will refer to the unit used for rule A as the "large unit," the unit used for rule B as the "middle unit," and the unit used for rule C as the "small unit."

Because the large unit is twice as long as the middle unit, it follows that 1 large unit has the same length as 2 middle units. Hence, we say that, in terms of their lengths,

$$1 \text{ large unit} = 2 \text{ middle units.}$$

Similarly,

$$1 \text{ middle unit} = 2 \text{ small units};$$
$$1 \text{ large unit} = 4 \text{ small units.}$$

We can use pictures A, B, and C to determine the inner and outer measures of segment PQ in terms of the three units used for rules A, B, and C. These measures are summarized below.

	Inner measure	Outer measure
Large units	3	4
Middle units	7	8
Small units	14	15

Certainly, we could have used other rules that involved either smaller or larger units than rules A, B, and C. However, the three different rules that we have used are sufficient to illustrate the ideas we have in mind.

Let us now interpret the measures that we have found for segment PQ in terms of a physical situation. Suppose that the measures of segment PQ represent the length of some physical object, such as a piece of cloth. Suppose further that the cloth is priced as follows.

$4 per large unit
$2 per middle unit
$1 per small unit

Notice how the prices and the units of measure are related to each other. For example, the large unit is 4 times as long as the small unit, and the price per large unit is 4 times as great as the price per small unit.

Next we need to use the inner and outer measures of segment PQ to determine the price of the cloth for each of the 3 units of measure. First let us consider the price of the cloth in terms of the large unit. To obtain the price of the cloth in terms of the large unit, we must first decide whether to use the inner measure or the outer measure of the cloth. If we look back at picture A on page 336, we can see that the dot representing endpoint Q of segment PQ is nearer to the numeral 4 on the rule than to the numeral 3. Hence, we say that the measure of segment PQ to the *nearer unit* is 4 large units. Therefore, the price of the cloth when we use the large unit is 4 × 4, or 16, dollars. In picture B, we see that, when segment PQ is measured in middle units, the measure to the nearer unit is 7 middle units. This means that the price of the cloth, when it is measured in middle units is 7 × 2, or 14, dollars. Finally, from picture C, we obtain 15 as the measure of segment PQ to the nearer small unit. Thus, the price of the cloth, when measured in small units is 15 × 1, or 15, dollars.

From this example, it would seem that the smaller the unit of measure used, the better the results we obtain. This is so because the price of $15 is fairer than either of the other prices, $14 or $16, to both the seller and the buyer.

Let us use another illustration to examine the reasons why the measure obtained with a smaller unit of measure is a fairer measure. In pictures D and E we have used two scales to measure segment AB. The unit of measure in picture D is 2 times as great as the unit of measure in picture E.

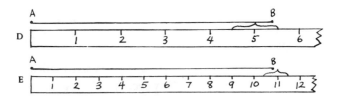

In picture D, we can see that the measure of segment AB is between 5 and 6 and is nearer to 5 than to 6. This means that the measure of segment AB is 5, to the nearer unit. Also, if the measure of segment AB were between 4 and 5, but nearer to 5 than to 4, we would say that the measure of the segment is 5 to the nearer unit. In fact, if the measure of the segment were anywhere between $4\frac{1}{2}$ and $5\frac{1}{2}$ units, we would say that the measure of AB is 5 to the nearer unit. Conversely, if we say that the measure is 5 units to the nearer unit, we know that this means that the measure of the segment is somewhere between $4\frac{1}{2}$ and $5\frac{1}{2}$ units. In picture D, we have used a brace to indicate the portion of the rule between $4\frac{1}{2}$ and $5\frac{1}{2}$ units. We can conclude that, for any measure, the *greatest possible error* in the measurement cannot be greater than $\frac{1}{2}$ the unit of measure.

In picture E, where we have used a smaller unit of measure, we note that, because the measure of segment AB is between $10\frac{1}{2}$ and $11\frac{1}{2}$ units, its measure is 11 units to the nearer unit. Again we say that the greatest possible error in the measure is $\frac{1}{2}$ the unit of measure.

The unit of measure in picture E is smaller than the unit of measure in picture D; consequently, $\frac{1}{2}$ the unit of measure in picture E is less than $\frac{1}{2}$ the unit of measure in picture D. This means that the greatest possible error of the measure illustrated in picture E is less than the greatest possible error of the measure illustrated in picture D. For this reason, we say that the measure illustrated in picture E is a more *precise* measure than the one illustrated in picture D. It should be apparent that, as the unit of measure becomes smaller, the greatest possible error ($\frac{1}{2}$ the unit of measure) becomes smaller, and the precision of the measure becomes greater.

One way of comparing two or more measures, then, is to compare them in terms of their precision. Thus, for the example given earlier concerning the length of the cloth, we note that the measure obtained by using rule C is the most precise of the three measures. Because the unit of measure is smallest on rule C, the greatest possible error is the least.

Another way to compare measures is to compare them in terms of their *relative errors.* We determine the relative error of a measure by comparing the greatest possible error with the total measure. We ordinarily express the relative error as the first component of a rate pair whose second com- Rate pairs, pages 178-179 ponent is 1. For example, if the measure of a segment XY is 7 units to the nearer unit, then we can use the rate pair $\frac{1}{2}/7$ to represent the comparison of the greatest possible error and the measure.

We can now use the method you learned in Chapter 8 to find the first Equivalent rate pairs, page 181 component, x, of an equivalent rate pair whose second component is 1. That is, we want to find the replacement for x that satisfies the following condition.

$$\tfrac{1}{2}/7 = x/1.$$

Using the definition of equal proportional relations, we obtain Equal proportional relations, page 184

$$\tfrac{1}{2} \times 1 = 7x.$$

Since $\frac{1}{2} \times 1 = \frac{1}{2}$ and since $\frac{1}{2} = 7x$ is equivalent to $\frac{1}{2} \div 7 = x$, we obtain

$$x = \tfrac{1}{2} \div 7.$$

Thus,

$$x = \tfrac{1}{14}.$$

Therefore, $\frac{1}{2}/7 = \frac{1}{14}/1$; and we conclude that the relative error in the measure of segment XY is $\frac{1}{14}$ of a unit.

Suppose that we measure segment XY again, using a unit of measure $\frac{1}{2}$ as long as the unit we used to obtain the measure of 7 units. Suppose further that the measure to the nearer unit is 13 units. This time, the relative error can be obtained by using the rate pair $\frac{1}{2}/13$. Because $\frac{1}{2}/13$ is equal to $\frac{1}{26}/1$, we conclude that the relative error in the measure obtained by using the smaller unit is $\frac{1}{26}$ of a unit. If the relative error in one measure is less than the relative error in another measure, then the first mentioned measure is said to be more *accurate* than the other. Therefore, the measure of segment XY obtained by using the smaller unit of measure is more accurate because the relative error is less.

We can summarize our discussion of measurement thus far as follows:

The measure of a segment is a number.
This number is the number of units of measure
that are included in the segment.

The inner measure of a segment is
the number of units of measure
that are completely included within the segment.

The outer measure of a segment is
the number of units of measure
that are required to include the segment completely.

When we are determining the measure of the segment
to the nearer unit,
we choose either the inner or the outer measure
of a segment as the measure of the segment.

The greatest possible error in a measure
is equal to $\frac{1}{2}$ the unit of measure.
The more precise of two measures is the measure
with the lesser greatest possible error.

The relative error of a measure
is the amount of error per unit,
which is determined by comparing
the greatest possible error with the total measure.
The more accurate of two measures is the measure
that has the lesser relative error.

297 Use the three unit segments represented below to measure segment **UV**. For each unit, give the inner and outer measures. Also give the measure of UV to the nearer unit in each case.

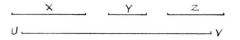

298 For each of the units A, B, and C represented below, construct a rule whose scale is determined by the given unit. Then use each of the rules to measure segment ST pictured below. Finally, copy and complete the chart with the results of your measurements.

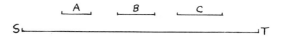

UNIT OF MEASURE	INNER MEASURE	OUTER MEASURE	NEARER UNIT OF MEASURE	GREATEST POSSIBLE ERROR	RELATIVE ERROR
A					
B					
C					

299 List the measures you obtained for exercise 298 in order of precision. Give the most precise measure first.

300 List the measures you obtained for exercise 298 in order of accuracy. Give the most accurate measure first.

Standard units of length

As we suggested earlier in this chapter, the development of standard units of measure is closely related to man's political, social, and economic history and to his scientific achievements. The two most widely used systems of standard units of measure are the metric system and the English system. The United States and the members of the British Commonwealth* use the English system of measures in their social and commercial transactions, but most of their scientific activities are carried on in the metric system. All of the other major countries of the world use the metric system for commercial and social purposes as well as for scientific work.

Because the metric system is a decimal system, it has certain advantages over the English system. For example, computation involving metric units is simpler than computation involving English units, and "converting" from one unit of measure to another is easier in the metric system. Since the metric system is so convenient and since it is so widely used throughout the world, many persons in the United States and Great Britain feel that we, too, should adopt this system for commercial and social use. But because custom and tradition are difficult to overcome and because of the inconvenience and cost the change-over would entail, there is still great reluctance in these countries to make the change.

In the first two tables presented below and on the next page, we list the more commonly used standard units of linear measure in both the English and the metric system. In the third table we show the relationship between certain of the English and metric units.

English units of linear measure
12 inches = 1 foot.
36 inches = 1 yard.
3 feet = 1 yard.
$16\frac{1}{2}$ feet = 1 rod.
5280 feet = 1 mile.
1760 yards = 1 mile.
320 rods = 1 mile.

---

* The Canadian and British Parliaments are currently considering the adoption of the metric system.

Metric units of linear measure
1000 millimeters = 1 meter.
100 centimeters = 1 meter.
10 decimeters = 1 meter.
10 meters = 1 decameter.
100 meters = 1 hectometer.
1000 meters = 1 kilometer.

English-metric units*
.039 inch = 1 millimeter.
25.4 millimeters = 1 inch.
.394 inch = 1 centimeter.
2.54 centimeters = 1 inch.
1.094 yards = 1 meter.
.914 meter = 1 yard.
.621 mile = 1 kilometer.
1.609 kilometers = 1 mile.

The remarks that we made in the preceding section concerning greatest possible error, relative error, precision, and accuracy apply to standard units of measure as well as to the arbitrary units we used in that section. That is, if the measure of a given segment MN is expressed as 14 inches, then we know that the unit of measure being used is the inch and that the measure of segment MN is between $13\frac{1}{2}$ and $14\frac{1}{2}$ inches. Furthermore, we know that the greatest possible error in the measure is $\frac{1}{2}$ inch and that the relative error is $\frac{1}{28}$ inch.

Now, however, suppose that the measure of segment MN is expressed as $14\frac{1}{4}$ inches. In this case, we know that the measure of segment MN is between $14\frac{1}{8}$ and $14\frac{3}{8}$ inches and that the unit of measure is $\frac{1}{4}$ inch rather than one inch. Because $\frac{1}{4}$ inch is the unit of measure, the greatest possible error is $\frac{1}{8}$ inch. The relative error is $\frac{1}{114}$ inch. Notice that the relative error is expressed in terms of the amount of error per inch, not in terms of the amount of error per $\frac{1}{4}$ inch. The relative error is always expressed in terms of error per *standard unit*; in this case, although $\frac{1}{4}$ inch is the unit of measure, $\frac{1}{4}$ inch is not a standard unit of measure. Hence, the relative error is expressed in terms of the amount of error per inch.

In this example, we can see that the measure of $14\frac{1}{4}$ inches is both more precise and more accurate than the measure of 14 inches for segment MN.

---

* In this table, all of the measures in the first column, except the number of millimeters and the number of centimeters in 1 inch, have been rounded off to the nearer thousandth. Thus, the corresponding measures are, strictly speaking, only *approximately* equal.

This is so because both the greatest possible error and the relative error are less in the measure of $14\frac{1}{4}$ inches than in the measure of 14 inches.

As a further example, suppose that one person finds the measure of a given segment CD to be 5.1 feet, while another person finds it to be 5.14 feet. How do these two measurements compare? First of all, the unit of measure used to obtain 5.1 feet is .1 foot, and the unit of measure used to obtain 5.14 feet is .01 foot. This means that the greatest possible error in the measure 5.1 feet is .05 foot, and the greatest possible error in the measure 5.14 feet is .005 foot. Therefore, 5.14 feet is a more precise measure than 5.1 feet. The relative error in 5.1 feet is $\frac{.05}{5.1}$, or approximately .01 foot. The relative error in 5.14 is $\frac{.005}{5.14}$, or approximately .001 foot. Therefore, 5.14 feet is also a more accurate measure than 5.1 feet.

From our discussion up to this point, it may seem that the more precise of two measures must also be the more accurate of the two measures in every instance; that is, it may seem that, if a first measure has a lesser greatest possible error than a second measure, then the relative error is also less for the first measure. Certainly, if we are comparing two measures of the same segment, as we have in the previous examples, it is true that the more precise measure is also the more accurate measure. This, however, is not necessarily the case when we are comparing the measures of *different* segments, because the total number of units of measure contained in the given measures is also a factor in determining relative error. For example, suppose that we compare a measure of $1\frac{1}{2}$ inches with a measure of 340 feet in terms of precision and accuracy. Obviously, $1\frac{1}{2}$ inches is more precise than 340 feet, since the greatest possible error in $1\frac{1}{2}$ inches is $\frac{1}{4}$ inch, while the greatest possible error in 340 feet is $\frac{1}{2}$ foot. But the relative error in $1\frac{1}{2}$ inches is $\frac{1}{4}/1\frac{1}{2}$, or $\frac{1}{6}$ inch; while the relative error in 340 feet is $\frac{1}{2}/340$, or $\frac{1}{680}$ foot. Certainly, a relative error of $\frac{1}{680}$ foot is less than a relative error of $\frac{1}{6}$ inch. Therefore, the measure of 340 feet is more accurate than the measure of $1\frac{1}{2}$ inches, even though $1\frac{1}{2}$ inches is more precise than 340 feet.

We should make one further observation at this time concerning the relationships between standard units of measure. In the table on page 341, we indicated that a measure of 12 inches is equal to a measure of 1 foot, that a measure of 5280 feet is equal to a measure of 1 mile, and so on. If, however, we compare these "equal" measures in terms of precision and accuracy, we see that, technically, they are not equal. For example, the greatest possible error in a measure of 12 inches is $\frac{1}{2}$ inch, while the greatest possible error in a measure of 1 foot is $\frac{1}{2}$ foot. Therefore, 12 inches is a more precise measure than 1 foot. If you compare the relative errors in these two measures, you will see that 12 inches is also a more accurate measure than 1 foot. Similarly, if you compare the greatest possible errors and the relative errors in 5280 feet and 1 mile, you will see that 5280 feet is more precise and more accurate than 1 mile. Thus, even though it is convenient to use the idea of equality to relate certain pairs of units of measure, we must keep in mind that in this case we are using the idea of equality in a very loose sense.

301 For each of the following measures, give the unit of measure, the limits between which the actual measure must lie, the greatest possible error of the measure, and the relative error of the measure.

a 5.81 feet   e 12 centimeters

b $3\frac{5}{8}$ inches   f 80 millimeters

c 36 yards   g .032 inch

d 1.9 miles   h .110 kilometer

302 Rank the measures given in exercise 301 with regard to precision, beginning with the most precise. Then rank the measures with regard to accuracy, beginning with the most accurate.

Square measure

In much the same way that we use linear measurement to determine the number that is the length of a segment, we use square measurement to determine the number that is the *area* of a region bounded by a simple closed curve. Examples of simple closed curves are figures such as a rectangle, a square, a triangle, or a circle. For simplicity, we will talk of "the area of a closed curve" instead of "the area of the region bounded by the curve." The area of a simple closed curve is the number of units of measure contained in the region bounded by the curve. Instead of using a segment as a unit of measure, however, we use the region bounded by a closed curve of some specific shape and size as our unit of measure.

Let us consider an example of the process whereby we determine the area of a simple closed curve like the one pictured below. First, we must

choose another simple closed curve and its interior as our unit of measure. Any of the curves pictured below might be used to provide an arbitrary unit of measure. Customarily, we use as our unit of measure a square and its

interior. The side of the square has a measure of one linear unit. The last picture at the right represents such a unit. We define a *unit square* as the union of a square and its interior. We can use this unit square to determine the area of the given curve just as we used a unit segment to determine the length of a segment. To do this, we cover the region bounded by the curve with as many of the unit squares as necessary, making sure that the interior is completely covered and that the unit squares do not overlap. In the following illustration, we have shown how a unit square of arbitrary size can be used to determine the area of the closed curve represented near the bottom of page 344.

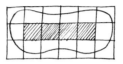

When we determine the area of a closed curve in this way, we obtain an inner and outer area of the curve just as we obtained an inner and outer measure of a segment. As you might expect, the *inner area* of the curve is the number of square units that are completely contained within the curve and its interior; while the *outer area* is the number of square units that are required to cover completely the curve and its interior. If you count the number of square units used in the illustration above, you will find that the outer area is 18, and the inner area is 4. This means that the area of the curve is some number between 18 and 4.

Obviously, the area of a curve, like the length of a segment, depends upon the size of the unit of measure. Suppose that we again find the area of the curve, this time using a unit square that is smaller than the one used in the previous illustration. Notice that, this time, the outer area is 57, and

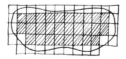

the inner area is 28. We can assume that the area found by using the smaller unit is more precise than the area found with the larger square unit.

Let us consider another example. Suppose that we want to determine the area of the rectangle pictured below. We will again use an arbitrary

unit square to determine the measure. We can use this unit square to develop a grid as a measuring device in the same way that we used a unit segment to develop a scale for measuring a segment. The grid shown below was constructed by marking off unit squares that touch each other but do not overlap.

We next put the grid on top of the region enclosed by the rectangle to determine the inner and outer area of the rectangle, as shown in the following picture. By counting the number of unit squares, we see that the inner area is 5 and the outer area is 12.

Now suppose that we use another unit of measure to determine the area of the given rectangle. The grid in the following picture was made by using a unit square whose side is $\frac{1}{2}$ as long as the side of the unit square used to make the first grid. With this grid, we find that the inner area of the rectangle is 33, and the outer area is 48.

If you compare the two pictures in which we found the area of the rectangle, you can see that the outer area is 4 times as great when we use the smaller unit of measure and the inner area is almost 7 times as great. Hence, by using smaller units we were able to include more of the interior of the rectangle in the inner area. In fact, if we were to continue to use smaller and smaller unit squares, we would arrive at more and more precise measures of the area of the rectangle. This is analogous to linear measurement, where we found that the use of a smaller unit segment resulted in a more precise measure of length.

From the examples we have discussed, you can see that the ideas involved in determining the area of a simple closed curve are analogous to the concepts involved in finding the length of a segment. In each case, we use some given unit of measure to determine a number that is the measure of the curve or segment. In each case, we do this by finding the number of units wholly contained in the object being measured (the inner measure) and the number of units required to cover the object completely (the outer measure). Also, in each case, we find a more precise measure by using a smaller unit of measure. These are the important ideas that elementary-school children ought to understand before they begin to work with standard units of square measure and before they learn to determine areas by using a rule or formula.

Probably most of you learned the following rule for finding the area of a rectangle:

> To determine the area of a rectangle,
> find the product of the length and the width.

Let us now use the ideas we have been discussing to see how this rule can be developed. To simplify this discussion, we will use an example in which the inner and outer measures of a rectangle are the same—that is, an example in which we have chosen a unit square so that the number of unit squares that are wholly contained in the rectangle and its interior is the same as the number of unit squares required to cover the rectangle and its interior completely. Thus, in the following illustration we see that 24 square units is both the inner and the outer area of the rectangle.

Note that we can determine the area of the rectangle by counting the number of unit squares required to cover the rectangle and its interior. However, we can use a short cut to determine the area. First, we observe that there are 6 unit squares in each row of the grid and that there are 4 rows of unit squares in the grid. So we can use the following condition to determine the number of unit squares in all.

$$6/1 = n/4.$$

In this condition, the rate pair $6/1$ represents the number of unit squares in 1 row, and $n/4$ represents the number of unit squares in 4 rows. We know that, because each row contains the same number of unit squares, these two rate pairs are equal.

Next we can use the definition of equal proportional relations to obtain

$$6 \times 4 = n \times 1.$$

Since $6 \times 4 = 24$ and $n \times 1 = n$, we obtain

$$24 = n.$$

Therefore, we know that the area of the rectangle is 24 unit squares.

Now think for a moment about the condition $6 \times 4 = n$. If we look again at the illustration, we can see that, since 6 unit squares are contained in each row, the length of the rectangle must be 6 units. This is so because each unit square is one unit long, and, therefore, 6 unit squares are 6 units long. By the same kind of reasoning, we see that the width of the rectangle must be 4 units, since 4 rows of unit squares are contained in the rectangle.

Hence, because the length of the rectangle is 6 units and the width is 4 units, we see that we can find the area of the rectangle by finding the product of the number that represents the length and the number that represents the width. You should be able to see that this short cut can be used generally to find the area of a rectangle, since the number of unit squares in 1 row is always the same as the length of the rectangle and the number of rows of unit squares is always the same as the width of the rectangle.

303 For each of the unit squares A, B, and C represented below, construct a grid whose scale is determined by the given unit. Then use each of the grids to measure the area of the closed curve pictured below. Finally, copy and complete the chart with the results of your measurements.

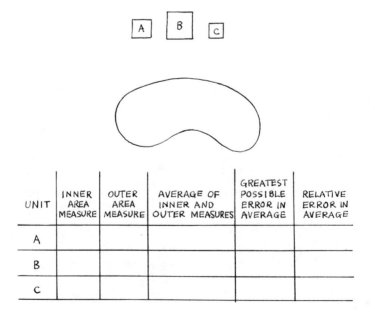

UNIT	INNER AREA MEASURE	OUTER AREA MEASURE	AVERAGE OF INNER AND OUTER MEASURES	GREATEST POSSIBLE ERROR IN AVERAGE	RELATIVE ERROR IN AVERAGE
A					
B					
C					

304 Suppose that the radius of a given circle is 3 feet. If the unit of measure is a square foot, what is the inner area of the circle? What is the outer area?

305 Suppose that the dimensions of a rectangle are $6\frac{2}{5}$ yards by $4\frac{1}{3}$ yards. If the unit of measure is the square yard, what are the inner and outer measures of the area of the rectangle?

306 Suppose that the unit of measure is the square foot. Now determine the inner and outer measures of the area of the rectangle described in exercise 305.

307 What is the area of the rectangle described in exercise 305 in square yards? What is the area in square feet?

Standard units of area

In the preceding discussion of area, we used arbitrary units to establish the meaning of area as the measure of a closed region, which is the union of a simple closed curve and its interior. You perhaps noticed that, although the units we used were arbitrary in size, they were always square in shape. In determining the area of any closed curve, such as those pictured below, it is convenient to use a square of some size as the unit of measure, no matter what the shape of the closed curve may be. Obviously, a circle or a rectangle that is not a square *could* have been chosen as a basis for the units used in determining area; in such an event, we would talk of "circular" measure or "rectangular" measure rather than square measure.

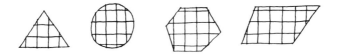

However, it is more convenient to use a square than to use some other kind of rectangle as the unit of area, since we can easily describe a 1-unit square (meaning a square region whose side is 1 unit in length). If the unit were a rectangle that is not a square, then it would be necessary to describe the rectangular unit as a 1-unit by 2-unit rectangle, or whatever its dimensions might be. A circular unit would also be inconvenient, since it is not possible to arrange circular units so that they cover the interior of a closed curve either without overlapping or without leaving portions of the closed region uncovered.

With the idea that the standard units of area are square in shape, we then derive the standard units of square measure from the standard units of length. Thus, a square region whose side is 1 inch long is a *square inch*, a square region whose side is 1 foot long is a *square foot*, and so on.

We can also use our knowledge of the relationships among various units of length to determine the relationships among various units of square measure. For example, because 1 foot is equal to 12 inches, we know that 1 square foot is equal to 12 × 12, or 144, square inches. Similarly, because 1 yard is equal to 3 feet, 1 square yard is equal to 3 × 3, or 9, square feet. In the following table, we have summarized the relationships among the more commonly used standard units of square measure in the English system.

$$144 \text{ square inches} = 1 \text{ square foot.}$$
$$9 \text{ square feet} = 1 \text{ square yard.}$$
$$43,560 \text{ square feet} = 1 \text{ acre.}$$
$$160 \text{ square rods} = 1 \text{ acre.}$$
$$640 \text{ acres} = 1 \text{ square mile.}$$

Notice that the acre is a square measure and not a linear measure. Thus, it would be incorrect to speak of "square acres," since the acre is itself a unit of square measure that has the same area as a square whose side is $\sqrt{160}$ rods long. Also keep in mind that we are using the idea of equality in a loose way when we say that a measure of 144 square inches is equal to a measure of 1 square foot. These two measures are not the same if we consider precision and accuracy. They are equal only if we disregard the fact that the process of measurement necessarily involves error and approximation.

308 For each of the following measures, give the unit of measure, the limits between which the actual measure must lie, the greatest possible error of the measure, and the relative error of the measure.
a 50.2 square miles   **c** $4\frac{1}{5}$ acres
b 41 square inches   **d** 4.124 square meters
309 Rank the measures given in exercise 308 with regard to precision and then with regard to accuracy.

Cubic measure and standard units of volume

In much the same way that we measure a segment or a closed region in the plane, we can measure the union of a solid figure, such as a prism, cylinder, or sphere, and its interior. The number that is the measure of a solid figure is the *volume* of the figure, and the volume is stated in terms of cubic units.

We will not discuss cubic measure in any great detail. But the process of determining the inner and the outer measure of a solid figure is analogous to the process of determining the inner and the outer measure of a segment or of a simple closed curve in a plane. This means that the inner measure of a solid would be the number of cubic units wholly contained within the solid, while the outer measure would be the number of cubes required to fill the solid completely. As you might expect, the smaller the cubic unit, the more precise the measure of the volume.

We can determine the volume of a prism or other solid in much the same way that we determine the length of a segment or the area of a simple closed curve. The picture below can be used to illustrate the process. Notice

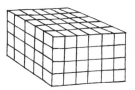

that the prism and its interior are filled with cubes of the same size and that there are 4 layers of cubes, each containing the same number of cubes. If we consider just one layer of cubes, we note that there are 5 rows of cubes in the layer and that each row contains 6 cubes. Thus, we see that there are 6×5, or 30, cubes in each layer and 30×4, or 120, cubes in the prism. Hence, the volume of the prism is 120 cubic units.

It is left as an exercise for the reader to explain how the following rule can be developed.

> To determine the volume of a prism,
> find the product of the length,
> the width, and the height of the prism.

The standard units of volume are derived from the standard units of linear and square measure. For example, the *cubic inch* is a cube each of whose edges is one inch long and, thus, each of whose faces is a one-inch square. Similarly, the *cubic centimeter* is a cube each of whose edges is 1 centimeter long and, thus, each of whose faces is a one-centimeter square.

In the English system of measures, the most commonly used cubic measures are the cubic inch, the *cubic foot*, and the *cubic yard*. We can use the relationships among linear measures to show how cubic measures are related. For example, because 1 foot is equal to 12 inches, 1 cubic foot is equal to $12 \times 12 \times 12$, or 1728, cubic inches. Similarly, because 1 yard is equal to 3 feet, 1 cubic yard is equal to $3 \times 3 \times 3$, or 27, cubic feet.

310 Suppose that the dimensions of a rectangular prism are $2\frac{1}{5}$ feet by $3\frac{3}{4}$ feet by $1\frac{2}{3}$ feet. If the unit of measure is the cubic foot, what is the inner volume of the prism? What is its outer volume?

311 If the unit of measure is the cubic inch, what is the inner volume of the prism described in exercise 310 on page 351? What is its outer volume?

312 What is the volume of the prism described in exercise 310 in cubic feet? What is its volume in cubic inches?

313 Suppose that the radius of a sphere is 3 feet. If the unit of measure is the cubic foot, what is the inner volume of the sphere? What is its outer volume?

314 If the volume of a solid is 54 cubic feet, what is its volume in cubic inches? What is its volume in cubic yards?

315 If the volume of a solid is 12.31 cubic centimeters, what is its volume in cubic meters? What is its volume in cubic millimeters?

Computation involving measures

When we "convert" a measure expressed in feet to a measure expressed in inches or find the sum of several measures or find the area of a rectangle, we are computing with measures. Computation involving measures is not really different from computation involving numbers of apples or numbers of children. Often, however, when the numbers represent measures, the results of the computation require some interpretation. This is so because all measurement is approximate and because we must consider precision in measure.

For example, if we are given the length and width of a rectangle to the nearer tenth of an inch, then we need to decide just how precise we should be in expressing the area—that is, we must decide if the area should be expressed to the nearer square inch, the nearer tenth of a square inch, or the nearer hundredth of a square inch. Certainly, the length and width are approximate measures that have been rounded to the nearer tenth of an inch; therefore, the area is an approximation and must be rounded off. But the question remains, what is an appropriate unit of measure for the area?

Let us answer this question by considering an example in which we measure the length and width of a rectangle, using several different units of measure. The results of these measurements are given in columns A and B of the table on page 353. Note that we have used successively smaller units of measure and, hence, have obtained more and more precise measures.

The first measures of the length and width, 4 and 4, are given to the nearer whole unit; the next, 4.2 and 3.7, are given to the nearer tenth of a unit; and so on. Each of the numerals in column C expresses the number

A	B	C	D
LENGTH	WIDTH	LENGTH TIMES WIDTH	AREA
4	4	16	16
4.2	3.7	15.54	15.5
4.24	3.71	15.7304	15.73
4.238	3.711	15.727218	15.727
4.2382	3.7109	15.72753638	15.7275

we obtain when we find the product of the length and width. Thus, 16 is the product of 4 and 4, 15.54 is the product of 4.2 and 3.7, and so on.

Now let us assume that each number named in column C represents the area of the rectangle to the nearer square unit. Notice that, if the numbers named in column C do represent the areas, then in every case except the first one, the area is more precise than the length and width. For example, in the second row, the length and width are given to the nearer tenth of a unit, while the area is given to the nearer hundredth of a square unit. Similarly, in the fourth row, the length and width are expressed to the nearer thousandth of a square unit, while the area is expressed to the nearer millionth of a square unit.

It does not seem justifiable that the area should be a more precise measure than the length or width, since the area is determined on the basis of these measurements. To avoid difficulties of this kind, some rather complex rules have been developed for computation involving measures. It is not necessary to discuss all of these rules in detail because elementary-school pupils are required to do only a limited amount of computation that involves measures. As a consequence, extended discussion of these complex rules is not appropriate. For our purposes, the following simple rule will suffice:

When two numbers that represent linear measures are multiplied,
both measures should have the same precision, and
the product should never be more precise
than the two measures that are being multiplied.

In the table shown above, the numbers expressed in column D represent the areas as determined by the rule just given. For example, the area expressed in the third row of column D has been rounded to the nearer hundredth of a square unit because the length and width in this case are expressed to the nearer hundredth of a unit; the area named in the fourth row of column D has been rounded to the nearer thousandth of a square

354

unit because the length and width in this case are expressed to the nearer thousandth of a unit.

In the table below, we have used the rule stated on the preceding page to determine the precision for the area of several rectangles. Notice that, in the first example, the length is expressed as 14.0 to show that the measure was determined to the nearer tenth of a unit. The product of the numbers that represent the two dimensions is 43.40 (3.1 × 14.0), but, since each of the dimensions is given to the nearer tenth, the area also is given to the nearer tenth, or as 43.4.

Length	Width	Area
14.0	3.1	43.4
5.16	4.33	22.34
6	8	48
5.281	2.222	11.734

A rule similar to the one we gave for the product of two measures can also be applied to the sum of two measures. Thus, the sum of two measures should have the same precision as the two measures being added. This means that the sum of 8.36 miles and 6.24 miles, for example, should be expressed as 14.60 miles, and not as 14.6 miles. Further, the sum of the two measures should never be more precise than either of the measures being added. For example, the sum of 8.36 miles and 6.2 miles should be expressed as 14.6 miles, and not as 14.56 miles.

When we convert from one unit of measure to another, we express a measure given in one unit by an equal measure in a different unit. Thus, we convert feet to inches when we express 1 foot as 12 inches. (Keep in mind, however, that we are using equality in a special sense. When we say that 12 inches = 1 foot, we do not mean that the two measures are equal in terms of precision or accuracy.)

316 C is a point in segment AB that is located between points A and B. Copy and complete the following chart.

	LENGTH OF SEGMENT AC	LENGTH OF SEGMENT CB	LENGTH OF SEGMENT AB
A	14.2 MILES	8.9 MILES	
B	8.572 CENTIMETERS	3.49 CENTIMETERS	
C	12 1/8 FEET	19 3/4 FEET	
D	.3486 MILLIMETERS	1.89 MILLIMETERS	

317 ABCD is a rectangle. Copy and complete the following chart.

	LENGTH OF SIDE AB	LENGTH OF SIDE BC	AREA OF RECTANGLE ABCD
A	2.4 MILES	6.7 MILES	
B	.034 YARDS	2.06 YARDS	
C	5.96 KILOMETERS	4.6 KILOMETERS	
D	1.200 INCHES	7.43 INCHES	
E	$3\frac{3}{5}$ FEET	$4\frac{3}{8}$ FEET	

318 A rectangular right prism has rectangle ABCD as its base and segment AE as its altitude. Copy and complete the following chart.

	LENGTH OF SIDE AB	LENGTH OF SIDE BC	LENGTH OF ALTITUDE AE	VOLUME OF PRISM
A	3.1 INCHES	2.6 INCHES	4.4 INCHES	
B	8 CENTIMETERS	4.1 CENTIMETERS	.78 CENTIMETERS	
C	$3\frac{1}{4}$ YARDS	$5\frac{1}{2}$ YARDS	$4\frac{1}{10}$ YARDS	
D	2.006 MILLIMETERS	4.20 MILLIMETERS	3.001 MILLIMETERS	

Traditionally, children have been taught some rule, such as the one stated below, for converting from one unit of measure to another.

If you are converting from a smaller unit of measure
to a larger unit of measure,
divide the number of smaller units
by the number of these units contained in the larger unit.
If you are converting from a larger unit
to a smaller unit,
multiply by the number of smaller units
contained in the larger unit.

Often children become confused by this kind of rule and have difficulty in deciding whether they should multiply or divide. A much more meaningful way of teaching children how to convert measures is to use the idea of rate pairs and proportional relations.

For example, suppose that we want to express a measure of 52 feet as a number of inches. First of all, we can use the rate pair 12/1 to represent the fact that there are 12 inches in 1 foot. To find the number of inches in 52 feet, we need to find another rate pair that is a member of the propor-

Rate pairs and proportional relations, pages 178-179

tional relation 12/1 and that has 52 as its second component. Thus, we can use the following condition, in which n represents the number of inches in 52 feet.

$$12/1 = n/52.$$

By the definition of equal proportional relations, we obtain

$$n = 12 \times 52.$$

Then, because $12 \times 52 = 624$, we obtain

$$n = 624.$$

Thus, we conclude that 52 feet is the same as 624 inches.

As another example, suppose that we want to convert 400 cubic feet to cubic yards. We can use the rate pair 27/1 to represent the number of cubic feet in 1 cubic yard and the rate pair $400/x$ to represent the number of cubic yards in 400 cubic feet.

We know that these two rate pairs are members of the same proportional relation, so we write

$$27/1 = 400/x.$$

Then we proceed in the usual manner to obtain

$$27x = 400,$$

and

$$x = \tfrac{400}{27}, \text{ or } 14\tfrac{22}{27}.$$

From this last condition, we know that 400 cubic feet is equal to $14\tfrac{22}{27}$ cubic yards.

For a child who is just beginning to work with measures and with problems involving measures, this approach to converting measures makes more sense than a short-cut rule. Eventually, of course, after a certain amount of practice, children can develop short cuts for themselves.

319 Convert each of the following measures as indicated.
  a 42 inches to feet
  b 8.5 centimeters to millimeters
  c 42 square yards to square feet
  d 12.31 square centimeters to square meters
  e 100 square inches to square millimeters
  f 9.4 cubic yards to cubic feet
  g 427.8 cubic millimeters to cubic centimeters
  h 100 square kilometers to square miles

CONCLUSION

In our discussion of measurement, we have been using some intuitive ideas that were not stated explicitly. Among them are the following basic notions: 1) A measure is always a positive real number; this means that a measure is always greater than 0. It also means that the scale on a measuring device is a physical representation of some portion of the real-number line. 2) Areas and volumes are additive. For example, if we wish to find the area of a curve like the one pictured below, we can first separate the interior of the curve into two parts, as indicated by the dotted line. We can then find the area of each part, and use the sum of the two areas as the area of the entire curve.

We have limited our discussion in this chapter to linear, square, and cubic measures. But the ideas we have discussed and the generalizations we have made also apply to other measures traditionally taught in the elementary school, such as measures of time and weight and liquid and dry measures. We have also limited our discussion to some very basic ideas about measurement because we feel that these ideas are most important to you as an elementary teacher.

CHAPTER QUIZ

1 Draw a rectangle 6 inches by 4 inches. Then make two grids for measuring the area of the rectangle. For one of the grids, use a rectangular unit 2 inches by $\frac{1}{2}$ inch, and for the other grid, use a 1-inch square. Use these two grids to find the area of the rectangle and then compare the results.

2 Find the area of each rectangle whose dimensions are expressed below.

RECTANGLE	LENGTH	WIDTH
A	15	26
B	1.5	2.6
C	.15	2.60
D	15.0	2.6
E	145	34.9
F	1.456	1.22
G	14.35	5.678

3 Use an equilateral triangle whose side is 1 inch long to find the area of an equilateral triangle whose side is 6 inches long.

4 Find the area of each of the figures pictured below. What basic principle of areas do you use to find these areas?

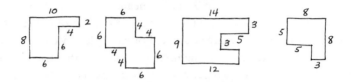

5 What is the formula for finding the area of a triangle? What is the formula for finding the area of a parallelogram? Use the discussion concerning the "length times width" formula for the area of a rectangle (page 347) to help you explain each formula in terms of the principles developed in this chapter.

6 Draw several lines that differ in length, but each of which has a measure of 1 foot to the nearer foot. Draw several lines that differ in length, but each of which has a measure of 12 inches to the nearer inch. In which case is there greater variation among the lengths?

7 Repeat exercise 6, but use the measures of 5 inches and 5.0 inches.

8 Convert each of the following measures as indicated.

A 5 kilometers to miles   D 75 cubic inches to cubic feet

B 45 cubic feet to cubic yards   E 28 yards to meters

C 64 feet to rods   F 56 inches to centimeters

SUPPLEMENTARY READINGS

National Council of Teachers of Mathematics, *Twenty-Second Yearbook*: *Emerging Practices in Mathematics Education*, pp. 310-338. This yearbook contains two articles on the terminology and computational procedures used when working with approximate data. Item 52 of Bibliography

Schaaf, William, *Basic Concepts of Elementary Mathematics*, Chapter 7. This is a very complete treatment of the nature of measurement, standard units, the reliability of measurement, and computing with approximate data. Item 30 of Bibliography

Smith, David Eugene, *History of Mathematics, Volume II*, Chapter 9. This selection contains a comprehensive history of the practical aspects of measurement through the ages. Item 46 of Bibliography

Van Engen, *et al.*, *Seeing Through Mathematics, Book 1*, Unit 8 and *Seeing Through Mathematics, Book 2*, Unit 12. These units provide an excellent source of information and exercise material on measurement. Items 21 and 48 of Bibliography

There are many books and pamphlets on the topic of measurement. All of those in the following list contain enrichment material that would be appropriate.

Bendick, Jeanne, *How Much and How Many?* Item 53 of Bibliography

Johnson, Donovan A. and Glenn, W. H., *The World of Measurement.* Item 54 of Bibliography

Lufkin Rule Co., *The Amazing Story of Measurement.* Item 55 of Bibliography

Newman, James, *The World of Mathematics*, pp. 1797-1813. Item 56 of Bibliography

Rassweiler, M. and Harris, J., *Mathematics and Measurement.* Item 57 of Bibliography

Chapter fifteen

Geometry for the elementary school

Geometric figures as sets of points
Some ideas from Euclidean geometry
Ideas from topology

For many years the teaching of geometry in the elementary school has been rather limited and haphazard. Textbooks often included, seemingly as an afterthought, several pages of pictures of common geometric figures, such as triangles, circles, squares, and so on. The pupils were expected to memorize the names of these figures and to recognize other examples of each kind of figure. This was often the extent of the "geometry" the elementary-school child was expected to learn.

While it is of course necessary that pupils be able to recognize the names, shapes, and simple properties of the more common geometric figures, this ability no more constitutes the subject of geometry than the ability to compute constitutes the subject of arithmetic. Rather, geometry may more accurately be characterized as the study of relations among sets of points in much the same way that arithmetic and algebra may be described as the study of relations among sets of numbers.

In this chapter we will first discuss some concepts of geometry that a child must understand, such as the meaning of a line, a segment, an angle, a plane, and a simple closed curve. We will then consider a few of the geometric relations that might profitably be presented to pupils in the elementary school.

Geometric figures as sets of points

Just as we work with sets of numbers in arithmetic, so do we work with sets of points in geometry. Similarly, points, like numbers, are ideational mathematical objects and are not to be confused with their physical representations. Just as children must learn that the meaning of the number 6 is independent of the way we choose to represent it, so they must learn that a line or a triangle or a single point also is independent of the way we choose to represent it. It is important for children to learn, for example, that, although the dots in the picture below are of different sizes, the points represented by these dots do *not* differ in "size." This is the case because a point is not a physical object and thus can be thought of as being without size in the physical sense.

● ·· ●● ● ·

From the notion of a single point as a geometric figure of "no dimension," we move next to the ideas of a line, a ray, and a segment. A line is an infinite set of points that extends indefinitely in opposite directions from Infinite set, page 30 any given point in the line. In the picture below, we have used arrows to show that the line "goes on and on" in opposite directions.

←――――――――――→

When we refer to a line, we will always mean "straight line." Points that are contained in the same line are *collinear* points. Sets of points such as those pictured below, which are not lines, will be called curves. Lines do belong to the general category of objects called curves, but a line does not "curve."

⌐ ⌒ ◯ ⌐ ⌐

One way of distinguishing between a line and other curves is to observe that two points determine exactly one line, but two points do not determine just one curve of any other kind. In fact, infinitely many curves contain any two given points. This distinction between a line and other curves is illustrated below, where we show the line determined by points P and Q and several other curves containing these points.

Because two points determine a line, we usually name a line by naming two points in it. For example, the line pictured at the left below, line AB, is named by the symbol $\overleftrightarrow{AB}$ ($\overleftrightarrow{BA}$ is also a name for this line). The second line from the left is named $\overleftrightarrow{PQ}$ or $\overleftrightarrow{QP}$, and so on.

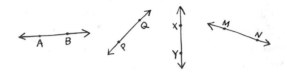

A given point in a line separates the line into two subsets, called *half-lines*. Each half-line extends endlessly in one direction from the given point, which is the boundary of each half-line. The union of the set containing the boundary and one of the half-lines is a *ray*. Several rays are pictured below. The first ray pictured at the left, ray CD, is named by the symbol $\overrightarrow{CD}$. In the second picture, $\overleftrightarrow{RT}$ is the union of the two rays, $\overrightarrow{SR}$ and $\overrightarrow{ST}$. Note that the endpoint and one other point in the ray are used, in that order, in naming a ray. You should be able to name the ray in the picture at the extreme right.

Subset, page 14

Union of two sets, page 20

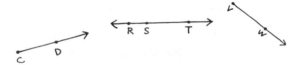

A *segment* is a subset of a line that includes two points in a line and all the points between the two given ones, which are called the *endpoints* of the segment. We usually use the two endpoints to name a segment. Thus, the segment at the left below is segment AB (symbolized as $\overline{AB}$); the second from the left is $\overline{JK}$; and so on.

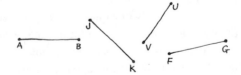

Just as two points determine a line, so two intersecting lines determine a *plane*. Since any three points that are not all contained in the same line (noncollinear points) determine two intersecting lines, it follows that three noncollinear points determine a plane. Thus, we name a plane, such as any of those pictured near the top of page 363, by naming three noncollinear

points in the plane. For example, the plane pictured at the left is plane
GHI; that pictured next is plane PQR; and so on. A plane, like a line, has
no boundary, and we can think of it as extending indefinitely.

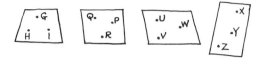

Certain subsets of a plane that are the union or the intersection of
lines, rays, and segments will be of interest to us later in this chapter. Two
lines that are included in the same plane may be related to each other in
two ways: their intersection may be a single point that is contained in
both lines; or they may not intersect, in which case, their intersection is the
empty set. In the latter case, we say that the two lines are parallel. Thus,
in picture A below, $\overleftrightarrow{AB}$ and $\overleftrightarrow{BC}$ intersect in point B, and the lines in picture C intersect in point H. The lines in picture B and those in picture D
do not intersect in a point and, hence, are parallel.

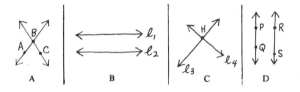

If two rays have a common endpoint and their union is not a straight
line, then their union is an *angle*. The common endpoint of the two rays
is the *vertex* of the angle. In the pictures below, angle CDE ($\angle$CDE) is the
union of $\overrightarrow{DC}$ and $\overrightarrow{DE}$; $\angle$OPQ is the union of $\overrightarrow{PO}$ and $\overrightarrow{PQ}$; and $\angle$JKL is
the union of $\overrightarrow{KJ}$ and $\overrightarrow{KL}$.

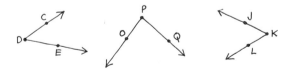

Much of plane geometry is devoted to the study of relations among
subsets of a plane that are called *simple closed curves*. Informally, we may
say that a simple closed curve is a geometric figure whose outline may be
traced with a pencil by starting at some point in the curve and ending at
that same point without lifting the pencil and without tracing the same
point more than once. The figure encloses a subset of the plane; the set

of points enclosed by the curve is called the *interior* of the curve, and the set of points outside the curve is called its *exterior*. One property of simple closed curves is that a segment determined by a point in the interior of a simple closed curve and a point in its exterior must contain a point in the curve.

In the figures represented below, pictures A, B, C, E, G, and J represent simple closed curves, while the others do not. Notice that we call figures like A, B, and E curves, even though they have "straight" sides. A simple closed curve may be the union of three or more segments that intersect in pairs, as in pictures A, B, and E. Such curves are called *polygons*. The segments that make up the polygon are called the *sides* of the polygon, and the points of intersection of pairs of sides are called the *vertices* of the polygon.

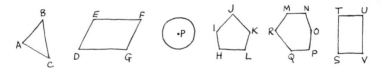

In naming a polygon, we ordinarily name the vertices in order, beginning with any vertex we choose. For example, the triangle pictured at the left below, which is the union of segments AB, BC, and AC, is called triangle ABC (symbolized as △ABC), △BCA, or △CAB. The polygon pictured next is called parallelogram DEFG, EFGD, FGDE, or GDEF. From these examples, you should be able to give several names for each of the other polygons pictured below. A circle, which is the set of all points in a plane that are the same distance from a point called the center of the circle, usually is given the same name as its center. Thus, the circle pictured below is called circle P.

We can also think of geometric figures that are subsets of the set of all points called *space*. Subsets of space, such as those pictured on page 365, are the union or the intersection of planes and curved surfaces in space. Thus, the faces and the base of the pyramid at the left are portions of intersecting planes, and each edge of the pyramid is the intersection of two of the portions of planes. The cylinder pictured next is the union of its two bases, which are portions of planes, and its lateral surface, which is a curved surface in space. The faces and bases of the prism pictured next are likewise portions of intersecting planes. The sphere is a curved surface consisting of all points in space that are the same distance from a given point called the center of the sphere.

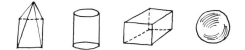

320 A plane geometric figure is represented below. Name two of each of the following geometric objects illustrated in the figure.

a points	**h** angles
b lines	**i** vertices of angles
c rays	**j** simple closed curves
d segments	**k** non-closed curves
e intersections of lines	**l** polygons
f intersections of rays	**m** triangles
g intersections of segments	**n** quadrilaterals

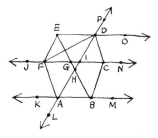

With this discussion of basic ideas and terminology, we are now ready to consider certain topics from geometry that we think are appropriate and interesting for elementary school children. In the remainder of this chapter we will use an informal approach to the ideas we discuss. We will rely heavily on intuition and imagination in arriving at generalizations, and we will not attempt to prove our conclusions. We do this because proof, in most cases, would require an extensive mathematical development. We also want to present the material in a form that can be easily adapted for use with children, and we feel strongly that *formal* geometry is not an appropriate part of the elementary school curriculum.*

---

* Van Engen, *et al.*, *Seeing Through Mathematics, Book 1*, Units 1, 2, and 8 and *Seeing Through Mathematics, Book 2*, Units 9 and 14. The geometric material in these units covers in detail the Euclidean relationships among points, lines, and planes. This is a more comprehensive development than the one given in this section. Items 21 and 48 of Bibliography

Some ideas from Euclidean geometry

In the first section of this chapter, we said that lines, rays, and segments are infinite sets of points and that rays and segments are subsets of lines. When we consider sets of points, we can arrive at certain results that are analogous to those we discovered when we worked with sets of numbers. For example, suppose that we want to compare the two segments represented below. Segment AB is 3 inches long, and segment CD is 1 inch long. Because $\overline{AB}$ is longer than $\overline{CD}$, it would seem natural to assume that

$\overline{AB}$ contains more points than $\overline{CD}$. However, let us see what happens when we compare these two infinite sets of points.

To make the comparison, we will use a line, which we will call $\overleftrightarrow{PX}$, that can be "moved" back and forth so that the location of point P is constant but the location of point X is variable. Thus, point P will act as a "pivotal" point. In picture A below, $\overleftrightarrow{PX}$ is shown to intersect $\overline{CD}$ in point L and $\overline{AB}$ in point M. In picture B we have "moved" $\overleftrightarrow{PX}$ very slightly so that $\overleftrightarrow{PX}$ now intersects $\overline{CD}$ and $\overline{AB}$ in points L' and M' respectively. In picture C, we have again "moved" $\overleftrightarrow{PX}$ so that it now intersects $\overline{CD}$ and $\overline{AB}$ in points L" (read "L double prime") and M" respec-

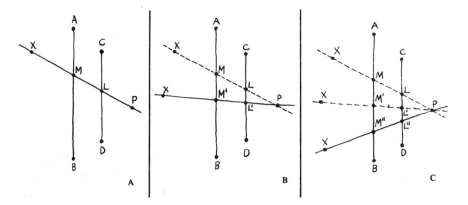

tively. If we were to continue this procedure, we would see that each "movement" of $\overleftrightarrow{PX}$ about point P will determine two more points of intersection, one in each segment. Thus, we can show that the points in $\overline{CD}$ can be put in one-to-one correspondence with the points in $\overline{AB}$. By the definition of equivalent sets, we conclude that the two sets of points,

One-to-one correspond-ence, page

Equivalent sets, page 1

$\overline{AB}$ and $\overline{CD}$, are equivalent. This seems rather surprising, since we began by assuming that, because $\overline{AB}$ is longer, $\overline{AB}$ probably contains more points than $\overline{CD}$. However, if we think back to the results we obtained when we compared an infinite set of numbers, like the set of natural numbers, with a proper subset of itself, we find that the results are not so surprising. In this respect, infinite sets of points behave like infinite sets of numbers.

Equivalent infinite sets, pages 32-33

321 Show that the following sets are equivalent.

    a The unit fractions between 0 and 1 and the natural numbers greater than 1

    b A segment 2 inches long and a semicircle

    c The two curves shown below

    In discussing the next idea, we need to keep in mind the following assumptions (usually called axioms) from plane geometry.

Two points determine exactly one line.

If two lines intersect,
their intersection consists of exactly one point.

    With these assumptions in mind, we now want to decide how many lines are determined by 25 points in a plane if no three of the points are contained in the same line. To solve this problem, we could represent 25 points on a piece of paper and then proceed to draw lines until each point was connected to each of the other points by means of a line. However, this would be rather tedious and we might make a mistake as our picture became more complicated. Furthermore, this method would not give us any basis for deciding how many lines are determined by 22 points, or 35 points, or 150 points. Let us instead see if we can find a relation between the number of lines determined and the increase in the number of points. If we can do this, we will be able to make a generalization to cover all particular examples.

    We already know, from the first assumption given above, that 2 points determine exactly 1 line. If we add a third point, we find that it is possible to draw 3 lines, since each pair of points determines 1 line. In the picture near the top of page 368, we show the number of lines determined first by 2 points, then by 3 points, by 4 points, and by 5 points. The picture also includes a table that summarizes the results so far. If you were to add a sixth point, you would find that it is possible to draw 5 more lines and, hence, a total of 15 lines for the 6 points. You should verify this by copying picture D, including 1 more point, and then drawing the additional lines.

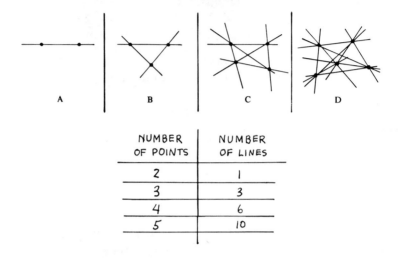

A   B   C   D

NUMBER OF POINTS	NUMBER OF LINES
2	1
3	3
4	6
5	10

We can now add a new entry in our table showing the numbers of points and the numbers of lines.

NUMBER OF POINTS	NUMBER OF LINES
2	1
3	3
4	6
5	10
6	15

Instead of putting more points and lines in the pictures, let us think about the results for the first six entries in the table. If you examine the numbers that represent the number of lines, you should be able to discern a pattern to this sequence. Thus, in going from 2 points to 3 points, the number of lines increases by 2; in going from 3 points to 4, the number of lines increases by 3; in going from 4 points to 5, the number of lines increases by 4; and in going from 5 points to 6, the number of lines increases by 5. The reason for this pattern of increases is quite apparent. Every time one more point is chosen, it is possible to draw as many lines as were drawn before the point was added *plus* the lines that connect the new point with each of the previously chosen points. For example, when there are 5 points, we are able to draw the 6 lines we drew when there were only 4 points plus the 4 lines that connect the fifth point with the 4 other points. Our intuition tells us that this pattern will hold for any number of points. Thus, when we add a seventh point, we will be able to draw 6 more lines than we drew with 6 points; with 15 points, we will be able to draw 14 more lines than with 14 points; and so on.

Notice that, once we have observed this pattern, we no longer need to locate the points and draw the lines. The table below shows the results for the first 13 points, and we know how many lines can be drawn through 7 to 13 points, even though we have not actually drawn the pictures.

NUMBER OF POINTS	NUMBER OF LINES	NUMBER OF POINTS	NUMBER OF LINES
2	1	8	28
3	3	9	36
4	6	10	45
5	10	11	55
6	15	12	66
7	21	13	78

So far we know that, to decide how many lines are determined by a given number of points, we can add the number of lines connecting the given point with all of the previously placed points to the number of lines determined by the previously placed points. Another way of saying this is to say that the number of lines determined by a given number of points is equal to the sum of the number that represents 1 point fewer and the number of lines determined by these points. We can express this idea more clearly if we develop some symbolism to represent the number of points and the number of lines determined. Suppose that we use P_1 to represent the number of points given in the first row of the table above and L_1 to represent the number of lines given in the first row of the table; that is, $P_1 = 2$ and $L_1 = 1$. Further, we will use P_2 and L_2 to represent the number of points and the number of lines, respectively, named in the second row of the table. In general, we will use P_n to represent the number of points in the nth row of the table and L_n to represent the number of lines determined by the P_n points. Now we can use this symbolism to express the relation that we have established. The sentence below expresses the idea that the number of lines in the second row of the table—that is, the number of lines determined by 3 points—is the sum of the number of points and the number of lines in the first row of the table. This statement is obviously true, since $P_1 = 2$, $L_1 = 1$, $2 + 1 = 3$, and $L_2 = 3$.

$$P_1 + L_1 = L_2.$$

We can now use our new notation and the information given in the table on page 369 to write the following pairs of sentences about the relation between the number of points given and the number of lines determined.

$$P_1 + L_1 = L_2, \text{ or } 2 + 1 = 3.$$
$$P_2 + L_2 = L_3, \text{ or } 3 + 3 = 6.$$
$$P_3 + L_3 = L_4, \text{ or } 4 + 6 = 10.$$
$$P_4 + L_4 = L_5, \text{ or } 5 + 10 = 15.$$

. .

. .

. .

Even though our table does not show a 20th row, we will assume that the same relationship still holds and that the following sentence expresses a true statement.

$$P_{20} + L_{20} = L_{21}.$$

Keep in mind that, since the table began with 2 points rather than 1, P_{20} represents 21 points, not 20 points. Thus, the statement $P_{20} + L_{20} = L_{21}$ means that the sum of 21 points and the number of lines that are determined by 21 points is equal to the number of lines that are determined by 22 points.

For the general case, we can write the following sentence to express the relationship between the number of points and the number of lines.

$$P_n + L_n = L_{n+1}.$$

From this statement, you know that the number of lines determined by $n + 2$ points is equal to the sum of $n + 1$ points and the number of lines determined by $n + 1$ points. The formula, $P_n + L_n = L_{n+1}$, is an example of a *recurrence formula*.* It is of the same type as the formula we developed for the Fibonacci sequence in Chapter 3. Notice that, because we know $P_1 = 2$ and $L_1 = 1$, by repeated use of the formula, we can find out how many lines are determined by any number of points that we are concerned with.

Fibonacci sequence, page 42

Another way of solving this same problem is to note that, when the nth point is chosen, $n - 1$ lines are determined by the nth point paired with each of the earlier points. That is, for n points, $n - 1$ lines can be drawn from each of the n points. Thus, we can think of $n(n - 1)$ lines in

---

* We have not proved this relationship for any number of points and lines; we have only assumed it to be true because it seems reasonable. However, it is possible to prove that the relationship expressed by this formula does hold for any n.

all for *n* points. But because each line contains *two* of the *n* points, the product $n(n - 1)$ includes each line twice. Hence, we must divide by 2. So we obtain $\dfrac{n(n - 1)}{2}$ as another expression for finding the number of lines determined by *n* points.

322 Continue the table given on page 370 until you have found how many lines are determined by 25 points if no three of the points are contained in the same line.

323 Suppose that three of the 25 points are contained in the same line. How does this affect the number of lines determined by the 25 points?

324 How many lines are determined by 1 point?

325 A checkerboard has 64 small squares. It also contains a number of larger squares that are formed by 4 of the smaller squares that are all adjacent to each other or by groups of smaller squares that contain a smaller square in the center. Determine the total number of squares of all sizes that are contained on a checkerboard. To help with this problem, first determine the number of squares contained on each of the following "checkerboards," and try to develop a relation between the number of smaller squares and the total number of squares.

a A checkerboard consisting of just one square

b A checkerboard consisting of four squares

c A checkerboard consisting of nine squares

In the example just discussed, we established a relation between points in a plane and the lines determined by those points. As another example of the kind of geometric idea that might be taught in the elementary school, we will discuss a relation between the number of sides a polygon has and the measures of the angles of the polygon. In this example, we will work only with *simple convex* polygons. A polygon is convex if no segment determined by two points in its interior intersects a side of the polygon. Thus, figures ABCD, IJKLMN, and STU below represent simple convex

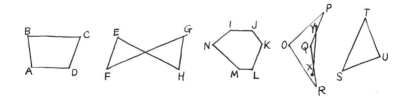

polygons. Figure EFGH is not a simple convex polygon, since sides EH and GF intersect in a point that is different from an endpoint of one of the sides. Neither is figure OPQR a simple convex polygon, since segment XY, which connects two points in the interior of the polygon, intersects sides QR and PQ. (Figure OPQR is a *concave* polygon.) From now on, we will use the word "polygon" to mean a simple convex polygon.

One further idea you need to recall at this time is how the measure of an angle is determined. In Chapter 14 we discussed how to measure a seg- Measure of a segment, page 334 ment by using a real-number line. Usually, we first make one endpoint of the segment correspond to point 0. We then use the coördinate in the number line that corresponds to the other endpoint as the measure of the segment. Thus, the measure of $\overline{AB}$, pictured below, is 4.5 units, since A corresponds to 0 and B corresponds to 4.5 on the real-number line.

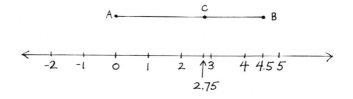

Of course, it is possible to determine the measure of a segment even if one of the endpoints does not correspond to point 0 in the number line. For example, we can find the measure of $\overline{CB}$ in the above illustration by subtracting the coördinate that corresponds to C from the coördinate that corresponds to B. Thus, the measure of $\overline{CB}$ is 4.5 − 2.75, or 1.75 units.

We can establish an analogous method for determining the measure of an angle by using a measuring device of a different form. The *degree* is the unit commonly used for measuring an angle. The unit called the degree is so chosen that the measure of a right angle is 90. Just as we assign numbers that represent units of linear measure to points in a number line, so we can assign numbers that represent degrees to rays that are included

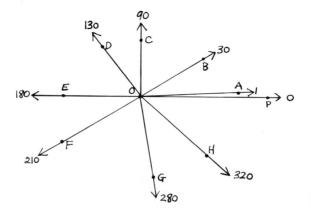

in the same plane. In the illustration at the bottom of page 372, we have used the degree as a unit of measure to assign numbers to the rays. All of the rays have a common endpoint, point O, and they are all included in the same plane.

We choose $\overrightarrow{OP}$ as the starting ray, assign the number 0 to it, and continue to assign numbers to the rays in a counterclockwise direction. To find the measure of an angle, we can use the difference of the numbers assigned to the rays in the same way that we used the difference of coördinates in a number line to find the measure of a segment. Because zero is assigned to $\overrightarrow{OP}$ and 1 is assigned to $\overrightarrow{OA}$, the measure in degrees of $\angle AOP$ is $1 - 0$, or 1. Similarly, the measure of $\angle DOP$ is $130 - 0$, or 130; the measure of $\angle COE$ is $180 - 90$, or 90; and so on.

Notice that our picture contains only a few of the rays in the plane that have point O as their common endpoint. Obviously, we could not show all of the rays, since there are infinitely many of them. If we had shown the ray associated with every degree, we would have shown 360 rays, and the ray associated with 360 would have been the same ray as $\overrightarrow{OP}$.

The measure of an angle need not be limited to a natural number, but may be any positive real number between 0 and 360. Thus, between $\overrightarrow{OP}$ and $\overrightarrow{OA}$, we could (at least theoretically) have located rays associated with $\frac{1}{4}$, $\frac{1}{2}$, .6, and so on. Note that, if the measure of an angle is 180 degrees, then the two rays form a straight line. In our discussion of angles, we will usually exclude angles with a measure of 180 degrees.

You probably made use of a protractor like the one pictured below when you studied geometry. Note that the scale on this protractor begins with 0 and ends with 180 and that numerals are shown at ten-degree

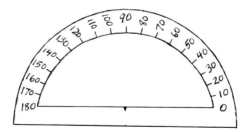

intervals. You can see how the scale on the protractor is derived from the idea of numbers associated with rays in a plane as shown in the illustration on page 372. This is analogous to the way the scale on a rule or a tape measure is derived from the idea of coördinates in a number line.

Now that we have seen how angles may be measured, we are ready to consider the relation between the number of sides a polygon has and the sum of the measures of its angles. You probably remember that the sum of the measures in degrees of the angles of a triangle is 180. Perhaps you were convinced of this fact by some device such as that shown below.

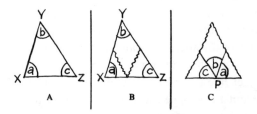

In picture A, we show a triangle with the vertices of the angles labeled X, Y, and Z. The letters a, b, and c represent the measures in degrees of the three angles of triangle XYZ. Then we "tear" the triangle into pieces, as shown in picture B. Finally, we arrange the portions of the triangle so that the angles all meet at a single point P and so that a segment is formed, as shown in picture C. If you look again at the illustration on page 373, you will see that "angle" EOP, whose two sides form a straight line, has a measure in degrees of 180. Such an "angle" sometimes is referred to as a "straight angle." Because the angles of the triangle pictured above can be fitted together so that a "straight angle" is formed, we conclude that $a + b + c = 180$; that is, the sum of the measures in degrees of the angles of the triangle is 180.

Since a triangle is a polygon with 3 sides, we know that the sum of the measures in degrees of the angles of a three-sided polygon is 180. But what about a polygon of 4 sides, or 8 sides, or n sides? Can we develop a generalization that will enable us to determine the sum of the measures of the angles of a polygon whenever we know how many sides the polygon has?

Let us first consider a polygon with 4 sides, like quadrilateral ABCD pictured below. Notice that the quadrilateral is separated into two triangles

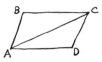

by diagonal AC. (A *diagonal* of a polygon is a segment determined by any two vertices that are not endpoints of the same side of the polygon. Thus, in quadrilateral ABCD, vertices A and C and vertices B and D determine diagonals of the quadrilateral.)

Diagonal AC separates angle BAD of the quadrilateral into two angles, one in each of the triangles; and it also separates angle BCD of the quadrilateral into two angles, one in each triangle. The sum of the measures of the two angles formed at vertex A is equal to the measure of angle BAD; similarly, the sum of the measures of the two angles formed at vertex C is equal to the measure of angle BCD. We know that the sum of the measures in degrees of the angles of each triangle is 180; so the sum of the measures in degrees of the angles of the quadrilateral is 2×180, or 360.

A polygon with 5 sides (a *pentagon*) can be separated into three triangles by drawing two of its diagonals, as shown in picture A below. The measures of the angles of the three triangles together make up the measures of the angles of the pentagon. This is so because one of the angles of the pentagon has been separated into three angles and two other angles of the pentagon have been separated into two angles in forming the angles of the three triangles. Hence, the sum of the measures in degrees of the angles of the pentagon must be 3×180, or 540. In picture B, we have used a similar procedure to separate the *hexagon*, which is a polygon with 6 sides, into four triangles. Because the hexagon can be separated into four triangles in this fashion, we know that the sum of the measures in degrees of the angles is equal to 4×180, or 720.

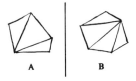

A   B

Let us summarize the results we have obtained so far to see if a pattern is evident.

NUMBER OF SIDES OF POLYGON	SUM OF MEASURES IN DEGREES OF THE ANGLES
3	1×180, OR 180
4	2×180, OR 360
5	3×180, OR 540
6	4×180, OR 720

In each case, we see that the sum of the measures of the angles is equal to the product of 180 and $n - 2$, where n represents the number of sides. We can assume that the same pattern will continue and that the sum of the measures of the angles of a polygon with 20 sides, for example, will be equal to the product of 18 (or $20 - 2$) and 180. More generally, if n represents the number of sides of a polygon of n sides, the sum of the measures of the angles of the polygon must be equal to $(n - 2) \times 180$.

326 Find a formula for the sum of the measures of the interior angles of a concave polygon of n sides. (A concave polygon is a simple polygon that is not convex, like the ones pictured below.)

327 A wheel makes 150 revolutions per minute. Describe the speed of a given point on the wheel first in terms of degrees per minute, then in terms of degrees per second, and finally in terms of degrees per hour.

We can use the generalization we developed in the preceding example to help solve another problem concerning polygons. In this example, we will be concerned with *regular* polygons. A regular polygon is one whose sides all have the same linear measure and whose angles all have the same angular measure. As you probably recall, a regular triangle may be called either an equilateral or an equiangular triangle; a regular quadrilateral is called a square. Several regular polygons are pictured below. Of course, the formula developed in the preceding example concerning the sum of the

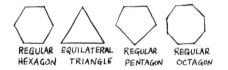

REGULAR   EQUILATERAL   REGULAR   REGULAR
HEXAGON   TRIANGLE   PENTAGON   OCTAGON

measures of the angles of a polygon of n sides applies to regular polygons as well as to those that are not regular.

Our next problem is to determine which kinds of regular polygons can be arranged as the squares in the picture below are arranged. Note that all of the squares have vertex X in common and that each pair of adjacent squares—A and B, B and C, C and D, and D and A—has a common side.

We want now to decide if any of the other kinds of regular polygons can be arranged in this way so that all of them have one vertex in common and each pair of adjacent polygons has one side in common. In other words, we want to arrange a certain number of regular polygons so that the polygons and their interiors fill the plane about a point. We can make an observation about the example we have illustrated that may give us a clue. The measure in degrees of each angle of a square is 90, since the sum of the measures of the angles of a quadrilateral is 360 and the four angles of the square all have the same measure. So each of the four angles with point X as a vertex has a measure in degrees of 90, and the sum of the measures of these four angles is 360. It seems that the sum of the measures in degrees of the angles that have a common vertex must be equal to 360.

Let us now use this idea in connection with some other kinds of regular polygons. Earlier in this section, we found that the sum of the measures in degrees of the angles of a polygon of n sides is equal to $(n - 2) \times 180$. The number of angles in a polygon is equal to the number of sides; hence, a polygon with n sides also has n angles. Because the angles of a regular polygon all have the same measure, each angle of a regular polygon with n angles has as its measure

Sum of measures of angles of polygons, page 375

$$\frac{(n - 2) \times 180}{n}.$$

If we replace the n in this formula by each of the numbers 3, 4, 5, 6, and so on, we will find the measure of each angle of the regular polygon with the given number of sides. The results are given for the regular polygons with 3 through 9 sides in the following table.

REGULAR POLYGON	MEASURE IN DEGREES OF EACH ANGLE
TRIANGLE	60
SQUARE	90
PENTAGON	108
HEXAGON	120
SEPTAGON	$128\frac{4}{7}$
OCTAGON	135
NONAGON	140

Notice that, as the number of sides increases, the measure of each angle also increases. In fact, as n is replaced by greater and greater numbers, the measure in degrees of each angle of the regular polygon gets closer and closer to 180. For example, the measure in degrees of each angle of a regular polygon of 20 sides is 174; and the measure of each angle of a regular polygon with 90 sides is 176.

We now return to the original problem concerning the kinds of regular polygons that can be placed so that the polygons and their interiors fill the plane about a single point. So far, we have decided that the sum of the measures in degrees of all the angles that have the given point as their vertex must be equal to 360. Since each angle in a regular polygon has the same measure, this means that the measure of one angle must be a factor of 360. In other words, the set of prime factors of the measure of each angle in a regular polygon must be a subset of the prime factors of 360. Prime factors page 216

To consider a specific example, can a certain number of equilateral triangles be arranged in such a way that all the plane about a single point is filled? The measure in degrees of each angle of an equilateral triangle is 60. Now $360 = 2 \cdot 2 \cdot 2 \cdot 3 \cdot 3 \cdot 5$, and $60 = 2 \cdot 2 \cdot 3 \cdot 5$. Since the prime factors of 60 form a subset of the prime factors of 360, we should be able to arrange a certain number of equilateral triangles so that they all have a common vertex and so that each pair of adjacent triangles has a common side. Furthermore, since $360 \div 60 = 6$, we ought to be able to do this with 6 equilateral triangles. As you can see from the following illustration, it is possible to do this.

We already know that four squares can be arranged according to our requirements. This is verified by the fact that $90 = 2 \cdot 3 \cdot 3 \cdot 5$, and, hence, the prime factors of 90 form a subset of the prime factors of 360.

Next, let us see whether or not a certain number of regular pentagons can be arranged in this way. From the table on page 377, we see that each angle of a regular pentagon has a measure in degrees of 108. Now $108 = 2 \cdot 2 \cdot 3 \cdot 3 \cdot 3$; hence, the prime factors of 108 are not a subset of the prime factors of 360. Therefore, we conclude that regular pentagons cannot be arranged in this way.

What about regular hexagons? Each angle of a regular hexagon has a measure in degrees of 120, and $120 = 2 \cdot 2 \cdot 2 \cdot 3 \cdot 5$. Thus, we should be able to arrange a certain number of regular hexagons so that they fill the space about a single point. It is left as an exercise for you to make an illustration showing this arrangement.

From the information given in the table on page 377, it should be apparent that none of the regular polygons having more than 6 sides can be arranged so that each of the polygons has a common vertex with all the other polygons and so that all pairs of adjacent polygons have a common side. First of all, $128\frac{4}{7}$, which is the measure in degrees of each angle of a septagon, cannot be expressed as the product of natural numbers. Second, the prime factors of 135, which is the measure in degrees of each angle of an octagon, are 5, 3, 3, 3. These factors do not form a subset of the prime factors of 360. You should determine the prime factors of 140, which is the measure in degrees of each angle of a nonagon, and verify that they do not form a subset of the prime factors of 360.

In this section we have considered several problems from Euclidean plane geometry that should be of interest to you. With these examples, we have tried to give you an idea of how generalizations can be arrived at by looking at several specific examples and then making an "educated guess" about what must be true for the general case. If geometry is approached in such a spirit, it can be much more interesting and enjoyable—and, in the long run, more profitable—for the elementary-school pupil.

328 Suppose that a regular polygon has the number of sides named in each of the following exercises. In each case, find the measure of an angle of the regular polygon.

a 10   c 50   e 180
b 25   d 100   f 1000

329 Suppose that a regular polygon has more than 1000 sides. The measure of each angle of the polygon must be between what two numbers?

330 Make an illustration to show how regular hexagons can be arranged so that the space about a given point is filled.

331 How many triangles are determined by 6 points, no 3 of which are collinear? By 10 points, no 3 of which are collinear? By n such points?

332 Let a, b, and c represent the lengths of the sides of a triangle. What relation must exist among a, b, and c?

Ideas from topology

In the preceding section we considered several problems from Euclidean geometry. The simple closed curves with which we worked either remained in one location in the plane or, if we thought of "moving them about," their size and shape remained the same. This kind of geometry is sometimes called the geometry of rigid motion, since it is assumed that figures can be moved about in the plane, or even transferred from one plane to another, without altering or destroying the properties we wish to investigate. It is possible, however, to examine what happens to geometric figures when their shapes or sizes are altered by "stretching" or "shrinking" or "twisting," but not by "tearing." If we imagine the plane figures as drawn on a rubber sheet that can be stretched and the solid figures as made of flexible material so that they can be squeezed or flattened out, then we can see which of the geometric properties of the figures are altered and which remain the same. The study of the properties of figures that remain unchanged under such circumstances is included in a branch of geometry called *topology*. More colloquially, topology has sometimes been referred to as "rubber sheet" geometry.

As an example of a simple geometric problem in topology, let us consider the two intersecting circles with their chords, shown in picture A below. Suppose that the plane in which these two circles are located has the characteristics of a rubber sheet that can be pulled and stretched. Picture B shows the figures that might result if the sheet is stretched in a certain way.

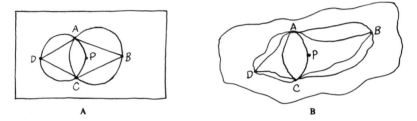

| A | B |

We know that the circles shown in picture A have certain properties that we can study, such as circumference, area, measure of radius, and so on. But what can we say about these circles after they have been distorted as in picture B? Certainly, the figures that were circles are no longer circles, and the circumferences and areas of the figures must have changed. The chords, like AD and CB, are no longer segments, but have become curves. The angles with vertex D and vertex B have changed in size. You might begin to think that nothing has remained the same and that there is no point in comparing the two pictures. However, there are some relations that have *not* changed (or have remained invariant). For example, the two segments that intersect at point D have become two curves that intersect at D; likewise, the two segments that intersect at B have become two curves that intersect at the same point. Furthermore, it is true for both pictures that, if you trace a path from point P to point D, for example, your path must include point A or point C, no matter how it is traced. Also, the number of curves that meet at any point is the same in both pictures.

All of the problems we will discuss in this section will involve examination of the properties of geometric figures that remain invariant no matter how the figures are changed in size or shape.

As the first problem, let us see what properties or relations we can determine for figures like the cube pictured on page 381. Figures whose faces are all plane surfaces, such as cubes or other prisms and pyramids, are called *polyhedra*. The Greek word from which "polyhedron" is derived literally means "having many bases or sides." Now let us imagine that this

cube is made of some flexible material such as foam rubber so that it can be distorted as shown in the following illustrations.

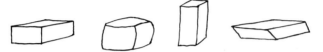

What properties of the cube can we discover that have not been changed by any of the distortions? It is apparent that the volume has been changed by twisting and flattening the cube. Also, it is certain that the surface area has changed. Further, the edges of the cube are no longer segments, the faces are no longer square in shape, and the edges are not perpendicular to each other. In fact, the "cube" is no longer a cube. However, if you again examine the original cube and the figures after distortion, you will see that the *number* of faces, the *number* of edges, and the *number* of vertices have not been altered by any of the distortions. This suggests that we might be able to make some generalization about the relations among the numbers of faces, edges, and vertices of a cube or some other polyhedron.

As we have done with earlier problems in this chapter, let us consider several examples, see whether or not we can formulate a generalization based upon these examples, and then check to see if the generalization holds for other examples. We will use the polyhedra pictured below to see what relations, if any, we can establish among the numbers of faces, vertices, and edges of these polyhedra. Note that some of the polyhedra are distorted, while others are not.

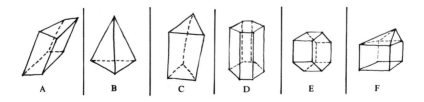

The table that follows summarizes the information concerning the numbers of faces (F), vertices (V), and edges (E) for each of these polyhedra.

POLYHEDRON	F	V	E
A	6	8	12
B	4	4	6
C	5	6	9
D	8	12	18
E	8	6	12
F	9	9	16

As we look at the information given in the table, no special relationship is immediately apparent. For example, it is not the case that, as the number of faces increases, the number of vertices or edges increases. Thus, polyhedron E, which has 8 faces, has only 6 vertices; while polyhedron A, which has 6 faces, has 8 vertices. Similarly, both polyhedra A and E have 12 edges, although A has 6 faces and E has 8 faces. Neither does an increase in the number of vertices necessarily imply an increase in the number of edges, as you can see by comparing polyhedra A and E. Hence, there is no pattern that relates an increase in the number of vertices or in the number of edges of a polyhedron to an increase in the number of faces of the polyhedron.

Suppose we now investigate the possibility of a relation between the sum of two of the numbers and the third number named in each row of the table. For polyhedron A, the sum of the faces and vertices is $6 + 8$, or 14. This is 2 more than the number of edges that polyhedron A has. This result does not seem promising, but let us see what happens for polyhedron B. In this case, $F + V = 4 + 4$, or 8, which again is 2 more than the number of edges. With this encouraging result, we check all of the other entries in our table to find that the sum of the number of faces and the number of vertices is 2 more than the number of edges in every case. We might suspect that the following generalization holds for all polyhedra: If F represents the number of faces; V, the number of vertices; and E, the number of edges, then

$$F + V = E + 2.$$

The first illustration on page 383 shows 3 more polyhedra, together with a table summarizing the numbers of faces, vertices, and edges for each of the polyhedra. If you check these three polyhedra, you will find that the formula $F + V = E + 2$ does hold for them. You might wish to sketch several polyhedra different from those we have considered to see if the relation still holds.

The formula

$$F + V = E + 2$$

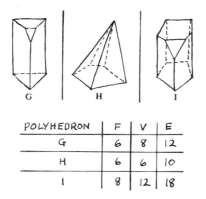

POLYHEDRON	F	V	E
G	6	8	12
H	6	6	10
I	8	12	18

is called *Euler's formula* after a German mathematician of the eighteenth century. Leonhard Euler produced an enormous amount of original work in mathematics and was one of the first mathematicians to consider problems of the kind discussed in this section. It is possible to prove Euler's formula for all polyhedra, but the proof requires certain ideas that are beyond the scope of this book.*

333 Check Euler's formula for each of the following polyhedra.
  a A cube with one corner cut off
  b A triangular prism with the top cut off at a slant
  c A pyramid with a square base and the top cut off
  d A pyramid with a triangular base and the top cut off
334 If a prism has *n* lateral faces (faces different from the two bases), how many faces in all does it have? It has how many vertices? How many edges does the prism have? Does Euler's formula hold for a prism with *n* lateral faces?
335 The figure represented below could be called a "square doughnut." Does Euler's formula hold for this figure?

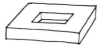

The next problem in topology that we will discuss is related to a kind of puzzle that you may have tried to solve when you were a child. You may have seen a diagram like the one at the top of page 384 in which you were

---

* You might be interested in reading G. Polya's *Induction and Analogy in Mathematics*, Chapter III, for a more complete treatment of this problem. Item 58 of Bibliography

to begin at some point of intersection in the figure and trace a path around the curve. The "rules of the game" required you to trace the curve without lifting your pencil from the curve and without tracing any segment or portion of a segment more than once, although you could pass through a point of intersection as often as necessary. You will find that it is not possible to trace this figure under the requirements that have been set up. We will now find out why it is not possible to do so.

Diagrams like those below, which consist of a number of intersecting segments or curves, are called *networks*. The points of intersection are called vertices and are classified as either even or odd, depending upon

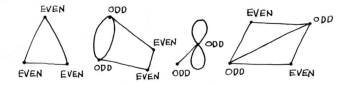

the number of curves that intersect at the vertex. If a curve leads away from one vertex and back to the same vertex without intersecting any other vertex, it will be counted as two curves. A *path* in a network is a set of one or more curves that can be traced without lifting the pencil from the network and without retracing a curve of the network.

We will develop a method for determining if networks such as the simple ones pictured above can be traced in a single path that includes all of the curves in the network or not. The observations we make for these simple examples will also apply to more complicated examples, since the same basic principles are involved.

For example, suppose that the following diagrams represent floor plans of houses. In the diagrams, the rectangles represent rooms, and the double marks are used to indicate doorways. The problem is to "tour each

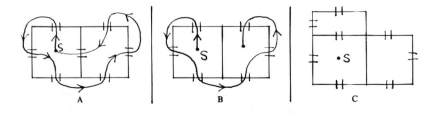

house" by tracing a continuous path that goes through each doorway just once from some point S in one of the rooms back to the same point.

The paths are shown for diagrams A and B. In diagram A, we see that it is possible to tour the house and return to point S by going through each doorway just once. In diagram B, it is not possible to tour the house and return to point S by going through each doorway just once, although it is possible to begin at point S and make a tour through the house in which you go through each doorway just once and end at a point different from S. (We have shown only one of the possible paths in diagram B; but, if you check the others, you will find that none of them will bring you back to S.) Neither is it possible to trace a path from point S, through each doorway, and back to point S in diagram C. In fact, it is not even possible to trace a path from point S through each doorway just once that ends in a room different from the one in which point S is located. You should check several possible paths for diagram C to convince yourself of this fact. What are the characteristics of these house plans that affect the results of our attempts to trace a path? Can we arrive at some generalization concerning the number of doorways or the arrangement of the doorways that will enable us to decide without having to test each possibility? As you can see, there are quite a few possible paths that would have to be checked for diagram C, and a more complicated plan could make the task quite tedious.

The problem concerning the floor plans can be explained as a problem involving networks; and, as you will see, the generalizations we make about networks in the following pages can be applied to the floor plans.

Another problem that can be treated as a network problem is one that has a long history in mathematics—the Königsberg bridge problem. This problem was first posed as a puzzle in the eighteenth century and was eventually explained by Euler, whom we have already mentioned in connection with the formula for polyhedra. A part of the city of Königsberg, Germany, was located on a small island situated at the fork of a river that runs through the city. There were seven bridges connecting the island and the different parts of the mainland, as shown in the illustration below.

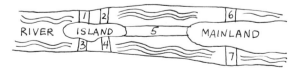

The problem was to determine whether or not a resident of Königsberg could walk around the mainland and the island along a route that would cross each of the 7 bridges just once. No one was ever able to devise such a route, and, eventually, Euler was able to give an explanation of why it is not possible. His explanation can best be given in terms of networks and paths around networks.

Before we show how the bridge picture can be translated into a network diagram, we will consider some simpler examples of networks. Our problem is to determine if a network that can be traced in a single path has certain properties that distinguish such a network from one that cannot be traced in a single path. Notice that this is properly a problem in topology since, as we have seen earlier, distortions that result from stretching or shrinking do not change the number of vertices or the number of curves that meet at a vertex.

We will consider the networks shown below one by one to see what relation exists among all of those networks that can be traced by a single

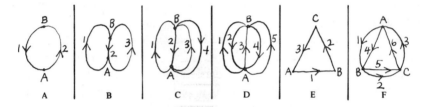

path. A glance at network A reveals that this network can be traced in a single path that begins at one of the vertices and ends at the same vertex. Such a path will be called a *closed* path. What are the characteristics of this network? Network A has two vertices, with two curves meeting at each vertex; thus, A is a network with two vertices, both of which are even. Next, consider network B, which is a network with two vertices, both of which are odd. This network can be traced in a single path that begins with one vertex and ends with the other. Such a path will be called an *open* path. However, network B cannot be traced in a single *closed* path, since you cannot return to the starting point without retracing some portion of the network.

Network C is again a network with two vertices, both of which are even; this time, 4 curves meet at each vertex. As the arrows indicate, this network can be traced in a single closed path. We can now tentatively formulate a generalization about networks with two vertices, both of which are even.

Any network with exactly two vertices that are both even
can be traced in a single closed path.

If you reflect for a moment, you will see why this is so. If a vertex is even, you can always group the curves at the vertex in pairs so that one curve in each pair leads you away from the vertex and the other curve leads you back to the vertex.

Network D, like B, has two odd vertices; this time, 5 curves meet at each vertex. The results for D are the same as those for B; that is, it is possible to trace network D in a single *open* path, but it is not possible to do so in a single *closed* path. Thus, we form a second generalization that seems reasonable from the examples considered so far.

> Any network with exactly two vertices that are both odd
> can be traced in a single open path
> but cannot be traced in a single closed path.

336 Explain why a network with exactly two vertices cannot have one even vertex and one odd vertex.

Now that we have examined networks with exactly two vertices and made generalizations about these networks, we next consider networks with 3 vertices. Networks E and F in the illustration on page 386 each have 3 even vertices. In network E, 2 curves meet at each vertex; in network F, 4 curves meet at each vertex. If you examine these networks carefully and follow the paths indicated by the arrows, you will find that each of them can be traced in a single closed path. Thus, you assume that the following generalization holds for networks with three even vertices.

> Any network with exactly three vertices that are all even
> can be traced in a single closed path.

So far, we have found it reasonable to assume that every network with exactly 2 vertices that are both even and every network with exactly 3 vertices that are all even can be traced in a single closed path. We might now begin to suspect that the following generalization holds for any network, all of whose vertices are even.

> If all the vertices of a given network with *n* vertices
> are even, then the network can be traced
> in a single closed path.

Network G shown below has 5 vertices, all of which are even, since 4 curves meet at vertices A, B, D, and E, and 6 curves meet at vertex C. If

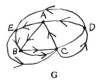

G

you trace the path indicated by the arrows, you will see that this network can be traced in a single closed path. Hence, the generalization just given does hold for this example. You may want to draw several other networks, all of whose vertices are even, to help convince yourself that all such networks can be traced in a single closed path. Even though we have not proved that every network that has only even vertices can be traced in a single closed path, we can see why this is a sensible assumption. As we mentioned earlier, if a vertex is even, then it is always possible to use pairs of curves to trace a path away from and back to the vertex without having to retrace any of the curves.

Let us now see if we can come to any conclusion concerning networks with a certain number of even and a certain number of odd vertices. If we think about this for a moment, it seems that any network that can be traced in a single open path can have only two odd vertices. This is so because the vertex we begin with and the one we end with can both be odd, but all other vertices must be even so that we can form pairs of arcs that lead to and from each vertex. In the networks shown below, networks H and I can be traced in a single open path, as indicated by the arrows, because each of these networks has just two odd vertices. If you experiment a bit with network J, you will see that it cannot be traced in a single path, since it has more than 2 odd vertices.

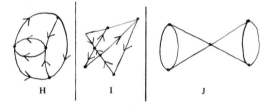

H   I   J

Our next generalization concerning networks can be expressed as follows.

A network that can be traced in a single path
cannot have more than two odd vertices.

337 Explain why the network shown on page 384 cannot be traced in a single path.

338 "Translate" each of the floor plans on page 384 into a network by using the exterior of the house and each room as a vertex and the doorways as curves. Then explain why each of the networks can or cannot be traced in a single path.

We can now return to the Königsberg bridge problem and use our generalization about networks to give an answer to this problem. The illustration on page 385 can be represented as a network by using each region of land as a vertex of the network and each bridge as a curve. Below, we have repeated the original diagram and then shown how this diagram can be translated into a network. The labels on the curves and vertices in the network correspond to those on the bridges and the regions of land in the original diagram.

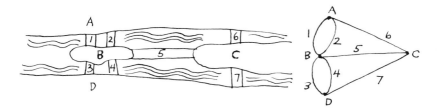

Notice that the network has 4 vertices, all of which are odd. Thus, by our fifth generalization about networks, we know that this network cannot be traced in a single path, and, consequently, the residents of Königsberg could not plan a route whereby they crossed every bridge exactly once.

339 Explain why it is not possible to draw a network with exactly 3 odd vertices.

340 For each of the following networks, first tell whether or not it can be traced in a single closed path. Then tell whether or not it can be traced in a single open path.

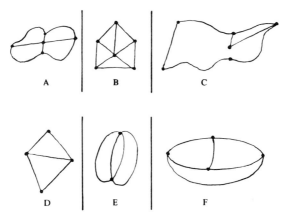

341 Translate each of the following floor plans into a network by considering the exterior and each room to be a vertex and each doorway to be a curve.

Then determine whether or not the network can be traced in a single path, either open or closed.

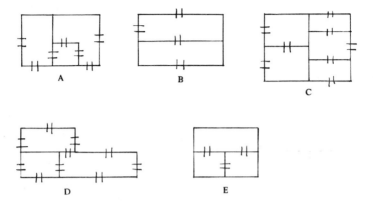

342 For each curve pictured below, determine the number of odd vertices and the number of even vertices. Do the generalizations we made concerning networks and paths around them (see pages 386, 387, and 388) hold for these curves?

In this section, we have considered a selection of problems from the branch of geometry that is called topology.* All of the properties of figures that we have discussed are those properties that remain invariant no matter how the figures are distorted by twisting or stretching, but not by tearing. We spent some time on networks and made several generalizations about them. Of course, we did not make all the generalizations it is possible to make about networks, but those that we did make enabled us to solve some interesting problems. The ideas and problems we discussed in this section were chosen for a special reason. They were chosen because, on the basis of two or three specific examples, we were able to make guesses about relations that we could check later. In other words, they were problems in which our intuition served us well. We feel that problems

* Johnson, D. A., *Topology: The Rubber-Sheet Geometry*. This booklet covers many of the interesting puzzle problems related to topology. An intuitive approach is used throughout. Item 59 of Bibliography

such as these could be quite useful in helping children develop their "geometric imaginations."

CONCLUSION

In the section on Euclidean geometry, we considered properties of figures —such as size and shape—that are not altered by rigid motion in a plane or from one plane to another. In the section on topology, we considered properties of figures—such as numbers of vertices and numbers of intersecting segments or curves—that are not changed by distortions resulting from shrinking, stretching, or twisting. There are other branches of geometry from which interesting problems like those discussed here could be obtained. For example, many problems that can be solved in an intuitive way are found in projective geometry, which is the study of the properties of figures that are not changed when the figures are projected from one plane to another. Similarly, finite geometries, in which the set of points that make up space is finite, offer some problems that can be solved by an intuitive or imaginative approach.

In this chapter, we have only begun to suggest the kinds of geometric ideas that might be taught informally and interestingly in the elementary school. We hope that what we have presented here will encourage you to look further and to use your imagination in selecting topics from geometry to interest the elementary school child.

CHAPTER QUIZ

1 What relation holds between the number of vertices and the number of sides a convex polygon has? Does this relation also hold for concave polygons?

2 Show how to establish a one-to-one correspondence between two perpendicular segments that have a common endpoint.

3 Suppose that you were to draw 25 lines, no two of which were parallel. How many points would be needed to determine these lines?

4 Suppose that two of the 25 lines mentioned in exercise 3 were parallel. How many points would be needed to determine these 25 lines?

5 A circle and its interior can be divided into separate areas or regions by segments, called *chords*, whose endpoints intersect the circle. Find the greatest number of regions determined by 5 chords.

6 Determine the number of diagonals that can be drawn in a polygon of n sides. You should begin by considering several specific cases in sequence. Then look for a pattern that you can assume will hold in general.

7 Explain why the measure in degrees of an angle of a convex polygon cannot be equal to or greater than 180.

8 Explain why you would not expect to find floor tile in the shape of a pentagon or an octagon. Which polygonal shapes would you expect to find?

9 One plane separates space into two regions. One region consists of all the points on one side of the plane; the other region consists of all the points on the opposite side of the plane. The points in the plane do not belong to either region. Two planes that are not parallel separate space into how many regions? Three planes that intersect in a line separate space into how many regions? Use these examples to form a generalization about the number of regions of space determined by a given number of planes that have a common line of intersection. Then check your generalization for several more cases.

10 For each of the following exercises, if it is possible to do so, draw a network having the given number of vertices and the given number of curves that can be traced in a closed path.

A Three even vertices and three curves

B Three even vertices and six curves

C Three even vertices and five curves

D Four even vertices and six curves

E Five even vertices and two odd vertices

F Six odd vertices

11 The diagram below represents a map. Think of the regions labeled with capital letters as countries, the curves as boundaries, and the intersections of the boundaries as "corners" of the countries. Investigate the relation among the number of countries C, the number of boundaries B, and the number of corners K. Express this relation as a formula.

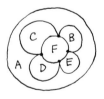

SUPPLEMENTARY READINGS

Abbott, E. A., *Flatland*. An interesting story about life in one-, two-, three-, and four-dimensional "worlds." Item 60 of Bibliography

Courant, R., and Robbins, H., *What Is Mathematics?*, Chapters 3, 4, and 5. Excellent material (but somewhat sophisticated) on geometric constructions, transformations, projective geometry, non-Euclidean geometry, and topology. Item 61 of Bibliography

Johnson, Donovan A., *Curves in Space*. This is an excellent booklet containing material on linkages, conic sections, cycloids, and curve stitching. Item 62 of Bibliography

Johnson, Donovan A., *Paper Folding for the Mathematics Class*. This booklet shows how it is possible to perform the constructions of plane Euclidean geometry by folding paper. It also includes procedures for constructing regular polyhedra. Item 63 of Bibliography

Montague, H. F. and Montgomery, M. D., *The Significance of Mathematics*, Chapter 1. This reference includes many examples of patterns in geometry. Item 64 of Bibliography

Norton, M. Scott, *Geometric Constructions*. This book illustrates not only the common geometric constructions, but also some of the more involved figures, too—for example, the nine-point circle, the golden section, and snowflake designs. Also discussed are such famous impossible problems as trisecting an angle, squaring the circle, and duplicating the cube. Item 65 of Bibliography

Ravielli, A., *An Adventure in Geometry*. The excellent illustrations in this book make it a good source of enrichment material for instruction dealing with geometric ideas. The book also contains some very fine examples of symmetry and shapes in nature. Item 66 of Bibliography

Schnell, L. H. and Crawford, M. G., *Plane Geometry: A Clear Thinking Approach*, Chapter 16. This chapter contains some very interesting material on reasoning by analogy and the fourth dimension. Item 67 of Bibliography

Bibliography

1 Price, G. Baley. "Progress in Mathematics and Its Implications for Schools," *The Revolution in School Mathematics*. Washington, D.C.: National Council of Teachers of Mathematics, 1961.

2 Van Engen, H. "Twentieth Century Mathematics in the Elementary School," *The Arithmetic Teacher*, VI (March 1959).

3 National Council of Teachers of Mathematics. *Instruction in Arithmetic*. Twenty-Fifth Yearbook. Washington, D.C.: National Council of Teachers of Mathematics, 1960.

4 "Mathematics," *Life Science Library*. Edited by David Benjamin. New York: Time Incorporated, 1963.

5 National Council of Teachers of Mathematics. *Learning of Mathematics: Its Theory and Practice*. Twenty-First Yearbook. Washington, D.C.: National Council of Teachers of Mathematics, 1953.

6 National Council of Teachers of Mathematics. *The Growth of Mathematical Ideas: Grades K-12*. Twenty-Fourth Yearbook. Washington, D.C.: National Council of Teachers of Mathematics, 1959.

7 Hartung, M. L. "Formalism in Arithmetic Programs," *The Arithmetic Teacher*, IX (November 1962).

8 Banks, J. Houston. *Learning and Teaching Arithmetic*. Boston: Allyn and Bacon, Inc., 1959.

9 Marks, John L.; Purdy, D. Richard; and Kinney, Lucien B. *Teaching Arithmetic for Understanding*. New York: McGraw-Hill Book Company, Inc., 1958.

10 Van Engen, H. "Which Way Arithmetic?" *The Arithmetic Teacher*, II (December 1955).

11 Wheat, Harry G. "The Fallacy of Social Arithmetic," *The Mathematics Teacher*, XXXIX (January 1946).

12 Evenson, A. B. *Modern Mathematics: Introductory Concepts and Their Implications*. Chicago: Scott, Foresman and Co., 1962.

13 Hamilton, Norman, and Landin, Joseph. *Set Theory: The Structure of Arithmetic*. Boston: Allyn and Bacon, Inc., 1961.

14 Breuer, Joseph. *Introduction to the Theory of Sets*. Translated by Howard Fehr. Englewood Cliffs, N.J.: Prentice-Hall, Inc., 1958.

15 Johnson, Donovan A., and Glenn, William H. *Sets, Sentences, and Operations*. St. Louis: Webster Publishing Company, 1960.

16 School Mathematics Study Group. *Mathematics for the Elementary School, Grade 4*. New Haven, Conn.: Yale University Press, 1963.

17 National Council of Teachers of Mathematics. *Insights into Modern Mathematics*. Twenty-Third Yearbook. Washington, D.C.: National Council of Teachers of Mathematics, 1957.

18 Report of the Commission on Mathematics. *Appendices*. New York: College Entrance Examination Board, 1959.

19 Tarski, Alfred. *Introduction to Logic*. New York: Oxford University Press, 1946.

20 University of Chicago College Mathematics Staff. *Concepts and Structure of Mathematics*. Chicago: University of Chicago Press, 1954.

21 Van Engen, H., *et al*. *Seeing Through Mathematics, Book 1*. Chicago: Scott, Foresman and Co., 1962.

22 Marston, Howard. *Worktext in Modern Mathematics*. Evanston, Ill.: Harper & Row, Publishers, 1962.

23 Levi, Howard. *Elements of Algebra*. New York: Chelsea Publishing Co., 1954.

24 Russell, Bertrand. *Introduction to Mathematical Philosophy*. London: George Allen and Unwin, Ltd., 1919.

25 Kerschner, R. B., and Wilcox, L. R. *The Anatomy of Mathematics*. New York: The Ronald Press Company, 1950.

26 Peterson, John A., and Hashisaki, Joseph. *Theory of Arithmetic*. New York: John Wiley and Sons, Inc., 1963.

27 Norton, M. Scott. *Finite Mathematical Systems*. St. Louis: Webster Publishing Company, 1963.

28 Sawyer, W. W. *Prelude to Mathematics*. Baltimore: Penguin Books, Inc., 1955.

29 Freund, John. *A Modern Introduction to Mathematics*. Englewood Cliffs, N.J.: Prentice-Hall, Inc., 1956.

30 Schaaf, W. L. *Basic Concepts of Elementary Mathematics.* New York: John Wiley and Sons, Inc., 1960.

31 Neugebauer, Otto. *The Exact Sciences in Antiquity.* Providence, R.I.: Brown University Press, 1957.

32 Johnson, Donovan A., and Glenn, William H. *Understanding Numeration Systems.* St. Louis: Webster Publishing Co., 1960.

33 Smith, David E.. and Ginsburg, J. *Numbers and Numerals.* Washington, D.C.: National Council of Teachers of Mathematics, 1951.

34 Van Der Waerden, B. L. *Science Awakening: Egyptian, Babylonian, and Greek Mathematics.* Groningen, Holland: P. Noordhoff, Ltd., 1954.

35 Chiera, Edward. *They Wrote on Clay.* Edited by George G. Cameron. Chicago: University of Chicago Press, 1955.

36 Glenn, William H., and Johnson, Donovan A. *Short Cuts in Computing.* St. Louis: Webster Publishing Company, 1961.

37 Johnson, Donovan A., and Glenn, William H. *Computing Devices.* St. Louis: Webster Publishing Company, 1961.

38 Larsen, Harold D., and Ludlow, H. Glenn. *Arithmetic for Colleges.* New York: Macmillan Co., 1963.

39 Swain, Robert L. *Understanding Arithmetic.* New York: Rinehart and Company, 1957.

40 Gardner, Martin. "The Remarkable Lore of Prime Numbers," *Scientific American,* CCX (March 1964).

41 Barnett, I. A. *Some Ideas About Number Theory.* Washington, D.C.: National Council of Teachers of Mathematics, 1961.

42 Bowers, Henry, and Bowers, Joan. *Arithmetical Excursions: An Enrichment of Elementary Mathematics.* New York: Dover Publications, Inc., 1961.

43 School Mathematics Study Group. *Essays on Number Theory.* 2 vols. New Haven, Conn.: Yale University Press, 1960.

44 Ore, Oystein. *Number Theory and Its History.* New York: McGraw-Hill Book Company, 1948.

45 National Council of Teachers of Mathematics. *Topics in Mathematics for Elementary Teachers.* Twenty-Ninth Yearbook. Washington, D.C.: National Council of Teachers of Mathematics, 1964.

46 Smith, David Eugene. *History of Mathematics, Vol. II.* New York: Dover Publications, Inc., 1958.

47 Sawyer, W. W. *Introducing Mathematics I: Vision in Elementary Mathematics.* Baltimore: Penguin Books, 1964.

48 Van Engen, H., *et al. Seeing Through Mathematics, Book 2.* Chicago: Scott, Foresman and Co., 1963.

49 Niven, Ivan. *Numbers: Rational and Irrational.* New York: Random House, 1961.

50 Adler, Irving, and Adler, Ruth. *The New Mathematics.* New York: The John Day Company, 1958.

51 Van Engen, H., *et al. Seeing Through Mathematics, Book 3.* Chicago: Scott, Foresman and Co., 1964.

52 National Council of Teachers of Mathematics. *Emerging Practices in Mathematics Education.* Twenty-Second Yearbook. Washington, D.C.: National Council of Teachers of Mathematics, 1954.

53 Bendick, Jeanne. *How Much and How Many?* New York: McGraw-Hill Book Co., 1947.

54 Johnson, Donovan A., and Glenn, W. H. *The World of Measurement.* St. Louis: Webster Publishing Co., 1961.

55 Lufkin Rule Company. *The Amazing Story of Measurement.* Saginaw, Mich. 1959.

56 Newman, James. *The World of Mathematics.* New York: Simon and Schuster, Inc., 1956.

57 Rassweiler, M., and Harris, J. *Mathematics and Measurement.* Evanston, Ill.: Row, Peterson and Co., 1955.

58 Polya, G. *Induction and Analogy in Mathematics.* Princeton, N.J.: Princeton University Press, 1954.

59 Johnson, D. A., and Glenn, W. H. *Topology: The Rubber Sheet Geometry.* St. Louis: Webster Publishing Co., 1960.

60 Abbott, E. A. *Flatland.* New York: Dover Publications, Inc., 1952.

61 Courant, R., and Robbins, H. *What Is Mathematics?* New York: Oxford University Press, 1941.

62 Johnson, Donovan A. *Curves in Space.* St. Louis: Webster Publishing Co., 1963.

63 ———. *Paper Folding for Mathematics Classes.* Washington, D.C.: National Council of Teachers of Mathematics, 1958.

64 Montague, H. F., and Montgomery, M. D. *The Significance of Mathematics.* Columbus, Ohio: Charles E. Merrill Books, Inc., 1963.

65 Norton, M. Scott. *Geometric Constructions.* St. Louis: Webster Publishing Co., 1963.

66 Ravielli, A. *An Adventure in Geometry.* New York: The Viking Press, 1961.

67 Schnell, L. H., and Crawford, M. G. *Plane Geometry: A Clear Thinking Approach.* New York: McGraw-Hill Book Co., 1953.

Responses

Responses to contextual exercises

The responses to all of the exercises within the chapters appear on pages 399 through 425. The responses for Chapter Quizzes are given on pages 426 through 437. If an exercise requires more than one response, the responses are separated by an asterisk.

1 a The set consisting of the "whole" numbers from 1 through 7.

  b The set consisting of **2,** the square of 2, the cube of 2, and the fourth and fifth powers of 2

  c The set consisting of the last day of the week and the first day of the week

  d The set consisting of the letters of the alphabet that are used as vowels

  e The set consisting of the multiples of 7 that are less than or equal to 35

2 a {Idaho, Illinois, Indiana, Iowa}

  b {4, 6, 8, 10, 12, 14}

  c {1, 4, 9, 16, 25, 36, 49, 64}

  d { }

  e {September, April, June, November}

3 a Yes   **b** No   **c** Yes   **d** Yes

4 One of the ways is:

  B = {2, 4, 6}.   D = {2, 4}.

  C = {2, 4}.   E = {2, 4, 6}.

5 a {Sam, Wayne}, {Sam}, {Wayne}, { }

  b {Nancy, Carl, Ed, Marie}, {Nancy}, {Carl}, {Ed}, {Marie}, {Nancy, Carl}, {Nancy, Ed}, {Nancy, Marie}, {Carl, Ed}, {Carl, Marie}, {Ed, Marie}, {Carl, Ed, Marie}, {Nancy, Ed, Marie}, {Nancy, Carl, Marie}, {Nancy, Carl, Ed}, and { }

6 Proper subsets are {5, 6}, {5, 7}, {6, 7}, {5}, {6}, {7}, and { }. Improper subset is {5, 6, 7}.* A has 8 subsets.

7 A set with n members has 2^n subsets. For example, a set with 1 member has 2^1, or 2, subsets; a set with 2 members has 2^2, or 4, subsets; a set with 3 members has 2^3, or 8, subsets.

8 X = {1, 3, 5}.

  Y = {Mary, John, Henry}.

{ 1,   3,   5 }

    ↓   ↓   ↓

{Mary, John, Henry}

9 X = {1, 5}.

  Y = {Mary, John, Henry, Sue}.

{   1,   5   }

  ↗↖   ↗↖

{Mary, John, Henry, Sue}

10 X = {   1,   10,   100 }.

    ↑   ↑   ↑

Y = {Mr. Smith, Mr. Brown, Mr. Hayes}.

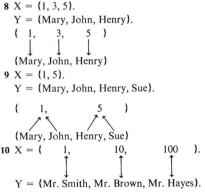

11 a False   **c** False   **e** False
b True   **d** True   **f** True
12 a One answer is K = {Bob, 5}.
b One answer is D = {Bob, 5, pencil,
Sara, the sun, the moon, Plato}.
13 Mapping 1: Many-to-one
Mapping 2: One-to-one and onto
Mapping 3: Many-to-one and onto
Mapping 4: One-to-one
14 Mappings 1 and 2: No
Mappings 3 and 4: Yes
Mappings 5 and 6: No
Mappings 7 and 8: Inverses; not one-to-one
15 a { }   **b** {a, b, c}
c {(Sue, 1), (Sue, 2), (Doris, 1),
(Doris, 2), (Tad, 1), (Tad, 2),
(Tom, 1), (Tom, 2)}
d {(1, Sue), (1, Doris), (1, Tad),
(1, Tom), (2, Sue), (2, Doris),
(2, Tad), (2, Tom)}
e {1, 2}
16 a {1, 3, 5}
b {1, 2, 3, 4, 5, 6, 7, 9}
c { }
d {2, 4, 6}
e {1, 2, 3, 4, 5, 6, 7, 8, 9, 10}
f {1, 3, 5}
17 a Yes
b $Z \cap Y$ or { }
c $Z \cap X$ or {2, 4, 6}
18 Yes * Let C = {1, 2, 3, 4}
and let D = {2, 4, 6}.
$C \cup D$ = {1, 2, 3, 4, 6} and
$D \cup C$ = {2, 4, 6, 1, 3}. Because order can
be disregarded, both $C \cup D$ and $D \cup C$
are equal to {1, 2, 3, 4, 6}. Thus,
$C \cup D = D \cup C$.
19 Yes * Let C = {1, 3, 5, 7} and let
D = {1, 2, 3, 4, 5, 6}. $C \cap D$ = {1, 3, 5} and
$D \cap C$ = {1, 3, 5}. So, $C \cap D = D \cap C$.
20 Yes * Let C = {1, 2} and let D = {1, 2}.
Both $C \times D$ and $D \times C$ are equal to
{(1, 1), (1, 2), (2, 1), (2, 2)}.
Thus, $C \times D = D \times C$. This is true only
when the two sets have the same members or
when one or both sets are the empty set.
21 C = {5, 10, 15}.   D = {5, 10, 15}.
22 a The National Baseball League can be interpreted as a set of teams. The teams themselves are sets of players.

b The Butler family reunion can be interpreted as a set of specific families. The
specific families are sets of people.
c The population of Canada can be interpreted as the set of populations of the
individual provinces. The populations of
the individual provinces can be interpreted
as sets of people.
d The faculty of a university can be interpreted as a set of faculties of specific departments. The faculties of the specific
departments are sets of teachers.
23 a {{ }}
b {1, 2, {1, 2}}
c {{a}, {a, b}, {{a}, {a, b}}}
24 a {0, 1, 2}
b {0, 1, 2, 3}
c {0, 1, 2, 3, 4, 5}
25 a {0, 1, 2}
b {0, 1, 2, 3, 4, 5, 6, 7, 8, 9, 10, 11, 12, 13,
14, 15, 16, 17, 18, 19, 20, 21, 22, 23}
26 a {0, 1, 2, 3, 4, 5, 6, 7, 8, 9, 10, 11}
b {0, 1, 2, 3, 4, 5, 6}
c {0}
d {0, 1, 2, 3, 4, 5, 6, 7}
e {0, 1, 2, 3, 4, 5, 6, 7, 8, 9}
27 A and B have the same number of members.
* n[A] = n[B].
28 R and S do not have the same number of
members. * n[R] is not equal to n[S]. Specifically, you know that n[R] is less than n[S].
29 n[X] = n[Y].
30 a 6   **c** 14   **e** 48   **g** 48
b 8   **d** 14   **f** 0
31 a Infinite   **c** Infinite
b Finite   **d** Finite
32 a { 5, 10, 15, 20, . . .}
↑   ↑   ↑   ↑
{15, 30, 45, 60, . . .}
b { 1,   2,   3,   4, . . .}
↑   ↑   ↑   ↑
{1004, 1005, 1006, 1007, . . .}
33 One example is {$\frac{1}{4}$, $\frac{1}{5}$, $\frac{1}{6}$, $\frac{1}{7}$, . . .}.
34 A: 11 * 135 * 5988
B: 30 * 278 * 11,984
C: 100 * 17,956 * 35,844,169
35 D: $3n - 2$
E: $2n$
F: $2n + 1$

36 A: 8, 10, 12, 14, 16, 18, 20, 22, 24, 26, . . .
B: 0, 3, 8, 15, 24, 35, 48, 63, 80, 99, . . .
C: 0, 2, 6, 12, 20, 30, 42, 56, 72, 90, . . .
D: 0, 0, 0, 0, 0, 0, 0, 0, 0, 0, . . .
37 a 4 **b** 5 **c** 5, 6, 7, and 8
d No members yield true statements.
e 0, 1, 2, 3, 4, and 5
f No members yield true statements.
38 a $3x > 25$. **c** $5x + 12 = 47$.
b $x - 7 < 15$. **d** $x + 11 = 6$.
39 For each x, $x \times 0 = 0$.
40 For each x, $x + x + x + x = 4 \times x$.
41 For each x, $x(x + 1) > x^2$.
42 For each x, $x^2 + (x + 1)^2 < \left(x + (x + 1)\right)^2$.
43 a U **b** A **c** A **d** A **e** A **f** { }
44 { }
45 A * B
46 a $8 + (2 + 34) = (8 + 2) + 34$
$= 10 + 34$
$= 44$.
b $(19 + 42) + 81 = (42 + 19) + 81$
$= 42 + (19 + 81)$
$= 42 + 100$
$= 142$.
c $(22 + 49) + (51 + 33) = 22 + (49 + 51) +$
33
$= 22 + 100 + 33$
$= 22 + 33 + 100$
$= (22 + 33) + 100$
$= 55 + 100$
$= 155$.
d $68 + (33 + 51) + 32 = 68 + 32 +$
$(33 + 51)$
$= (68 + 32) +$
$(33 + 51)$
$= 100 + (33 + 51)$
$= 100 + 84$
$= 184$.
47 b $(a + b) + c = c + (a + b)$. For any two natural numbers a and b, $a + b = b + a$.
c $(a + b) + c = (a + c) + b$. For any three natural numbers a, b, and c, $(a + b) + c = a + (b + c)$. For any two natural numbers a and b, $a + b = b + a$.
e $a + (b + c) = a + (c + b)$. For any two natural numbers a and b, $a + b = b + a$.
f $c + b + a = a + b + c$.
For any three natural numbers a, b, and c, $(a + b) + c = a + (b + c)$. For any two natural numbers a and b, $a + b = b + a$.

48 By the definition of the product of two natural numbers, $n[A] \times n[B] = n[A \times B]$. Since $n[A] = 4$ and $n[B] = 5$, $4 \times 5 = n[A \times B]$. If you tabulate $A \times B$, you will find that it contains 20 ordered pairs; that is, $n[A \times B] = 20$. Thus, $4 \times 5 = 20$.
49 The standard set of 2 is {0, 1} and the empty set is { }. The product of 2 and 0 is the number associated with the Cartesian product of {0, 1} and { }. But the Cartesian product of any set and the empty set is the empty set. Also, $n[\{ \}] = 0$. Thus, $2 \times 0 = 0$.
50 a $4 \times (5 \times 7) = (4 \times 5) \times 7$
$= 20 \times 7$
$= 140$.
b $(25 \times 19) \times 4 = 4 \times (25 \times 19)$
$= (4 \times 25) \times 19$
$= 100 \times 19$
$= 1900$.
c $(11 \times 50) \times (20 \times 63) = (11 \times 50) \times$
20×63
$= 11 \times (50 \times 20)$
$\times 63$
$= 11 \times 63 \times$
(50×20)
$= 11 \times 63 \times 1000$
$= 693 \times 1000$
$= 693,000$.
d $50 \times (26 \times 6) \times 40 = 50 \times 40 \times$
(26×6)
$= 2000 \times (26 \times 6)$
$= 2000 \times 156$
$= 312,000$.
51 a $(ab)c = c(ab)$. For any two natural numbers a and b, $ab = ba$.
c $cba = abc$. For any three natural numbers a, b, and c, $(ab)c = a(bc)$. For any two natural numbers a and b, $ab = ba$.
e $a(bc) = a(cb)$. For any two natural numbers a and b, $ab = ba$.
f $(ab)c = (ac)b$. For any three natural numbers a, b, and c, $(ab)c = a(bc)$. For any two natural numbers a and b, $ab = ba$.
52 a $37 \times 82 + 37 \times 18 = 37 \times (82 + 18)$
$= 37 \times 100$
$= 3700$.
b $239 \times 124 + 239 \times 876 = 239 \times$
$(124 + 876)$
$= 239 \times 1000$
$= 239,000$.

c $25 \times (8 + 5) = 25 \times 8 + 25 \times 5$
$= 200 + 125$
$= 325.$

d $5137 \times 56 + 5137 \times 44 = 5137 \times$
$(56 + 44)$
$= 5137 \times 100$
$= 513,700.$

53 e $a \times (b + c) = (a \times b) + (a \times c).$

54 $(a + b)c = c(a + b)$. For any two natural numbers a and b, $ab = ba$.
$c(a + b) = ca + cb$. For any three natural numbers a, b, and c, $a(b + c) = ab + ac$.
$ca + cb = ac + bc$. For any two natural numbers a and b, $ab = ba$. Therefore, $(a + b)c = ac + bc$.

55 One example is the following: Replace a by 2, b by 3, and c by 4 in $a + (b \times c) = (a + b) \times (a + c)$. You obtain $2 + (3 \times 4) = (2 + 3) \times (2 + 4)$, which is not true.

56 a $8 + 8 + 8 + 8 + 8$
b $5 + 5 + 5 + 5 + 5 + 5 + 5 + 5$
c $5 \times 8 = 8 + 8 + 8 + 8 + 8$
$= (8 \times 1) + (8 \times 1) + (8 \times 1) +$
$(8 \times 1) + (8 \times 1)$
$= 8 \times (1 + 1 + 1 + 1 + 1).$
We know that $(1 + 1 + 1 + 1 + 1) = 5$. Therefore, $8 \times (1 + 1 + 1 + 1 + 1) = 8 \times 5$. Thus, we have shown that $5 \times 8 = 8 \times 5$.

57 a $(1 + 2) + (1 + 2) + (1 + 2) + (1 + 2)$
b $(1 + 2) + (1 + 2) + (1 + 2) + (1 + 2) = (1 + 1 + 1 + 1) + (2 + 2 + 2 + 2).$
We know that $(1 + 1 + 1 + 1) = 4 \times 1$ and that $(2 + 2 + 2 + 2) = 4 \times 2$. Therefore, $(1 + 1 + 1 + 1) + (2 + 2 + 2 + 2) = (4 \times 1) + (4 \times 2).$
Thus, we have shown that
$(1 + 2) + (1 + 2) + (1 + 2) + (1 + 2)$
is the sum of the products 4×1 and 4×2.

58 Sums and products have similar properties. Thus, when we add numbers or multiply numbers, comparable "rules" apply.

59 $(2x + 1)(2x) = \underbrace{2x + 2x + \ldots + 2x}_{2x + 1 \text{ addends of } 2x}.$

The sum of $2x + 1$ addends of $2x$ is even since the sum of any number of even numbers is always even. Thus, $(2x + 1)(2x)$, or the product of an odd number and an even number, is even.

60 a $(5 + 2) + 6 = (2 + 5) + 6$
$= 2 + (5 + 6).$
b $6 \times (1 + 4) = (6 \times 1) + (6 \times 4)$
$= 6 + (6 \times 4)$
$= (6 \times 4) + 6$
$= (4 \times 6) + 6.$
c $6 \times (a + 1) = (6 \times a) + (6 \times 1)$
$= 6a + 6$
$= 6 + 6a.$
d $4 \times 3 + 4 \times 5 = 4(3 + 5)$
$= 4(5 + 3).$
e $a \times 2 + 5a = (5 \times a) + (a \times 2)$
$= (a \times 5) + (a \times 2)$
$= a(5 + 2)$
$= (5 + 2)a.$
f $ac + cb = ca + cb$
$= c(a + b)$
$= c(b + a).$

61 From the definition of product, we know that $a(b + c + d) =$
$$\underbrace{(b + c + d) + \ldots + (b + c + d)}_{a \text{ addends of } (b + c + d)}.$$
Using properties concerning sums, we can regroup addends as follows:
$$\underbrace{(b + c + d) + \ldots + (b + c + d)}_{a \text{ addends of } (b + c + d)} =$$
$$\underbrace{(b + \ldots + b)}_{a \text{ addends of } b} + \underbrace{(c + \ldots + c)}_{a \text{ addends of } c} + \underbrace{(d + \ldots + d)}_{a \text{ addends of } d}.$$
From the definition of product, we know that
$$\underbrace{(b + b + \ldots + b)}_{a \text{ addends of } b} = ab, \text{ that}$$
$$\underbrace{(c + c + \ldots + c)}_{a \text{ addends of } c} = ac, \text{ and that}$$
$$\underbrace{(d + d + \ldots + d)}_{a \text{ addends of } d} = ad.$$
Thus, $a(b + c + d) = ab + ac + ad.$

62 a $x = 5.$ **f** $8 = z.$
b $x = 7.$ **g** $y + 5 = x.$
c $6 = z.$ **h** $y = z.$
d $y = 9.$ **i** $y = 2.$
e $z = 7.$ **j** $xz = y.$

63 a $5x = 55.$
$5x = 5 \times 11.$
$x = 11.$
Thus, 11 is the solution of $5x = 55.$

b $2x + 3 = 15.$
$2x + 3 = 12 + 3.$
$2x = 12.$
$2x = 2 \times 6.$
$x = 6.$

c $7 + 4x = 35.$
$7 + 4x = 7 + 28.$
$4x = 28.$
$4x = 4 \times 7.$
$x = 7.$

d $3x + 5 = 23.$
$3x + 5 = 18 + 5.$
$3x = 18.$
$3x = 3 \times 6.$
$x = 6.$

e $3a + 11 = 14.$
$3a + 11 = 3 + 11.$
$3a = 3.$
$3a = 3 \times 1.$
$a = 1.$

f $43b + 14 = 100.$
$43b + 14 = 86 + 14.$
$43b = 86.$
$43b = 43 \times 2.$
$b = 2.$

64 According to the definition of product given on page 68, $ac = \underbrace{c + c + \ldots + c}_{a \text{ addends of } c}$ and

$bc = \underbrace{c + c + \ldots + c}_{b \text{ addends of } c}.$ If $ac = bc$, then

$\underbrace{c + c + \ldots + c}_{a \text{ addends of } c} = \underbrace{c + c + \ldots + c}_{b \text{ addends of } c}.$

Thus, a must be equal to b.

65 a In the discussion in the text, it was established that the sum of any natural number and 3 is equal to the successor of the successor of the successor of the given number; so, we can find the sum of 5 and 7 as follows:
$5 + 7 = 7 + 5$
$= 7 + (3 + 2)$
$= (7 + 3) + 2$
$= 10 + 2.$
Also, the sum of any natural number and 2 is the successor of the successor of the given number. So, $10 + 2 = 12$. Thus, $5 + 7 = 12.$

b Similarly,
$6 + 6 = 6 + (3 + 3)$
$= (6 + 3) + 3$
$= 9 + 3 = 12.$
Thus, $6 + 6 = 12.$

c We can use the same method as for the previous examples to show that
$3 + 4 = 4 + 3 = 7.$

d $4 + 5 = 5 + 4$
$= 5 + (2 + 2)$
$= (5 + 2) + 2.$
We know that the sum of any natural number and 2 is equal to the successor of the successor of the given number. Therefore, $(5 + 2) + 2 = 7 + 2 = 9.$
Thus, $4 + 5 = 9.$

66 The successor of $5 + 10$ is $(5 + 10) + 1$, and the successor of $10 + 5$ is $(10 + 5) + 1$. Since, for any two natural numbers a and b, $a + b = b + a$, we know that $5 + 10 = 10 + 5$. Hence, $(5 + 10) + 1 = (10 + 5) + 1.$

67 a $8 \times 2 = 8 \times (1 + 1)$
$= (8 \times 1) + (8 \times 1) = 8 + 8.$
Using the successor idea for addition, we can show that
$8 + 8 = 8 + (3 + 5)$
$= (8 + 3) + 5$
$= 11 + 5$
$= 11 + (3 + 2)$
$= (11 + 3) + 2$
$= 14 + 2 = 16.$

b $4 \times 3 = 4 \times (1 + 1 + 1)$
$= (4 \times 1) + (4 \times 1) + (4 \times 1)$
$= 4 + 4 + 4.$
Further,
$4 + 4 + 4 = (4 + 2) + (2 + 4)$
$= 6 + (2 + 4)$
$= (6 + 2) + 4$
$= 8 + 4$
$= 8 + (2 + 2)$
$= (8 + 2) + 2$
$= 10 + 2 = 12.$

c Similarly, we can show that $5 \times 5 = 5 + 5 + 5 + 5 + 5$. By repeated use of the successor idea, we can show that $5 + 5 + 5 + 5 + 5 = 25.$

d Using the method of the previous examples, we have $6 \times 4 = 6 + 6 + 6 + 6$. And, by the successor idea,
$6 + 6 + 6 + 6 = 24.$

68 No

69 $2 * (0, 1)$ and $(1, 0)$

70 $(2, 0)$, $(0, 2)$, and $(1, 1)$

71 $4 * (3, 0)$, $(0, 3)$, $(2, 1)$, and $(1, 2)$

72 $n + 1$ pairs map onto a number n under addition mapping.

73 a Replacement for x is 24.

b Replacement for x is 4.

c Replacement for y is 3.

d Replacement for both x and y is 0.

e Each entry in the first row of the table below indicates a possible replacement for x. Each entry in the second row indicates the corresponding replacement for y.

x	0	1	2	3	4	5	6	7
y	7	6	5	4	3	2	1	0

f Replacement for x is 6.

g Replacement for y is 1.

h The entries in the first row of the table below indicate the possible replacements for x. The entries in the second row indicate the corresponding replacements for y. Note that there are 121 possible replacements for x and that, for each of these, there is a replacement for y.

x	0	1	2	3	4	...	118	119	120
y	120	119	118	117	116	...	2	1	0

74 0

75 $1 * (1, 1)$

76 $2 * (2, 1)$ and $(1, 2)$

77 $(1, 3)$ and $(3, 1) * (1, 4)$, $(4, 1)$, and $(2, 2) * (5, 1)$ and $(1, 5) * (1, 6)$, $(6, 1)$, $(3, 2)$, and $(2, 3) * (1, 7)$ and $(7, 1) * (1, 8)$, $(8, 1)$, $(4, 2)$, and $(2, 4)$

78 $2 * 2 * 2 * 2$

79 $3 * 5 * 6$

80 One way in which $A \times A$ can be mapped onto A is by mapping each pair whose first component is a onto a, each pair whose first component is b onto b, and each pair whose first component is d onto d. This mapping is shown below. Other mappings are possible.

$(a, a) \rightarrow a$ $(b, a) \rightarrow b$ $(d, a) \rightarrow d$

$(a, b) \rightarrow a$ $(b, b) \rightarrow b$ $(d, b) \rightarrow d$

$(a, d) \rightarrow a$ $(b, d) \rightarrow b$ $(d, d) \rightarrow d$

81 a Replacement for x is 28.

b Replacement for x is 3.

c Replacement for x is 6.

d Each entry in the first row of the table below indicates a possible replacement for x. Each entry in the second row indicates the corresponding replacement for y.

x	1	2	3	4	6	9	12	18	36
y	36	18	12	9	6	4	3	2	1

e Replacement for both x and y is 1.

f Replacement for y is 8.

g Replacement for y is 12.

h Each entry in the first row of the table below indicates a possible replacement for x. Each entry in the second row indicates the corresponding replacement for y.

x	1	2	3	5	6	9	10	15	18	30	45	90
y	90	45	30	18	15	10	9	6	5	3	2	1

i There is no proper replacement for x.

j Any natural number is a possible replacement for x if the replacement for y is 0. If the replacement for y is different from 0, there are no proper replacements for x.

82 a The even numbers

b The multiples of 7

83 Examples are the set of numbers that are less than 100 and the set of multiples of 4 that are less than 20.

84 All of the subsets of N listed in exercise 82 are closed with respect to multiplication.

85 Examples are the set of numbers that are less than 50 and the set of powers of 2 that are less than 128.

86 c Turning on the light and opening the window

87 One example is unlocking a door and opening the door. Another example is shampooing one's hair and setting one's hair.

88 The following foods are not associative: toast, jelly, coffee. "(Toast and jelly) and coffee" is different from "toast and (jelly and coffee)."

89 Yes * Yes * Yes * Yes

90 No * Yes * No. Note that since addition is not closed in P, there is really no operation of addition. Hence, it would not make sense to speak of properties of addition. * No

91 Yes * Yes * Yes * Yes

92 No * Yes * No (See response for exercise 90.) * No

93 No. Not all properties of a number system are satisfied. For example, "circle times" is not commutative.

94 a $5 \times 102 = 5(100 + 2) = 500 + 10 = 510.$
b $20 \times 91 = 20(90 + 1) = 1800 + 20 = 1820.$
c $25 \times 14 = 25(10 + 4) = 250 + 100 = 350.$

95 No. For example, $6 + (2 \times 3)$ is not equal to $(6 + 2) \times (6 + 3).$

96 No. For example, $2 \times (3 \times 4)$ is not equal to $(2 \times 3) \times (2 \times 4).$

97 Yes

98 Yes * Yes. For example, let A = {1, 2}, B = {3, 4}, and C = {5, 6}. Both A × (B ∪ C) and (A × B) ∪ (A × C) are equal to {(1, 3), (1, 4), (1, 5), (1, 6), (2, 3), (2, 4), (2, 5), (2, 6)}.

99 a Jim bought 2 balloons at 10¢ apiece and 2 whistles at 10¢ apiece. How much did the four items cost?
$(2 \times 10) + (2 \times 10) = 2 \times (10 + 10).$
b Mrs. Allen bought 4 packages of hamburger buns and 5 packages of hot dog buns. Each package contained 8 buns. How many buns in all did she buy?
$(4 \times 8) + (5 \times 8) = (4 + 5) \times 8.$
c Mr. Harris spends 45 minutes getting to work in the morning and 55 minutes getting home at night. How much time does he spend getting to and from his office in 5 days?
$5 \times (45 + 55) = (5 \times 45) + (5 \times 55).$
d For each machineful of laundry, Jean spends 25¢ for washing and 20¢ for drying. How much does she spend in doing 4 machinefuls of laundry?
$4 \times (25 + 20) = (4 \times 25) + (4 \times 20).$

100 $0 + a = a + 0.$
Commutative property of addition
$a + 0 = a.$
Identity-element property of addition
$0 + a = a.$
Transitive property of equality

101 $1 \times a = a \times 1.$
Commutative property of multiplication
$a \times 1 = a.$
Identity-element property of multiplication
$1 \times a = a.$
Transitive property of equality

102 a Stand up.
b Drive two miles south.
c Go down three floors.
d Deposit $10 in a savings account.
e Buy ten shares of stock.

103 Examples are:
Walking 2 blocks east and walking 2 blocks west
Putting on a tie and taking off a tie
Buying a car and selling a car
Walking from your home to the store and walking from the store to your home
Putting wallpaper on a wall and taking wallpaper off a wall

104 a $10 - 7 = 3.$ $10 - 3 = 7.$
b $5 - 5 = 0.$ $5 - 0 = 5.$
c $9 - 1 = 8.$ $9 - 8 = 1.$
d $14 - 3 = x.$ $14 - x = 3.$
e $13 - y = 6.$ $13 - 6 = y.$
f $z - y = x.$ $z - x = y.$

105 a $30 \div 6 = 5.$ $30 \div 5 = 6.$
b $14 \div 7 = 2.$ $14 \div 2 = 7.$
c $0 \div 8 = 0.$
d $4 \div 4 = 1.$ $4 \div 1 = 4.$
e $45 \div 5 = 9.$ $45 \div 9 = 5.$
f $36 \div 3 = 12.$ $36 \div 12 = 3.$

106 $(24 \div 6) \div 2 = 2.$
$24 \div (6 \div 2) = 8.$
$(24 \div 6) \div 2$ is not equal to $24 \div (6 \div 2).$

107 For natural numbers:
a 3   **b** 1   **c** 3
For members of U in clock arithmetic:
a 3 and 9   **b** 1, 3, 5, 7, 9, and 11
c 3, 7, and 11

108 Three. The numbers are 5, 7, and 11.

109 a Yes   **b** Yes   **c** No   **d** Yes

110

Addition table

+	1	2	3	4	5	6	7
1	2	3	4	5	6	7	1
2	3	4	5	6	7	1	2
3	4	5	6	7	1	2	3
4	5	6	7	1	2	3	4
5	6	7	1	2	3	4	5
6	7	1	2	3	4	5	6
7	1	2	3	4	5	6	7

Multiplication table

×	1	2	3	4	5	6	7
1	1	2	3	4	5	6	7
2	2	4	6	1	3	5	7
3	3	6	2	5	1	4	7
4	4	1	5	2	6	3	7
5	5	3	1	6	4	2	7
6	6	5	4	3	2	1	7
7	7	7	7	7	7	7	7

Addition is closed, commutative, and associative. Multiplication is closed, commutative, and associative. Multiplication distributes over addition. * None, as far as properties above are concerned.

111　**a** β　**b** α　**c** α　**d** α

112　If operation arrowhead is distributive with respect to operation star, then the following is true: $\beta \triangledown (\alpha \star \beta) = (\beta \triangledown \alpha) \star (\beta \triangledown \beta)$.
However, $\beta \triangledown (\alpha \star \beta) = \beta$ and $(\beta \triangledown \alpha) \star (\beta \triangledown \beta) = \alpha$. Thus, $\beta \triangledown (\alpha \star \beta)$ and $(\beta \triangledown \alpha) \star (\beta \triangledown \beta)$ are not equal, and we have shown one instance where operation arrowhead is not distributive with respect to operation star. This is sufficient to show that operation arrowhead does not distribute over operation star.

113　**a** ‹ �　**b** ⟨ ᛏ
c ᛏ ᛏᛏ　**d** ᛏᛏ ⟨⟨ ᛏᛏᛏ
e ᛏ ⟨⟨ ᛏᛏᛏ　**f** ᛏᛏᛏ ⟨ ᛏ
g ⟨ ᛏᛏ ⟨ ᛏᛏ　**h** ᛏ ⟨⟨ ᛏᛏ ⟨⟨⟨ ᛏᛏᛏ

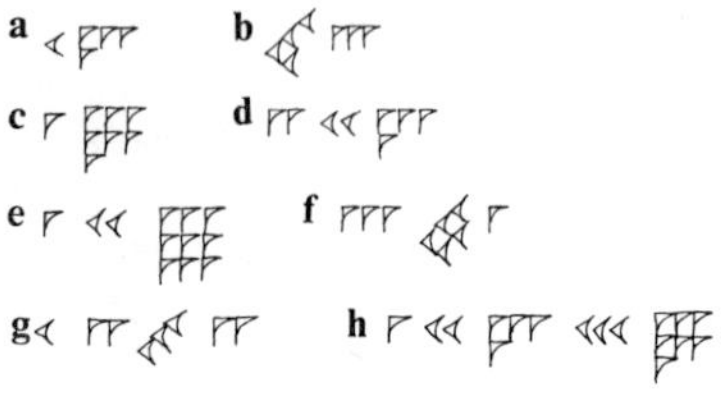

114　**a** ⟨ ᛏᛏ　**b** ᛏ ⟨⟨ ᛏᛏᛏ
c ᛏᛏ ⟨⟨　**d** ⟨ ᛏᛏᛏ

115　**a** ∩IIIII　**b** ∩∩∩∩∩∩∩ IIIIIII
c 9∩∩∩∩IIII　**d** 99∩∩∩I
e 99999999∩∩∩∩∩II　**f** 𒐚𒐚𒐚𒐚𒐚 9∩∩∩IIIIII

116　**a** ∩IIIII　**b** 9∩∩∩∩ IIIIIIIII
c 999999991　**d** 𒐚𒐚𒐚𒐚𒐚𒐚𒐚𒐚 9∩∩∩∩

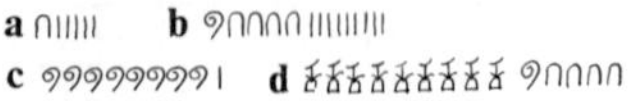

117　**a** XIV　　　**c** CXLIV or
　　　b LXXXIX　　　 CXXXXIV

d CCXXXI　　　**h** CDXCIII
e DCCLII　　　**i** MCDXCII
f MMMMCXXXVII　**j** MMDCCCXCIX
g MCMLXV

118　**a** ⟨ ᛏᛏᛏ　∩∩∩∩IIIIIII　XLVIII

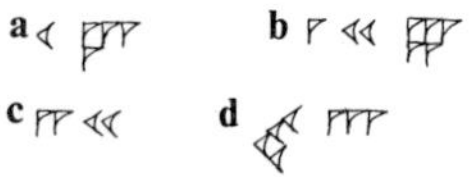

b ᛏ⟨ᛏᛏ　∩∩∩∩∩∩∩II　LXXII

c ᛏ⟨ ᛏᛏ 𒐚𒐚𒐚 999999∩∩∩II　MMDLXLII

d ᛏ⟨ ᛏᛏ 99II　CII

e ᛏ⟨ 9 C

f ⟨ᛏ⟨ ᛏᛏ
𒐚99999999999∩∩∩∩∩IIIII　MCMLXIV

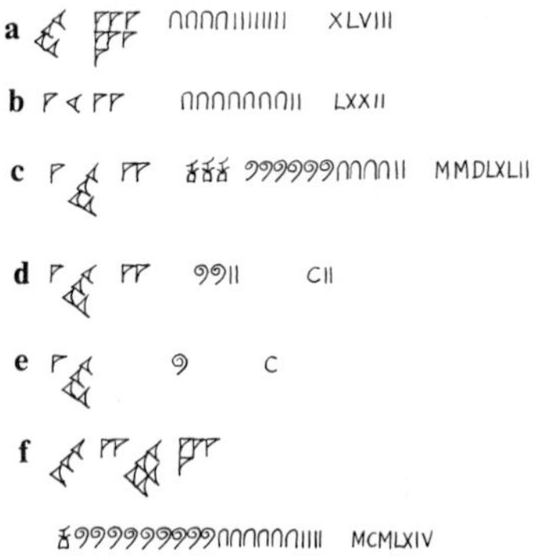

119

ᛏ	I	I	ᛏᛏᛏ	IIIIIIIII	IX
ᛏᛏ	II	II			
ᛏᛏᛏ	III	III	⟨	∩	X
ᛏᛏ ᛏᛏ	IIII	IV	⟨ᛏ	∩I	XI
ᛏᛏ ᛏᛏᛏ	IIIII	V	⟨ᛏᛏ	∩II	XII
ᛏᛏᛏ ᛏᛏᛏ	IIIIII	VI	⟨ᛏᛏᛏ	∩III	XIII
ᛏᛏ ᛏᛏ	IIIIIII	VII	⟨ᛏᛏ	∩IIII	XIV
ᛏᛏ ᛏᛏᛏ	IIIIIIII	VIII	⟨ᛏᛏᛏ	∩IIIII	XV

120　15,055 seconds * Bases ten and sixty

121　58 + 39 = 97. *

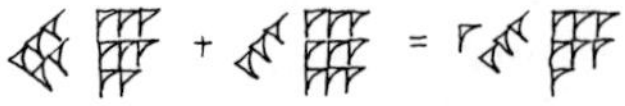

⟨ᛏᛏ + ⟨ᛏᛏ = ᛏ⟨ᛏᛏ

∩∩∩∩∩IIIIIIII + ∩∩IIIIIIIII = ∩∩∩∩∩∩∩∩IIIIIII.

LVIII + XXXIX = XCVII.

* Computation with any of the above symbols is somewhat tedious. These systems are not as efficient as base ten.

122　**a** 3^4　**d** $2^3 \cdot 5^2$　**g** $9^1 \cdot 4^4$
　　　b 5^2　**e** 10^3　**h** $7^2 \cdot 8^1 \cdot 6^2$
　　　c $6^1 \cdot 8^1$　**f** $5^1 \cdot 10^2$

123　**a** 8^{10}　**c** 15^3　**e** 5^3
　　　b 10^{14}　**d** 35^1　**f** 4^6

124　**a** 125　**c** 2016　**e** 36
　　　b 1024　**d** 256　**f** 45

125 a $1 \cdot 10^3 + 5 \cdot 10^2 + 6 \cdot 10^1 + 0 \cdot 10^0 =$
        $1000 + 500 + 60 + 0 = 1560.$
  b $0 \cdot 10^3 + 9 \cdot 10^2 + 0 \cdot 10^1 + 9 \cdot 10^0 =$
        $0 + 900 + 0 + 9 = 909.$
  c $0 \cdot 10^3 + 0 \cdot 10^2 + 0 \cdot 10^1 + 1 \cdot 10^0 =$
        $0 + 0 + 0 + 1 = 1.$
  d $6 \cdot 10^3 + 1 \cdot 10^2 + 1 \cdot 10^1 + 1 \cdot 10^0 =$
        $6000 + 100 + 10 + 1 = 6111.$

126 a 19 b 66 c 397 d 123 e 586 f 733

127 a 24_5 d 1411_5 g 14411_5
  b 324_5 e 11002_5 h 222_5
  c 1034_5 f 131022_5

128 a 25 b 29 c 13 d 125 e 69

129 a 11111_2 c 111_2 e 1100_2
  b 110010_2 d 1100011_2 f 1000000_2

130 a $15 + 43$
In expanded form, $15 = 1 \cdot 10^1 + 5 \cdot 10^0$
and $43 = 4 \cdot 10^1 + 3 \cdot 10^0.$
By the substitution property, we obtain
$15 + 43 = (1 \cdot 10^1 + 5 \cdot 10^0) +$
        $(4 \cdot 10^1 + 3 \cdot 10^0).$
By the associative property of addition,
$15 + 43 =$
$\left(1 \cdot 10^1 + (5 \cdot 10^0 + 4 \cdot 10^1)\right) + 3 \cdot 10^0.$
By the commutative and associative
properties of addition,
$15 + 43 =$
$\left(1 \cdot 10^1 + (4 \cdot 10^1 + 5 \cdot 10^0)\right) + 3 \cdot 10^0$
    $= (1 \cdot 10^1 + 4 \cdot 10^1) +$
        $(5 \cdot 10^0 + 3 \cdot 10^0).$
By the distributive property of
multiplication over addition,
$1 \cdot 10^1 + 4 \cdot 10^1 = (1 + 4)10^1$ and
$5 \cdot 10^0 + 3 \cdot 10^0 = (5 + 3)10^0.$
By the substitution property,
$15 + 43 = (1 + 4)10^1 + (5 + 3)10^0.$
From our knowledge of basic facts for
addition and the substitution property,
we obtain
$15 + 43 = 5 \cdot 10^1 + 8 \cdot 10^0.$
Using properties of the decimal
numeration system and also the transitive
property of equality, we obtain
$15 + 43 = 58.$ * 15
          $\underline{43}$
          58

  b $27 + 65 = (2 \cdot 10^1 + 7 \cdot 10^0) +$
           $(6 \cdot 10^1 + 5 \cdot 10^0).$
Expanded form of decimals

        $= (2 \cdot 10^1 + 6 \cdot 10^1) +$
            $(7 \cdot 10^0 + 5 \cdot 10^0)$
Associative and commutative
properties of addition
$= (2 + 6)10^1 + (7 + 5)10^0$
Distributive property
$= 8 \cdot 10^1 + 12 \cdot 10^0$
Basic facts for addition
$= 8 \cdot 10^1 + 1 \cdot 10^1 + 2 \cdot 10^0$
Expanded form of decimals
$= (8 + 1)10^1 + 2 \cdot 10^0$
Distributive property
$= 9 \cdot 10^1 + 2 \cdot 10^0$
Basic facts for addition
$= 92.$
Meaning of expanded form *

      27
      $\underline{65}$
      92

c $293 + 172 = (2 \cdot 10^2 + 9 \cdot 10^1 + 3 \cdot 10^0)$
           $+ (1 \cdot 10^2 + 7 \cdot 10^1 + 2 \cdot 10^0)$
Expanded form of decimals
$= (2 \cdot 10^2 + 1 \cdot 10^2) +$
    $(9 \cdot 10^1 + 7 \cdot 10^1) +$
    $(3 \cdot 10^0 + 2 \cdot 10^0)$
Commutative and associative
properties of addition
$= (2 + 1)10^2 + (9 + 7)10^1 +$
         $(3 + 2)10^0$
Distributive property
$= 3 \cdot 10^2 + 16 \cdot 10^1 + 5 \cdot 10^0$
Basic facts for addition
$= 3 \cdot 10^2 + 1 \cdot 10^2 + 6 \cdot 10^1$
         $+ 5 \cdot 10^0$
Expanded form of decimals
$= (3 + 1)10^2 + 6 \cdot 10^1 +$
         $5 \cdot 10^0$
Distributive property
$= 465.$
Meaning of expanded form
and basic facts for addition *

     293
     $\underline{172}$
     465

d $4 + 8 + 9 + 3 = 4 \cdot 10^0 + 8 \cdot 10^0 +$
$$9 \cdot 10^0 + 3 \cdot 10^0$$
Expanded form of
decimals
$$= (4 + 8 + 9 + 3)10^0$$
Distributive property
$$= 24 \cdot 10^0$$
Combination of several
steps involving basic
facts for addition,
associative and
commutative
properties, and so on
$$= 2 \cdot 10^1 + 4 \cdot 10^0$$
Expanded form
$$= 24.$$
Meaning of expanded
form *

$$\begin{array}{r} 4 \\ 8 \\ 9 \\ 3 \\ \hline 24 \end{array}$$

131 a $847 - 514$

In expanded form,
$$\begin{array}{r} 847 = 8 \cdot 10^2 + 4 \cdot 10^1 + 7 \cdot 10^0 \\ 514 = 5 \cdot 10^2 + 1 \cdot 10^1 + 4 \cdot 10^0 \\ \hline 3 \cdot 10^2 + 3 \cdot 10^1 + 3 \cdot 10^0 \end{array}$$
Since $3 \cdot 10^2 + 3 \cdot 10^1 + 3 \cdot 10^0 = 333$,
it follows that $847 - 514 = 333.$ *

$$\begin{array}{r} 847 \\ 514 \\ \hline 333 \end{array}$$

b $31 = 3 \cdot 10^1 + 1 \cdot 10^0$
$19 = 1 \cdot 10^1 + 9 \cdot 10^0$

$$\begin{array}{r} 3 \cdot 10^1 + 1 \cdot 10^0 = 2 \cdot 10^1 + 11 \cdot 10^0 \\ 1 \cdot 10^1 + 9 \cdot 10^0 = 1 \cdot 10^1 + 9 \cdot 10^0 \\ \hline 1 \cdot 10^1 + 2 \cdot 10^0 \end{array}$$
Since $1 \cdot 10^1 + 2 \cdot 10^0 = 12$,
it follows that $31 - 19 = 12.$ *

$$\begin{array}{r} {}^2\!\!\not{3}\ {}^1 1 \\ 1\ 9 \\ \hline 1\ 2 \end{array}$$

c $625 = 6 \cdot 10^2 + 2 \cdot 10^1 + 5 \cdot 10^0$
$268 = 2 \cdot 10^2 + 6 \cdot 10^1 + 8 \cdot 10^0$

$$\begin{array}{r} 6 \cdot 10^2 + 2 \cdot 10^1 + 5 \cdot 10^0 = 6 \cdot 10^2 + 1 \cdot 10^1 + 15 \cdot 10^0 \\ 2 \cdot 10^2 + 6 \cdot 10^1 + 8 \cdot 10^0 = 2 \cdot 10^2 + 6 \cdot 10^1 + 8 \cdot 10^0 \\ \hline \end{array}$$

$$\begin{array}{r} 6 \cdot 10^2 + 1 \cdot 10^1 + 15 \cdot 10^0 = 5 \cdot 10^2 + 11 \cdot 10^1 + 15 \cdot 10^0 \\ 2 \cdot 10^2 + 6 \cdot 10^1 + 8 \cdot 10^0 = 2 \cdot 10^2 + 6 \cdot 10^1 + 8 \cdot 10^0 \\ \hline 3 \cdot 10^2 + 5 \cdot 10^1 + 7 \cdot 10^0 \end{array}$$

$3 \cdot 10^2 + 5 \cdot 10^1 + 7 \cdot 10^0 = 357$;
thus, $625 - 268 = 357.$ *

$$\begin{array}{r} {}^5\ {}^{11} \\ \not{6}\ \not{2}\ {}^1 5 \\ 2\ 6\ 8 \\ \hline 3\ 5\ 7 \end{array}$$

132 a 847 **b** ${}^3\!1\!1$ **c** $6\ {}^1 2\ {}^1 5$

$$\begin{array}{r} 514 \\ \hline 333 \end{array} \qquad \begin{array}{r} 2 \\ \not{3}\ 9 \\ \hline 1\ 2 \end{array} \qquad \begin{array}{r} 3\ 7 \\ \not{2}\ \not{6}\ 8 \\ \hline 3\ 5\ 7 \end{array}$$

133 a $8 \times 63 = 8 \times (6 \cdot 10^1 + 3)$
Expanded form of decimals
$$= (8 \times 6 \cdot 10^1) + (8 \times 3)$$
Distributive property
$$= (8 \times 6)10^1 + (8 \times 3)$$
Associative property of
multiplication
$$= 48 \cdot 10^1 + 24$$
Basic facts for multiplication
$$= (4 \cdot 10^2 + 8 \cdot 10^1) +$$
$$(2 \cdot 10^1 + 4)$$
Expanded form
$$= 4 \cdot 10^2 + (8 \cdot 10^1 + 2 \cdot 10^1) + 4$$
Associative property of addition
$$= 4 \cdot 10^2 + 10 \cdot 10^1 + 4$$
Distributive property and basic
facts for addition
$$= 4 \cdot 10^2 + 1 \cdot 10^2 + 4$$
Expanded form
$$= 5 \cdot 10^2 + 4$$
Distributive property and basic
facts for addition
$$= 504.$$
Meaning of expanded form
Thus, by the transitive property of equality,
$8 \times 63 = 504.$
b $10 \times 759 = 1 \cdot 10^1 \times$
$$(7 \cdot 10^2 + 5 \cdot 10^1 + 9)$$
Expanded form
$$= (10^1 \times 7 \cdot 10^2) +$$
$$(10^1 \times 5 \cdot 10^1) + (10^1 \times 9)$$
Distributive property

$$= \left(7 \times (10^1 \cdot 10^2)\right) +$$
$$\left(5 \times (10^1 \cdot 10^1)\right) + (9 \cdot 10^1)$$

Commutative and associative
properties of multiplication

$$= (7 \cdot 10^3) + (5 \cdot 10^2) +$$
$$(9 \cdot 10^1)$$

Product of two powers

$$= 7590.$$

Meaning of expanded form

Thus, by the transitive property of equality,
$10 \times 759 = 7590.$

134 a

63	63	63	
8	8	8	
24	24	24	8×3
48	480	480	8×60
504	504	504	

b

759	759	759	
10	10	10	
7590	7590	90	10×9
		500	10×50
		7000	10×700
		7590	

For both examples, we have shown only
one way of using the third algorism.

135 a

89		**b**	325	
36			84	
54	6×9		24000	80×300
480	6×80		1600	80×20
270	30×9		400	80×5
2400	30×80		1200	4×300
3204			80	4×20
			20	4×5
			27300	

c

709		**d**	1234	
235			562	
1800	200×9		8	2×4
140000	200×700		60	2×30
270	30×9		400	2×200
21000	30×700		2000	2×1000
45	5×9		240	60×4
3500	5×700		1800	60×30
166615			12000	60×200
			60000	60×1000
			2000	500×4
			15000	500×30
			100000	500×200
			500000	500×1000
			693508	

Note that, for each example, we have shown
only one way of using the algorism.

136

```
 20
  4  1
 16
  4  1
 12
  4  1
  8
  4  1
  4
  4  1
  0  5
```

137 a The Calandri algorism is shown at the left,
and one version of the Greenwood
algorism is shown at the right.

```
        25
  16)400       16)400  | 20
     32           320  |
     80            80  | 5
     80            80  |
                      | 25
```

b The Calandri algorism is shown at the left,
and one version of the Greenwood
algorism is shown at the right.

```
       108
  19)2052       19)2052  | 100
     19           1900   |
    152            152   | 8
    152            152   |
                         | 108
```

c The Calandri algorism is shown at the left,
and one version of the Greenwood
algorism is shown at the right.

```
         30
  115)3450      115)3450  | 20
      345           2300  |
        0           1150  | 10
        0           1150  |
                          | 30
```

138 a $462 = 28 \times 16 + 14.$

b $4289 = 11 \times 364 + 285.$

c $20 = 0 \times 21 + 20.$

d $372 = 31 \times 12 + 0.$

139 a $\{(1, 1), (1, 2), (1, 3),$
$(2, 1), (2, 2), (2, 3),$
$(3, 1), (3, 2), (3, 3)\}$

b {$(a, a), (a, b), (a, c), (a, d), (b, a), (b, b),$
$(b, c), (b, d), (c, a), (c, b), (c, c), (c, d),$
$(d, a), (d, b), (d, c), (d, d)$}

c {(s, s)}

d {(cat, cat), (cat, dog), (cat, rat),
(dog, cat), (dog, dog), (dog, rat),
(rat, cat), (rat, dog), (rat, rat)}

e { }

f {$(2, 10), (4, 10), (6, 10), (8, 10)$} *
{$(10, 2), (10, 4), (10, 6), (10, 8)$} * No

g {$(1, 2), (1, 4), (1, 6),$
$(3, 2), (3, 4), (3, 6),$
$(5, 2), (5, 4), (5, 6)$} *
{$(2, 1), (2, 3), (2, 5),$
$(4, 1), (4, 3), (4, 5),$
$(6, 1), (6, 3), (6, 5)$}

h Yes. Each is the empty set.

140 a For convenience, we have rearranged the
members of C in order, beginning with
the least number.
{$(1, 3), (1, 6), (1, 9), (1, 12), (1, 15),$
$(1, 18), (1, 24), (1, 30), (1, 36),$
$(2, 3), (2, 6), (2, 9), (2, 12), (2, 15),$
$(2, 18), (2, 24), (2, 30), (2, 36),$
$(3, 3), (3, 6), (3, 9), (3, 12), (3, 15),$
$(3, 18), (3, 24), (3, 30), (3, 36),$
$(4, 3), (4, 6), (4, 9), (4, 12), (4, 15),$
$(4, 18), (4, 24), (4, 30), (4, 36),$
$(5, 3), (5, 6), (5, 9), (5, 12), (5, 15),$
$(5, 18), (5, 24), (5, 30), (5, 36),$
$(6, 3), (6, 6), (6, 9), (6, 12), (6, 15),$
$(6, 18), (6, 24), (6, 30), (6, 36)$}
The grid for A $\times$ C is shown below.

b See graph.   **c** See graph.

141 a {$(1, 1), (1, 2), (1, 3), (1, 4),$
$(1, 5), (1, 6), (2, 1), (2, 2),$
$(2, 3), (2, 4), (2, 5), (2, 6),$
$(3, 1), (3, 2), (3, 3), (3, 4),$
$(3, 5), (3, 6), (4, 1), (4, 2),$
$(4, 3), (4, 4), (4, 5), (4, 6)$}

The grid for X $\times$ Y is shown below.
b See graph.   **c** See graph.

142 a {(spider, cat), (spider, dog), (spider, bird),
(cat, cat), (cat, dog), (cat, bird),
(man, cat), (man, dog), (man, bird),
(rat, cat), (rat, dog), (rat, bird)}

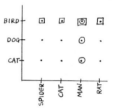

b See graph.   **d** Point is both encircled and
c See graph.   enclosed with a square.

143 a {$(210, 70), (210, 66), (210, 72), (210, 61),$
$(190, 70), (190, 66), (190, 72), (190, 61),$
$(150, 70), (150, 66), (150, 72), (150, 61),$
$(120, 70), (120, 66), (120, 72), (120, 61)$}

b See graph at left below.

c {$(210, 72), (150, 66), (190, 70), (120, 61)$}

144 100 * See graph at right above. * No * 45

145 See graph at left below. * No * 6

146 See graph at right above. * Yes * Y is an
infinite set.

147

(graph)

* See graph. * No * Infinitely many

148 a $\{(1, 3), (2, 6), (3, 9),$
$(4, 12), (5, 15), (6, 18), \ldots\}$
* Proportional relation

b $\{(4, 1), (6, 2), (8, 3),$
$(10, 4), (12, 5), (14, 6), \ldots\}$
* Not a proportional relation

c $\{(1, 1), (1, 2), (1, 3), (1, 4), (1, 5), (1,6), \ldots\}$
* Not a proportional relation

d $\{(2, 3), (4, 6), (6, 9),$
$(8, 12), (10, 15), (12, 18), \ldots\}$
* Proportional relation

e $\{(2, 5), (4, 5), (6, 5),$
$(8, 5), (10, 5), (12, 5), \ldots\}$
* Not a proportional relation

f $\{(1, 1), (2, 2), (3, 3), (4, 4), (5, 5), (6, 6), \ldots\}$
* Proportional relation

g $\{(1, 1), (2, 4), (3, 9),$
$(4, 16), (5, 25), (6, 36), \ldots\}$
* Not a proportional relation

h $\{(5, 3), (10, 6), (15, 9),$
$(20, 12), (25, 15), (30, 18), \ldots\}$
* Proportional relation

149 As shown in the following graph, each set is a subset of $C \times C$.

(graph)

150 a Examples are (2, 6), (3, 9), (100, 300), (300, 900), (3000, 9000), and (2000, 6000).

b Examples are (10, 2), (15, 3), (20, 4), (200, 40), (2000, 400), and (5000, 1000).

c Examples are (4, 6), (6, 9), (40, 60), (60, 90), (2000, 3000), and (4000, 6000).

d Examples are (10, 4), (20, 8), (40, 16), (150, 60), (500, 200), and (2500, 1000).

e Examples are (2, 2), (3, 3), (100, 100), (1000, 1000), (2000, 2000), and (5000, 5000).

f Examples are (3, 5), (6, 10), (60, 100), (300, 500), (1500, 2500), and (3000, 5000).

g Examples are (1, 5), (2, 10), (20, 100), (200, 1000), (2000, 10000), and (4000, 20000).

h Examples are (27, 34), (54, 68), (270, 340), (540, 680), (1080, 1360), and (1350, 1700).

151 $\{5/8, 10/16, 15/24, 20/32, 25/40,$
$30/48, 35/56, 40/64, 45/72,$
$50/80, 500/800, \ldots\}$
* The graph of this proportional relation is shown at the left below.

(graphs)

152 $3/2$ * Examples are 6/4, 9/6, 12/8, 30/20, 60/40, and 450/300. * The graph is shown at the right above.

153 $2/50$ * Examples are 4/100, 6/150, 8/200, 10/250, 100/2500, and 400/10000.

154 $45/120$ * $\{3/8, 6/16, 9/24, 12/32,$ $15/40, 18/48, \ldots\}$

155 $\{10/2, 15/3, 40/8, 60/12\}$ is an example. * The graph is shown below.

156 a No   c Yes   e No   g Yes
b Yes   d Yes   f No   h Yes

157 **a** {5/2, 10/4, 15/6, 20/8, . . .} *
The graph is shown below.
b {9/10, 18/20, 27/30, 36/40, . . .} *
The graph is shown below.
c {3/4, 6/8, 9/12, 12/16, . . .} *
The graph is shown below.
d {4/3, 8/6, 12/9, 16/12, . . .} *
The graph is shown below.

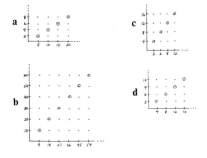

158 The graph is shown below. For each ordered
pair associated with a point in the graph,
the first component refers to a number of
inches and the second component refers
to a number of feet. If we wish to
"convert" 24 inches to feet, for example,
we locate the point associated with the
rate pair whose first component is 24 and
note that its second component is 2. Hence,
we know that 24 inches is equal to 2 feet.

159 **a** 3 feet is the same length as 1 yard.
This fact can be represented by the rate
pair 3/1. Thus, the graph of the
proportional relation whose members
are of the form 3n/n can be used to
convert feet to yards, as shown below.
If we wish to convert 9 feet to yards,
we locate the point associated with the
rate pair whose first component is 9.
Since the second component is 3, we
know that 9 feet is the same as 3 yards.

b We can make use of the graph of the
proportional relation whose members
are of the form 2n/n for converting pints
to quarts. This graph is shown at the
right at the bottom of column 1. A method
similar to the one described in part a can
be used for converting pints to quarts.
c We can make use of the graph of the
proportional relation whose members
are of the form 4n/n to convert pecks to
bushels. This graph is shown below.

d We can make use of the graph of the
proportional relation whose members
are of the form 3n/2n to convert gluz to
murds. This graph is shown above.

160

The points in the graph of A are encircled.
The points in the graph of B are enclosed
by squares. From the graphs, it is
apparent that A and B are linear relations
and that the points in the graphs are
contained in different straight lines that
do not intersect. Thus, it appears that no
point is in both graphs, and, hence, no
element of either relation belongs to the
other relation.

161 $3/15 = 39/x$. $3x = 585$.
$x = 195$. 195 cents, or \$1.95
162 $30/100 = x/210$. $6300 = 100x$.
$63 = x$. 63 dozen eggs
163 $65/100 = 611/x$. $65x = 61100$.
$x = 940$. 940 lb.
164 $35/50 = x/100$. $3500 = 50x$. $x = 70$. 70%
165 $21/100 = 840/x$. $21x = 84,000$.
$x = 4000$. \$4000
166 $5280/1 = x/60$. $x = 316,800$.
$316,800/60 = y/1$. $316,800 = 60y$.
$5280 = y$. 5280 feet per minute
167 From exercise 166, you know that 60 miles
per hour is the same as 5280 feet per

minute. Since 1 minute is the same as
60 seconds, you can proceed as follows.
5280/60 = x/1. 5280 = 60x.
88 = x. 88 feet per second

168 12/80 = x/100. 1200 = 80x. 15 = x. 15%
169 5 − 4 = 1. 1/4 = x/100. 100 = 4x.
25 = x. 25%
170 5/100 = 150/x. 5x = 15,000.
x = 3000. $3000
171 1/45,000 = x/900,000. 900,000 = 45,000x.
20 = x. 20 cows
* 1/45,000 = 15/x. x = 675,000.
675,000 head of cattle
172 80/100 = 44/x. 80x = 4400. x = 55. $55
* 80/100 = x/120. 9600 = 100x. 96 = x. $96
173 1/4 = 56/x. x = 224. 224 guilders
174 10 men. This problem cannot be solved by
using equivalent rate pairs. It is a problem
involving inverse variation and must be
solved by another method.
175 The methods discussed in this section do
not apply to this situation. Actually,
3 boys can probably see the same distance
as 1 boy. That is a distance of 5 miles,
in this case.
176 The graph is shown at the left below.

* Yes * No
177 The graph is shown at the right above.
* No * No
178 The graph is shown below.

* No * No
179 No * No
180 1, 3, 6, 10, 15, 21, 28, 36, 45, 55, 66, 78,
91, 105, 120, 136, 153, 171, 190, and 210
181 5050 * 7626 * 500,500 * 758,296

182 We can represent any two consecutive
triangular numbers by $\frac{n(n+1)}{2}$
and $\frac{(n+1)(n+2)}{2}$. Note that
$$\frac{n(n+1)}{2} + \frac{(n+1)(n+2)}{2} =$$
$$\frac{n^2+n}{2} + \frac{n^2+3n+2}{2} =$$
$$\frac{2n^2+4n+2}{2} = n^2+2n+1 = (n+1)^2.$$
For any n, $(n+1)^2$ is obviously a square
number. Therefore, the sum of any two
consecutive triangular numbers is a
square number.

183
2 = 1 + 1.   14 = 10 + 3 + 1.
3 = 1 + 1 + 1.   15 = 6 + 6 + 3.
4 = 3 + 1.   16 = 10 + 6.
5 = 3 + 1 + 1.   17 = 10 + 6 + 1.
6 = 3 + 3.   18 = 15 + 3.
7 = 6 + 1.   19 = 15 + 3 + 1.
8 = 6 + 1 + 1.   20 = 10 + 10.
9 = 6 + 3.   21 = 15 + 6.
10 = 6 + 3 + 1.   22 = 21 + 1.
11 = 10 + 1.   23 = 21 + 1 + 1.
12 = 10 + 1 + 1.   24 = 21 + 3.
13 = 10 + 3.   25 = 10 + 15.

184
1 = 1 + 0 + 0 + 0.
2 = 1 + 1 + 0 + 0.
3 = 1 + 1 + 1 + 0.
4 = 4 + 0 + 0 + 0.
5 = 4 + 1 + 0 + 0.
6 = 4 + 1 + 1 + 0.
7 = 4 + 1 + 1 + 1.
8 = 4 + 4 + 0 + 0.
9 = 9 + 0 + 0 + 0.
10 = 9 + 1 + 0 + 0.
11 = 9 + 1 + 1 + 0.
12 = 9 + 1 + 1 + 1.
13 = 9 + 4 + 0 + 0.
14 = 9 + 4 + 1 + 0.
15 = 9 + 4 + 1 + 1.
16 = 16 + 0 + 0 + 0.
17 = 16 + 1 + 0 + 0.
18 = 16 + 1 + 1 + 0.
19 = 16 + 1 + 1 + 1.
20 = 16 + 4 + 0 + 0.
21 = 16 + 4 + 1 + 0.
22 = 16 + 4 + 1 + 1.

23 = 9 + 9 + 4 + 1.
24 = 16 + 4 + 4 + 0.
25 = 25 + 0 + 0 + 0.

185 The pattern for the 1000th rectangular number would be 1000 rows of dots with 1001 dots in each row. From this we can conclude that the 1000th rectangular number is 1001 · 1000, or 1,001,000.

186 $(n + 1)n$, or $n^2 + n$

187 1, 5, 12, 22, 35, 51, 70, 92, 117, 145, 176, 210, 247, 287, 330, 376, 425, 477, 532, and 590

188 Including zero as a triangular number and including 0 and 1 as square numbers, we find that the expression for the nth triangular number is $\dfrac{(n-1)n}{2}$ and the expression for the nth square number is $(n-1)^2$. Thus, the expression for the $(n+1)$st square number is n^2. We are considering a pentagonal number as the sum of an nth triangular number and the $(n+1)$st square number.

Thus, we can obtain $\dfrac{(n-1)n}{2} + n^2 =$

$\dfrac{n^2-n}{2} + n^2 = \dfrac{3n^2-n}{2} = \dfrac{n(3n-1)}{2}$.

Thus, $\dfrac{n(3n-1)}{2}$ is an expression for the nth pentagonal number.

189
1 = 1 + 0 + 0 + 0 + 0.
2 = 1 + 1 + 0 + 0 + 0.
3 = 1 + 1 + 1 + 0 + 0.
4 = 1 + 1 + 1 + 1 + 0.
5 = 5 + 0 + 0 + 0 + 0.
6 = 5 + 1 + 0 + 0 + 0.
7 = 5 + 1 + 1 + 0 + 0.
8 = 5 + 1 + 1 + 1 + 0.
9 = 5 + 1 + 1 + 1 + 1.
10 = 5 + 5 + 0 + 0 + 0.
11 = 5 + 5 + 1 + 0 + 0.
12 = 12 + 0 + 0 + 0 + 0.
13 = 12 + 1 + 0 + 0 + 0.
14 = 12 + 1 + 1 + 0 + 0.
15 = 12 + 1 + 1 + 1 + 0.
16 = 12 + 1 + 1 + 1 + 1.
17 = 12 + 5 + 0 + 0 + 0.
18 = 12 + 5 + 1 + 0 + 0.
19 = 12 + 5 + 1 + 1 + 0.
20 = 12 + 5 + 1 + 1 + 1.

190 If you continue the process with 64,

you will find that the last difference is 0. ∗
As examples, we will use the square numbers 9, 16, and 36.

9	16	36
−1	−1	−1
8	15	35
−3	−3	−3
5	12	32
−5	−5	−5
0	7	27
	−7	−7
	0	20
		−9
		11
		−11
		0

The results are always the same. That is, the last difference is always 0.

191 Let $2n$ represent any even number, and let $2m + 1$ represent any odd number. $2n + (2m + 1) = 2(n + m) + 1$. Since $2(n + m)$ is even, $2(n + m) + 1$ is odd.

192 Let $2n$ and $2m$ represent any two even numbers. $2n \times 2m = 4nm = 2(2mn) = 2k$, where $k = 2nm$. $2k$ is of the form $2n$ and, hence, represents an even number.

193 Let $2n + 1$ represent any odd number. $(2n + 1)^2 = 4n^2 + 4n + 1 = 2(2n^2 + 2n) + 1 = 2k + 1$, where $k = 2n^2 + 2n$. $2k + 1$ is of the form $2n + 1$ and, hence, represents an odd number.

194 Let $2n$ represent any even number. $(2n)^2 = 4n^2$, and $(2n)^2 + 1 = 4n^2 + 1 = 2(2n^2) + 1 = 2k + 1$, where $k = 2n^2$. $2k + 1$ is of the form $2n + 1$ and, hence, represents an odd number.

195 Let $2n$ represent any even number. $3(2n) + 1 = 6n + 1 = 2(3n) + 1 = 2k + 1$, where $k = 3n$. $2k + 1$ is of the form $2n + 1$ and, hence, represents an odd number.

196 The following sentences show how 149 can be expressed as the sum of a power of 2 and another number.
149 = 2^1 + 147.   149 = 2^5 + 117.
149 = 2^2 + 145.   149 = 2^6 + 85.
149 = 2^3 + 141.   149 = 2^7 + 21.
149 = 2^4 + 133.

Because none of the numbers 147, 145, 141, 133, 117, 85, or 21 is a prime number, 149 cannot be expressed as the sum of a power of 2 and a prime number.

197 All of the even numbers between 50 and 150 can be expressed as the sum of two prime numbers. Below are 10 specific examples.

$56 = 43 + 13.$ $66 = 59 + 7.$
$58 = 47 + 11.$ $68 = 37 + 31.$
$60 = 31 + 29.$ $70 = 41 + 29.$
$62 = 43 + 19.$ $72 = 61 + 11.$
$64 = 61 + 3.$ $74 = 43 + 31.$

198 $13! + 2; 13! + 3; 13! + 4; 13! + 5; \dots;$ $13! + 13$, which is equal to $6,227,020,802;$ $6,227,020,803; 6,227,020,804; 6,227,020,805;$ $\dots; 6,227,020,813.$ This sequence does not contain a prime because the first number is divisible by 2, the second by 3, the third by 4, and so on.

199 $2(1)^2 + 29 = 31.$ $2(4)^2 + 29 = 61.$
$2(2)^2 + 29 = 37.$ $2(5)^2 + 29 = 79.$
$2(3)^2 + 29 = 47.$ $2(6)^2 + 29 = 101.$

* You might make the conjecture that a prime number is always obtained from $2n^2 + 29.$ * $2(29)^2 + 29 = 2(29)(29) + 29 = 58(29) + 1(29) = 59(29)$, which is not a prime number.

200
a 2 and 3   i 1009
b 2, 3, and 5   j 2, 3, and 7
c 2 and 3   k 3 and 107
d 3 and 5   l 2, 3, and 11
e 3 and 5   m 2 and 3
f 2, 3, 5, and 7   n 2, 3, and 7
g 3 and 11   o 3, 13, and 17
h 7

201 Examples are 9, 21, 33, and 49.
202 9 and 25, 1 and 225, 5 and 45 $* 5 \cdot 5 \cdot 9$
* Yes

203
a $5 \cdot 21$ c $9 \cdot 21$
b $9 \cdot 9$ d $21 \cdot 21$; also, $9 \cdot 49$

204 No. For example, there are two prime factorizations of 441, $21 \cdot 21$ and $9 \cdot 49$.

205
a 24   c 16   e 42
b 2   d 35   f 63

206
a $16380 = 1 \cdot 10200 + 6180.$
$10200 = 1 \cdot 6180 + 4020.$
$6180 = 1 \cdot 4020 + 2160.$
$4020 = 1 \cdot 2160 + 1860.$
$2160 = 1 \cdot 1860 + 300.$
$1860 = 6 \cdot 300 + 60.$
$300 = 5 \cdot 60 + 0.$
The gcd is 60.

b $7553 = 2 \cdot 3071 + 1411.$
$3071 = 2 \cdot 1411 + 249.$
$1411 = 5 \cdot 249 + 166.$
$249 = 1 \cdot 166 + 83.$
$166 = 2 \cdot 83 + 0.$
The gcd is 83.

207
a 60   c 120   e 100   g 240
b 20   d 90   f 144

208

$\frac{1}{4}$ $\frac{3}{12}$

$\frac{2}{8}$ $\frac{4}{16}$

* Yes

209

$\frac{1}{5}$ $\frac{3}{15}$

$\frac{2}{10}$ $\frac{4}{20}$

* Yes

210
a Examples are $\frac{10}{12}, \frac{15}{18}, \frac{20}{24}, \frac{30}{36}, \frac{500}{600},$ and $\frac{600}{720}.$
b Examples are $\frac{30}{68}, \frac{45}{102}, \frac{75}{170}, \frac{105}{238}, \frac{120}{272},$ and $\frac{1500}{3400}.$
c Examples are $\frac{4}{14}, \frac{6}{21}, \frac{8}{28}, \frac{16}{56}, \frac{200}{700},$ and $\frac{400}{1400}.$
d Examples are $\frac{8}{10}, \frac{16}{20}, \frac{20}{25}, \frac{28}{35}, \frac{32}{40},$ and $\frac{8000}{10000}.$
e Examples are $\frac{0}{1}, \frac{0}{7}, \frac{0}{11}, \frac{0}{16}, \frac{0}{100},$ and $\frac{0}{1200}.$

211
a Examples are $\frac{1}{2}, \frac{2}{4}, \frac{8}{16},$ and $\frac{20}{40},$ which you obtain by replacing a by 1, 2, 8, and 20 respectively. You obtain a set of equivalent fractions.
b Examples are $\frac{1}{2}, \frac{1}{6}, \frac{1}{10},$ and $\frac{1}{20},$ which you obtain by replacing b by 2, 6, 10, and 20 respectively. You do not obtain a set of equivalent fractions.
c Examples are $\frac{2}{4}, \frac{7}{14}, \frac{9}{18},$ and $\frac{21}{42},$ which you obtain by replacing n by 1, 6, 8, and 20 respectively. You obtain a set of equivalent fractions.
d Examples are $\frac{2}{4}, \frac{3}{5}, \frac{9}{11},$ and $\frac{14}{16},$ which you obtain by replacing n by 3, 4, 10, and 15 respectively. You do not obtain a set of equivalent fractions.

212
a $\frac{2}{3}$ b $\frac{3}{5}$ c $\frac{1}{3}$ d $\frac{3}{10}$ e $\frac{9}{2}$ f $\frac{3}{1}$

213
a Examples are $\frac{8}{14}, \frac{12}{21},$ and $\frac{48}{84}.$
b Examples are $\frac{3}{4}, \frac{6}{8},$ and $\frac{30}{40}.$
c Examples are $\frac{5}{8}, \frac{20}{32},$ and $\frac{50}{80}.$

d Examples are $\frac{4}{18}, \frac{40}{180},$ and $\frac{48}{216}.$

e Examples are $\frac{6}{1}, \frac{12}{2},$ and $\frac{36}{6}.$

214 **a** $\frac{4}{7}$ **b** $\frac{3}{4}$ **c** $\frac{5}{8}$ **d** $\frac{2}{9}$ **e** $\frac{6}{1}$

215 $\frac{a}{c} = \frac{b}{c}.$

Given

$ac = bc.$

Definition of equal rational numbers of arithmetic

$ac + cd = bc + cd.$

Addition property of equality for natural numbers

$ca + cd = cb + cd.$

Commutative property of multiplication of natural numbers

$c(a + d) = c(b + d).$

Distributive property for natural numbers

$(a + d)c = (b + d)c.$

Commutative property of multiplication of natural numbers

$\frac{a+d}{c} = \frac{b+d}{c}.$

Definition of equal rational numbers of arithmetic

$\frac{a}{c} + \frac{d}{c} = \frac{b}{c} + \frac{d}{c}.$

Definition of sum of two rational numbers of arithmetic

216 $\frac{a}{b} + \frac{c}{d} = \frac{ad + bc}{bd}.$

Sum of two rational numbers of arithmetic

$\frac{ad + bc}{bd} = \frac{bc + ad}{bd}.$

Commutative property of addition of natural numbers

$\frac{bc + ad}{bd} = \frac{cb + da}{db}.$

Commutative property of multiplication of natural numbers

$\frac{cb + da}{db} = \frac{c}{d} + \frac{a}{b}.$

Definition of the sum of two rational numbers of arithmetic

$\frac{a}{b} + \frac{c}{d} = \frac{c}{d} + \frac{a}{b}.$

Transitive property of equality

217 $\left(\frac{a}{b} + \frac{c}{d}\right) + \frac{e}{f} = \frac{ad + bc}{bd} + \frac{e}{f}.$

Definition of sum of two rational numbers of arithmetic

$\frac{ad + bc}{bd} + \frac{e}{f} = \frac{(ad + bc)f + bde}{bdf}.$

Definition of sum of two rational numbers of arithmetic

$\frac{(ad + bc)f + bde}{bdf} = \frac{(abf + bcf) + bde}{bdf}.$

Distributive property for natural numbers

$\frac{(adf + bcf) + bde}{bdf} = \frac{adf + (bcf + bde)}{bdf}.$

Associative property of addition of natural numbers

$\frac{adf + (bcf + bde)}{bdf} = \frac{adf + b(cf + de)}{bdf}.$

Distributive property for natural numbers

$\frac{adf + b(cf + de)}{bdf} = \frac{a}{b} + \frac{cf + de}{df}.$

Definition of sum of two rational numbers of arithmetic

$\frac{a}{b} + \frac{cf + de}{df} = \frac{a}{b} + \left(\frac{c}{d} + \frac{e}{f}\right).$

Sum of two rational numbers of arithmetic

$\left(\frac{a}{b} + \frac{c}{d}\right) + \frac{e}{f} = \frac{a}{b} + \left(\frac{c}{d} + \frac{e}{f}\right).$

Transitive property of equality

218 **a** $\frac{3}{1}$ **c** $\frac{16}{9}$ **e** $\frac{37}{15}$ **g** $\frac{94}{45}$

b $\frac{11}{5}$ **d** $\frac{3}{2}$ **f** $\frac{19}{2}$ **h** $\frac{37}{9}$

219 **a** One example is $\frac{4}{6} + \frac{2}{9}.$ Sum is $\frac{3}{1}.$

b One example is $\frac{18}{10} + \frac{20}{50}.$ Sum is $\frac{11}{5}.$

c One example is $\frac{45}{27} + \frac{10}{90}.$ Sum is $\frac{16}{9}.$

d One example is $\frac{35}{40} + \frac{25}{40}.$ Sum is $\frac{3}{2}.$

e One example is $\frac{6}{9} + \frac{27}{15}.$ Sum is $\frac{37}{15}.$

f One example is $\frac{14}{2} + \frac{25}{10}.$ Sum is $\frac{19}{2}.$

g One example is $\frac{42}{27} + \frac{40}{75}.$ Sum is $\frac{94}{45}.$

h One example is $\frac{30}{270} + \frac{16}{4}.$ Sum is $\frac{37}{9}.$

220 $\frac{a}{b} = \frac{c}{d}.$

Given

$ad = cb.$

Definition of equal rational numbers of arithmetic

$(ad)(ef) = (cb)(ef).$

Multiplication property of equality for natural numbers

$(ae)(df) = (ce)(bf).$

Associative and commutative properties of multiplication of natural numbers

$\frac{ae}{bf} = \frac{ce}{df}.$

Definition of equal rational numbers of arithmetic

$\frac{a}{b} \cdot \frac{e}{f} = \frac{c}{d} \cdot \frac{e}{f}.$

Definition of product of two rational numbers of arithmetic

221 $\frac{a}{b} \cdot \frac{c}{d} = \frac{ac}{bd}.$

Definition of product of two rational numbers of arithmetic

$\frac{ac}{bd} = \frac{ca}{db}.$

Commutative property of multiplication of natural numbers

$\frac{ca}{db} = \frac{c}{d} \cdot \frac{a}{b}.$

Definition of product of two rational numbers of arithmetic

$\frac{a}{b} \cdot \frac{c}{d} = \frac{c}{d} \cdot \frac{a}{b}.$

Transitive property of equality

222 $\left(\frac{a}{b} \cdot \frac{c}{d}\right) \cdot \frac{e}{f} = \frac{ac}{bd} \cdot \frac{e}{f}.$

Definition of product of two rational numbers of arithmetic

$\frac{ac}{bd} \cdot \frac{e}{f} = \frac{(ac)e}{(bd)f}.$

Definition of product of two rational numbers of arithmetic

$\frac{(ac)e}{(bd)f} = \frac{a(ce)}{b(df)}.$

Associative property of multiplication of natural numbers

$\frac{a(ce)}{b(df)} = \frac{a}{b} \cdot \frac{ce}{df}.$

Definition of product of two rational numbers of arithmetic

$\frac{a}{b} \cdot \frac{ce}{df} = \frac{a}{b} \cdot \left(\frac{c}{d} \cdot \frac{e}{f}\right).$

Definition of product of two rational numbers of arithmetic

$\left(\frac{a}{b} \cdot \frac{c}{d}\right) \cdot \frac{e}{f} = \frac{a}{b} \cdot \left(\frac{c}{d} \cdot \frac{e}{f}\right).$

Transitive property of equality

223 **a** $\frac{3}{10}$ **b** $\frac{9}{20}$ **c** $\frac{33}{8}$ **d** $\frac{15}{52}$ **e** $\frac{4}{1}$

224 $\frac{0}{1} \cdot \frac{a}{b} = \frac{0 \cdot a}{1 \cdot b}.$

Definition of product of two rational numbers of arithmetic

$\frac{0 \cdot a}{1 \cdot b} = \frac{0}{b}.$

Zero property of multiplication of natural numbers and identity-element property of multiplication of natural numbers

$\frac{0}{b} = \frac{0}{1}.$

Definition of equal rational numbers of arithmetic

$\frac{0}{1} \cdot \frac{a}{b} = \frac{0}{1}.$

Transitive property of equality

225 **a** $\frac{9}{5}$ **b** $\frac{3}{7}$ **c** $\frac{11}{37}$ **d** $\frac{15}{13}$ **e** $\frac{21}{10}$ **f** $\frac{1}{3}$

226 **a** $\frac{2}{3}(\frac{1}{5} + \frac{5}{6}) = \frac{2}{3}(\frac{31}{30}) = \frac{31}{45}.$

$\frac{2}{3} \cdot \frac{1}{5} + \frac{2}{3} \cdot \frac{5}{6} = \frac{2}{15} + \frac{5}{9} = \frac{31}{45}.$

Since both $\frac{2}{3}(\frac{1}{5} + \frac{5}{6})$ and $\frac{2}{3} \cdot \frac{1}{5} + \frac{2}{3} \cdot \frac{5}{6}$ are equal to $\frac{31}{45}$, we know the distributive property holds for this example.

b $\frac{6}{1}(\frac{1}{2} + \frac{2}{3}) = \frac{6}{1}(\frac{7}{6}) = \frac{7}{1}.$

$\frac{6}{1} \cdot \frac{1}{2} + \frac{6}{1} \cdot \frac{2}{3} = 3 + \frac{4}{1} = \frac{7}{1}.$

Since both $\frac{6}{1}(\frac{1}{2} + \frac{2}{3})$ and $\frac{6}{1} \cdot \frac{1}{2} + \frac{6}{1} \cdot \frac{2}{3}$ are equal to $\frac{7}{1}$, we know the distributive property holds for this example.

227 **a** Three examples are:

$\frac{3}{4} + \frac{1}{2} > \frac{1}{4} + \frac{1}{2}.$

$\frac{5}{8} + \frac{7}{3} > \frac{1}{3} + \frac{7}{3}.$

$\frac{13}{2} + \frac{1}{6} > \frac{5}{2} + \frac{1}{6}.$

b Three examples are:

$\frac{3}{4} \cdot \frac{1}{3} > \frac{1}{8} \cdot \frac{1}{3}.$

$\frac{17}{4} \cdot \frac{5}{6} > \frac{1}{4} \cdot \frac{5}{6}.$

$\frac{9}{10} \cdot \frac{7}{10} > \frac{1}{2} \cdot \frac{7}{10}.$

228 **a** $<$ **c** $<$ **e** $=$ **g** $>$
b $>$ **d** $<$ **f** $>$ **h** $=$

229 It is less than $\frac{1}{1}$. * It is greater than $\frac{1}{1}$.

230 **a** $\frac{a}{b} > \frac{463}{198}$, since $\frac{581}{580} > \frac{1}{1}.$

b $\frac{x}{y} > \frac{1}{1}$, since $\frac{a}{b} > \frac{1}{1}$ and $\frac{c}{d} > \frac{1}{1}.$

c $\frac{c}{d} = \frac{1}{1}.$ **d** $\frac{c}{d} > \frac{1}{1}.$ **e** $\frac{c}{d} < \frac{1}{1}.$

231 **a** $\frac{1}{2} = \{\frac{1}{2}, \frac{2}{4}, \frac{3}{6}, \frac{4}{8}, \frac{5}{10}, \frac{6}{12}, \dots\}.$

$\frac{1}{3} = \{\frac{1}{3}, \frac{2}{6}, \frac{3}{9}, \frac{4}{12}, \frac{5}{15}, \frac{6}{18}, \dots\}.$

b $\frac{3}{4} = \{\frac{3}{4}, \frac{6}{8}, \frac{9}{12}, \frac{12}{16}, \frac{15}{20}, \frac{18}{24}, \dots\}.$

$\frac{1}{7} = \{\frac{1}{7}, \frac{2}{14}, \frac{3}{21}, \frac{4}{28}, \frac{5}{35}, \frac{6}{42}, \dots\}.$

c $\frac{5}{7} = \{\frac{5}{7}, \frac{10}{14}, \frac{15}{21}, \frac{20}{28}, \frac{25}{35}, \frac{30}{42}, \dots\}.$

$\frac{3}{11} = \{\frac{3}{11}, \frac{6}{22}, \frac{9}{33}, \frac{12}{44}, \frac{15}{55}, \frac{18}{66}, \dots\}.$

d $\frac{1}{2} = \{\frac{1}{2}, \frac{2}{4}, \frac{3}{6}, \frac{4}{8}, \frac{5}{10}, \frac{6}{12}, \dots\}.$

$\frac{2}{4} = \{\frac{1}{2}, \frac{2}{4}, \frac{3}{6}, \frac{4}{8}, \frac{5}{10}, \frac{6}{12}, \dots\}.$

232 **a** $\{\frac{5}{6}, \frac{10}{12}, \frac{15}{18}, \frac{20}{24}, \frac{25}{30}, \frac{30}{36}, \dots\}$

b $\{\frac{25}{28}, \frac{50}{56}, \frac{75}{84}, \frac{100}{112}, \frac{125}{140}, \frac{150}{168}, \dots\}$

c $\{\frac{76}{77}, \frac{152}{154}, \frac{228}{231}, \frac{304}{308}, \frac{380}{385}, \frac{456}{462}, \dots\}$

d $\{\frac{1}{1}, \frac{2}{2}, \frac{3}{3}, \frac{4}{4}, \frac{5}{5}, \frac{6}{6}, \dots\}$

233 **a** $\{\frac{1}{6}, \frac{2}{12}, \frac{3}{18}, \frac{4}{24}, \frac{5}{30}, \frac{6}{36}, \dots\}$

b $\{\frac{3}{28}, \frac{6}{56}, \frac{9}{84}, \frac{12}{112}, \frac{15}{140}, \frac{18}{168}, \dots\}$

c $\{\frac{15}{77}, \frac{30}{154}, \frac{45}{231}, \frac{60}{308}, \frac{75}{385}, \frac{90}{462}, \dots\}$

d $\{\frac{1}{4}, \frac{2}{8}, \frac{3}{12}, \frac{4}{16}, \frac{5}{20}, \frac{6}{24}, \dots\}$

234 **a** $1\frac{2}{3}$ **b** 0 **c** $1\frac{5}{16}$ **d** $\frac{76}{113}$ **e** $\frac{45}{139}$

235 An example of the reflexive property is:

$\frac{5}{8} = \frac{5}{8}.$

An example of the symmetric property is:
If $\frac{1}{2} = \frac{28}{56}$, then $\frac{28}{56} = \frac{1}{2}.$

An example of the transitive property is:
If $\frac{3}{4} = \frac{9}{12}$ and $\frac{9}{12} = \frac{30}{40}$, then $\frac{3}{4} = \frac{30}{40}.$

236 Let us assume that there are two identity elements, 0 and 0', such that $\frac{a}{f} + 0 = \frac{a}{f}$ and $\frac{a}{f} + 0' = \frac{a}{f}$. Then from properties of equality, it follows that $\frac{a}{f} + 0 = \frac{a}{f} + 0'$; so 0 and 0' must be the same number. Hence, there is exactly one identity element for addition of rational numbers of arithmetic.

237 No $* \frac{3}{4} - \frac{1}{2}$ is not equal to $\frac{1}{2} - \frac{3}{4}$. $\frac{3}{4} - \frac{1}{2} = \frac{1}{4}$, but there is no rational number of arithmetic that is equal to $\frac{1}{2} - \frac{3}{4}$.

238 No $* (\frac{15}{16} - \frac{1}{4}) - \frac{1}{8}$ is not equal to $\frac{15}{16} - (\frac{1}{4} - \frac{1}{8})$. $(\frac{15}{16} - \frac{1}{4}) - \frac{1}{8} = \frac{9}{16}$, but $\frac{15}{16} - (\frac{1}{4} - \frac{1}{8}) = \frac{13}{16}$.

239 From $\frac{a}{b} + \frac{4}{5} = \frac{8}{3}$, we can obtain $\frac{5a + 4b}{5b} = \frac{8}{3}$. From this we obtain $3(5a + 4b) = 40b$, or $15a + 12b = 40b$. $15a + 12b = 40b$ is the same as $15a + 12b = 28b + 12b$. By the cancellation property of addition of natural numbers, we obtain $15a = 28b$, or $a \cdot 15 = 28 \cdot b$. By the definition of equal rational numbers of arithmetic, $a \cdot 15 = 28 \cdot b$ is the same as $\frac{a}{b} = \frac{15}{28}$.

240 a $\frac{7}{24}$ b $\frac{11}{60}$ c $\frac{11}{12}$ d $\frac{11}{10}$

241 a One such number is $\frac{x}{y} = \frac{2997}{4000}$.
b One such number is $\frac{x}{y} = \frac{665}{888}$.

242 $\frac{a}{b} \cdot \frac{3}{4} = \frac{9}{5}$.
$\frac{a \cdot 3}{b \cdot 4} = \frac{9}{5}$.
$\frac{3a}{4b} = \frac{9}{5}$.
$a \cdot 15 = 36 \cdot b$.
$\frac{a}{b} = \frac{36}{15}$.
Hence, $\frac{a}{b} = \frac{36}{15}$, or $\frac{12}{5}$.

243 Let $\frac{a}{b} \div \frac{c}{d} = \frac{x}{y}$ and let $(\frac{a}{b} \cdot \frac{e}{f}) \div (\frac{c}{d} \cdot \frac{e}{f}) = \frac{u}{v}$.
$\frac{a}{b} = \frac{x}{y} \cdot \frac{c}{d}$.
Assumption and relation between multiplication and division
$\frac{a}{b} = \frac{xc}{yd}$.
Definition of multiplication of rational numbers of arithmetic
$ayd = xcb$.
Definition of equal rational numbers of arithmetic
$xbc = ady$.
Symmetric property of equality and commutative property of multiplication of rational numbers of arithmetic
$\frac{x}{y} = \frac{ad}{bc}$.
Definition of equal rational numbers of arithmetic
$(\frac{a}{b} \cdot \frac{e}{f}) = \frac{u}{v} \cdot (\frac{c}{d} \cdot \frac{e}{f})$.
Assumption and relation between division and multiplication
$\frac{ae}{bf} = \frac{uce}{vdf}$.
Definition of multiplication of rational numbers of arithmetic

$aevdf = ucebf$.
Definition of equal rational numbers of arithmetic
$ubcef = adefv$.
Symmetric property of equality and commutative property of multiplication of rational numbers of arithmetic
$\frac{u}{v} = \frac{adef}{bcef}$.
Definition of equal rational numbers of arithmetic
$\frac{u}{v} = \frac{ad}{bc} \cdot \frac{e}{e} \cdot \frac{f}{f}$.
Definition of multiplication of rational numbers of arithmetic
$\frac{u}{v} = \frac{ad}{bc}$.
Identity-element property of multiplication of rational numbers of arithmetic [That is, $\frac{e}{e} = \frac{1}{1} = \frac{f}{f}$.]
$\frac{x}{y} = \frac{u}{v}$.
Transitive property of equality [Both $\frac{x}{y}$ and $\frac{u}{v}$ have been shown to be equal to $\frac{ad}{bc}$.]
Thus, $\frac{a}{b} \div \frac{c}{d} = (\frac{a}{b} \cdot \frac{e}{f}) \div (\frac{c}{d} \cdot \frac{e}{f})$.

244 a $\frac{5}{12}$ b $\frac{7}{32}$ c $\frac{27}{5}$ d $\frac{7}{4}$ e $\frac{2}{5}$

245 a Examples are $\frac{11}{16}, \frac{41}{64}$, and $\frac{23}{32}$.
b Examples are $\frac{43}{440}, \frac{21}{220}$, and $\frac{41}{440}$.
c Examples are $\frac{1}{2}, \frac{3}{2}$, and $\frac{5}{2}$.
d Examples are $\frac{19}{80}, \frac{9}{40}$, and $\frac{17}{80}$.

a

b

c

d

246 a Since one of the factors is $\frac{3}{16}$ and the product is also $\frac{3}{16}$, the other factor must be $\frac{1}{1}$, the identity element for multiplication. Thus, $u = 25$ since $\frac{25}{25} = \frac{1}{1}$.
b $n = 40$. c $n = 5$. d $n = 56$.

247 a $\frac{3}{5} + \frac{1}{6} = \frac{18}{30} + \frac{5}{30} = \frac{23}{30}$.
b $\frac{7}{10} + \frac{11}{24} = \frac{84}{120} + \frac{55}{120} = \frac{139}{120}$.
c $6\frac{3}{4} + 3\frac{5}{8} = (\frac{6}{1} + \frac{3}{4}) + (\frac{3}{1} + \frac{5}{8})$
$= (\frac{6}{1} + \frac{3}{4}) + (\frac{3}{1} + \frac{5}{8})$
$= (\frac{6}{1} + \frac{3}{1}) + (\frac{3}{4} + \frac{5}{8})$
$= \frac{9}{1} + \frac{11}{8} = \frac{72}{8} + \frac{11}{8} = \frac{83}{8}$.

d $\frac{23}{18} - \frac{9}{14} = \frac{161}{126} - \frac{81}{126} = \frac{80}{126} = \frac{40}{63}$.

e $8\frac{1}{3} - 5\frac{4}{5} = \frac{25}{3} - \frac{29}{5} = \frac{125}{15} - \frac{87}{15} = \frac{38}{15}$.

f $\frac{16}{5} \cdot \frac{1}{4} = \frac{4}{5}$.

g $4\frac{1}{12} \cdot 2\frac{11}{14} = \frac{49}{12} \cdot \frac{39}{14} = \frac{91}{8}$.

h $6\frac{2}{3} \cdot \frac{9}{10} = \frac{20}{3} \cdot \frac{9}{10} = \frac{6}{1}$.

i $\frac{12}{5} \div \frac{21}{40} = \frac{12}{5} \cdot \frac{40}{21} = \frac{32}{7}$.

j $5\frac{13}{15} \div 2\frac{2}{9} = \frac{88}{15} \div \frac{20}{9} = \frac{88}{15} \cdot \frac{9}{20} = \frac{66}{25}$.

248 a 49.6301 c .00608 e 9009.09
b 500.06 d 500.38 f 40,030.00

249 a $4 \cdot 1 + 6 \cdot \frac{1}{10} + 2 \cdot \frac{1}{100} + 3 \cdot \frac{1}{1000}$ *
$4 \cdot 10^0 + 6 \cdot 10^{-1} + 2 \cdot 10^{-2} + 3 \cdot 10^{-3}$

b $5 \cdot 100 + 8 \cdot 10 + 0 \cdot 1 + 0 \cdot \frac{1}{10} + 4 \cdot \frac{1}{100}$ *
$5 \cdot 10^2 + 8 \cdot 10^1 + 0 \cdot 10^0 + 0 \cdot 10^{-1} + 4 \cdot 10^{-2}$

c $9 \cdot 1 + 0 \cdot \frac{1}{10} + 0 \cdot \frac{1}{100} + 5 \cdot \frac{1}{1000}$ *
$9 \cdot 10^0 + 0 \cdot 10^{-1} + 0 \cdot 10^{-2} + 5 \cdot 10^{-3}$

d $0 \cdot \frac{1}{10} + 0 \cdot \frac{1}{100} + 5 \cdot \frac{1}{1000}$ *
$0 \cdot 10^{-1} + 0 \cdot 10^{-2} + 5 \cdot 10^{-3}$

e $5 \cdot \frac{1}{10} * 5 \cdot 10^{-1}$

f $1 \cdot 100 + 0 \cdot 10 + 0 \cdot 1 + 0 \cdot \frac{1}{10} + 0 \cdot \frac{1}{100} + 1 \cdot \frac{1}{1000}$ *
$1 \cdot 10^2 + 0 \cdot 10^1 + 0 \cdot 10^0 + 0 \cdot 10^{-1} + 0 \cdot 10^{-2} + 1 \cdot 10^{-3}$

250 a .4 d 13.2 g 1.82
b .56 e 1.463 h .72
c 5.6 f .015 i .95

251 a $\frac{4}{1} + \frac{1}{2} * 4.5$ d $\frac{3}{1} + \frac{1}{2}$ 3.5
b $\frac{32}{1} + \frac{1}{4} * 32.25$ e $\frac{1}{1} + \frac{7}{8} * 1.875$
c $\frac{20}{1} + \frac{3}{8} * 20.375$ f $\frac{6}{1} + \frac{3}{16} * 6.1875$

252 a $\frac{379}{100} + \frac{1245}{100} = \frac{1624}{100} = 16.24$. *
3.79
12.45
16.24

b $\frac{67180}{10000} + \frac{549}{10000} = \frac{67729}{10000} = 6.7229$. *
6.7180
.0549
6.7729

c $\frac{4582}{1000} - \frac{916}{1000} = \frac{3666}{1000} = 3.666$. *
4.582
.916
3.666

d $\frac{3483}{100} - \frac{1974}{100} = \frac{1509}{100} = 15.09$. *
34.83
19.74
15.09

e $\frac{81700}{1000} + \frac{4593}{1000} = \frac{86293}{1000} = 86.293$. *
81.700
4.593
86.293

f $\frac{5412}{100} - \frac{1986}{100} = \frac{3426}{100} = 34.26$. *
54.12
19.86
34.26

253 a $\frac{2}{3} + \frac{5}{6} = \frac{4}{6} + \frac{5}{6} = \frac{9}{6} = \frac{3}{2}$.

b $\frac{1}{2} + \frac{5}{8} = \frac{4}{8} + \frac{5}{8} = \frac{9}{8}$.

c $\frac{5}{1} + \frac{3}{11} = \frac{55}{11} + \frac{3}{11} = \frac{58}{11}$.

d $\frac{2}{5} + (\frac{1}{2} + \frac{1}{3}) = \frac{2}{5} + (\frac{3}{6} + \frac{2}{6}) = \frac{2}{5} + \frac{5}{6}$
$= \frac{12}{30} + \frac{25}{30} = \frac{37}{30}$.

e $(\frac{2}{5} + \frac{1}{2}) + \frac{1}{3} = (\frac{4}{10} + \frac{5}{10}) + \frac{1}{3} = \frac{9}{10} + \frac{1}{3}$
$= \frac{27}{30} + \frac{10}{30} = \frac{37}{30}$.

f $\frac{11}{3} + \frac{5}{9} = \frac{33}{9} + \frac{5}{9} = \frac{38}{9}$.

g $\frac{5}{2} + \frac{3}{1} = \frac{5}{2} + \frac{6}{2} = \frac{11}{2}$.

h $\frac{9}{5} + \frac{9}{4} = \frac{36}{20} + \frac{45}{20} = \frac{81}{20}$.

i $\frac{3}{8} + \frac{2}{8} = \frac{5}{8}$.

254 a $\frac{3}{4} \times \frac{6}{5} = \frac{9}{10}$.

b $6\frac{1}{2} \times 2 = \frac{13}{2} \times \frac{2}{1} = \frac{13}{1}$.

c $\frac{8}{3} \times \frac{3}{8} = \frac{1}{1}$.

d $\frac{7}{14} \times \frac{15}{6} = \frac{7}{1}$.

e $3\frac{2}{3} \times \frac{4}{11} = \frac{11}{3} \times \frac{4}{11} = \frac{4}{3}$.

f $6 \times \frac{1}{3} = \frac{6}{1} \times \frac{1}{3} = \frac{2}{1}$.

g $\frac{7}{2} \times \frac{12}{21} = \frac{2}{1}$.

h $\frac{5}{8} \times \frac{3}{10} = \frac{3}{16}$.

i $\frac{2}{3} \times \frac{1}{2} = \frac{1}{3}$.

255 a $1 \cdot 10^4 + 4 \cdot 10^3 + 5 \cdot 10^2 + 6 \cdot 10^1 + 2 \cdot 10^0$

b $1 \cdot 10^3 + 9 \cdot 10^2 + 0 \cdot 10^1 + 0 \cdot 10^0$
$\qquad + 0 \cdot 10^{-1} + 0 \cdot 10^{-2} + 2 \cdot 10^{-3}$

c $5 \cdot 10^3 + 0 \cdot 10^2 + 0 \cdot 10^1 + 5 \cdot 10^0$

d $5 \cdot 10^7 + 6 \cdot 10^6 + 9 \cdot 10^5 + 0 \cdot 10^4$
$\qquad + 2 \cdot 10^3 + 0 \cdot 10^2 + 0 \cdot 10^1 + 5 \cdot 10^0$

e $4 \cdot 10^{-1} + 5 \cdot 10^{-2} + 9 \cdot 10^{-3}$

f $0 \cdot 10^{-1} + 0 \cdot 10^{-2} + 0 \cdot 10^{-3} + 4 \cdot 10^{-4}$
$\qquad + 0 \cdot 10^{-5} + 9 \cdot 10^{-6}$

g $0 \cdot 10^{-1} + 0 \cdot 10^{-2} + 0 \cdot 10^{-3} + 0 \cdot 10^{-4}$
$\qquad + 0 \cdot 10^{-5} + 5 \cdot 10^{-6} + 0 \cdot 10^{-7}$
$\qquad + 0 \cdot 10^{-8} + 9 \cdot 10^{-9}$

h $4 \cdot 10^3 + 5 \cdot 10^2 + 0 \cdot 10^1 + 0 \cdot 10^0$
$\qquad + 0 \cdot 10^{-1} + 0 \cdot 10^{-2} + 0 \cdot 10^{-3}$
$\qquad + 5 \cdot 10^{-4} + 6 \cdot 10^{-5}$

i $1 \cdot 10^1 + 5 \cdot 10^0 + 6 \cdot 10^{-1} + 7 \cdot 10^{-2}$

256 **a** $\frac{56}{1}$ **d** $\frac{45,666,666}{1000}$ **g** $\frac{5006}{1000}$

b $\frac{98}{1000}$ **e** $\frac{400,001}{1000}$ **h** $\frac{809}{1,000,000}$

c $\frac{15}{10}$ **f** $\frac{145,145}{1000}$ **i** $\frac{40}{100,000}$

257 **a** $2.04 * .578 * 1.36 * 5$

b $5.64 * 1.088 * 5.24 * 27.2$

c $165.66 * 2349 * 134.34 * 9.58$

d $4545.009 * 40.905 * 4544.991 * 505,000$

e $4590.45 * 206,570.25 * 4499.55 * 100$

f $.3003 * .00009 * .2997 * 1000$

258 **a** $\frac{155}{10}, \frac{34}{100}, \frac{5270}{1000} * 5.27$

b $\frac{734}{100}, \frac{96}{10}, \frac{70.464}{1000} * 70.464$

c $\frac{999}{10}, \frac{111}{1000}, \frac{110,889}{10,000} * 11.0889$

d $\frac{101}{1000}, \frac{5}{1000} * \frac{505}{1,000,000} * .000505$

e $\frac{4567}{10}, \frac{15,055}{100} * \frac{68,756.185}{1000} * 68,756.185$

f $\frac{441}{1000}, \frac{51}{100,000} * \frac{22,491}{100,000,000} * .00022491$

259 **a** The digit 3 in .003 is associated with 10^{-3}. The digit 3 in .0003 is associated with 10^{-4}. Since $3 \cdot 10^{-3}$ (or .003) is greater than $3 \cdot 10^{-4}$ (or .0003), .003 is greater than .0003.

b The final digit in 7.45 expresses $5 \cdot 10^{-2}$ (or .05) and the final digit in 7.44 expresses $4 \cdot 10^{-2}$ (or .04). Thus, 7.45 is greater than 7.44.

c The digit 1 in .1 is associated with 10^{-1} and the digit 1 in 1 is associated with 10^0. Since $1 \cdot 10^{-1}$ (or .1) is less than $1 \cdot 10^0$ (or 1), .1 is less than 1.

d The digit 9 in 956.0 is associated with 10^2. The digit 9 in 95.60 is associated with 10^1. Since $9 \cdot 10^2$ (or 900) is greater than $9 \cdot 10^1$ (or 90), 956.0 is greater than 95.60.

e The final digit in .36 expresses $6 \cdot 10^{-2}$ (or .06) and the final digit in .38 expresses $8 \cdot 10^{-2}$ (or .08). Thus, .36 is less than .38.

f The digit 1 in .0001 is associated with 10^{-4}. The digit 1 in .001 is associated with 10^{-3}. Since $1 \cdot 10^{-4}$ is less than $1 \cdot 10^{-3}$, .0001 is less than .001.

260 **a** 4.56456×10^5

b 9.0009×10^{-8}

c 1.500083×10^{-1}

d $1.234089000045 \times 10^7$

e 6.5×10^0

f 1×10^{-4}

261 $-6, -\frac{22}{7}, -3, -\frac{12}{5}, -\frac{7}{3}, +\frac{2}{5}, +\frac{5}{12}, +\frac{13}{3}, +5, +\frac{27}{5}$

262 **a** $+\frac{29}{15}$ **b** $+\frac{31}{36}$ **c** $+\frac{4}{3}$ **d** $+\frac{14}{15}$

263 No. The additive inverse of 0 is 0. Thus, the additive inverse of a given rational number may be equal to the given number. The additive inverse of a negative number is a positive number. Any positive number is greater than any negative number. Thus, the additive inverse of a given rational number may be greater than the given number.

264 **a** -6 **c** $+\frac{5}{4}$ **e** $-\frac{10}{3}$ **g** 0

b $-\frac{3}{5}$ **d** $+4$ **f** $+\frac{2}{7}$

265 From the additive-inverse property, you know that the sum of a rational number and its additive inverse is the identity element for addition, 0. From the multiplicative-inverse property, you know that the product of a rational number of arithmetic and its multiplicative inverse is the identity element for multiplication, $\frac{1}{1}$, or 1.

266 **a** $15 + (-6) = (9 + 6) + (-6)$.
$15 + (-6) = 9 + \left(6 + (-6)\right)$.
$15 + (-6) = 9 + 0 = 9$.

b $(-18 + 16) + \left(18 + (-16)\right) = (-18 + 18) + \left(16 + (-16)\right)$.
$(-18 + 16) + \left(18 + (-16)\right) = 0$.
$(-18 + 16) + \left([2 + 16] + (-16)\right) = 0$.
$(-18 + 16) + \left(2 + [16 + (-16)]\right) = 0$.
$(-18 + 16) + 2 = 0$.
$(-18 + 16) + \left(2 + (-2)\right) = 0 + (-2)$.
$-18 + 16 = -2$.

c $\left(-7 + (-3)\right) + (7 + 3) =$
$\qquad (-7 + 7) + (-3 + 3).$
$\left(-7 + (-3)\right) + (7 + 3) = 0.$
$\left(-7 + (-3)\right) + 10 = 0.$
$\left(-7 + (-3)\right) + \left(10 + (-10)\right) =$
$\qquad 0 + (-10).$
$\left(-7 + (-3)\right) = -10.$

d $18 + (-8) = (10 + 8) + (-8).$
$18 + (-8) = 10 + \left(8 + (-8)\right).$
$18 + (-8) = 10.$

e $\left(14 + (-3)\right) + 26 =$
$\qquad \left([11 + 3] + (-3)\right) + 26.$
$\left(14 + (-3)\right) + 26 =$
$\qquad \left(11 + [3 + (-3)]\right) + 26.$
$\left(14 + (-3)\right) + 26 = 11 + 26.$
$\left(14 + (-3)\right) + 26 = 37.$

f $-9 + (-10 + 9) = \left(-9 + (-10)\right) + 9.$
$-9 + (-10 + 9) = \left(-10 + (-9)\right) + 9.$
$-9 + (-10 + 9) = -10 + (-9 + 9).$
$-9 + (-10 + 9) = -10.$

267 Positive

268 a $(-5 + 5) \cdot 2 = 0.$
$(-5 + 5) \cdot 2 = 2 \cdot (-5) + 2 \cdot 5.$
$2 \cdot (-5) + 2 \cdot 5 = 0.$
$2 \cdot (-5) + 10 = 0.$
$2 \cdot (-5) = -10.$
$-5 \cdot 2 = -10.$

b $-8 \cdot (-9 + 9) = 0.$
$-8 \cdot (-9 + 9) = -8 \cdot (-9) + (-8 \cdot 9).$
$-8 \cdot (-9) + (-8 \cdot 9) = 0.$
Now you must find $-8 \cdot 9$.
$(-8 + 8) \cdot 9 = 0.$
$(-8 + 8) \cdot 9 = 9 \cdot (-8) + 9 \cdot 8.$
$9 \cdot (-8) + 9 \cdot 8 = 0.$
$9 \cdot (-8) + 72 = 0.$
$9 \cdot (-8) = -72.$
$-8 \cdot 9 = -72.$
Next, substitute -72 for $-8 \cdot 9$ in
$-8 \cdot (-9) + (-8) \cdot 9 = 0$, obtaining
$-8 \cdot (-9) + (-72) = 0$. From this, you
can obtain $-8 \cdot (-9) = 72$.

c $14 \cdot (-21 + 21) = 0.$
$14 \cdot (-21 + 21) = 14 \cdot (-21) + 14 \cdot 21.$
$14 \cdot (-21) + 14 \cdot 21 = 0.$
$14 \cdot (-21) + 294 = 0.$
$14 \cdot (-21) = -294.$

d You can first find $(-3) \cdot (-4)$.
$-3 \cdot (-4 + 4) = 0.$
$-3 \cdot (-4 + 4) = -3 \cdot (-4) + (-3 \cdot 4).$
$-3 \cdot (-4) + (-3 \cdot 4) = 0.$

Before you can complete the procedure
for finding $(-3) \cdot (-4)$, you must find
$-3 \cdot 4$.
$(-3 + 3) \cdot 4 = 0.$
$(-3 + 3) \cdot 4 = 4 \cdot (-3) + 4 \cdot 3.$
$4 \cdot (-3) + 4 \cdot 3 = 0.$
$4 \cdot (-3) + 12 = 0.$
$4 \cdot (-3) = -12.$
$-3 \cdot 4 = -12.$
Now, substitute -12 for $-3 \cdot 4$ in
$-3 \cdot (-4) + (-3 \cdot 4) = 0$. You obtain
$-3 \cdot (-4) + (-12) = 0$, from which
you can obtain $-3 \cdot (-4) = 12$.
Now that you know that
$-3 \cdot (-4) = 12$, you can substitute 12
for $(-3) \cdot (-4)$ in $(-3) \cdot (-4) \cdot (-2)$,
obtaining $12 \cdot (-2)$. To find $12 \cdot (-2)$,
you proceed as follows.
$12 \cdot (-2 + 2) = 0.$
$12 \cdot (-2 + 2) = 12 \cdot (-2) + 12 \cdot 2.$
$12 \cdot (-2) + 12 \cdot 2 = 0.$
$12 \cdot (-2) + 24 = 0.$
$12 \cdot (-2) = -24.$
Thus, $(-3) \cdot (-4) \cdot (-2) = -24.$

269 Positive

270 Negative

271 a $-\frac{9}{4}$ **b** $+\frac{16}{105}$ **c** $-\frac{8}{45}$

272 The quotient of two non-zero rational
numbers is equal to the product of the
dividend and the multiplicative inverse of
the divisor. Since the multiplicative inverse
of a rational number is a rational number
and since the set of rational numbers is
closed under multiplication, non-zero
rational numbers are closed under division.

273 No. We can consider 1 as the right-identity
element for division, since $x \div 1 = x$ for
each x. However, for 1 to be the identity
element for division, $1 \div x = x$ must also
always be true. This is not the case.

274 a $-\frac{11}{15}$ **b** $-\frac{31}{36}$ **c** $+\frac{123}{120}$ **d** $-\frac{155}{98}$

275 No. We can consider 0 as the right-identity
element for subtraction, since $x - 0 = x$
for each x. However, for 0 to be the
identity element for subtraction,
$0 - x = x$ must also always be true.
This is not the case.

276 a $.8333\ldots$ **c** $-.111\ldots$ **e** $.090909\ldots$
    b $.32$ **d** 6.4 **f** -3.1416

277 $\frac{5}{16}, \frac{6}{125}, \frac{9}{40}, -\frac{6}{75}, \frac{9}{50}$

278 a $.\overset{.}{1}4285\overset{.}{7}$ d $.\overset{.}{5}7142\overset{.}{8}$

   b $.\overset{.}{2}8571\overset{.}{4}$ e $.\overset{.}{7}1428\overset{.}{5}$

   c $.\overset{.}{4}2857\overset{.}{1}$ f $.\overset{.}{8}5714\overset{.}{2}$

   * The repetends contain the same six digits, and these digits occur in the same order in the repetends.

279 a 4 non-zero remainders

   b 10   c 22   d 24   e 30

280 a $.2$ (or $.2\overset{.}{0}$)   c $-.04$ (or $-.04\overset{.}{0}$)

   b $.\overset{.}{4}$ d $-.0\overset{.}{3}225806451612\overset{.}{9}$

281 a $10x = 69.\overset{.}{9}.$ b $10x = 55.\overset{.}{5}.$

$\quad \underline{x = 6.\overset{.}{9}.}$ $\underline{x = 5.\overset{.}{5}.}$

$\quad 9x = 63.$ $9x = 50.$

$\quad x = \frac{63}{9}$ or $7.$ $x = \frac{50}{9}$ or $5\frac{5}{9}.$

   c $10x = 161.6\overset{.}{6}.$ d $100x = 1616.\overset{.}{1}\overset{.}{6}.$

$\quad \underline{x = 16.1\overset{.}{6}.}$ $\underline{x = 16.\overset{.}{1}\overset{.}{6}.}$

$\quad 9x = 145.5.$ $99x = 1600.$

$\quad x = \frac{1455}{90}$ or $16\frac{1}{6}.$ $x = \frac{1600}{99}$ or $16\frac{16}{99}.$

   e $1000x = 101.\overset{.}{1}0\overset{.}{1}.$

$\quad \underline{x = .\overset{.}{1}0\overset{.}{1}.}$

$\quad 999x = 101.$

$\quad x = \frac{101}{999}.$

   f $10,000x = 1001.\overset{.}{1}00\overset{.}{1}.$

$\quad \underline{x = .\overset{.}{1}00\overset{.}{1}.}$

$\quad 9999x = 1001.$

$\quad x = \frac{1001}{9999}.$

282 a $.\overset{.}{6}2\overset{.}{0}$ and $.61\overset{.}{9}$ d $.1875\overset{.}{0}$ and $.1874\overset{.}{9}$

   b $4.\overset{.}{0}$ and $3.\overset{.}{9}$ e $.8\overset{.}{0}$ and $.7\overset{.}{9}$

   c $.04\overset{.}{0}$ and $.03\overset{.}{9}$

283 Assume that $\sqrt{3}$ is a rational number. If this is so, there are two integers a and b, with b not equal to zero, for which it is true that $\frac{a}{b} = \sqrt{\frac{3}{1}}.$ If $\frac{a}{b} = \sqrt{\frac{3}{1}},$ it follows that $\frac{3}{1} = \frac{a^2}{b^2}$ and that $3b^2 = a^2.$ From this last condition, we know that $3b^2$ is to be equal to $a^2.$ a^2 has an even number of prime factors. So does $b^2.$ However, $3b^2$ has an odd number of prime factors, since it has a factor of 3 in addition to the prime factors of $b^2.$ Thus, a^2 and $3b^2$ represent two different ways of factoring the same number into the product of primes. This contradicts the fundamental theorem of arithmetic. So, by assuming that $\sqrt{3}$ is a rational number $\frac{a}{b}$, we arrive at a conclusion that contradicts the fundamental theorem of arithmetic. Therefore, we must reject our assumption that $\sqrt{3}$ is a rational number.

284 You obtain $4b^2 = a^2$, or $2^2b^2 = a^2.$ Both $4b^2$ (or 2^2b^2) and a^2 have an even number of prime factors, so there is no contradiction of the fundamental theorem of arithmetic. Hence, you cannot show that $\sqrt{4}$ is an irrational number by this method.

285 No. All it shows is that we cannot prove $\sqrt{4}$ to be irrational by that method. (Actually, $\sqrt{4}$ is rational. However, not being able to prove $\sqrt{4}$ is irrational does not prove that it is rational.)

286 $\frac{4}{5}, \frac{3}{7}, \sqrt{\frac{4}{9}}, -\frac{5}{9}, \sqrt{16},$ and $-\sqrt{9}.$

287 No * $\sqrt{5} + (-\sqrt{5}) = 0.$ ($\sqrt{5}$ and $-\sqrt{5}$ are irrational numbers, but 0 is not an irrational number.)

288 No * $\sqrt{5} \cdot \sqrt{5} = 5.$ ($\sqrt{5}$ is irrational, but 5 is not an irrational number.)

289 3.1623

290 $3\sqrt{10}$

291 $\sqrt{10} - 1.4$

292 You know that $6 > 2.$ If a first number is greater than a second number, the principal square root of the first number is greater than the principal square root of the second number. * You know that $7 = \sqrt{49}$ and that $49 < 50.$ If a first number is less than a second number, the principal square root of the first number is less than the principal square root of the second number. * The principal square root of any number is a positive number. The product of 2 and a given positive number is greater than the given number.

293 A number t is a greatest lower bound of a set of real numbers if $t \geq m$ for all numbers m that are lower bounds of the given set.

294 $2 < \sqrt{6} < 3.$
$2.4 < \sqrt{6} < 2.5.$
$2.44 < \sqrt{6} < 2.45.$
$2.449 < \sqrt{6} < 2.450.$

295 $3 < \sqrt{12} < 4.$
$3.4 < \sqrt{12} < 3.5.$
$3.46 < \sqrt{12} < 3.47.$
$3.464 < \sqrt{12} < 3.465.$

296 a $\sqrt{2}$ * Irrational   c $\sqrt{10}$ * Irrational
b $\frac{3}{2}$ * Rational   d $\sqrt{\frac{2}{3}}$ * Irrational

297 Using segment X as the unit of measure, you obtain 2 as the inner measure of segment UV, 3 as the outer measure, and 3 as the measure to the nearer unit.
With segment Y: 5, 5, 5
With segment Z: 3, 4, 3

298

Unit of measure	A	B	C
Inner measure	8	6	5
Outer measure	8	7	6
Nearer unit of measure	8	7	5
Greatest possible error	$\frac{1}{2}$ A	$\frac{1}{2}$ B	$\frac{1}{2}$ C
Relative error	$\frac{1}{16}$	$\frac{1}{14}$	$\frac{1}{10}$

299 8 (in terms of unit A)
7 (in terms of unit B)
5 (in terms of unit C)
The measure obtained by using unit A is the most precise because it is the measure with the least greatest possible error.

300 8 (in terms of unit A)
7 (in terms of unit B)
5 (in terms of unit C)
The measure obtained by using unit A is the most accurate because it has the least relative error.

301 a .01 foot * 5.805 feet and 5.815 feet * .005 foot * Approximately .0009 foot
b $\frac{1}{8}$ inch * $3\frac{9}{16}$ inches and $3\frac{11}{16}$ inches * $\frac{1}{16}$ inch * $\frac{1}{58}$ inch or approximately .017 inch
c 1 yard * $35\frac{1}{2}$ yards and $36\frac{1}{2}$ yards * $\frac{1}{2}$ yard * $\frac{1}{72}$ yard or approximately .014 yard
d .1 mile * 1.85 miles and 1.95 miles * .05 mile * Approximately .026 mile
e 1 centimeter * 11.5 centimeters and 12.5 centimeters * .5 centimeter * Approximately .042 centimeter
f 1 millimeter * 79.5 millimeters and 80.5 millimeters * .5 millimeter * Approximately .006 millimeter
g .001 inch * .0315 inch and .0325 inch * .0005 inch * Approximately .016 inch
h .001 kilometer * .1095 kilometer and .1105 kilometer * .0005 kilometer * Approximately .0045 kilometer

302 .032 in., 80 mm., 5.81 ft., $3\frac{5}{8}$ in., 12 cm., 36 yd., .110 km., 1.9 mi. * 80 mm., 5.81 ft., .032 in., $3\frac{5}{8}$ in., 12 cm., 36 yd., .110 km., 1.9 mi.

303

Unit	A	B	C
Inner area measure	11	4	21
Outer area measure	32	18	55
Average	21.5	11	38
Greatest possible error in average	$\frac{1}{2}$ A	$\frac{1}{2}$ B	$\frac{1}{2}$ C
Relative error in average	$\frac{1}{43}$	$\frac{1}{22}$	$\frac{1}{76}$

304 16 sq. ft. * 36 sq. ft.

305 24 sq. yd. * 35 sq. yd.

306 247 sq. ft. (inner) and 260 sq. ft. (outer)

307 $27\frac{11}{15}$ sq. yd. * $249\frac{3}{5}$ sq. ft.

308 a .1 sq. mi. * 50.15 sq. mi. and 50.25 sq. mi. * .05 sq. mi. * Approximately .001 sq. mi.
b 1 sq. in. * 40.5 sq. in. and 41.5 sq. in. * .5 sq. in. * Approximately .012 sq. in.
c $\frac{1}{5}$ acre * $4\frac{1}{10}$ acres and $4\frac{3}{10}$ acres * $\frac{1}{10}$ acre * Approximately .024 acre
d .001 sq. m. * 4.1235 sq. m. and 4.1245 sq. m. * .0005 sq. m. * Approximately .0001 sq. m.

309 41 sq. in., 4.124 sq. m., $4\frac{1}{5}$ acres, 50.2 sq. mi. * 41 sq. in., 4.124 sq. m., $4\frac{1}{5}$ acres, 50.2 sq. mi.

310 6 cu. ft. * 24 cu. ft.

311 23,400 cu. in. * 24,300 cu. in.

312 $13\frac{3}{4}$ cu. ft. * 23,760 cu. in.

313 Inner volume is 56 cu. ft. Outer volume is 184 cu. ft.

314 93,312 cu. in. * 2 cu. yd.

315 .00001231 cu. m. * 12,310 cu. mm.

316 A 23.1 miles   C $32\frac{0}{8}$ feet
B 12.06 centimeters   D 2.24 millimeters

317 A 16.1 miles   D 8.9 inches
B 70 yards   E $15\frac{4}{5}$ feet
C 27.4 kilometers

318 A 35.6 inches   C $73\frac{1}{2}$ yards
B 26 centimeters   D 25.30 millimeters

319 a $12/1 = 42/x.$ $3\frac{1}{2}$ ft.
b $10/1 = x/8.5.$ 85 mm.
c $9/1 = x/42.$ 378 sq. ft.

d $10000/1 = 12.31/x.$ .001231 sq. meter
e $645.16/1 = x/100.$ Approximately
  64516 sq. mm.
f $27/1 = x/9.4.$ 253.8 cu. ft.
g $1000/1 = 427.8/x.$ .4278 cu. cm.
h $.385641/1 = x/100.$
  Approximately 38.5641 sq. mi.

320 a B and F   **e** I and A
   b $\overleftrightarrow{LP}$ and $\overleftrightarrow{JN}$ **f** G and I
   c $\overrightarrow{AL}$ and $\overrightarrow{HD}$ **g** G and F
   d $\overline{EB}$ and $\overline{DH}$ **h** $\angle$KAL and $\angle$BHP
   i D and I
   j $\triangle$AHB and quadrilateral FEDI
   k JFAK and NCIGEDO
   l AFDCB and GIH
   m $\triangle$FDC and $\triangle$AHB
   n BHIC and AFED

321 a The unit fractions between 0 and 1 and
the natural numbers greater than 1 can
be put in one-to-one correspondence in
the following way.
Pair the numbers $\frac{1}{2}$ and 2 with each
other; pair the numbers $\frac{1}{3}$ and 3 with
each other; pair the numbers $\frac{1}{4}$ and 4
with each other; and so on. Any sets
that can be put in one-to-one
correspondence with each other are
equivalent sets.
b See the sketch below. Every line
through P that intersects the segment
also intersects the semicircle. Thus, the
two sets of points can be put in
one-to-one correspondence.

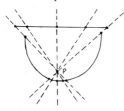

c See the sketch below.

322

Number of points	Number of lines
14	91
15	105
16	120
17	136
18	153
19	171
20	190
21	210
22	231
23	253
24	276
25	300

323 The number of lines determined will then
be 298. There will be 2 fewer lines because
3 of the points, which determine 3 lines
if they are noncollinear, now determine
only 1 line.

324 0 lines

325 a Total number of squares is 1.
b Total number of squares is 5.
c Total number of squares is 14.
From a, b, and c it appears that a (the
total number of squares) is equal to
$n + (\sqrt{n} - 1)^2 + (\sqrt{n} + 2)^2$
$+ \ldots + (\sqrt{n} - \sqrt{n})^2$, where n is the
number of smaller squares and where
n is an integer that is a perfect square.
Using this relation, we see that the
total number of squares contained on a
checkerboard with 64 small squares is
equal to $64 + (8 - 1)^2 + (8 - 2)^2$
$+ (8 - 3)^2 + (8 - 4)^2 + (8 - 5)^2$
$+ (8 - 6)^2 + (8 - 7)^2 + (8 - 8)^2$,
or 204.

326 $S = (n - 2) \times 180.$
A concave polygon of n sides can be
separated into $n - 2$ triangles. Thus, the
sum of the measures in degrees of the
angles is equal to $(n - 2) \times 180.$

327 54,000 degrees per minute ∗ 900 degrees
per second ∗ 3,240,000 degrees per hour

328 a 144 degrees   **d** $176\frac{2}{5}$ degrees
   b $165\frac{3}{5}$ degrees   **e** 178 degrees
   c $172\frac{4}{5}$ degrees   **f** $179\frac{16}{25}$ degrees

329 From exercise 328, you know that
$179\frac{16}{25}$ degrees is the measure of each angle
of a regular polygon of 1000 sides. The
greater the number of sides, the greater the

measure of each angle of a regular polygon. A polygon with more than 1000 sides will therefore have a number greater than $179\frac{16}{25}$ as the measure in degrees of each angle. However, each angle of a polygon is less than 180 degrees. Thus, the measure in degrees of each angle of a polygon that has more than 1000 sides will be between $179\frac{16}{25}$ and 180.

330

331 $4 * 8 * n - 2$

332 If a represents the length of the longest side of the triangle, then it must be true that $b + c > a$. Similarly, if b or c represents the length of the longest side, then it must be the case that the sum of the lengths of the two shorter sides is greater than the length of the third side.

333 **a** F = 7. V = 10. E = 15. Substituting in F + V = E + 2, we obtain 7 + 10 = 15 + 2, which is true. Euler's formula holds in this case.
b F = 5. V = 6. E = 9. Substituting in F + V = E + 2, we obtain 5 + 6 = 9 + 2, which is true. Euler's formula holds in this case.
c F = 6. V = 8. E = 12. Substituting in F + V = E + 2, we obtain 6 + 8 = 12 + 2, which is true. Euler's formula holds in this case.
d F = 5. V = 6. E = 9. Substituting in F + V = E + 2, we obtain 5 + 6 = 9 + 2, which is true. Euler's formula holds in this case.

334 $n + 2 * 2n * 3n *$ Yes. Substituting in F + V = E + 2, we obtain $(n + 2) + 2n = 3n + 2$, which is true.

335 Yes. F = 10, V = 16, and E = 24. When you substitute in F + V = E + 2, you obtain a true statement.

336 Suppose that a network has two vertices, A and B. Suppose also that vertex A is even. In this case, you can group the curves at vertex A in pairs so that one

curve leads you away from vertex A and the other curve leads you back to vertex A. However, the curve that leads you away from vertex A leads you to vertex B and the curve that leads you back to vertex A leads you away from vertex B. Thus, in grouping the curves at A in pairs, you are also grouping the curves at B in pairs. This means that vertex B is even. Thus, a network with exactly two vertices cannot have one even vertex and one odd vertex.

337 The network has 4 odd vertices. A network that can be traced in a single path cannot have more than 2 odd vertices.

338 All the vertices of Network A are even. A network that has all even vertices can be traced in a single closed path.
* Network B has 2 odd vertices and one even vertex (the exterior). A network that has 2 odd vertices can be traced in a single open path.
* Network C has 3 odd vertices. A network that can be traced in a single path cannot have more than 2 odd vertices. Thus, this network cannot be traced in a single path.

339 A network consists of intersecting segments or curves. If there are n intersecting segments or curves, there are $2n$ "ends" of segments or curves. In other words, the number of "ends" in the network is even. All the "ends" must intersect at a vertex. If a network had exactly 3 odd vertices, it would follow that the number of "ends" in the network was odd. This is impossible because, as stated above, the number of "ends" in a network is even.

340 A No * No   D No * Yes
B No * No   E Yes * No
C No * Yes   F No * No

341 Network A can be traced in a single path. * Network B can be traced in a single open path. * Network C can be traced in a single path. * Network D can be traced in a single path.
* Network E can be traced in a single path.

342 Three even vertices * Four even vertices * Yes

Responses for chapter quizzes

Chapter one,
pages 8 and 9

These exercises are intended for class discussion. Space limitations prevent us from giving complete responses. The following responses express one viewpoint and should serve as a guide for discussion.

1 A Traditional   G Traditional
   B Modern   H Modern
   C Both   I Traditional
   D Modern   J Both
   E Traditional   K Traditional
   F Both

2 Use of ideas involving measurement, formulas, rounding off numbers, charts and graphs, and so on * Use of charts and graphs, per cent, averages, and so on

3 A Although sound mathematically, too sophisticated for second graders
   B Some discussion of the basic concepts of area should precede work in determining areas by a rule or formula.
   C Memorization of the *names* of numbers without any understanding of the concept of number is not desirable.

4 This exercise, in particular, is intended for class discussion.

5 No * No

6 The sum of any two even numbers is an even number. * The sum of any two odd numbers is an even number.

7 For any triangle, the sum of the lengths of the two shorter sides is greater than the length of the longest side.

Chapter two,
pages 38 and 39

1 6 * The letters $a, b,$ and c in the following diagrams represent objects.

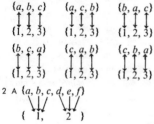

2 A $\{a, b, c, d, e, f\}$

$$\{\ 1, \quad 2\ \}$$

B $\{a, b, c, d, e, f, g, h\}$

$$\{1, \quad 2, \quad 3, \quad 4\}$$

C $\{a, b, c, d\}$

$$\{1, 2, 3, 4\}$$

3 S = $\{0, 1, 2, 3\}$.   T = $\{0, 1, 2, 3, 4, 5\}$.

4 V = $\{1, 3, 5\}$ and W = $\{1, 3, 5\}$.
   * V and W are equal.

5 $\{1, 3, 5, 6, 8, 10\}$

6 $\{5, 8\}$

7 $\{\ \}$

8 $\{3, 5, 6, 8, 10\}$

9 $\{(3, 1), (3, 5), (3, 8), (5, 1), (5, 5),$
   $(5, 8), (6, 1), (6, 5), (6, 8), (8, 1),$
   $(8, 5), (8, 8), (10, 1), (10, 5), (10, 8)\}$

10 $\{\ \}$

11 $\{1, 5, 8\}$

12 $\{\ \}$

13 15

14 A $\{\frac{1}{2}, \frac{1}{3}, \frac{1}{4}, \ldots, \quad \frac{1}{n}, \ldots\}$

$$\{0, 1, 2, \ldots, n - 2, \ldots\}$$

B $\{\frac{1}{4}, \frac{1}{5}, \frac{1}{6}, \ldots, \quad \frac{1}{n}, \ldots\}$

$$\{0, 1, 2, \ldots, n - 4, \ldots\}$$

C Any set that can be put in one-to-one correspondence with a proper subset of itself is an infinite set. Since this can be done with F, as shown below, F is an infinite set.

$$\{\frac{1}{2}, \frac{1}{3}, \frac{1}{4}, \frac{1}{5}, \ldots, \quad \frac{1}{n}, \quad \ldots\}$$

$$\{\frac{1}{5}, \frac{1}{6}, \frac{1}{7}, \frac{1}{8}, \ldots, \quad \frac{1}{n + 3}, \ldots\}$$

15 5   17 2   19 1

16 3   18 7   20 12

21 $n' = n \cup \{n\}$.
    = $\{0, 1, 2, \ldots, n - 1\} \cup \{n\}$.
    = $\{0, 1, 2, \ldots, n\}$.

22 A Example of a natural number
   B Example of an ordinal or identification numeral
   C Example of a natural number or an identification numeral
   D Example of an identification numeral
   E Example of an identification numeral
   F Example of a natural number
   G Example of a natural number

Chapter three,
pages 53 and 54

	U_1	U_2	U_3	U_4
1	Yes	Yes	No	Yes
2	No	No	No	Yes
3	No	No	Yes	No
4	Yes	Yes	No	Yes
5	Yes	Yes	Yes	Yes
6	Yes	Yes	Yes	Yes
7	Yes	Yes	Yes	Yes
8	Yes	Yes	Yes	Yes
9	Yes	Yes	Yes	Yes

10 2, 4, 6, 8, 10, 12, 14, 16, 18, 20, . . .

$* S_n + 2 = S_{n+1}.$

11 1, 4, 9, 16, 25, 36, 49, 64, 81, 100, . . . $*$
$S_n + (2n + 1) = S_{n+1}.$

12 $\frac{2}{2}, \frac{4}{3}, \frac{6}{4}, \frac{8}{5}, \frac{10}{6}, \frac{12}{7}, \frac{14}{8}, \frac{16}{9}, \frac{18}{10}, \frac{20}{11}, \ldots$

$* S_n + \dfrac{2}{(n+1)(n+2)} = S_{n+1}.$

13 $\frac{1}{2}, \frac{2}{3}, \frac{3}{4}, \frac{4}{5}, \frac{5}{6}, \frac{6}{7}, \frac{7}{8}, \frac{8}{9}, \frac{9}{10}, \frac{10}{11}, \ldots$

$* S_n + \dfrac{1}{(n+1)(n+2)} = S_{n+1}.$

14 4, 7, 10, 13, 16, 19, 22, 25, 28, 31, . . .

$* S_n + 3 = S_{n+1}.$

15 2, $1\frac{1}{2}$, $1\frac{1}{3}$, $1\frac{1}{4}$, $1\frac{1}{5}$, $1\frac{1}{6}$, $1\frac{1}{7}$, $1\frac{1}{8}$, $1\frac{1}{9}$, $1\frac{1}{10}$, . . .

$* S_n - \dfrac{1}{n(n+1)} = S_{n+1}$ or

$S_n - \dfrac{1}{n^2 + n} = S_{n+1}.$

16 $n * 6, 7, 8, 9, 10$

17 $n - 1 * 5, 6, 7, 8, 9$

18 $2n - 2 * 10, 12, 14, 16, 18$

19 $2n - 1 * 11, 13, 15, 17, 19$

20 $\dfrac{n-1}{2} * \frac{5}{2}, 3, \frac{7}{2}, 4, \frac{9}{2}$

21 $n + 4 * 10, 11, 12, 13, 14$

22 $2 * 2, 2, 2, 2, 2$

23 $n^2 - 2n + 2 * 26, 37, 50, 65, 82$

24 For each x, if x is non-zero, $x \div x = 1$.

25 For each x, $x + 0 = x$.

26 For each x, if x is non-zero, $0 \div x = 0$.

27 For each x, $0 \times x = 0$.

28 For each x, $1 \times x = x$.

Chapter four,
pages 82 and 83

1 $n[A] = 0.$ $n[B] = 1.$ $n[C] = 4.$ $n[D] = 2.$

2 1 3 0 4 5 5 0 6 1 7 0 8 6 9 8 10 1

11 {(a, Sue),   (a, Jane),   (a, Carol),
↕   ↕   ↕
{(Don, Sue), (Don, Jane), (Don, Carol),
(b, Sue),   (b, Jane),   (b, Carol)}
↕   ↕   ↕
(Nancy, Sue), (Nancy, Jane), (Nancy, Carol))

$*$ S $\times$ R and L $\times$ R are equivalent sets.

$*$ n[S $\times$ R] = n[L $\times$ R].

12 "Order in sums" property

13 Property concerning product of 3 numbers

14 "Order in products" property and property concerning product of 3 natural numbers

15 "Order in sums" property

16 "Order in sums" property

17 "Order in products" property

18 Property concerning sums and products and "order in products" property

19 Property concerning sums and products and "order in sums" property

20 Property concerning sums and products, "order in sums" property, and "order in products" property

21 Property concerning sums and products

22 Property concerning sums and products and "order in products" property

23 rs 26 $r + a$

24 rsa 27 $sa + b$

25 $ab + rs$ 28 $(a + b)(r + s)$

29 {(cat, dog), (cat, rat), (cat, mouse)}
↕   ↕   ↕
{dog,   rat,   mouse}

30 "Order in products" property

31 Property concerning sums and products

32 First change 5×6 to $5(4 + 2)$. Then use property concerning sums and products.

33 Cancellation property of products

Chapter five,
pages 118 and 119

1 $(6, 12) \xrightarrow{+} 18 * (6, 12) \xrightarrow{\times} 72$

2 $(0, 14) \xrightarrow{+} 14 * (0, 14) \xrightarrow{\times} 0$

3 $(10, 10) \xrightarrow{+} 20 * (10, 10) \xrightarrow{\times} 100$

4 $(18, 1) \xrightarrow{+} 19 * (18, 1) \xrightarrow{\times} 18$

5 $(55, 3) \xrightarrow{+} 58 * (55, 3) \xrightarrow{\times} 165$

6 $(78, 39) \xrightarrow{+} 117 * (78, 39) \xrightarrow{\times} 3042$

7 (1) No (2) No (3) Yes (4) Yes
(5) Yes (6) Yes $*$ (1) No (2) Yes
(3) Yes (4) Yes (5) No (6) Yes

8 He is using the multiplication property of equality, the substitution property, the

distributive property, and the transitive property of equality.

9 He is using the addition property of equality, the substitution property, the distributive property, and the transitive property of equality.

10 A Suppose you know that $9 \times 4 = 36$.
Then $(9 \times 4) + (9 \times 4) = 36 + (9 \times 4)$.
Addition property of equality

$9(4 + 4) = 36 + 36$.
Distributive property

$9 \times 8 = 72$.
Substitution $(4 + 4 = 8$ and $36 + 36 = 72$.)

B Another method: Suppose you know that $9 \times 4 = 36$. Then $(9 \times 4) \times 2 = 36 \times 2$.
Multiplication property of equality

$9 \times (4 \times 2) = 36 \times 2$.
Associative property of multiplication

$9 \times 8 = 72$.
Multiplication and substitution property

C Suppose you know that $9 \times 2 = 18$ and that $9 \times 6 = 54$. Then
$(9 \times 2) + (9 \times 6) = 18 + (9 \times 6)$.
Addition property of equality

$9(2 + 6) = 18 + 54$.
Distributive and substitution properties

$9 \times 8 = 72$.
Addition and multiplication

D Suppose you know that $3 \times 8 = 24$. Then
$(3 \times 8) \times 3 = 24 \times 3$.
Multiplication property of equality

$(3 \times 3) \times 8 = 24 \times 3$.
Commutative and associative properties of multiplication

$9 \times 8 = 72$.
Multiplication and substitution property

11 If you add 3 to 4 and multiply the result by 2, you obtain 14.
If you multiply 3 by 2 and add the result to 4, you obtain 10.

12 If you multiply 5 by 6 and add 8 to the result, you obtain 38.
If you add 8 to 6 and multiply the result by 5, you obtain 70.

13 If you multiply 3 by 4 and 6 by 2 and add the results, you obtain 24. If you add 6 to 4, you obtain 10; then, if you multiply 3 by 10, you obtain 30; finally, if you multiply 30 by 2, you obtain 60.

14 Yes * We agree that the operations within parentheses will be performed first. If no parentheses are used, multiplication and division are to be performed before addition and subtraction.

15 No. For example, let $A = \{1, 2\}$ and let $B = \{3, 4\}$. Then
$A \times B = \{(1, 3), (1, 4), (2, 3), (2, 4)\}$,
and $B \times A = \{(3, 1), (3, 2), (4, 1), (4, 2)\}$.
$A \times B$ and $B \times A$ are not the same set.

16 $A \times B = \{(1, a), (1, b), (1, c), (2, a),$
$\qquad (2, b), (2, c)\}$.
$B \times C = \{(a, k), (b, k), (c, k)\}$.
$(A \times B) \times C = \{((1, a), k), ((1, b), k),$
$\qquad ((1, c), k), ((2, a), k), ((2, b), k),$
$\qquad ((2, c), k)\}$.
$A \times (B \times C) = \{(1, (a, k)), (1, (b, k)),$
$\qquad (1, (c, k)), (2, (a, k)), (2, (b, k)),$
$\qquad (2, (c, k))\}$.
From the tabulations above, it is evident that $(A \times B) \times C$ and $A \times (B \times C)$ are not equal sets.
* The operation of forming a Cartesian product is not associative for all sets X, Y, and Z.

Chapter six,
page 143

1 Base six: 0, 1, 2, 3, 4, 5, 10, 11, 12, 13, 14, 15, 20, 21, 22, 23, 24, 25, 30, 31
* Base three: 0, 1, 2, 10, 11, 12, 20, 21, 22, 100, 101, 102, 110, 111, 112, 120, 121, 122, 200, 201

2 The circles shown below represent objects. We use the base-ten numeral 11 to describe the number of objects because there is 1 group of ten and 1 single object.

    O O O
O O O O   O
   O O O

We group the objects into as many groups of 8 as possible, as shown below.

O O O O
O O O O   O O O

We use the base-eight numeral 13 to describe the number of objects. Since both numerals name the same number, we know that $13_8 = 11$.

3 A 30   B 200   C 10010   D 20   E 10
4 {a, b, c, d, e, f, g, h, i, j, k, l, m, n, o} *

{a, b, c, d, e, f, g, h, i, j, k, l, m, n, o, p,
q, r, s, t, u}

5

+	0	1	2
0	0	1	2
1	1	2	10
2	2	10	11

×	0	1	2
0	0	0	0
1	0	1	2
2	0	2	11

6 A 31   B 15   C 78   D 10   E 12   F 15

7 A 50   B 140   C 1200   D 101101

8 In a numeration system with a base of one, we would have only one digit. Such a numeration system is essentially a tally system of the kind used by primitive man, with 1 tally mark corresponding to each object. A tally system is not useful for computing and is very cumbersome for representing large numbers.

9 It would simplify the writing of fraction numerals since 12 has more factors than 10. A base-twelve system would also be convenient for representing large numbers. Since some of our units of measure make use of twelve as a base, it might be convenient to use 12 as the base of a numeration system.

10 Base eight: 0, 1, 2, 3, 4, 5, 6, 7, 10, 11, 12, 13, 14, 15, 16, 17. Base two: 0, 1, 10, 11, 100, 101, 110, 111, 1000, 1001, 1010, 1011, 1100, 1101, 1110, 1111 * Since $8 = 2^3$, the powers of 10_8 are equal to the cubes of the powers of 10_2. That is, $10_8 = (10_2)^3$; $(10_8)^2 = (10_2)^6$; $(10_8)^3 = (10_2)^9$; and so on. Thus, the relation between the powers of 10_8 and the powers of 10_2 provide a useful first step in converting from base eight to base two and conversely.

Chapter seven,
pages 165 and 166

1 A 5 * 4 * 2 * 6

  B n[A ∪ B] = 9.
    n[A ∪ D] = 11.
    n[B] + n[D] = 10.
    n[C] + n[B] = 6.
    n[A ∪ C] = 7.
    n[D] + n[A] = 11.

  C n[C] + n[D] is equal to n[C ∪ D] only if C and D are disjoint sets. In this case, C and D are not disjoint sets.
    n[C] + n[D] = 8 and n[C ∪ D] = 7.

2 A $3 \cdot 10^2 + 4 \cdot 10^1 + 5 \cdot 10^0$

  B $1 \cdot 10^4 + 5 \cdot 10^3 + 6 \cdot 10^2 + 9 \cdot 10^1 + 0 \cdot 10^0$

  C $5 \cdot 10^3 + 0 \cdot 10^2 + 0 \cdot 10^1 + 0 \cdot 10^0$

  D $4 \cdot 10^2 + 0 \cdot 10^1 + 9 \cdot 10^0$

  E $1 \cdot 10^0$

3 $56 = 5 \cdot 10^1 + 6 \cdot 10^0$ and $11 = 1 \cdot 10^1 + 1 \cdot 10^0$.

  A $56 + 11 = (5 \cdot 10^1 + 6 \cdot 10^0) + (1 \cdot 10^2 + 1 \cdot 10^0)$.
    Expanded form and substitution property

  B $(5 \cdot 10^1 + 6 \cdot 10^0) + (1 \cdot 10^1 + 1 \cdot 10^0) = (5 + 1)10^1 + (6 + 1)10^0$.
    Commutative and associative properties of addition and distributive property

  C $(5 + 1)10^1 + (6 + 1)10^0 = 6 \cdot 10^1 + 7 \cdot 10^0$.
    Basic facts and substitution property

  D $6 \cdot 10^1 + 7 \cdot 10^0 = 67$.
    Meaning of expanded form

  E $56 + 11 = 67$.
    Transitive property of equality

4
$(6 + 9) + 3$ $(9 + 6) + 3$ $(3 + 6) + 9$
$6 + (9 + 3)$ $9 + (6 + 3)$ $3 + (6 + 9)$
$6 + (3 + 9)$ $9 + (3 + 6)$ $3 + (9 + 6)$
$(6 + 3) + 9$ $(9 + 3) + 6$ $(3 + 9) + 6$
* Associative and commutative properties of addition

5
$(6 \times 9) \times 3$ $(9 \times 6) \times 3$ $(3 \times 6) \times 9$
$6 \times (9 \times 3)$ $9 \times (6 \times 3)$ $3 \times (6 \times 9)$
$6 \times (3 \times 9)$ $9 \times (3 \times 6)$ $3 \times (9 \times 6)$
$(6 \times 3) \times 9$ $(9 \times 3) \times 6$ $(3 \times 9) \times 6$
* Associative and commutative properties of multiplication

6 To simplify notation, you can dispense with the zero power of 10 in the expanded form. Thus, $45 = 4 \cdot 10^1 + 5$ and $14 = 1 \cdot 10^1 + 4$. Several steps have been combined at various steps in the following example.

$$45 \times 14 = (4 \cdot 10^1 + 5) \times (1 \cdot 10^1 + 4)$$
$$= ((4 \cdot 10^1 + 5) \cdot (1 \cdot 10^1)) + ((4 \cdot 10^1 + 5) \cdot 4)$$
$$= ((4 \cdot 10^1 \cdot 10^1) + 5 \cdot 10^1) + ((4 \cdot 4 \cdot 10^1) + 5 \cdot 4)$$
$$= ((4 \cdot 10^2) + 5 \cdot 10^1) + (16 \cdot 10^1 + 20)$$
$$= 4 \cdot 10^2 + (5 + 16) \cdot 10^1 + 20$$
$$= 4 \cdot 10^2 + 2 \cdot 10^2 + 1 \cdot 10^1 + 2 \cdot 10^1$$
$$= 6 \cdot 10^2 + 3 \cdot 10^1 = 630.$$

7 A Correct   B Incorrect

  C Incorrect. $1 \times 4 = 4$.

  D Incorrect. $0 \div 0$ does not equal 0.

  E Incorrect. $0 \div 0$ does not equal 1.

F Correct   G Correct

8 A Calandri's method is shown at the left below. An example of Greenwood's method is shown at the right below.

```
        60
  16)965      16)965 | 60
     96          960 |
    ---          --- |
      5            5 | 60
```

$965 = 60 \times 16 + 5.$

B Calandri's method is shown at the left below. An example of Greenwood's method is shown at the right below.

```
         29
  34)1004      34)1004 | 20
     68           680  |
    ----        -----  |
     324          324  | 9
     306          306  |
    ----        -----  |
      18           18  | 29
```

$1004 = 29 \times 34 + 18.$

C Calandri's method is shown at the left below. An example of Greenwood's method is shown at the right below.

```
         229
 199)45600     199)45600 | 200
     398           39800 |
    -----         ------ |
      580           5800 | 20
      398           3980 |
    -----         ------ |
     1820           1820 | 9
     1791           1791 |
    -----         ------ |
       29             29 | 229
```

$45600 = 229 \times 199 + 29.$

D Calandri's method is shown at the left below. An example of Greenwood's method is shown at the right below.

```
       309
 66)20400      66)20400 | 100
    198           6600  |
   -----        ------  |
     600         13800  | 200
     594         13200  |
   -----        ------  |
       6           600  | 9
                   594  |
                 -----  |
                     6  | 309
```

$20400 = 309 \times 66 + 6.$

E Calandri's method is shown at the left at the top of the next column. An example of Greenwood's method is shown at the right in column 2.

```
      3666
 12)44000      12)44000 | 2000
    36            24000  |
   -----         ------  |
    80            20000  | 1000
    72            12000  |
   -----         ------  |
    80             8000  | 500
    72             6000  |
   -----         ------  |
    80             2000  | 100
    72             1200  |
   -----         ------  |
     8              800  | 60
                    720  |
                   ----  |
                     80  | 6
                     72  |
                   ----  |
                      8  | 3666
```

$44000 = 3666 \times 12 + 8.$

F Calandri's method is shown at the left below. An example of Greenwood's method is shown at the right below.

```
      3200
 16)51210      16)51210 | 3000
    48            48000  |
   -----         ------  |
    32             3210  | 200
    32             3200  |
   -----          -----  |
    10               10  | 3200
```

$51210 = 3200 \times 16 + 10.$

9 $3^2 = 9.$ $15^2 = 225.$ $25^2 = 625.$
$7^2 = 49.$ $17^2 = 289.$ $31^2 = 961.$
$11^2 = 121.$ $21^2 = 441.$
$13^2 = 169.$ $23^2 = 529.$

* $9 - 1 = 8.$ $289 - 1 = 288.$
$49 - 1 = 48.$ $441 - 1 = 440.$
$121 - 1 = 120.$ $529 - 1 = 528.$
$169 - 1 = 168.$ $625 - 1 = 624.$
$225 - 1 = 224.$ $961 - 1 = 960.$

* Yes * No * Yes * No * 8 * It appears that 8 is the greatest common divisor of all numbers obtained by subtracting 1 from the square of an odd number.

10 The sum of any two odd numbers is an even number. The product of any two odd numbers is an odd number. If the difference of two odd numbers is a natural number, it is an even number. If the quotient of two odd numbers is a natural number, it is an odd number. * The sum of any two even numbers is an even number. The product of any two even numbers is an even number. If the difference of two even numbers

is a natural number, it is an even number. If
the quotient of two even numbers is a natural
number, it may be an even number or it may
be an odd number.

11 A $(5 \times 6) + 5$ and $5 \times (6 + 5)$
B $(12 \div 3) + 1$ and $12 \div (3 + 1)$
C $(5 + 6) \times 7$ and $5 + (6 \times 7)$
D $(15 - 3) \times 4$ and $15 - (3 \times 4)$
E Both $(15 \times 6) \div 2$ and $15 \times (6 \div 2)$
are equal to 45.
F $(16 - 5) \times 2$ and $16 - (5 \times 2)$
G Both $(36 \times 6) \div 6$ and $36 \times (6 \div 6)$
are equal to 36.
H $(52 - 5) \times 3$ and $52 - (5 \times 3)$
I $(12 \div 4) - 1$ and $12 \div (4 - 1)$

12 B, D, F, H, and I are meaningless because
division by zero is not defined. I is also
meaningless when we are dealing with natural
numbers because there is no natural number
that is equal to $8 - 9$.

Chapter eight,
page 197

1 A Examples are 7/50, 21/150, 28/200, 35/250,
42/300, 49/350, 63/450, 70/500, 700/5000,
and 7000/50000.
B Examples are 12/50, 18/75, 24/100, 30/125,
36/150, 42/175, 60/250, 120/500, 600/2500,
and 1200/5000.
C Examples are 16/6, 24/9, 80/30, 160/60,
240/90, 320/120, 480/180, 640/240,
800/300, and 8000/3000.
D Examples are 1/1, 2/2, 3/3, 4/4, 5/5, 6/6,
7/7, 8/8, 9/9, and 20/20.
E Examples are 2/22, 3/33, 4/44, 5/55, 6/66,
7/77, 8/88, 9/99, 10/110, and 100/1100.
F Examples are 2/8, 3/12, 4/16, 5/20, 6/24,
7/28, 20/80, 200/800, 300/1200, and
1000/4000.

2 A 8% B 170% C 50% D 30% E 100%

3 Examples are (2, 4), (3, 9), (4, 16), and (5, 25).
* The graph is shown below. * No * No

4 {(2, 1), (3, 2), (4, 3), . . .} * Yes * No *
The graph is shown at the top of column 2.

5 16 ft. in 1 sec., 64 ft. in 2 sec., 144 ft. in
3 sec., 256 ft. in 4 sec., 400 ft. in 5 sec.,
576 ft. in 6 sec. * The graph is shown below.
* No

6 {(1, 1), (1, 2), (1, 3), (1, 4), (1, 5), (1, 6), (1, 7),
(1, 8), (2, 1), (2, 2), (2, 3), (2, 4), (2, 5), (2, 6),
(2, 7), (3, 1), (3, 2), (3, 3), (3, 4), (3, 5), (3, 6),
(4, 1), (4, 2), (4, 3), (4, 4), (4, 5), (5, 1), (5, 2),
(5, 3), (5, 4), (6, 1), (6, 2), (6, 3), (7, 1), (7, 2),
(8, 1)} * The graph is shown below. * Yes
* No

7 A {(1, 1), (2, 2), (3, 3), (4, 4), . . .} * Both a
linear relation and a proportional relation
B {(1, 2), (2, 4), (3, 6), (4, 8), . . .} * Both a
linear relation and a proportional relation
C {(1, 3), (2, 3), (3, 3), (4, 3), . . .} * A linear
relation, but not a proportional relation
D {(1, 1), (4, 2), (9, 3), (16, 4), . . .} *
Neither a linear relation nor a proportional
relation
E {(1, 6), (2, 7), (3, 8), (4, 9), . . .} * A linear
relation, but not a proportional relation
F {(1, 1), (2, 4), (3, 9), (4, 16), . . .} *
Neither a linear relation nor a
proportional relation

8

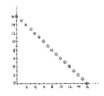

Chapter nine,
pages 226 and 227

1 A True C False E True G False
  B False D False F False H True

2 101 ~~102~~ 103 ~~104~~ ~~105~~ ~~106~~ 107 ~~108~~
  109 ~~110~~ ~~111~~ ~~112~~ 113 ~~114~~ ~~115~~ ~~116~~
  ~~117~~ ~~118~~ ~~119~~ ~~120~~ ~~121~~ 122 ~~123~~ ~~124~~
  ~~125~~ ~~126~~ 127 ~~128~~ ~~129~~ ~~130~~ 131 ~~132~~
  ~~133~~ ~~134~~ ~~135~~ ~~136~~ 137 ~~138~~ 139 ~~140~~
  ~~141~~ ~~142~~ ~~143~~ ~~144~~ ~~145~~ ~~146~~ ~~147~~ ~~148~~
  149 ~~150~~ 151 ~~152~~ ~~153~~ ~~154~~ ~~155~~ ~~156~~
  157 ~~158~~ ~~159~~ ~~160~~ ~~161~~ ~~162~~ 163 ~~164~~
  ~~165~~ ~~166~~ 167 ~~168~~ ~~169~~ ~~170~~ ~~171~~ ~~172~~
  173 ~~174~~ ~~175~~ ~~176~~ ~~177~~ ~~178~~ 179 ~~180~~
  181 ~~182~~ ~~183~~ ~~184~~ ~~185~~ ~~186~~ ~~187~~ ~~188~~
  ~~189~~ ~~190~~ 191 ~~192~~ 193 ~~194~~ ~~195~~ ~~196~~
  197 ~~198~~ 199 ~~200~~

The primes are 101, 103, 107, 109, 113, 127, 131, 137, 139, 149, 151, 157, 163, 167, 173, 179, 181, 191, 193, 197, and 199.

3 641, 691, 743, 797, 853, 911, 971, 1033, 1097, 1163, 1231, 1301, 1373, 1447, 1523, 1601, 1681, 1763, 1847, 1933, 2021, 2111, 2203, 2297, 2393, and 2491

∗ The result obtained by replacing n by 41, 42, 45, or 50 is a composite number. The result obtained by replacing n by each of the other numbers from 25 through 50 is a prime number. ∗ No

4 No. For example, $4 \times (4)^2 + 1$, or 65, is not a prime number.

5 First, we establish that the product of two even numbers is even, the product of two odd numbers is odd, and the product of an even number and an odd number is even.

We can represent any two even numbers by $2m$ and $2n$. The product of $2m$ and $2n$ is $4mn$, or $2(2mn)$, which represents an even number. We can represent any two odd numbers by $2m + 1$ and $2n + 1$. The product of $2m + 1$ and $2n + 1$ is $4mn + 2m + 2n + 1$, or $2(2mn + m + n) + 1$, which represents an odd number. We can represent any even number by $2m$ and any odd number by $2n + 1$. The product of $2m$ and $2n + 1$ is $4mn + 2m$, or $2(2mn + m)$, which represents an even number.

The above establishes that the product of two natural numbers is even unless both

numbers are odd. Next, consider the product of any three natural numbers. The numbers may be three even numbers, three odd numbers, two even numbers and one odd number, or two odd numbers and one even number. We can use e to represent an even number and o to represent an odd number. Since multiplication is associative and commutative, the following represent all possible combinations.

$$e \cdot e \cdot e$$
$$o \cdot o \cdot o$$
$$e \cdot e \cdot o$$
$$o \cdot o \cdot e$$

The result of multiplying an even number by another even number is an even number; the product of this result and a third even number is an even number. Thus,
$(e \cdot e) \cdot e = e \cdot e = e.$
Similarly, we can show that
$(o \cdot o) \cdot o = o \cdot o = o,$
$(e \cdot e) \cdot o = e \cdot o = e,$
and $(o \cdot o) \cdot e = o \cdot e = e.$
Thus, the product of three natural numbers is odd only if all three numbers are odd.

We could continue in a similar fashion to consider the product of any four natural numbers, any five natural numbers, and so on. We would find that the product is even unless all the numbers are odd.

6 The sum of two or more natural numbers is even unless there is an odd number of addends, and each addend is an odd number.

7 197 and 199

8 A $2 \cdot 2 \cdot 2 \cdot 2 \cdot 3 \cdot 3$
  B $2 \cdot 3 \cdot 23$
  C $2 \cdot 3 \cdot 163$
  D $11 \cdot 13$
  E $2 \cdot 3 \cdot 13 \cdot 13$
  F $2 \cdot 2 \cdot 2 \cdot 2 \cdot 5 \cdot 307$

9 A number whose digit in the ones' place is even can be represented by
$\ldots c \cdot 10^3 + b \cdot 10^2 + a \cdot 10^1 + n,$
where a, b, and c are natural numbers and n is an even number. Since the product of two numbers is even unless both of the numbers are odd, each of the products $a \cdot 10^1$, $b \cdot 10^2$, $c \cdot 10^3$, etc., represents an even number. Since n is even and since the sum of any number of even numbers is even,

$\ldots c \cdot 10^3 + b \cdot 10^2 + a \cdot 10^1 + n$
represents an even number. An even
number is a number that is divisible by 2.

10 A number whose digit in the ones' place is 0
can be represented by
$\ldots c \cdot 10^3 + b \cdot 10^2 + a \cdot 10^1 + 0$,
where a, b, and c are natural numbers. A
number whose digit in the ones' place
is 5 can be represented by
$\ldots c \cdot 10^3 + b \cdot 10^2 + a \cdot 10^1 + 5$, where
a, b, and c are natural numbers. In all cases,
each of the products $a \cdot 10^1$, $b \cdot 10^2$,
$c \cdot 10^3$, etc., represents a number that is
divisible by 5; so
$\ldots c \cdot 10^3 + b \cdot 10^2 + a \cdot 10^1$ represents a
number that is divisible by 5. Therefore,
$\ldots c \cdot 10^3 + b \cdot 10^2 + a \cdot 10^1 + 0$ and
$\ldots c \cdot 10^3 + b \cdot 10^2 + a \cdot 10^1 + 5$
represent numbers that are divisible by 5.

11 We can represent such a number by
$\ldots b \cdot 10^3 + a \cdot 10^2 + 4n$ where a, b, and
and n are natural numbers. In all cases, each
of the products $4n$, $a \cdot 10^2$, $b \cdot 10^3$, etc.,
represents a number that is divisible by 4.
Therefore, $\ldots b \cdot 10^3 + a \cdot b^2 + 4n$
represents a number that is divisible by 4.

12 No. For any two consecutive natural numbers
greater than 2, one of them is an even
number that is divisible by 2. Such a number
is not a prime number.

13 Two examples are $2^1 + 1 = 3$ and
$2^8 + 1 = 257$.

14 Examples are $1^2 + 1 = 2$, $2^2 + 1 = 5$,
$4^2 + 1 = 17$, $6^2 + 1 = 37$, $10^2 + 1 = 101$,
$14^2 + 1 = 197$.

15 5 is a prime number that is between 3 and
2×3, or 6. 7 is a prime number that is
between 4 and 2×4, or 8. 17 is a prime
number that is between 10 and 2×10, or 20.
19 is a prime number that is between 15 and
2×15, or 30.

16 A $5 + 13$ B $7 + 137$ C $37 + 61$

17 $3! + 1$, or 7 * The product of two or more
natural numbers is even unless all of the
numbers are odd. From this, we know that,
for every replacement of n by a number
greater than or equal to 2, $n!$ is an even
number. The sum of two even numbers is an
even number. Thus, we know that the sum
of $n!$ and 2 is an even number. We also
know that the sum of $n!$ and 2 is greater
than 2. Thus, $n! + 2$ is an even number that
is greater than 2, and every even number
greater than 2 is composite.

18 A 2   B 45   C 5   D 16   E 1   F 1

19 A 84   C 352   E 23,490
   B 24   D 31,824   F 135

20 The divisors of 6 (other than 6) are 1, 2,
and 3. The sum of 1, 2, and 3 is 6. * 28

21 The lcm is the greater of the two numbers. *
The gcd is the lesser of the two numbers.

22 The lcm of two numbers that are relatively
prime is the product of the two numbers.

23 A $q = 7, r = 3$.   C $q = 105, r = 310$.
   B $q = 11, r = 1$.   D $q = 10, r = 0$.

24 $d \mid a$ means that there is a counting number n
such that $d \cdot n = a$. $d \mid b$ means that there is
a counting number m such that $d \cdot m = b$.
By the relation between addition and
subtraction, we know that $a = b + c$
also means $a - b = c$. We can replace
a in $a - b = c$ by $d \cdot n$ and b by
$d \cdot m$ (the substitution property) to
obtain $(d \cdot n) - (d \cdot m) = c$. Using the
distributive property, we obtain $d(n - m) = c$.
Since $d(n - m) = c$, we know that $d \mid c$.

Chapter ten,
pages 271 and 272

1 Such numbers behave like their mates when
we are adding, subtracting, multiplying, or
dividing, since they are closely associated
with their mates in terms of properties.
Because computation involving natural
numbers is simpler than computation
involving rational numbers of arithmetic, we
compute with natural numbers when possible.

2 Division by zero is undefined.

3 A $\frac{2}{1}$ B $\frac{5}{3}$ C $\frac{3}{10}$ D $\frac{1}{5}$ E $\frac{1}{12}$ F $\frac{100}{7}$

4 $\frac{0}{1}$ * There is no number such that the product
of $\frac{0}{1}$ and the number is equal to 1.

5 $abn = abn$.
Reflexive property of equality

$a(bn) = (an)b$.
Commutative and associative properties of
multiplication

$\frac{a}{b} = \frac{an}{bn}$.
Definition of equal rational numbers of
arithmetic

6 19. The numbers from $\frac{181}{240}$ through $\frac{199}{240}$.

7 A Least member is 2. Greatest member is 999.

B There is no greatest member. There is no least member.

C There is no greatest member. The least member is 0.

D The greatest member is $\frac{1}{1}$, or 1. There is no least member.

E There is no greatest member. The least member is $\frac{0}{1}$, or 0.

8 Suppose that the fractions represent the rational numbers $\frac{a}{b}$ and $\frac{c}{b}$, and that $\frac{a}{b} > \frac{c}{b}$. Then, because of the definition of "greater than" for rational numbers, $ab > cb$. Since $ab > cb$, a must be greater than c. Thus, the fraction that represents the greater rational number has the greater numerator.

9 A Suppose that we select $\frac{1}{100}$ as the least member of the set. By the density property of the set of rational numbers of arithmetic, we know there is at least one number between 0 and $\frac{1}{100}$ that is a member of the set determined by $0 < \frac{a}{b}$ and that is less than $\frac{1}{100}$. We can show that $\frac{1}{1000}$ meets these requirements. However, $\frac{1}{1000}$ is not the least member of the set determined by $0 < \frac{a}{b}$ because, by the density property, we can find a number between 0 and $\frac{1}{1000}$. This number will be a member of the set determined by $0 < \frac{a}{b}$ and will be less than $\frac{1}{1000}$, but it will not be the least member of the set determined by $0 < \frac{a}{b}$. We can continue as before but we will not be able to find the least member of the set determined by $0 < \frac{a}{b}$.

B Suppose that we select $100\frac{1}{4}$ as the least member of the set determined by $100 < \frac{a}{b} < 200$. By the density property of the set of rational numbers of arithmetic, we know there is at least one number between 100 and $100\frac{1}{4}$. This number, which must be less than $100\frac{1}{4}$ and greater than 100, also is in the set determined by $100 < \frac{a}{b} < 200$. We can show that $100\frac{1}{8}$ meets these requirements. Thus, we know that $100\frac{1}{4}$ is not the least member of the set determined by $100 < \frac{a}{b} < 200$. By continuing this line of reasoning, we can conclude that there is no least member of the set determined by $100 < \frac{a}{b} < 200$.

C By using the same line of reasoning as we used to answer part B of this exercise, we can conclude there is no least member of the set determined by $\frac{1}{2} < \frac{a}{b} < \frac{3}{4}$. No matter what number we select as the least member of the set, the density property enables us to find another number in the set that is less than the number we selected.

10 A Examples are $\frac{201}{100}, \frac{21}{10}, \frac{5}{2}, \frac{21}{8}, \frac{11}{4}$, and $\frac{29}{10}$.

B Examples are $\frac{33}{64}, \frac{11}{16}, \frac{19}{32}, \frac{20}{32}, \frac{5}{8}$, and $\frac{47}{64}$.

C Examples are $\frac{22,502}{250,000}, \frac{9001}{100,000}, \frac{1803}{20,000}, \frac{19}{200}, \frac{97,000}{1,000,000}$, and $\frac{99,999}{1,000,000}$.

D Examples are $\frac{560}{831}, \frac{224}{333}, \frac{112}{167}, \frac{1120}{1673}, \frac{560}{837}$, and $\frac{560}{839}$.

11 Examples are $\frac{1}{2} < \frac{1+3}{2+4} < \frac{3}{4}$, or $\frac{1}{2} < \frac{4}{6} < \frac{3}{4}$, and $\frac{9}{10} < \frac{9+3}{10+2} < \frac{3}{2}$, or $\frac{9}{10} < \frac{12}{12} < \frac{3}{2}$. *
a, b, c, and d must be replaced by natural numbers so that the number obtained from $\frac{a}{b}$ is less than the number obtained from $\frac{c}{d}$. Also, b and d cannot be replaced by 0.

12 829 * 999,999 * $\frac{x-1}{x}$

13 Either $\frac{a}{b}$ is 0 or $\frac{a}{b}$ is not 0. First, assume that $\frac{a}{b}$ is 0. Then we can conclude that at least one of the numbers is 0. Next, assume that $\frac{a}{b}$ is not 0. Then $\frac{a}{b}$ has a reciprocal, which is $\frac{b}{a}$.

$\frac{a}{b} \cdot \frac{c}{d} = 0$.
Given

$\frac{a}{b} \cdot \frac{c}{d} \cdot \frac{b}{a} = 0 \cdot \frac{b}{a}$.
Multiplication property of equality

$\left(\frac{a}{b} \cdot \frac{b}{a}\right) \cdot \frac{c}{d} = 0 \cdot \frac{b}{a}$.
Commutative and associative properties of multiplication

$\frac{1}{1} \cdot \frac{c}{d} = 0 \cdot \frac{b}{a}$.
Inverse property of multiplication

$\frac{c}{d} = 0$.
Identity-element and zero properties of multiplication

Thus, if $\frac{a}{b}$ is not 0, then $\frac{c}{d}$ is 0. Again, we can conclude that at least one of the numbers is 0.

14 A $\frac{0}{1}$ B $\frac{0}{1}$

Chapter eleven,
pages 295 and 296

1 $\frac{1}{1}, \frac{2}{2}, \frac{3}{3}, \frac{5}{5}, \frac{10}{10}, \frac{15}{15}, \frac{20}{20}, \frac{25}{25}, \frac{50}{50}$, and $\frac{100}{100}$

2 $\frac{0}{1}, \frac{0}{2}, \frac{0}{3}, \frac{0}{4}, \frac{0}{5}, \frac{0}{50}, \frac{0}{60}, \frac{0}{80}, \frac{0}{100}$, and $\frac{0}{200}$

3 A $\frac{59}{13}$ C $\frac{13}{45}$ E $\frac{52}{31}$ G $\frac{61}{17}$

B $\frac{0}{1}$ D $\frac{1}{1}$ F $\frac{107}{72}$ H $\frac{4}{45}$

4 $\frac{1}{a} + \frac{1}{b} = \frac{a+b}{ab}$.

5 A $20{,}000 + 3000 + 400 + 50 + 6 + \frac{2}{10} + \frac{1}{100}$ *

$2 \cdot 10{,}000 + 3 \cdot 1000 + 4 \cdot 100 + 5 \cdot 10 +$
$\qquad 6 \cdot 1 + 2 \cdot \frac{1}{10} + 1 \cdot \frac{1}{100}$ *

$2 \cdot 10^4 + 3 \cdot 10^3 + 4 \cdot 10^2 + 5 \cdot 10^1 +$
$\qquad 6 \cdot 10^0 + 2 \cdot 10^{-1} + 1 \cdot 10^{-2}$

B $5 + \frac{6}{100} + \frac{5}{1000} + \frac{1}{10{,}000}$ *

$5 \cdot 1 + 0 \cdot \frac{1}{10} + 6 \cdot \frac{1}{100} + 5 \cdot \frac{1}{1000} +$
$\qquad 1 \cdot \frac{1}{10{,}000}$ *

$5 \cdot 10^0 + 0 \cdot 10^{-1} + 6 \cdot 10^{-2} +$
$\qquad 5 \cdot 10^{-3} + 1 \cdot 10^{-4}$

C $\frac{9}{100{,}000} + \frac{3}{1{,}000{,}000} + \frac{4}{10{,}000{,}000}$ *

$9 \cdot \frac{1}{100{,}000} + 3 \cdot \frac{1}{1{,}000{,}000} + 4 \cdot \frac{1}{10{,}000{,}000}$ *

$9 \cdot 10^{-5} + 3 \cdot 10^{-6} + 4 \cdot 10^{-7}$

D $1 + \frac{5}{10} + \frac{5}{10{,}000}$ *

$1 \cdot 1 + 5 \cdot \frac{1}{10} + 0 \cdot \frac{1}{100} + 0 \cdot \frac{1}{1000} +$
$\qquad 5 \cdot \frac{1}{10{,}000}$ *

$1 \cdot 10^0 + 5 \cdot 10^{-1} + 0 \cdot 10^{-2} +$
$\qquad 0 \cdot 10^{-3} + 5 \cdot 10^{-4}$

6 A $\frac{5601}{10{,}000}$　B $\frac{1136}{25}$　C $\frac{17}{5000}$　D $\frac{100{,}001}{1000}$　E $\frac{10{,}003}{50}$

7 A .5　C .56　E .312
  B .75　D .16　F 1.5

8 When you use this property to convert a fraction numeral to a decimal, you choose n and b so that the product bn is 10 or a power of 10, such as 10^2 or 10^5 or 10^{-3}. There is no counting number by which you can multiply 3 and obtain 10 or a power of 10. * $\frac{1}{6}, \frac{1}{7}, \frac{1}{9}, \frac{1}{11},$ and $\frac{3}{13}$

9 $.7 = \frac{7}{10}, .70 = \frac{70}{100}, .700 = \frac{700}{1000},$ and $.7000 = \frac{7000}{10{,}000}.$ You can use the definition of equal rational numbers of arithmetic to show that $\frac{7}{10} = \frac{70}{100},$ that $\frac{7}{10} = \frac{700}{1000},$ and that $\frac{7}{10} = \frac{7000}{10{,}000}.$

10 A Greater than .00056 but less than 45.9023
   B Greater than .909 but less than 1.11
   C Greater than .0101099 but less than 3
   D Less than both factors
   E Greater than both factors
   F Less than both factors
   * The product of two rational numbers is greater than either of the numbers if both factors are greater than 1; the product is less than either of the numbers if both factors are less than 1; the product is greater than one of the factors but less than the other if one of

the numbers is greater than 1 and the other is less than 1.

11 A About 3　B About 46　C About 2

12 The quotient of two numbers is not affected if both the dividend and the divisor are multiplied by the same non-zero number.

13 A $<$　B $<$　C $>$　D $<$　E $=$　F $>$

14 For the rational numbers of arithmetic $\frac{a}{b}, \frac{c}{d}, \frac{e}{f},$ and $\frac{g}{h},$ where $\frac{c}{d}$ and $\frac{g}{h}$ are non-zero, if $\frac{a}{b} < \frac{e}{f}$ and if $\frac{c}{d} = \frac{g}{h},$ then $\frac{a}{b} \cdot \frac{c}{d} < \frac{e}{f} \cdot \frac{g}{h}.$

15 A 1.456092×10^3　E 4.4×10^{-1}
   B 1×10^9　F 4.500056×10^1
   C 1.000923×10^9　G 4.500056×10^4
   D 4.9×10^{-16}　H 1.5632×10^{-2}

16 A $4.9995 < 5.00 < 5.005 < 5.01.$
   B $.00445 < .0045 < .004501 < .00451.$
   C $6.5 \cdot 10^{-6} < 6.501 \cdot 10^{-6} < 6.4909 \cdot 10^{-5} <$
   $\qquad 6 \cdot 50 \cdot 10^{-5}.$
   D $7.334 \cdot 10^8 < 7.34 \cdot 10^8 < 7.34 \cdot 10^9 <$
   $\qquad 7.3401 \cdot 10^9.$
   E $9.4401 \cdot 10^{-3} < 9.44999 \cdot 10^{-3} <$
   $\qquad 9.45 \cdot 10^{-3} < 9.451 \cdot 10^{-3}.$
   F $.000\ 004\ 4 < .000\ 044\ 01 < .000\ 045 <$
   $\qquad .000\ 45.$

Chapter twelve,
pages 309 and 310

1 Your number line should show the points, from left to right, that are associated with the following numbers: $-2, -1\frac{1}{2}, -\frac{1}{3},$ $-\frac{1}{4}, \frac{3}{4}, 1, \frac{5}{2}.$

2 No. There is not at least one integer between any two given integers. For example, there is no integer between 3 and 4 or between -9 and $-10.$

3 Yes. There exists at least one rational number between any two given rational numbers.

4 A $-\frac{1}{2} * 2$　D $\frac{1}{10} * -10$　G $-\frac{7}{8} * \frac{8}{7}$
   B $\frac{3}{4} * -\frac{4}{3}$　E $-6\frac{1}{2} * \frac{2}{13}$　H $\frac{11}{2} * -\frac{2}{11}$
   C $2 * -\frac{1}{2}$　F $3\frac{2}{3} * -\frac{3}{11}$　I $\frac{5}{4} * -\frac{4}{5}$

5 Negative * Positive

6 A $6\frac{3}{8} * 4\frac{5}{8}$　C $0 * 1\frac{1}{5}$　E $-\frac{1}{3} * \frac{1}{3}$
   B $-5 * 1$　D $-\frac{4}{5} * -3\frac{1}{5}$　F $-\frac{1}{3} * -\frac{1}{3}$

7 A $\frac{15}{32} * 1\frac{1}{5}$　C $-8 * -1\frac{7}{25}$　E $-1\frac{1}{3} * -2\frac{1}{2}$
   B $1 * \frac{1}{4}$　D $\frac{9}{10} * \frac{9}{10}$　F $-1 * -1$

8 A -1　C $\frac{1}{2}$　E -12　G $-\frac{3}{5}$
   B 7　D $1\frac{1}{2}$　F $-1\frac{1}{6}$　H $-10\frac{1}{2}$

Chapter thirteen,
pages 329 and 330

1 A 6.75   C .583   E −.6   G 4.8
   B −.625   D 3.2   F −.857142   H .6

2 $\frac{9}{12} = \frac{3}{4}$. Since 2 is the only factor of the denominator of $\frac{3}{4}$, the decimal for the rational number is a terminating decimal.

3 A $\frac{26}{125}$ C $\frac{2039}{1000}$ E $\frac{36}{5}$ G $\frac{623}{100}$
   B $\frac{69}{20}$ D $\frac{719}{100}$ F $-\frac{4}{25}$ H $\frac{647}{2000}$

4 A .750 and .749
   B 2.40 and 2.39
   C −6.50 and −6.49
   D 7.0 and 6.9

5 $\sqrt{14}$, $-\sqrt{11}$, $\sqrt{18}$, and $-\sqrt{12}$

6 1.4142

7 2.8284

8 Yes. 2.8284 (rational approximation for $\sqrt{8}$) is equal to the product of 2 and 1.4142 (rational approximation for $\sqrt{2}$).

9 No. This relation does not have the transitive property. Suppose, for example, two numbers are considered to be approximately equal if their difference is less than or equal to .1. Then 3.1 ≈ 3 and 3 ≈ 2.9. But it is not the case that 3.1 ≈ 2.9.

10 All of the statements are true except $6 < \sqrt{36}$.

11 A A least upper bound ∗ Rational number
    B A least upper bound ∗ Irrational number
    C A greatest lower bound ∗ Irrational number
    D A greatest lower bound ∗ Rational number
    E A greatest lower bound ∗ Rational number
    F A least upper bound ∗ Irrational number

12 Your chart should include the following properties of real numbers.

    Addition

    1 Closure: For each x and y, $x + y$ is a real number.
    2 Commutativity: For each x and y, $x + y = y + x$.
    3 Associativity: For each x, y, and z, $(x + y) + z = x + (y + z)$.
    4 Identity element: For each x, $x + 0 = x$.
    5 Inverse: For each x, $x + (-x) = 0$.
    6 Cancellation: For each x, y, and z, if $x + z = y + z$, then $x = y$.

    Multiplication

    7 Closure: For each x and y, xy is a real number.

8 Commutativity: For each x and y, $xy = yx$.
9 Associativity: For each x, y, and z, $(xy)z = x(yz)$.
10 Identity: For each x, $x \cdot 1 = x$.
11 Inverse: For each x, if x is non-zero, then $x \cdot \frac{1}{x} = 1$.
12 Zero: For each x, $x \cdot 0 = 0$.
13 Cancellation: For each x, y, and z, if z is non-zero and if $xz = yz$, then $x = y$.
14 Distributivity: For each x, y, and z, $x(y + z) = xy + xz$.
15 Completeness: For every set of real numbers that has an upper bound, there exists a real number that is the least upper bound of the set.

Chapter fourteen,
pages 357 and 358

1 Using the first grid, you obtain 24 square inches as the area. Using the second grid, you obtain 24 square inches as the area. The same result is obtained in either case.

2 A 390 square units   E 5060.5 square units
   B 3.9 square units   F 1.78 square units
   C .39 square units   G 81.48 square units
   D 39.0 square units

3 Using an equilateral triangle each side of which is 1 inch long as the unit of measure, you should obtain 36 square units as the area.

4 56 square units
   68 square units
   105 square units
   49 square units
   ∗ You use the basic principle that the areas of adjacent regions that have a common side may be added together to find a total area.

5 $A = \frac{1}{2}ab$. In this formula, A stands for area, a for the measure of an altitude, and b for the measure of the base. ∗ $A = ab$. In this formula, A stands for area, a for the measure of an altitude, and b for the measure of the base. ∗ The explanation of each of these formulas should be covered in class discussion.

6 The greater variation is among the lengths of the lines that have a measure of 1 foot to the nearer foot. In the first case, the lengths might vary between .5 feet and 1.5 feet. In the second case, the lengths might vary between 11.5 inches and 12.5 inches.

7 The greater variation is among the lengths of the lines that have a measure of 5 inches to the nearer inch.

8 A $1.6/1 = 5/x.$

Approximately 3.1 miles

B $27/1 = 45/x.$

$1\frac{2}{3}$ cubic yards

C $16\frac{1}{2}/1 = 64/x.$

$3\frac{29}{33}$ rods or approximately 3.9 rods

D $1728/1 = 75/x.$

$\frac{25}{576}$ cubic feet or approximately .04 cubic feet

E $1.094/1 = 28/x.$

Approximately 25.6 meters

F $.394/1 = 56/x.$

Approximately 142 centimeters

Chapter fifteen,
pages 391 and 392

1 The number of vertices is equal to the number of sides. ∗ Yes

2 Use a line that can be "moved" so that the location of one point, point A, is constant. Point L, the endpoint of the first segment that is not contained in the second segment, and the endpoint of the second segment that is not contained in the first segment should be collinear, as shown below.

The line intersects each of the segments and we have two points, one in each segment, that are mapped onto each other.

If we "move" the line slightly (keeping the location of point A the same) we can map two more points, one in each segment, onto each other. If we "move" the line a bit more, we can again map two points, one in each segment, onto each other. We can continue in this manner until we have established a one-to-one correspondence between the two perpendicular segments. The diagram at the top of column 2 illustrates this correspondence. Note that, with the last "movement" of the line, the point in the first segment and the point in the second segment that are mapped onto each other is the common endpoint.

3 8 points, no 3 of which are collinear (8 points actually determine 28 lines; but, since 7 points determine only 21 lines, 8 points are needed.)

4 8 points, no 3 of which are collinear

5 16 regions

6 $\dfrac{n(n-3)}{2}$

7 The measure of an angle is a positive real number between 0 and 180. Thus, the measure of an angle of a convex polygon cannot be equal to 180. If, for certain reasons, we want to let the measure of an angle of a polygon be more than 180, the polygon is not convex, because, in such a case, there are segments determined by two points in the interior of the polygon that intersect sides of the polygon.

8 The only shapes suitable for floor tile are regular polygons that can be arranged so that each of the polygons has a common vertex with all the other polygons and so that all pairs of adjacent polygons have a common side. Neither pentagons nor octagons can be arranged in this way. ∗ Equilateral triangles, squares, and regular hexagons

9 $4 ∗ 6 ∗ n$ planes that all intersect in 1 line separate space into $2n$ regions. ∗ According to this generalization, 10 intersecting planes should separate space into 20 regions; 12 intersecting planes should separate space into 24 regions; and 15 intersecting planes should separate space into 30 regions. We can easily verify that the generalization holds for these specific cases.

10 A ▷

B

C

D

E

F Impossible

11 $C + K = B + 2.$

Index

441

1 2 3 4 5 6 7 8 9 10 11 12 13 14 15 16 17 18 19 20 21 22 23 24 25   RM   70 69 68 67 66 65